HARCOURT, BRACE & WORLD SCIENCE PROGRAM

Under the General Editorship of Paul F. Brandwein

General Science

Health

The Biological Sciences

▶ The Physical Sciences

Texts and Correlated Workbooks, Laboratory Manuals, Tests, and Teacher's Manuals

Professional Books for the Teacher

THE PHYSICAL SCIENCES

EXPLORING PHYSICS
by Richard Brinckerhoff, Judson B. Cross, and Arthur Lazarus

With Correlated Laboratory Manual, Workbook, Tests, and Teacher's Manual

▶ THE PHYSICAL WORLD
by Richard Brinckerhoff, Burnett Cross, Fletcher Watson, and Paul F. Brandwein

With Correlated Tests and Teacher's Manual

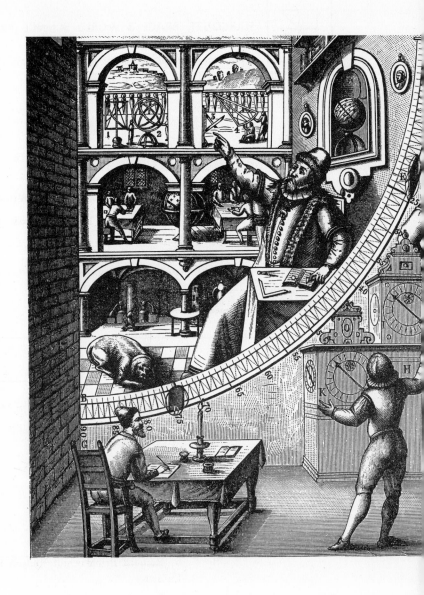

 HARCOURT, BRACE & WORLD, INC.

New York   Chicago   Atlanta   Dallas   Burlingame

THE PHYSICAL WORLD

SECOND EDITION

A COURSE IN PHYSICAL SCIENCE

RICHARD BRINCKERHOFF
BURNETT CROSS
FLETCHER WATSON
PAUL F. BRANDWEIN

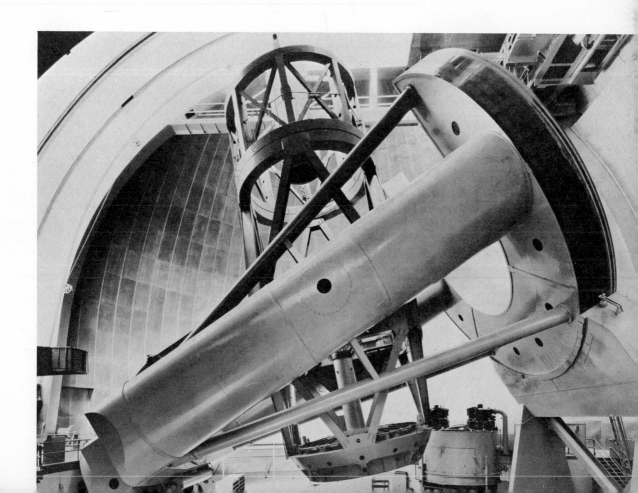

THE AUTHORS

RICHARD BRINCKERHOFF   Science Instructor, Phillips Exeter Academy, Exeter, New Hampshire

BURNETT CROSS   Instructor, Teachers College, Columbia University, New York

FLETCHER WATSON   Professor of Education, Harvard University, Cambridge, Massachusetts

PAUL F. BRANDWEIN   Director of Education, The Conservation Foundation; General Editor and Consultant to Schools, Harcourt, Brace & World; formerly Chairman, Science Department, Forest Hills High School, New York

COLLABORATOR

SIDNEY ROSEN   Associate Professor of Physical Science, College of Liberal Arts and Sciences, University of Illinois, Urbana

DRAWINGS

MILDRED WALTRIP

PICTURE CREDITS

TITLE PAGE: *Left-hand page: Illustration of 1587 showing the great 16th-century pretelescopic astronomer Tycho Brahe. His specially constructed observatory, or " celestial palace," included a large quadrant, or quarter circle, and highly accurate clocks. With these he made thousands of careful measurements of the positions and apparent motions of the stars and planets. Right-hand page: The Hale telescope at Mt. Palomar Observatory in California with its 200-inch perfectly ground mirror, the largest in the world — gathers in light from stars billions of trillions of miles away. The photograph was supplied through courtesy of the Mt. Wilson and Palomar Observatories.*

FRONT COVER: *Model of a molecule: American Cyanamid; the Moon: Mt. Wilson and Palomar Observatories; Geologist: Standard Oil Co. (N.J.).*

UNIT 1, *p. XIV, NASA;* UNIT 2, *p. 50, Dr. Erwin W. Müller;* UNIT 3, *p. 70, E. R. Squibb and Sons;* UNIT 4, *p. 106, Westinghouse Electric Corp.;* UNIT 5, *p. 134, Copyright 1956, by American Society of Civil Engineers;* UNIT 6, *p. 198, Scientific American — photo by D. E. Scherman;* UNIT 7, *p. 234, Black Star Photo by Hein Gorny;* UNIT 8, *p. 266, General Electric Co.;* UNIT 9, *p. 334, Standard Oil Co. (N.J.);* UNIT 10, *p. 376, Mount Wilson and Palomar Observatories*

PRINTED IN THE UNITED STATES OF AMERICA

Contents

UNIT 2   THE ABC OF THINGS AROUND YOU

UNIT 3   COMBINING ATOMS

UNIT 4 SPLITTING ATOMS

UNIT 5 EASING WORK WITH MACHINES

THE PHYSICAL WORLD

UNIT 1

Our Home in Space

◀ *From Atlas ICBM nose cone, earth curvature shows clearly. Main stage of missile is seen falling away.*

THE EARTH on which you live is only a very tiny speck compared with the universe. Yet you will agree that it is a very important speck. This unit will help you take a new look at the earth on which you will spend your life.

In your own home town and on trips through the country you can learn much about the earth. Thousands of people, for one example, are " rock hounds " in their spare time. They collect and study rocks and minerals gathered on field trips. Some of them exchange samples with other people in distant lands. The variety of earth materials is so great that no one has samples of them all.

Rocks, minerals, fossilized remains of living things, farmlands, river valleys, hills and mountains, beaches — each has its own story, and each story is a part of the history and development of the earth. You must know something of how to " read " the " pages " of the earth that you see about you before you can understand how scientists learn what they do about the earth. In this unit you can make a start on learning how to interpret what you see.

Study of the earth is important, as well as fun. As people have developed increasing needs for materials — and for more power to shape or control them — we must seek greater supplies of more and more materials on our earth. We also need to understand more about the earth because it is sometimes the source of great disasters: earthquakes, floods, storms, and volcanic explosions. Even the expanding exploration of space will not lessen our interest in studying our home planet. Indeed, as you shall soon learn, space efforts have yielded much new and valuable information about the earth.

The Earth in Space

At this moment, you are hurtling through space many miles per second on a moving object that is several billions of years old. Yes, of course, the object is our earth — our home in space.

What sort of a home is it?

SHAPE AND SIZE

As you stand on an open plain or on the deck of a ship at sea, the landscape or seascape around you looks flat — as flat as a carpet in all directions. For thousands of years some people who saw this were sure the earth *was* flat. In fact, when Columbus sailed west and discovered America, many people thought he might reach the edge of the flat earth and fall off it, much as you might fall off the edge of a cliff.

Nowadays you don't worry about falling off the edge of the earth when you take a long trip. You are used to thinking of the earth as a giant ball. But how do you *know* it is a ball?

Some Evidence

One easy way to see that the earth's surface is not flat is to watch an eclipse of the moon. Fig. 1-1 shows clearly what you might expect to see.

Another way is to have pictures of the earth transmitted from artificial satellites or rockets.

Such pictures may be picked up and recorded on film at special receiving stations on the earth, hundreds of miles beneath the orbits of the satellites. Or they may be recovered directly from the spent rocket. You can see the curvature of the earth quite clearly in rocket pictures, as in the one you saw two pages earlier in this book (photograph opposite page 1).

Can you think of other evidence for confirming the shape of the earth? What, for example, did Columbus suspect from watching a ship sail off into the distance? How else did men in early times demonstrate that the earth was not flat?

How Big?

If the earth is more or less a sphere, how large a sphere is it? You cannot measure it with a tape measure or pace off the distance around the equator. But you could measure the distance between some pair of fairly close points, M and N, on the equator or some other circumference. And then you could figure out how great the circumference is *if you knew what fraction of it you had measured.*

American Museum of Natural History

1-1. When the earth passes between the sun and the moon, an eclipse of the moon occurs. The shape of the earth's shadow on the moon is evidence that the earth is round.

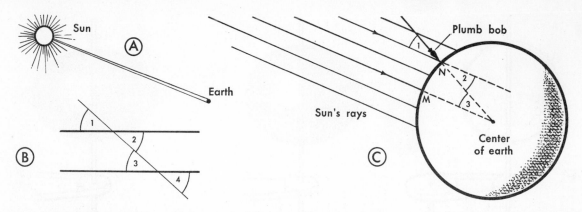

1-2. Eratosthenes' method of finding the earth's circumference depends on: A, the sun's rays being very nearly parallel as they hit the earth; B, equal angles formed by a line cutting two parallel lines; C, multiplying the known distance MN by the number of times angle 3 goes into the 360° of a circle.

Look at the points M and N in the third part of Fig. 1-2 (1-2C). If M and N are two points on the earth's circumference, what fraction of the circumference is the distance between these two points? If you can imagine drawing lines from M and N to the center of the earth you are on your way to finding this fraction. Remember that there are 360° in a circle or in the circumference of a sphere. Now how many degrees are in the angle formed by the two lines you drew to the center of the earth? Perhaps about 36°? If so, the portion of the circumference between M and N would be about 1/10 of the total circumference, because 36° is 1/10 of the total of 360°. Guesses aren't close enough, however. We need to measure the angle fairly accurately. Over 2,000 years ago, the Greek geometer Eratosthenes (ehr-uh-TOS-theh-neez) found a simple way to do this.

Eratosthenes knew that when two parallel lines are crossed by a third line, several pairs of equal angles are formed. For example, in Fig. 1-2, part B, angles 1, 2, 3, and 4 are equal. This can be proved in geometry. Eratosthenes also knew that the sun is so far from the earth that its rays are almost parallel to each other when they hit two different points on the earth. (See Fig. 1-2, part A.)

Look at the picture of the earth again in Fig. 1-2, part C. The sun's rays hitting at point M are on the same line that goes to the center of the earth from point M. (This will happen if you wait, at point M, for the sun to be directly overhead.) At the same time the rays hitting at point N to the north make an angle with the line going to the center of the earth (as the plumb bob shows).

Now, since the sun's rays are almost parallel, angles 1, 2, and 3 must be almost equal. Angle 1 can be measured easily on the surface of the earth; thus we can find the value of angle 3 at the center of the earth! We can then divide the value of the angle by 360° to find what fraction of the whole circumference lies between the measured distance MN. Our problem is solved!

Though his instruments were simple, Eratosthenes was able to get a measurement that was extremely close to our present-day figure for the circumference of the earth — about 25,000 miles. (From the formula for the circumference of a circle you could also find that the center of the earth lies about 4,000 miles beneath your feet.)

Today we know that the earth is not perfectly round. It bulges somewhat at the equator, where its diameter is about 1/300 greater than the diameter through the poles. Somewhat like the hoop in Fig. 1-3, the earth bulges in relation to the rate at which it rotates. (In comparison, the planet Jupiter, which rotates once almost every 10 hours, shows much more bulge.)

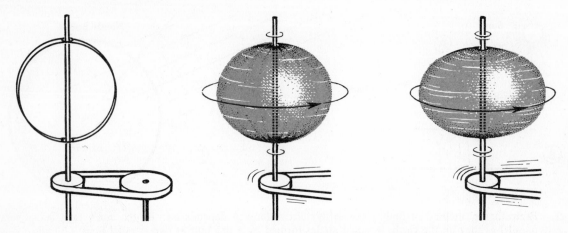

1-3. The bulging of the earth is due to the same forces which cause a rotating hoop to bulge.

ROTATION, GRAVITY, AND MAGNETISM

The earth turns round on its axis once every day. You may say, " Of course, it's easy to see that. The sun only *seems* to move across the sky each day. Actually, it is the earth that is turning on its axis."

For many centuries people believed this was not so. They believed the sun really did move across the sky on its way round and round a motionless earth. But at last, in 1851, a Frenchman named Foucault (foo-ko) did a famous experiment, and proved once and for all that it really *was* the earth that was turning. And he did it without even having to go outdoors!

Foucault built a very long pendulum and set it going in one of the largest halls in Paris. All day long the pendulum swung back and forth. But as it swung, the path of its back-and-forth motion seemed to change direction around the hall (Fig. 1-4).

Foucault analyzed what happened and showed that the only possible explanation for the effect was that the path of the swinging pendulum remained motionless in space as the earth turned round and round beneath it. Today you can see a Foucault pendulum in action if you visit United Nations Headquarters in New York, or Golden Gate Park in San Francisco.

You Can't Fall Off

You have probably heard the expression " He doesn't know which end is up." Of course, you think *you* know the direction of " up." But now look at Fig. 1-5 and see if you agree with the Australian's idea of " up." All over this round earth of ours people have different directions for " up "! Which way *is* " up "? Do *you* know the answer?

You can see from the picture that all " ups " have one thing in common. They all point away from the center of the earth. " Down " is toward the center of the earth, the direction an object falls when you drop it. Wherever you are on the earth, the direction of your " up " and " down " is decided by the *pull of gravity* toward the center of the earth. Thus you can never fall off this space platform even in Australia, where " up " and " down " may seem to you to be reversed (Fig. 1-5).

What is this pull of gravity that tells us which way is up and which way is down?

What Is Gravity?

You may be surprised to learn that something so familiar as gravity has not been completely explained, even by the efforts of Albert Einstein. Yet you do not need to fall off a stepladder or slip on the ice to know that the earth does pull on

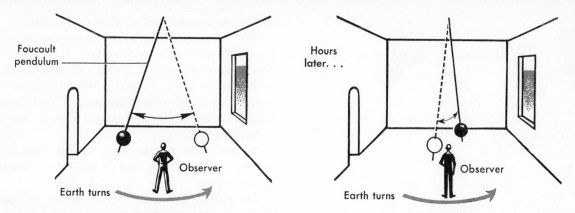

1-4. A Foucault pendulum keeps swinging in one direction. However, as the earth rotates under it, the direction of the swing of the pendulum appears to change clockwise in the northern hemisphere in relation to its surroundings. At the equator a Foucault pendulum would not change its apparent direction.

you. And you are pulling on the earth with as much force as the earth pulls on you.

Other objects exert a pull on you, too. Someone sitting one yard away from you pulls you toward him with a force of about seven millionths of an ounce, far too small a pull for you to notice without sensitive instruments.

When you stand beside a big building it pulls on you more strongly — as much as a few hundredths of an ounce. A big mountain pulls on you even more if you stand near its base. In Chapter 3 you will learn how the gravitational pull of mountains creates real difficulties for surveyors of large areas of land.

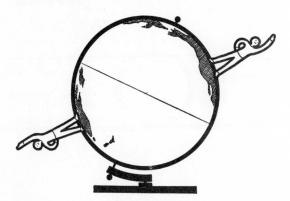

1-5. "Down" means toward the center of the earth. All objects on the earth are pulled down toward the center.

A still bigger object exerts an even greater pull on you. If you could travel to the surface of the moon, you would find yourself being pulled downward with a force of about one sixth of your present weight (Fig. 1-6).

But of course, the earth is bigger and heavier than any of these objects and pulls on you with a still stronger force. You can probably see that the heavier a body is, the stronger its pull on nearby bodies.

Isaac Newton's Idea

It was Isaac Newton who, in 1666, first suggested that *each object in the entire universe* (people, clouds, ants, stars, mountains, etc.) *exerts a pull on every other object in the universe.* He called this pull "universal gravitation."

If Newton is right, it means that even something as far away as the moon or the sun is pulling on the earth and everything on it (including you) this very moment.

Calculations show that gravity pulls the earth and the moon toward each other with a force of about 20,000 billion tons. This enormous force, the weight of nearly a billion battleships, keeps pulling the moon around and around the earth. Without such a pull of gravity attracting it, our moon would coast away in a straight line.

Not only does the earth pull the moon, the

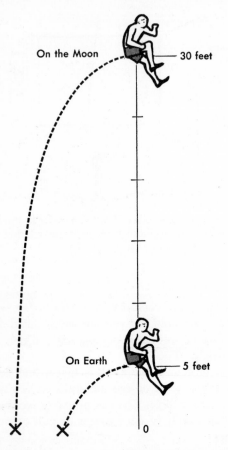

On the Moon — 30 feet

On Earth — 5 feet

0

1-6. The gravity on the surface of the moon is only one sixth that of the earth. On the moon you could jump six times higher than on the earth and it would take you more time to get back to the surface.

moon also pulls on the earth. It pulls hard enough to draw the oceans of the earth upward toward it by several feet, creating *tides* (Fig. 1-7). Does high tide occur exactly when the moon is overhead? No, it doesn't. The expanse of the high tide is many miles — very great as compared with the average depth of the oceans, two and one-half miles. The earth's rotation changes the relative position of the moon to the earth faster than the massive tide can keep up. In short, the tides act somewhat like giant brake shoes around the turning earth, creating *tidal friction*. This friction tends to slow down the rotation of the earth. Yes, our days are growing longer, but only by a small part

(16 ten-thousandths) of a second every century.

The moon pulls on more than the earth's oceans. It pulls on everything else on earth, too. For instance, it pulls on the nation's gold supply stored at Fort Knox, Kentucky. When the moon is overhead, pulling upward, the gold at Fort Knox weighs one pound less than it does when the moon is on the horizon.

Do you think you weigh a bit less when the moon is overhead than you do when the moon is on the horizon?

The pull of gravity of the sun affects us, too. If the sun did not pull on the earth as it does, you would quickly freeze to death, for at once the earth would shoot off into outer space beyond the warming rays of the sun. The sun's gravity keeps pulling our moving earth into a curved path that causes the earth to travel around the sun once each year (Fig. 1-8).

By now you can guess that the gravitational attraction between bodies becomes weaker as the distance between them increases. That is why the millions of stars in outer space have little influence upon the earth's path, even though, all told, these stars outweigh our sun billions of times.

To summarize what we have said about gravity:

1. Every object in the universe pulls on every other object with a force we call gravity.

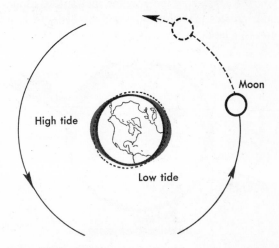

High tide

Low tide

Moon

1-7. High tides occur on the sides nearest and opposite to the moon. The pull of the sun also affects the tides.

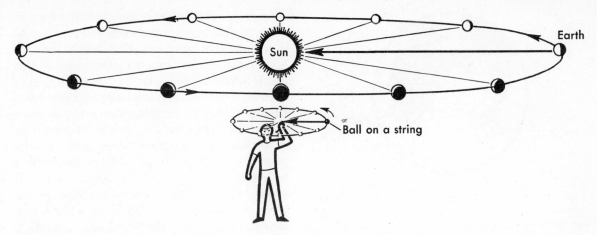

Ball on a string

1-8. Like a string holding a revolving ball, the gravitational pull of the sun on the earth prevents the earth from flying off into space. The same is true for the pull of the earth on the moon or on an orbiting man-made satellite.

2. The earth's pull of gravity on you is defined as your *weight*.
3. The heavier an object is, the stronger is its pull on nearby objects.
4. The farther apart two objects are, the less is the gravitational pull between them.

Magnetic Effects

You know that, in addition to gravity, the earth has another strange pull on materials near it. This is what we call *magnetism*. Its effect is most easily seen on steel and certain other forms of iron. But nearly every material is at least slightly sensitive to magnetic forces.

For many hundreds of years, magnetism has been important to navigators. They used magnetic compasses to show them the direction to sail during dark nights and cloudy days.

In western Europe at the time of Columbus, the crude compasses then in use pointed a bit eastward of the North Pole. But imagine the amazement and worry of Columbus when he found that in the middle of the Atlantic Ocean the compass pointed *west* of north! When he found land, the compass was again pointing nearly to north. If the compass was to be used and trusted by sailors, they needed to know how much the compass pointed away from true north in different parts of the world. Many expeditions and

careful observations were made to measure this deflection of the compass from true north. Since about 1700, this information has been printed on charts of the seas and on maps of the land.

If the compass does not point to true north, where does it point? In the northern half of the world, the compass now points toward a place north of Canada near latitude 75°N and longitude 101°W.

The more we learn about this magnetic force of the earth, the stranger it seems. For example, at London in 1580 the compass, instead of pointing true north, pointed 11° east of north; but this angle diminished to 0° by 1660. Then the compass swung westward to 24° by 1820. Now, the angle away from true north has diminished to about 8° westward. We must conclude that during past centuries, the position of the north *magnetic* pole of the earth slowly wanders from true north. It used to be near Greenland, but has slowly drifted westward toward Canada. Now it may again be moving eastward.

Apparently the magnetic pole has always been on the move. There is geological evidence that about 200 million years ago, the north magnetic pole was located in eastern Asia! And before that it may have been somewhere in the western Pacific Ocean (Fig. 1-9).

There is a southern magnetic pole, too. Where

1-9. Geologists have reason to believe the North magnetic pole has wandered considerably for the last two hundred million years.

would you expect it to be? If you said right op-posite the north magnetic pole, you are wrong! The south magnetic pole is in Antarctica (close to 68°S and 145°E). A line between it and the north magnetic pole misses the center of the earth by about 400 miles.

But even stranger things have been observed. The *amount* of the earth's magnetic pull changes. Over the years at some places the magnetic attraction has decreased; at other places it has increased. Also, it has changed direction. At the magnetic poles, a suspended bar magnet would stand straight up and down. Halfway between the magnetic poles, the pull is parallel to the ground. But at other places, the pull is partly along the ground and partly down. A suspended magnet then tends to *dip* toward the earth along the direction of the pull. And over the years, the dip has changed, too. As Alice in Wonderland said, " Things are getting curiouser and curiouser! "

Very careful observations show that the amount and the direction of magnetic forces change slightly when the sun rises and sets. At certain other times, magnets swing wildly and give no reliable reading; these situations are called magnetic storms. We know that magnetic storms are caused by activity on the sun that affects the upper atmosphere of the earth. When we have magnetic storms, radio transmissions may be blanked out.

We are led to conclude that part of the magnetic force arises from effects on the earth's upper

atmosphere. This is one reason there has been so much interest in sending rockets and satellites up to measure the earth's magnetic field at different heights and places. But our atmosphere is thin gas. How can it have magnetic effects? .

Perhaps you know that an electric current in a wire gives rise to magnetic forces in the space around the wire. Now the gases at the top of our atmosphere are electrified — the atoms of these gases carry electric charges just like the gas in a fluorescent tube. In addition, these atoms are moving rapidly. Thus, even though there are no wires, the motion of the charged gases makes an electric current, and like all electric currents, it gives rise to magnetic effects.

What accounts for the biggest part of the magnetic pull, which seems to come from within the earth (Fig. 1-10)? As we shall soon see, the earth has a large core surrounded by a thick layer of hot rock. The earth, then, has a structure somewhat like a baseball — large core, thick surrounding layer, and thin covering. The outer core might be iron; at any rate, it is very hot and much of it reacts like a liquid.

Present attempts to explain the earth's magnetism (and they are not overly successful) are based on the likelihood that electric currents circulate within the hot, liquefied materials deep inside the earth. But how and why these currents change is far from clear.

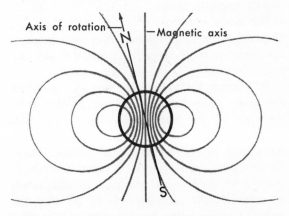

1-10. The earth's magnetic field spreads out into space much as though we imagined a huge bar magnet to be buried under the crust.

Perhaps the next time you look at a compass you will think of the strange force of magnetism that is acting upon it.

LAND MASSES

Less than one-millionth part of all the earth — the surface of its crust (and a bit of the subsurface of the crust) — has ever been seen by man. Yet this millionth part of the great ball you live on includes all the oceans of the world, the wood, metal, and rock you see all about you, your body and all the food that nourishes it — in fact, nearly everything that you will ever see and touch during your lifetime. The surface of the earth's crust together with the air above it is your storehouse and your home.

The Crust You Live On

We have learned most of what we know about the earth's crust from the land masses that rise above the surface of the oceans. The largest of these land masses are called continents; the smallest, islands. What are these land masses made of?

The largest part of them is rock, and there are many different kinds of rock. One of the distinguishing characteristics of rocks results from the way in which a particular rock was formed. Some rocks were formed by the sticking together of many tiny particles of sand, others by the cooling of hot, molten material, still others by the combined effect of heat and pressure on the first two types. Later in this unit we shall discuss the process of formation of the different types of rocks and how these types can be identified.

Besides rocks in the crust, there are other materials that form a surface coat on the earth's crust; these exist chiefly as soil and sand. The most important soil is the thin layer that contains the minerals and dead plant and animal material needed by growing plants. This soil, usually only a few inches thick, is called *topsoil*. It is necessary to the preservation of human and animal life, for without it trees and food plants would not grow. *Subsoil,* the soil below the topsoil, usually cannot support growing plants.

TABLE **1-1** THE MOST ABUNDANT ELEMENTS IN THE EARTH'S CRUST

Atomic number	Name	Per cent of crust by no. of atoms	Per cent of crust by volume
8	Oxygen	62	91.83
14	Silicon	21	0.83
13	Aluminum	6	0.79
26	Iron	2	0.58
20	Calcium	2	1.50
11	Sodium	2.6	1.64
19	Potassium	1.4	2.19
12	Magnesium	2	0.60

Chemical Composition of the Earth's Crust

The rocks and other materials in the earth's crust are made of chemical *elements.* An element is a basic, simple substance made of only one kind of atom. For example, copper is an element (it is made up of atoms of copper). Gold, mercury, sulfur, and oxygen are also elements. Water is not; it is made up of the elements hydrogen and oxygen. Less than a dozen of the more than 100 known elements make up over 98 per cent of the volume of all substances in the earth's crust. These are arranged for you in Table 1-1.

Of course, when you go out for a walk in the country you don't see many of these elements lying about in their pure form. You probably know that most of them are chemically combined with one another. They are in the form of *compounds.* The earth in your garden, for example, is probably made mostly of silicon atoms and oxygen atoms chemically combined to form the compound called silicon dioxide. The same earth may also contain a compound of calcium, carbon, and oxygen called calcium carbonate (or limestone), as well as many other compounds of iron, aluminum, magnesium, and other elements. Table 1-2 shows a list of just a few of the useful compounds and elements that are taken out of the earth's crust every day.

The chemical elements present in the earth limit

TABLE 1-2 SUBSTANCES IN THE EARTH'S CRUST

Compound or element	Used to make
Iron oxide	Iron and steel
Carbon (coal)	Coke and gas fuel
Aluminum oxide (bauxite)	Aluminum
Sulfur	Sulfuric acid
Zinc oxide	Zinc
Silicon dioxide (silica)	Glass
Methane and ethane (natural gas)	Fuel, plastics, medicine
Calcium sulfate	Plaster

or determine what types of *compounds* (chemical combinations of elements) can be formed. We can do a fairly good job of analyzing elements and compounds in the earth's crust. For example, you can see in Table 1-1 that 62 per cent of all atoms in the earth's crust are oxygen atoms. Note that they take up almost 92 per cent of the available room. Silicon atoms are the next most plentiful by number of atoms, 21 per cent, but they take up only a tiny fraction of the available space. While there are only about 3 times as many oxygen atoms as silicon atoms, the oxygen atoms take up over 100 times more space than the silicon atoms!

Chemists have found that silicon atoms can get into, and fit into, the spaces between closely packed oxygen atoms in a compound. As a result of this and the equally important chemical characteristics of oxygen and silicon atoms, these two elements pull strongly on each other and make compounds that are difficult to pull apart. One of these compounds, silicon dioxide, is the principal component of all rock and soil.

THE OCEANS

So far we have not considered the elements and compounds that cover almost three fourths of the surface of the earth — yes, the elements and compounds that make up the oceans. Rapidly we are coming to realize the importance of the oceans of the world. Look at a globe or a map of the world, and you will see how vast the oceans are. On the *average,* they are two and one-half miles deep!

For billions of years, the rivers of the world have been carrying salt and many other materials down to the sea. Today we have begun to realize the value of the minerals of the oceans, and we are finding ways to " mine " them.

Mines in the Sea

If you could boil away all the water of the oceans, you would have left about 30,000 hundreds of billions of tons of salt, enough to cover the entire earth (including the ocean bottom) with a layer 150 feet thick!

What is the salt in the ocean made of? About three fourths of it is ordinary table salt (sodium chloride). In fact, much of the world's supply of table salt is obtained from the ocean by using the warmth of the sun to evaporate sea water in shallow ponds. The remaining one fourth of the deposits dissolved in sea water is a surprisingly large collection of useful elements. Besides sodium and chlorine, each cubic mile of sea water has in it:

5,000,000 tons of magnesium
4,300,000 tons of sulfur
3,300,000 tons of potassium
2,400,000 tons of calcium
310,000 tons of bromine

as well as smaller — but important — amounts of the following: carbon, iodine, phosphorus, iron, and copper. There are even about 47 lbs. of gold, worth roughly $26,000. Moreover there are 320,-000,000 such cubic miles of sea water!

We have already begun to extract from sea water large amounts of table salt, magnesium, and bromine. The next airplane ride you take may be in a plane whose magnesium-aluminum alloy frame was made with magnesium extracted from sea water. And the plane may be driven through the sky by fuel containing bromine extracted from sea water.

Some large lumps of matter rich in the important element *manganese* have been dredged from the ocean bottom. How these concentrations were formed is not known. But inexpensive ways to get more of them up are being sought. There are probably many other mineral deposits on the ocean floors. We must look for them and for ways to bring them to the surface.

Mysteries of the Sea

There are great currents in the ocean that strongly influence how we live. Best known is the Gulf Stream, which originates in the warm Caribbean Sea and the Gulf of Mexico. The warm water at the surface flows to the north over cooler, sinking water, then swings eastward across the Atlantic Ocean. Because of the Gulf Stream, the west coast of Europe is much warmer than other places with the same latitude.

The Gulf Stream and all other great currents are parts of a general circulation pattern of the surface waters in each ocean. Near the equator there are westerly flowing currents, with nearby countercurrents. Then, along the western sides of the oceans, the warm surface currents turn poleward and swing around toward the east (Fig. 1-11).

What do you think could account for these ocean-wide patterns? Although there are many local irregularities, the motion of major surface currents is largely caused by prevailing winds and the earth's rotation. The rotation also influences the direction of prevailing winds (Fig. 1-12).

In addition to surface currents, there are deeper (or subsurface) ocean currents, too. These sometimes run opposite to the surface currents. The

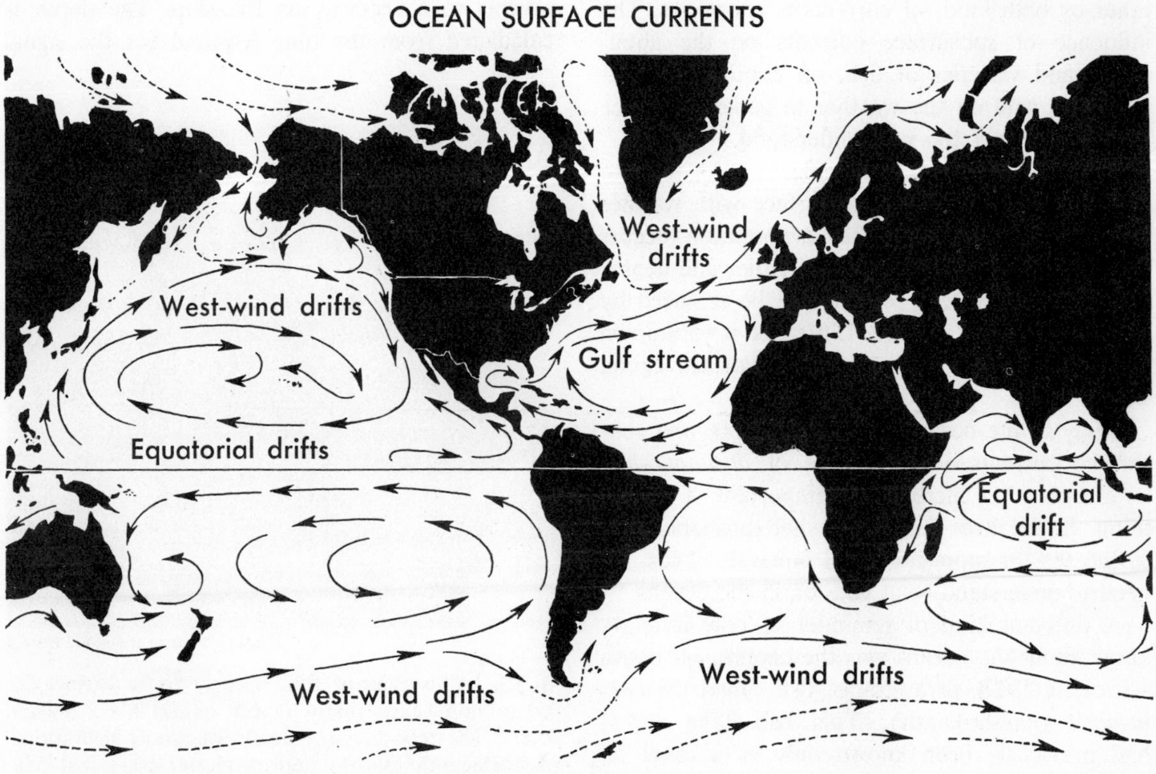

OCEAN SURFACE CURRENTS

1-11. The major ocean surface currents follow the pattern shown above due mainly to the action of prevailing winds (see Fig. 1-12) and the effect of the earth's rotation.

PREVAILING WINDS

N North Pole

Westerlies

Trade winds

Trade winds

Westerlies

South Pole S

1-12. In the days of the sailing ship, reaching your destination depended in large measure upon these patterns of prevailing winds.

amount of heat carried from one region to another by both kinds of currents is enormous. The influence of subsurface currents on the abundance and varieties of fish, on continental temperatures, and on the weather in general may be great, but is not too well understood.

We do know that cold, polar waters tend to sink and be replaced at the surface with warmer waters. We also know that evaporation occurs from the surface waters, leaving saltier and denser waters that may tend to sink and be replaced by cool water forced upward. Little else is yet known about the details of how the subsurface ocean waters move.

Study of the oceans and their surface and subsurface currents — the science of *oceanography* — is becoming increasingly important. For one thing, in the near future we shall probably turn to the sea for more food and minerals. Thus, we need to understand what goes on in the oceans.

A different kind of reminder of how little we know about the oceans was the capture off South Africa, in 1938, of a strange fish called the *coelacanth* (SEE-la-kanth). This fish (Fig. 1-13) had previously been known only as a fossil 60 million years old. Yet, here it was alive! Since then others have been captured and kept alive for

a very brief time. What other strange creatures and surprises are awaiting discovery in the oceans?

The difficulties of ocean study are many and great. The number of vessels equipped for this work is very small, and the oceans are large. In any one ocean area chosen for study, information is wanted at many depths on differences in temperature, in salinity (or degree of saltiness), in the amount of light present, in kinds of fish and living materials, in the flow of currents at various places and depths, and in the depth and nature of the ocean floor at different places (Fig. 1-14).

Until recently, the only way to get information on the depth of water was to drop a long sounding line with a weight attached. But now sound-echo equipment can be operated continuously, so that a great number of soundings can be obtained by each ship. On the ship a sounder sends out a sharp signal down through the water. At the ocean bottom the signal is reflected and eventually returns to a receiver on the ship. The depth is calculated from the time required for the signal

American Museum of Natural History

1-13. This type of fish, thought to be extinct for 60 million years, might report, as did Mark Twain, that "The report of my death was an exaggeration." A coelacanth (shown here in plaster cast) had relatives which later gave rise to amphibians which invaded the land.

1-14. Not all scientists wear white coats! These investigators of the ocean are lowering a specially designed underwater camera from a research vessel that regularly journeys forth from Woods Hole, Mass.

to make the trip down and back again. (See Fig. 29-5 on page 339.)

In the Pacific Ocean are mountains whose tops are as much as a mile below the surface. Study of the shape and composition of these submerged mountains, known as *seamounts,* is producing some surprising results. For example, samples dredged from some of the seamount tops contain coral. Yet we know that coral will not grow below a depth of about 200 feet. How did these deeply submerged peaks come to have a coral topping?

Immediately you begin to wonder if in times past the level of the sea was perhaps a mile lower than it is now. If so, then where did all the water in the top mile of the oceans come from? As an alternate theory, could these mountains and the sea bottom around them once have been much

higher? If so, what caused them to sink? Here is one of the many mysteries of the sea.

Another exciting, but still unexplained, feature of the ocean floors is its ridges, including the recently discovered Great Atlantic ridge. This ridge, which stretches over a thousand miles, seems to be a great volcanic hump. Along with other recent ocean-floor discoveries, it provides material for new theories of changes in the earth's crust — including one which sees the earth as having expanded slightly over the ages.

There are also great submarine canyons. The Monterey Canyon, off Monterey Bay in California, has a size and structure comparable to that of the Grand Canyon of the Colorado River.

There are deep trenches and vast plains, and near the continents, there are continental slopes and shelves. The structure of the earth's crust at

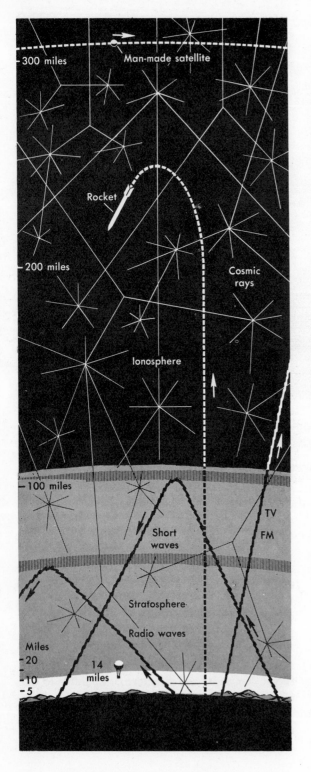

- 300 miles — Man-made satellite

Rocket

- 200 miles — Cosmic rays

Ionosphere

- 100 miles

TV

FM

Short waves

Stratosphere

Radio waves

Miles
- 20
- 10
- 5

14 miles

the bottom of an ocean is as varied and fascinating as the structure of any continent.

There is increasing evidence of over-all circulation of ocean waters. As very cold water in the arctic regions sinks and flows along the bottom, it pushes out the water that had been on the bottom. Such a circulation of water would be important to all forms of marine life. New water from the surface would carry dissolved oxygen down into the ocean depths where some fish and snails are found. And water recirculated upward would bring with it some of the rich organic sediment from the ocean floor, helping maintain the plant life near the surface.

THE OCEAN OF AIR

Did you know that you live at the bottom of an ocean — an ocean several hundred miles deep? It is an ocean of air, not of water. It is called the *atmosphere.*

Because we cannot see the air, taste it, or often even feel it, we sometimes forget that air, too, is made up of elements and compounds and that it has weight. Yet the weight of air in one room is much greater than your own.

The Weight of Air

Why aren't you crushed flat by the weight of the air above you? The answer is that the pressure of the atmosphere is exerted on you equally from *all* sides — even outward from inside your lungs, stomach, and blood stream. (It is easy to blow a hole through a sheet of tissue paper, but not if two people blow equally hard at the same time from opposite sides of the tissue.) We are not damaged by air pressure because the pressure

1-15. Up to about 6 miles clouds and weather fronts move. Higher is the cloudless stratosphere. At 35 to 60 miles is the first and most intense portion of an electrified region — the ionosphere, which reflects radio waves back to the earth. Still higher in the very thin air, rockets and man-made satellites will move readily.

TABLE 1-3 COMPOSITION OF AIR

Element or compound	Percentage (approximate)
Nitrogen	78.084
Oxygen	20.946
Argon	0.934
Carbon dioxide	0.033
Helium, Krypton, Neon, Ozone, Xenon, Methane, Hydrogen	.003
Water vapor	varies up to 4%

Water vapor is listed separately because its amount changes considerably from day to day.

The percentages of carbon dioxide and of even less abundant substances, such as ozone, may seem insignificant. Yet small changes in such percentages could have a long-range effect upon life on earth, because they affect the amount of solar radiation getting through to the earth's surface.

(with a force of about 14.7 pounds on each square inch) exists equally on both the inside and the outside of our bodies.

If a man jumped out of the pressurized cabin of an airplane into the thin air 15 miles above the earth, the air pressure inside his body would cause him to burst like a toy balloon. On the other hand, if you removed the air from the inside of a tin can nearer the earth's surface, the pressure of the air outside the can would easily crush it.

The mixture of elements and compounds that make up the part of the air nearest the surface of the earth (Table 1-3) are crowded closely together by the weight of those higher above. As we fly upward in an open airplane, we would find that the air at higher altitudes is thinner — it pushes on us with less force. Fewer and fewer molecules remain above us to weigh down upon our bodies. It becomes difficult to breathe enough air into our lungs.

Above an altitude of six miles, three fourths of all the air lies below. Here, in the region called the *stratosphere,* there is not enough air to breathe — or to supply enough oxygen to let a match burn.

There is not enough air to make possible the rains or sudden changes in temperature that we call "weather." The stratosphere is a thin, cold, almost dustless region. Fig. 1-15 shows this and other layers of the atmosphere. (For another view of the layers in the atmosphere see Fig. 3-19.)

Above the Stratosphere

Ordinary airplanes cannot fly higher than the lower regions of the stratosphere. But we have several ingenious ways of finding out what lies still higher.

One way is by watching "shooting stars," called *meteors.* Have you ever seen one? You will read about them in Chapter 32 and learn that most of them are really rocks, usually the size of gravel or sand grains, but sometimes much larger. Like the earth, they are moving around the sun and have speeds up to 25 miles per second (90,-000 miles per hour). Since the earth is also moving rapidly, 18 miles per second, meteors that hit us head on may have speeds of 43 miles per second. As they pass through the atmosphere, friction with the air heats them up until they turn to hot, glowing gas (Fig. 1-16). Most burn up more than 40 miles high. Measurements show that they start

Yerkes Observatory

1-16. Most meteors burn up in the atmosphere, but some are large enough to have remains that crash to earth as meteorites.

to burn as high as 60 miles above the ground. We can then be certain that our ocean of air extends at least that high.

Another way of learning about the upper air is through the study of radio waves that are beamed upward from the earth. They bounce back to the earth some distance away from the radio station. This is the principle of radio communication that enables people to hear shortwave broadcasts from the other side of the world.

Why do radio waves bounce back from the upper air? The only kind of obstacle in the air that would bounce radio waves back to earth this way would be a layer of electricity, and it is easy to see why such a layer of electricity exists high in the air. Unprotected from the intense light, the atoms of air near the top of the atmosphere are struck so strongly by sunlight that some of their electrons are knocked off. These electrons, and the atoms that have lost them, form moving layers of electricity several miles thick. We know now that there are several such layers ranging from 50 to more than 200 miles up. These layers of electricity, lying above the stratosphere, form a third region of our ocean of air, called the *ionosphere* (see Fig. 1-15). You will learn more about the electricity and the radiation in the ionosphere when you read about space travel in Chapter 34.

Still another way to explore our upper air is to send measuring instruments up in a rocket or a satellite. These report back by radio and television. But at what height do we separate the earth and its atmosphere from space? Actually, the atmosphere doesn't end abruptly; it thins out. At several hundred miles above the earth, virtually all traces of the atmosphere are left behind.

From now on, when you think of the planet Earth, you will find it more accurate to think of a globe whose outer covering is the atmosphere, rather than a globe whose outer covering is considered to be the land and water surface familiar to the geography classroom. By now, you should understand that the gaseous atmosphere is as *real* a part of planet Earth itself as the entire gaseous mass of the sun is real.

Looking Back . . . .

VOCABULARY

Each term in the following list is a key word or phrase in the chapter you have just studied. Define each term to be sure that you understand its meaning.

1. gravity
2. tide
3. tidal friction
4. Foucault pendulum
5. weight
6. magnetic pole
7. topsoil
8. ocean currents
9. oceanography
10. atmosphere
11. stratosphere
12. meteor
13. ionosphere
14. Earth

REVIEW QUESTIONS

1. Where is " up "?
2. What is weight?
3. Why don't we fall off the earth?
4. How can we measure the size of the earth?
5. How are we sure that the earth turns daily?
6. Why doesn't the gravitational pull of a large building make you move toward it?
7. What are some of the strange changes in the earth's magnetism?
8. Name six common chemical elements or compounds in the earth's crust.
9. How did so much salt get into the oceans?
10. Why are ocean currents important to us?
11. What evidence do we have that the earth is somewhat like a round ball?
12. How can we study the upper parts of the earth's atmosphere?

Going Further . . . .

THOUGHT QUESTIONS

1. How would you define " the top of the earth's atmosphere "?
2. When the sun and the moon are in line (at the time of new moon and of full moon), will the tide be higher or lower than when the moon pulls sideways to the sun (at first quarter and at last quarter)?
3. What are four things about oceans that we need to investigate further?

4. What is an important difference between topsoil and subsoil?

5. It has been estimated that 90% of the atmospheric oxygen, upon which all animal life depends, is produced by tiny ocean plants — the algae. What, then, is the importance of the oceans as a future source of food?

6. How can you use a knowledge of common elements and compounds to convince someone that the atmosphere is a *real* part of the earth?

THINGS TO DO

1. Watch an eclipse of the moon and observe the shape of the earth's shadow on the surface of the moon.

2. List the elements common in the earth's crust (see Table 1-2). Beside each element indicate the commonest compounds in which it occurs. Also indicate whether the element is found in a pure or almost pure state or only in compounds.

3. Using a world atlas and a physical geography textbook, make a drawing showing the major currents in the ocean. Distinguish between warm and cool currents.

4. At night, locate the Pole star (see Fig. 33-14).

Estimate the angle by which a compass points to the east or west of the star in the part of the earth where you live.

5. Locate the latitude of your home on a globe or map. What latitude would this become if the north pole of the earth were located at Peiping, China?

6. Find a nearby road cut on a highway or railroad. Observe the sequence of soil types there, from topsoil down to gravel or bedrock. Make a model of such a cross-section of soil types and display it in the classroom.

TRY THIS PROBLEM

Suppose, in an effort to determine the earth's circumference, you established two posts, one 200 miles north of the other. When the sun's rays fall directly on the southern post, the rays make an angle of 3° with the northern post. Referring to the discussion on pages 2–3, and Fig. 1–2, can you calculate the earth's circumference?

READING FURTHER

IGY: Year of Discovery by Sydney Chapman, Univ. of Michigan Press, 1959.

The Aging Face of the Earth

How many thousands of things have people said are "as old as the hills"? But is it true that "the hills" age indefinitely — that they will always be there? In terms of three or four — or even thirty or forty — generations of people, perhaps so. Yet in terms of the earth's lifetime, our hills, too, will have their day.

WATER, WIND, AND WEATHER — AGENTS OF CHANGE

Try this experiment. Spread up to an inch of soft dirt in a pie pan. At a few places put a small solid object, like a coin or flat stone. Tip the plate slightly. Then, from a watering can, let "rain" fall on the whole pan. What happens to the exposed dirt? What about the dirt under the coins? Have you ever seen this effect in a yard after a hard rain?

You can see a similar effect on a grand scale in such places as Bryce Canyon National Park and Monument Valley in Utah and Arizona (Fig. 2-1).

Erosion of the Earth's Crust

Water and, to a lesser extent, wind are changing the face of the earth every day. So far as we know, wind and water *erosion* have gone on ever since the earth's crust and bodies of water were formed.

In fair weather, water evaporates, cools, and forms clouds from which rain or snow may later fall. The fallen rain runs downhill under the pull of gravity and, on the way, carries off the loose sand and silt. This erosion, working year after year, forms gullies and river valleys.

Josef Muench

2-1. The "Three Sisters" were carved by water wearing away softer rock year after year in Monument Valley, Arizona.

South Dakota Dept. of Highways

2-2. Although generally less effective than water, the wind also contributes to weathering and erosion, as shown in the legendary Badlands of South Dakota.

Winds can whip waves of rain or sleet against hillsides or rocks with such force that the water erodes whatever its strikes at a much greater rate than it otherwise would. Even in dry weather, winds pick up loose sand and "sandblast" rocks and hillsides with it. Here, then, is another form of erosion (Fig. 2-2).

At the seashore, the breaking waves of the oceans pound away at the shoreline. Waves roll the rocks around and grind them to sand.

Not even mountains are immune to erosion. Before the erosion takes place, *weathering processes* prepare the way, breaking down large rock formations. For one thing, alternate heating (expansion) and cooling (contraction) of rocks between night and day may cause some degree of cracking and peeling of rock layers. Also, water

that seeps into cracks in large rock formations may freeze. You probably know that when water freezes, it expands. The ice takes up more space than the liquid. The freezing water exerts great pressure on the surrounding rock and causes it to crack. Alternate freezing and thawing slowly break up large blocks of rock. Furthermore, when water runs off rock formations, it dissolves some of the minerals out of the rock, creating more space for more water to invade the rock formations and freeze.

Weathering processes (and even growth of plant roots) slowly break up massive rock formations (Fig. 2-3). Then erosion (the carrying away of broken pieces) takes place. Yes, even mountains yield — but slowly, ever so slowly. It will take perhaps eight hundred million years to wear the Rocky Mountains away completely (assuming no further mountain-building takes place there).

Weathering and the erosion of weathered crust are not the only agents of inland wear and tear. Large sheets of ice called *continental glaciers* have carved and shaped many land areas in the past. In mountain ranges today, *valley glaciers* erode

U.S. Geological Survey

2-3. Weathering breaks up surface rock. The chips may then be carried away by water or wind, the agents of erosion.

2-4. The Grand Canyon — a mile deep from rim to river. During millions of years the Colorado River has cut through the higher soft-layered sedimentary rock and into the hard rocks below.

the mountainsides, as you will shortly read in greater detail in the section on glacial changes.

All around us we can see the forces of erosion working, but how do we know they have always worked in the same way? We don't know for sure, but so far, the evidence we find of the earth's past seems to uphold the truth of this idea: that all the reactions and processes we observe today have been operating throughout hundreds of millions of years. This assumption, known as *uniformi-*

tarianism, has become a basic principle for geologists as they reconstruct the earth's past.

From Rock to Soil

As water runs down mountainsides, it tends to carry away sand, soil, gravel (all of these are weathered rock), and pieces of floating plants. As the water later swirls and washes against the bottom of a fast-moving stream, the sand wears away the rock layers underlying the stream. More and more material is then carried by the water.

At the Grand Canyon, the Colorado River is carrying more soil and sand than an endless freight train loaded with dirt and running past at the same speed as the water. What you see in Fig. 2-4 is the effect of the scouring action of what the river carries.

As already mentioned, running water dissolves chemical compounds out of rocks: sodium chloride (common table salt) and carbonates. As the water moves out onto the plains below mountains, some of it is absorbed as ground water. Thus many of the dissolved chemicals and bits of plants contribute toward forming the rich topsoil that is so necessary for our existence.

GLACIAL CHANGES

Wherever all of the snow of winter does not melt during the summer — generally in high mountains — valley glaciers may form. As the snow piles up, pressure squeezes it together to form ice, like a hard-packed snowball. This ice mass will begin to move slowly downhill as the immense pressure from the ice on top causes a semiplastic flow of the ice underneath. As more snow piles up, the pressure below increases and the ice mass moves on (Fig. 2-5, *top*).

The outward pressure at the upper end of a glacier, combined with the shattering of surrounding rock by pressure and freezing, eats out a large circular basin called a *cirque* (SIRK). If the glacier later disappears, the cirque will show high on the mountain. The next time you travel in mountainous country, look for the kind of circular basin you see in Fig. 2-5, *bottom*.

Valley glaciers are easily identified as narrow rivers of ice, moving downward between mountains or eating out valleys on mountain slopes. Continental glaciers, on the other hand, form as

2-5. Glaciers cause changes in the earth's surface not only as they move forward (upper picture) but also at their origin. The cirques (lower picture) are an example.

Canadian National Railways

Spence Air Photo

huge sheets of ice in the cold Arctic and Antarctic regions. They move, too, but not necessarily downhill. They spread out from the region of greatest accumulation of ice, moving outward in all directions.

Continental glaciers do not characteristically cut valleys. They more often tend to level the land over which they move, carrying debris with them and pushing it before them, often for hundreds of miles. Long Island, near New York City, was built up of glacial debris from two different continental glaciers of long ago. Under certain circumstances, continental glaciers can eat out areas of land that dwarf by comparison the cirques of valley glaciers. The Great Lakes, for example, are the product of continental glaciers of past ages.

The Glacial Record

Glaciers now cover about ten per cent of our land masses, about one third of the area originally covered by the glaciers of a great ice age of 11,000 or more years ago. Many examples of glacial changes exist. Two — the Great Lakes and Long Island, both in the United States — have

Charles C. Bradley

2-6. Drumlins, such as this one in Wisconsin, are piles of glacial till — debris scraped from the bottom of a glacier or left behind when it melts.

already been mentioned. The rocks strewn on the vast flatlands of Canada are a good example of glacial debris scattered widely.

Valley glaciers produced the fiords of Greenland and Norway and Yosemite Valley in California. The glacial erosion in Yosemite Valley is so deep that many side valleys, or " hanging valleys," have been left high above the main valley. Streams that run from the side valleys create startling waterfalls whose water tumbles thousands of feet to the bottom of the glaciated valley.

Where do glaciers end? If, as with the continental icecaps of Greenland or Antarctica, they end in the sea, great masses of ice may break up and float as ice packs or ice floes. Lesser pieces may break off and fall into the sea with a spectacular splash to become icebergs.

Valley glaciers formed high in the mountains of a region with a warmer climate rarely end in the sea. As the glaciers move down off the high slopes, they begin to melt. Where the ice ends, a U-shaped embankment of debris (surrounding the end of the glacier) is deposited. This is the *terminal moraine*. The debris or mixture of boulders, gravel, sand, and sediment that makes up the moraine is known as *glacial till*.

Continental glaciers form moraines, too, often as great oblong piles or hills called *drumlins*. In Massachusetts, New York, Michigan, Wisconsin, and Minnesota there are many drumlins (Fig. 2-6).

Hard rock surfaces, polished smooth by glacial flow, often have long, thin scratches whose direction indicates the direction in which the glacier was moving. Often large chunks of rock have been dislodged, scoured into the form of boulders, carried many miles by a continental glacier, and then left in a " strange " place. The composition of these boulders is quite unlike that of nearby rocks, but matches that of rocks far away in the direction along which the glacial scratches point. Such " erratic " boulders — clearly out of place — are unmistakable evidence of glacial action.

From what geologists have found, we can conclude that great continental glaciers covered the northern United States and Canada during the

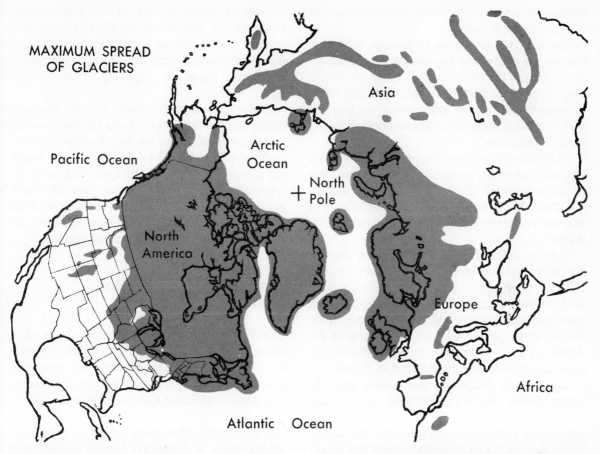

MAXIMUM SPREAD OF GLACIERS

Asia

Pacific Ocean

Arctic Ocean

+ North Pole

North America

Europe

Africa

Atlantic Ocean

2-7. The maximum spread of continental glaciers over the northern hemisphere, seen from the North Pole. The cause of the periodic advance and retreat of these giant ice sheets is still under dispute.

past million years. In fact, four separate glacial advances have been identified and named after the Midwestern states in which evidence for each was found. Fig. 2-7 shows the extent of this ice sheet when it covered the greatest areas of the United States and Europe.

Glacial changes, then, are responsible for many of the present forms of our land masses. The Cape Cod area in Massachusetts was formed from rock pushed and washed down to the sea. Glacial debris also formed the sandbars south of the New England coast that forced the Pilgrims to turn northward to Massachusetts. Much of the fine farm land near the Great Lakes came from *silt* — very small rock particles in solution — deposited during the melting of the great icecaps.

Causes of the Continental Glacial Cycle

What accounts for the Ice Ages — the repeated advance and retreat of great ice sheets which have, at least four times, covered and uncovered much of the United States and Europe?

This is a difficult scientific problem that is still unresolved. But we can look at two attempts to explain the glacial cycle as good examples of how scientists search for explanations.

Suppose that the growth and decline of glaciers is related to corresponding changes in the earth's average temperature. Then it is certainly likely that such temperature changes are due, in turn, to variations in the amount of the sun's heat reaching the earth's surface. Now the problem is: what are possible reasons for long-term, recurring changes in the amount of solar heat received? At least two come to mind.

The heat and brightness of the sun itself may change. Or changes in the earth's atmosphere — particularly in the percentage of carbon dioxide — may be partly responsible. Carbon dioxide tends to absorb infrared, or heat, waves, so that the heat reradiated from the earth's surface is trapped, as in a greenhouse.

Unfortunately, it is not known how to check on long-term changes in the brightness of the sun or in percentages of carbon dioxide in the atmosphere. We have no records of observations of the sun or atmosphere going back thousands of years.

Quite a different sort of explanation for the Ice Ages is offered by yet another theory. Instead of being based upon variations in the amount of heat received on the earth, this theory is based upon alternate freezing and melting of the Arctic Ocean. Although we are used to thinking of the Arctic Ocean as almost completely choked by polar ice, consider the reasoning that follows:

Suppose the Arctic ice sheet melts and the Arctic Ocean becomes relatively open water. From an increased expanse of open water greater evaporation takes place and the polar atmosphere would then be full of moisture capable of forming snow. The resultant heavy snows would, over the years, contribute to the formation of a new Arctic ice sheet, an advancing Ice Age.

Eventually so much water could be " captured " by this new ice sheet that the world's ocean level would fall. It would then be difficult for warmer Atlantic Ocean water to circulate northward over submarine ledges that ridge the North Alantic.

Now the conditions are present for a halt in the further growth of the ice sheet. For now there would be less of the open Arctic water and, therefore, less evaporation of the moisture that forms snow. Also, the cutting off of warmer Atlantic Ocean currents, as the ocean level falls, contributes to the next general freezing of the Arctic. Thus the very growth of the ice sheet is the cause of the halt in its spread. Once halted, it will start to melt, and the cycle will start all over again. If

this theory proves correct (it is highly speculative), we are now witnessing the beginning of a new cycle in which the Arctic Ocean is warming up and will become open. According to the theory, this would signal the beginning of another Ice Age.

Perhaps the next few years will see new evidence for one or another of the theories that explains the origins of an Ice Age. Perhaps, too, entirely new theories will be developed. The search for the causes of the glacial cycle will surely be reported as it develops. During your life much more will be learned about the cold regions of the earth. Even now, scientists of many countries are co-operating in studies of the polar regions.

THE WATER CYCLE, EROSION, AND SEDIMENTATION

We have dealt much with water as the chief agent of erosion — erosion by rainfall, by river flow, by glacial action, by breaking waves on beaches. It is time now to investigate the reasons *why* water is the chief agent of erosion.

Try this experiment. Fill a pie tin with water and set it aside. How many days does it take for all the water to disappear? Unless you live in a very damp climate, the water should all be gone in a day or two. Of course you knew that the water would evaporate into the air.

All over the earth exposed surfaces of water are evaporating in the same way this very moment. Water is also evaporating from damp land surfaces. In warm climates several tons of water may evaporate from each acre each day.

When you remember that almost three fourths of the earth's surface is covered by the oceans, and that most of the land is moist enough to support some form of plant life, you can agree that a lot of water is escaping into the air every minute. Unless that water came down again somewhere, the oceans would presently evaporate and disappear. Of course, water does come out of the air every time rain or snow falls, and whenever there is dew or frost. Rivers of it flow off the land and

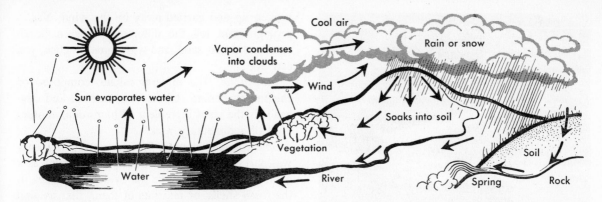

2-8. Evaporation of water from oceans, lakes, and the land is part of an endless cycle. Begin with any one of these bodies of water or land and trace the course a drop of water might take. The energy for "pumping" water around this cycle may be traced to the heat provided by sunlight.

back into the sea. Around and around the water goes — into the air as water vapor, down again as rain or snow — an endless process that is called the *water cycle* (Fig. 2-8).

The Force of Water

The important part of our story is what happens when water has come down onto the earth as rain or snow or frost. We have already seen that water rushing downhill can wash down rocks and cause them to grind each other to bits. This kind of moving water also washes down large amounts of soil and even dissolves some chemical compounds out of rocks that are not themselves washed away. (Rainwater that has carbon dioxide in it can dissolve limestone rocks completely. This limestone-dissolving water explains the formation of great underground caves.) What happens to the materials picked up by the rushing waters? Most of them are carried into rivers and down toward the sea.

Sedimentation

As rivers flow on toward the sea, the silt and the sand they carry are dropped when the water slows up in the sea beyond the mouths of the rivers. In many cases, great deltas form, like the one at the end of the Mississippi River. Some of the area becomes fine farm land, but some of the silt and sand is carried down and deposited

under the ocean. The underwater accumulation that piles up along the shore builds up the top layers of what we call the *continental shelf*.

All materials carried by a river, such as sand, gravel, and mud, are known as *sediments*. As new sediments are deposited over successive layers of older ones below them, the deeper, buried layers of sediments begin to undergo changes.

Sedimentary Rocks

Gradually, beneath the top layers of sediment, buried layers begin to harden. Circulation of underground water adds deposits of silicon dioxide and other materials to the buried sediments. Silicon dioxide and also calcium carbonate begin cementing buried deposits together. In the older, deeper, layers, the cementation process has been going on so long, aided by pressure from new sediments deposited high above, that solid rock has formed. The deeply buried sediments have become *sedimentary rock* — one of the three major groups into which rocks are classified according to how they were formed.

There are four important types of sedimentary rock. Each of the first three, shale, sandstone, and limestone, have distinctly different basic ingredients.

Shale. Clay is a sediment that is laid down in thin layers, then pressed and compacted to form a mudstone. It continues to undergo cemen-

2-9. Shale is recognizable by many thin layers in the deposits. A pick or other tool is often included in geological photos to indicate comparative size.

tation until increasing pressure from new sediments drives out all the water. At this point it has become *shale,* a sedimentary rock easily broken into thin plates. Look for shale the next time you ride a train over a track bed that lies below a cutaway cliff (Fig. 2-9).

Sandstone. The chemical combination of oxygen and silicon known as silica is a common material in sedimentary rocks. Silica is merely another name for silicon dioxide. It is found most commonly in the earth's crust in the form of the tiny quartz crystals we call sand. Under a small magnifying glass, sand grains look almost like glass.

Sand is deposited along ocean and lake shores. Over long periods of time, as sand piles up, cementing occurs, and a new kind of sedimentary rock called *sandstone* is formed. Of course, not all the world's sand is on the beaches. Some forms sand dunes on land. Here, too, buried deposits undergo cementation and form sandstone.

Did you know that you can tell the difference between beach sand and desert sand? One of the materials in sand — a silicate crystal called *mica,* which occurs in little fragile flakes — is missing in desert sand. The mica flakes have all been

broken up and carried away by the wind. Yes, a geologist can tell the difference between beach sand and desert sand, and with some practice, you can, too.

Limestone. The mineral calcite, composed of calcium carbonate (or calcium, carbon, and oxygen), is the chief ingredient of *limestone,* another kind of sedimentary rock.

The calcium in most limestone probably once was part of the shell of some sea animal, such as a clam or oyster. We have the evidence for this in the fossil shells, or imprints of them, that we find in rocks. Imagine how the great limestone cliffs, the White Cliffs of Dover, must have been formed: day after day, year after year, century after century, a thin rain of shells from dead animals fell to the floor of a sea. As they piled up, the lower shells began to get crushed and cemented together to form an early stage of rock made up of shell fragments. The more the shell fragments became crushed, the more cementation occurred. Eventually limestone resulted.

The next time you are in a bank or public building, look around to see if the counters or walls are made of limestone. Often, a few shells (or imprints of shells) of ancient animals are clearly visible embedded in the limestone.

Conglomerates. The fourth type of sedimentary rock may contain materials found in all three of the other types. It may result from a stream depositing a variety of rounded pebbles in a sandy bed. When such a mixture has been cemented into rock, it looks just like its name: *conglomerate rock.*

Sedimentary rocks tell us much about the history of the earth. Sometimes they are found in surprising places, not just in railroad cuts, mine shafts, etc. You will read more about how they provide clues to the earth's history in Chapter 3.

SOIL CONSERVATION

Erosion by water and wind is continually shaping the land, wearing away the face of the earth at high places and building it up at low places. In steep regions, great canyons and valleys have been

2-10. Whole sections of the country have been laid waste by winds blowing away soil. This results when the soil is dry and not sufficiently bound by the network of roots provided by certain plants and grasses.

formed, and along rivers and at their mouths, layers of sediment have piled up. Much of our fine farm land today is old "bottom land" — old riverbeds.

Erosion Control

Man can upset nature's processes and bring about undesirable results. If you were asked, "Where is the nearest desert?" you might name a place miles away. Yet wherever you stand on the earth, the nearest desert is really only a few inches away from you!

Beneath the few inches (at most a few feet) of precious topsoil is the desert — silt, clay, and sand that cannot support plant life. Remove the topsoil, and there go your chances to raise a lawn, flowers, or tomatoes. No topsoil, no food — except sea food.

Yet the very act of plowing a field leaves the topsoil at the mercy of the raindrops and the winds. Thus, farmers have to learn the many ways of preventing, or at least reducing, what you see in Fig. 2-10.

Many farmers plow so that the furrows run around a hill, rather than up and down. This is known as *contour plowing* (Fig. 2-11). Rain will

2-11. Both strip cropping and contour plowing are used to fight erosion by water and wind.

then catch in many little basins, instead of running downhill and making gullies from which the topsoil has been washed away.

Strip cropping also helps control erosion. Fields of open-tilled crops, such as corn, leave too much bare earth exposed. If corn is to be planted, it can be planted in alternate strips between which other strips are planted with close-growing crops like alfalfa. Alfalfa both covers the soil from above and binds it with a complex root system below the soil surface. Fig. 2-11 shows both strip cropping and contour plowing.

Really steep hills should be covered with growing grass and trees, and their slopes should not be used for open cultivation. In windy places, even flat lands may be kept under a cover of grass all the time. Roots of grass and close-growing crops hold topsoil down and slow up running water.

Flood Control

Too much water can be as dangerous as too little. In many areas of the southwestern part of our country, the rainfall is only a few inches each year. Trees and grass are sparse; wind and water erosion are active. When rain does fall, it often comes down in heavy showers, or cloudbursts, and runs off quickly. Then floods occur. Rushing waters carry off the loose topsoil and cut out deep gullies.

A flood is a serious matter, whether it happens in the Connecticut Valley of New England or along the Mississippi River or on the Rio Grande. Too much water in a short time, caused by heavy rain or rapidly melting snows, runs together to flood the surrounding lowlands. Erosion of precious topsoil is then great.

One way we have learned to stop floods is by using dams. These can hold back some of the rushing waters upstream and prevent flooding downstream. The water caught behind the dams can be used to irrigate nearby farms or to operate electrical generators. The electricity can be used to pump the water where it is needed, or for lighting or many other purposes.

As you may suspect, dams are only a temporary answer to flood control. Over the years, the dam basins will fill with sediments and their storage of water will become too limited. Long-term flood control must begin on the slopes of the hills down which the water first runs. Grass and plants on these slopes can catch and hold the water. Then it will sink into the ground and move slowly to other regions where it seeps up to the surface or can be pumped from wells.

Of the 1500 million acres available for farming or grazing in the United States, nearly 300 million acres, that is, 20 per cent, had been ruined by erosion by 1947! You can see why so much effort has been put into farm and conservation activities to save our topsoil.

Without man on the landscape, natural processes slowly reach a kind of balance. But man can quickly upset that balance with a plow, a bulldozer, forest fires, or overgrazing. Then centuries may have to pass before a new balance develops — and it may not be one that provides more topsoil.

You can see why it is important that we understand the physical, chemical, and biological processes of the world in which we live. Otherwise, we may do great harm to ourselves and to those who live after us.

Looking Back . . . .

VOCABULARY

Each of the following terms relates to one or more key ideas in the chapter you have just studied. Be sure that you know each term and the ideas or processes or events to which it relates.

1. erosion
2. agents of erosion
3. uniformitarianism
4. weathering
5. valley glacier
6. continental glacier
7. cirque
8. glacial till
9. erratic boulder
10. terminal moraine
11. water cycle
12. sediment
13. continental shelf
14. sedimentary rock
15. silica (silicon dioxide)
16. conglomerate
17. contour plowing
18. strip cropping

REVIEW QUESTIONS

1. What are some possible causes of glaciers?
2. Distinguish between weathering and erosion.
3. In what ways does water move in a cycle?
4. How do soft sediments form into hard rocks?
5. Why should we bother to preserve our topsoil?
6. What are the four major types of sedimentary rocks?
7. How can floods best be prevented?
8. How do winds change the face of the earth?
9. Where are sediments deposited?
10. What processes act to wear down the land?
11. What is the evidence for ancient glaciers?

Going Further . . . .

THOUGHT QUESTIONS

1. Do you suppose the surface of the earth in the past was more or less mountainous and uneven than it is today?
2. Why does the geologist begin his study of the earth's past with some assumptions?
3. How might you tell if a new glacial period was developing?
4. How did so much salt get into the oceans?
5. From where have the thousands of square miles of Mississippi River delta come?
6. Why do you suppose the coast of Maine is so rocky and rugged, when the coast of Delaware or Texas is not?

THINGS TO DO

1. Make a collection of stones from your home town. Identify the sedimentary rocks among them. What can you conclude about their past history from the shapes of the stones? What can you conclude about their origin from their internal structure?

2. Look for layers of shale or slate in cuts made through hills for highways or railroads. From the appearance and thickness of the layers of exposed rock, estimate how long it might have taken for the material in these rocks to be deposited as sediments.

3. Pour a thin stream of vinegar or weak hydrochloric acid over limestone or marble. Does the stone dissolve away? Are channels formed?

4. Drop some vinegar or weak hydrochloric acid on a seashell and on an eggshell. What do you see? Put a few drops on limestone and calcite. What evidence do you have that limestone is chemically similar to seashells? What should you do to make sure that many other rocks and minerals do not react like limestone when tested this way?

TRY THESE PROBLEMS

1. If, on the average, rainfall causes the erosion of 15 tons of rock each year from a given mountain whose total mass is 500 million tons, how many years will it take for erosion to level the mountain?

2. If a glacier moves at the rate of 200 feet per year, how many years ago did it start " growing " if it is now 3 miles long?

READING FURTHER

The Earth We Live On by Ruth Moore, Alfred A. Knopf, Inc., 1956.
Water for People by Sarah R. Reidman, Abelard, 1955, discusses one of the most vital national resources.

CHAPTER 3

The Restless Earth

Montana Highway Commission

Weathering and erosion have worn away so many mountains and hills in the earth's past that the oldest known rocks today, from miles deep within the crust, bear unmistakable evidence of having once been sediments, deposited following erosion. Nothing on earth could have withstood what are now known to be billions of years of wear and tear.

How is it, then, that so many high mountain ranges exist even today?

DISTURBANCES OF THE EARTH'S CRUST

Some of the highest mountains on earth are made up primarily of sedimentary rock. *How can this be?* Everyone knows that sediments are deposited in low areas, not on mountains!

Look at Fig. 3-1. You can see clearly the layers of sedimentary rock aligned in a mountain high in the Rockies. Some of these rock layers contain imprints of animals that lived long ago in the seas. What can you gather from this evidence? Two things might occur to you — one, that the rock layers of this mountain once must have been at the bottom of an ancient sea, and two, that somehow, part of the ancient sea bottom has come to be high in the air.

Now look at Fig. 3-2. Do you see the layers of sedimentary rock? If you don't, perhaps it is

3-1. The occurrence of sedimentary layers high up in mountains seems a puzzle since such sediments must be deposited in low-lying areas by erosion. How do attempts to solve this puzzle lead to ideas of mountain formation?

because you didn't expect them to be folded and mutilated as they are. Originally, the layers of rock were flat and level, like any other sedimentary rock. What violent force can have crumpled them in this way?

Evidence of upheavals in the earth's crust, many of them fairly recent in geologic time, is recorded in rock formations all over the world.

A. Keith, U.S. Geological Survey

3-2. Earth movements produce these patterns from sedimentary layers originally deposited in level strata.

Figs. 3-2 and 3-3 are but two examples.

Every mountain range — almost every individual mountain — has its own story of how and (approximately) when it came to be where it is. The part of each story that is least well known is the why of it — the underlying causes of mountain building.

Determining the Ages of Mountain Formations

The age of any mountain can be determined, at least roughly. Scientists have found a geological "clock" that "tells the time" through the ages for any rock formation that contains uranium or certain other *radioactive elements*. Radioactivity, as you may know, is a process of self-distintegration of certain elements. The atoms of these elements are not stable — they break up or decay continually, giving off atomic particles, heat, and light.

Uranium decays to form several other unstable elements, one at a time. At each stage certain particles known as *alpha* particles are given off. These ultimately become helium. The larger part of what once was uranium finally ends up as lead. From experiments with the rate at which uranium decays, we know that half of any sample of uranium will be converted to lead and helium in 4.56 billion years. We have no reason to believe that this rate has ever changed. Thus, if we analyze the amounts of uranium, lead, and helium in rock

R. H. Chapman, U.S. Geological Survey

3-3. The huge forces at work in the earth's crust are evident not only in earthquakes but also in this instance of folding and tilting of sedimentary layers.

3-4. The contrast between old and young mountain ranges is clearly shown by the Appalachians pictured above and the Rocky Mountains shown to the right. The Appalachians exhibit the relatively smooth and rounded features of a range worn by over a hundred million years of erosion.

samples, we can estimate how old the rock samples are, since no lead was present originally.

Helium, however, is a gas. Some of the helium from uranium decay has been trapped within rock formations, but most of it has escaped into the air. Lead, on the other hand, is a heavy metal. The lead from uranium decay has remained with the rock formations of which uranium is a part.

Using the method of *uranium-lead dating,* scientists have worked backward and calculated that certain rock formations are almost three and one-half billion years old. They have checked these estimates by following the same process with other radioactive elements — thorium, for example. Like uranium, thorium disintegrates to form lead — but at a different rate. Can scientists distinguish which element yielded the lead in a rock sample? Yes. The lead yielded by thorium decay is a heavier form than the lead yielded by uranium decay.

Thus, *thorium-lead dating* makes a good check for results obtained by uranium-lead dating.

None of the rugged mountain ranges of today is three and one-half billion years old, or even one tenth that age. Any mountains that may have existed then were worn away millions of years ago. There are not even any rocks today that are thought to have been a part of the earth's original crust. The oldest known rocks are some that once were sedimentary rocks and that later underwent further changes.

How old is the earth itself? It is worth pausing a moment to confess that we do not know. Perhaps we never will find out through study of the earth alone. (Another hope lies in astronomy, as you will read in Chapter 33.) If the oldest known rocks on earth are sedimentary in origin, then they must have been deposited as sediments long before they hardened into rock. Thus, an

3-5. An aerial view of the Rocky Mountains — a chain of young mountains (only about 60 million years old). The extensive folding, faulting, and uplift that resulted in the Rocky Mountains was a world-wide process. In the western hemisphere, it produced the Andes Mountains as well.

age of erosion and sedimentation considerably older than three and one-half billion years is indicated. Was this the *first* age of earth erosion and sedimentation? Or was it merely an age that eliminated the last traces of even older ages of erosion and sedimentation? No one knows for sure, but hard as it is to believe, the latter may be true. (We suspect so because two meteors that struck the earth long ago have been dated at roughly four and one-half billion years or more of age. Since it is believed that the earth was formed at the same time as the other planets and the meteors, the age of a meteorite — the remains of a meteor — should be related to the age of the earth.)

The oldest major mountain range in North America is the Appalachian range (Fig. 3-4), dating back about 200 million years. The Rockies (Fig. 3-5), the Cascades, the Sierra Nevadas —

all are younger. Some — the Arbuckles of Oklahoma, the Ozarks of Arkansas and Missouri, and a few of the Appalachians generally east of the main range — are older than the 200 million years indicated for most of the Appalachians. These older mountains are so worn away that reconstruction of their original sizes is impossible. The Killarneyan Mountains of Minnesota, Wisconsin, and Southern Canada are perhaps the oldest United States range from which a few small hills remain. These mountains are 800 million years old. Probably they were high and rugged once. Today their remains (the Penokee Hills in northern Wisconsin and a few hills in northeastern Minnesota) are very small.

Mountain-building Processes

How are mountain ranges built? Most are pushed up at least partly by folding and crum-

Ⓐ **Folded mountains**

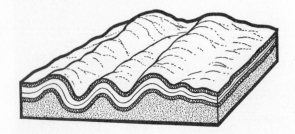

Ⓑ **Normal fault**

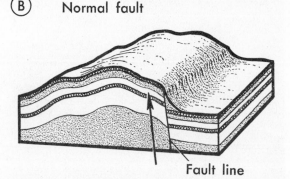

Fault line

3-6. Mountains are built by various processes. A range like this one appears when forces acting upon the earth's crust cause it to buckle and fold.

When layers of rock resist folding but cannot resist the tremendous pressures being exerted on them, faults, or breaks, such as this one occur.

Ⓔ **Fault-block mountains**

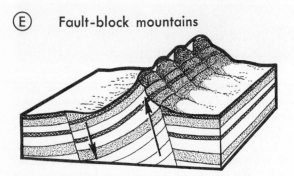

Ⓕ₁ **Formation of residual mountain**

Softer rock layers

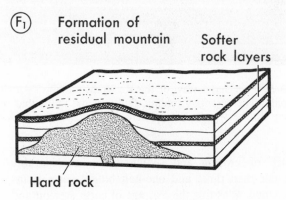

Hard rock

A block of crust between two fault lines is tilted and thrust up; fault-block mountains result.

Another type is the residual mountain, formed when a broad land area is eroded away.

pling of the earth's crust. You can see *folds* in Fig. 3-2 and Fig. 3-6a. Those in Fig. 3-6a have produced a range of young *folded mountains.*

Sometimes layers of rock resist folding but cannot resist the tremendous pressures being exerted on them from other parts of the crust beneath and around them. Earthquakes occur, and *faults* form — definite lines of break in the rock formations (Figs. 3-6b and c).

Lines of faulting — as well as folding — may be hundreds of miles long. Thus, mountain ranges tend to be long and narrow. Layers of rock on one

side of a line of fault may be lifted upward (or they may slip downward) perhaps only a few inches or feet. Or, the layers of rock on one side of the fault line may be lifted upward considerably, forming mountains.

Fault lines rarely are vertical; thus, one part of the earth's crust tends to be *on one side and below* the fault line, another part *on the other side and above* the fault line. You can see this effect in differing degrees in Figs. 3-6b, c, and d. If the rock layers on one side of the fault line are pushed up, *normal-fault mountains* may result (Fig.

TO THE FORMATION OF MOUNTAINS

Ⓒ Thrust fault

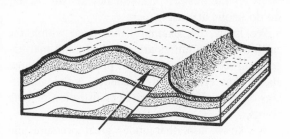

Fault lines are rarely vertical. If the portion to one side of the fault line is thrust sideways and upward, thrust fault mountains result.

Ⓓ Overthrust fault

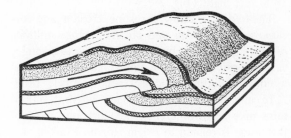

If layers on one side of a fault are raised and thrust completely over the layers on the other side, overthrust mountains materialize.

F₂ Residual mountain

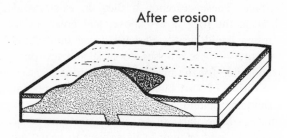

After erosion

Layer by layer, softer rock gradually disappears, leaving a protruding area of hard rock.

Ⓖ Volcano

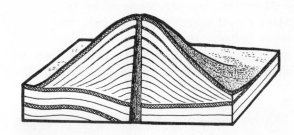

A volcano appears when extreme heat deep in the earth forces rock to melt and escape upward.

3-6b). If the rock layers are pushed upward and sideways, *thrust-fault mountains* result (Fig. 3-6c). If the angle of the fault line is extreme, layers of the earth's crust on one side of a fault may be raised and thrust completely over the layers on the other side, forming *overthrust-fault mountains* (Fig. 3-6d). In some of the mountains of the western United States, parts of the earth's crust have been lifted up and thrust eastward ten miles or more over other parts of the crust! The Rockies in Montana may still be building up this way.

There are still other types of mountains. When a block of the earth's crust between *two* different fault lines is tilted and thrust up (Fig. 3-6e), *fault-block mountains* result. And when a broad land area is eroded away except for certain harder rock that resisted erosion, *residual mountains* are left (Fig. 3-6f).

Volcanic activity also contributes to mountain building. *Volcanic mountains* (Fig. 3-6g) exist in many parts of the world. One of the most famous volcanoes, however, did not exist at all before 1943. In that year, a Mexican farmer saw a crack appear in the earth in his cornfield. Before his eyes, steam and lava began to pour out. A volcano was born! When the activity ceased for a time, the new volcanic " mountain " was already 1400 feet high! (Fig. 3-7.)

The folding, faulting, thrusting, erosion, and volcanic activity go on and on. Sometimes millions of years go into the building of a mountain range; yet in terms of geologic time (*billions* of years) mountain-building processes are relatively brief.

In any one mountain range, different mountains may be of different types, although most of the range is related in origin. In the Rockies, for example, there are folded mountains, normal-fault mountains, thrust-fault mountains, over-thrust-fault mountains, block-fault mountains, residual mountains (Pikes Peak is residual), and others. In the Cascades are many of these same types of mountains plus volcanic mountains (Mt. Shasta, Mt. Rainier, Mt. Lassen, Mt. Hood).

Mountains are not restricted to land areas. Many rugged mountain ranges exist on the earth's ocean bottoms. Here, too, the ranges tend to be long, narrow, and often curved. When some of these mountains break the ocean's surface they become islands, as with the Hawaiian chain.

Ewing Galloway

3-7. A farmer in Mexico plants corn and is surprised by what " grows."

The Forces Behind Mountain Building

The question of why mountains are built — what the tremendous forces are that buckle parts of the surface of the earth — is difficult to answer. Many of the answers are still not known. A few we do know, at least in part.

We know, for example, that deep within the earth the temperatures are very high, and that underlying rocks are under great pressure from those above. The eruption of volcanoes, with outpourings of molten rock, is one demonstration of both points.

We know, too, that under great pressure and heat, many solid materials become somewhat plastic even though they are not molten. And just as *convection currents* (p. 212) of air circulate in a room with a window on one side and a heater on the other, so it is possible that slow convection currents of somewhat plastic rock exist at different depths (and temperatures) under the earth's surface. These currents, if they do exist, would drag on the rock layers above, and great surface stresses could result. Perhaps — we don't know for sure — these stresses do exist and are partly responsible for the buckling of the crust.

Erosion of vast high areas may leave residual mountains behind, but how is it that such broad areas — large parts of an entire continent — become elevated enough to be subject to heavy erosion? What can influence such broad continental uplift, as opposed to long, narrow regions of folding and faulting?

Isostasy and Uplift

It was in a mountain range that a good theory of uplift on a continental scale had its beginning. Near the Himalaya mountains of India, one hundred years ago, a party of surveyors was at work on a new map of the region.

Using surveying methods, they measured the length of a long north-south line. They then found, by star-sightings, the latitude at each end of their line. Using these latitudes, they found the length of their north-south line again to use as a check against their original measurement. But the two figures differed by almost 500 feet. What could

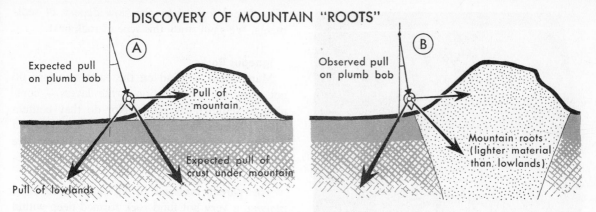

DISCOVERY OF MOUNTAIN "ROOTS"

A

Expected pull on plumb bob

Pull of mountain

Expected pull of crust under mountain

Pull of lowlands

B

Observed pull on plumb bob

Mountain roots (lighter material than lowlands)

3-8. What would you have suggested to explain the smaller-than-expected pull on the plumb bob? Some thought the mountains might be hollow. Can you see how low-density mountain roots would be a solution?

be the cause of this great difference? Since determinations of latitude by star-sighting are extremely accurate, they thought their surveying was faulty. But they had been very careful to estimate how much the gravitational pull of the mountains would affect their plumb bob (Fig. 3-8a).

A thorough check revealed that the sideways pull of the mountains on the plumb bob was one third less than their most careful estimate of what it should have been. At first it was suggested that the mountains might be hollow, or at least of very low density. But sometime later a more thorough explanation was offered.

Suppose that the mountain ranges are considered as merely the topmost portion of much greater extents of low-density rock. If this were the case, then the pull on the plumb bob by the mountains would be less than expected because of the relatively greater influence of the denser continental plains pulling away from the mountains (Fig. 3-8b).

Since that time, measurements all over the world support the idea that mountain ranges do have deep "roots" far below the surface of the earth where the inner crust is under so much pressure that it forms a somewhat plastic rock "ocean."

Picture the mountains and their deep roots as floating in an ocean of denser, semiplastic rock (much as icebergs float in water with less than one seventh of their volume above the surface). The

idea that mountain ranges "float" in subsurface rock and that all other parts of the upper structure of the earth's crust are in a floating balance with lower portions, is known as *isostasy* (eye-sos-tuh-si).

The theory of isostasy is widely applied to the problem of what causes uplift or sinkage of vast land areas. Imagine, for example, that one part of the earth once was covered by a great glacier that exerted tremendous pressure downward on the earth beneath it. Under the ice load, the crust would sink lower. Elsewhere, vast areas of crust might be uplifted.

The theory of isostasy is important in geology. The more we learn about the float-balance that appears to exist between upper and lower portions of the earth's crust, the better able we should be to investigate the tremendous forces that act to change the face of the earth.

TYPES OF ROCK — EVIDENCE OF PAST ACTIVITY

You already know of *sedimentary rocks* (pp. 25–26) and their origin. Sedimentary rocks are the earth's salvage from countless ages of erosion. They tell a story not only of the changing face of the earth but also of the history of life on earth, for within the layers of sediment of bygone ages were buried the remains of ancient living things.

American Museum of Natural History

3-9. The trilobite fossil occurs widely. Extinct for 300 million years, it was an ancestor of crabs and insects.

In time these remains or imprints turned to rock, forming what we call *fossils* (Figs. 3-9 and 3-10).

There are other kinds of rocks besides sedimentary rocks. Volcanic lavas are good examples of rock not formed by the slow deposit of sediments. We shall study this type of rock next.

Igneous Rocks

Many rocks we find on the earth's surface do not show the stratification — the layers — common to sedimentary rocks. Nor do they contain fossils. They look as though they had once been liquid and had cooled and hardened. These are known as *igneous* (IG-nee-us) *rocks,* or " firerocks."

The parent material of all igneous rocks is *magma,* a very hot fluid rock formed deep within the earth's crust and made up largely of compounds of silicon, oxygen, and sulfur. Certain volcanic lavas are the only magma that is ever seen in its molten state on the earth's surface. These are *basaltic lavas,* which cool to form *basalt* — a dense, dark rock that occurs widely in subsurface layers of the crust. Hawaii, our newest state, owes its origin to basaltic lavas.

American Museum of Natural History

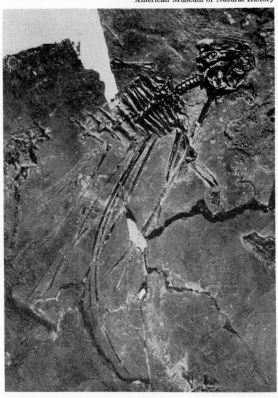

The New York Times

3-10. Collecting fossils not only is fun but also may lead to important finds that advance science. In 1961 these New Jersey students were the first to discover a type of reptile which may have been the earliest flying animal.

3-11. Granite is a common igneous rock whose mineral content is often easy to detect. This sample contains quartz, feldspar, and black mica.

3-12. Quartz, one of the hardest of the common minerals, is shown here in its six-sided crystalline form. Chemically it is silicon dioxide.

The most common type of igneous rock is *granite,* with the typical blotched or speckled appearance you see in Fig. 3-11. The part of granite that is most clear and glassy in appearance is *quartz* (Fig. 3-12), almost pure silicon dioxide. Small amounts of impurities often color quartz rosy, purple, or gray. Amethysts are purple quartz in the form of six-sided, pointed crystals.

The milky white or pink part of granite is an important group of minerals called *feldspars,* which make up about sixty per cent of the volume of granite. Feldspar is softer than quartz. In the presence of water, it decomposes at a faster rate than quartz, becoming clay.

Also found in granite are glittering pieces of *mica,* which flake off in brittle sheets, and dark crystals called *hornblendes.*

If you look for igneous rocks, you will often find them in *dikes* (Fig. 3-13). A dike is a narrow, vertical band of dark rock (usually basalt) that has pushed up as molten rock through a crack in other rocks. Any pushing up or intrusion of molten rock into cracks in the rock layers above it is known as an *igneous intrusion.* These intrusions are not always dikes; they may be *sills* — intru-

sions that spread out horizontally between two layers of rock.

Still other intrusions may form large blocks in the rock layers they invade. If widespread erosion then wears down the surface of the land, the intrusions may be left as residual mountains or buttes. In the mountain ranges of the western United States, huge igneous intrusions make up a large part of the mountain substructures. These intrusions are not widely exposed, however, nor are they thought to be a cause of the mountain building, but rather one of the many results, along with folding, faulting, and other processes.

Igneous extrusions, as opposed to intrusions, are the outpourings of lavas onto the surface of the earth from volcanoes or fissures.

If you look at igneous rocks through a magnifying glass, you will notice that the grained appearance seems to be caused by many small parts with regular shapes. In granite, for one example, you can see the regularly shaped crystals of *minerals.* (The quartz, feldspars, mica, and hornblendes are all minerals, and crystalline.) We class as minerals many different substances, all of which have some form of crystalline structures

C. P. Ross, U.S. Geological Survey

3-13. Igneous intrusions — molten rock forced through fissures or between layers of other rock — take two forms. Shown here is a dike, an intrusion in a vertical fissure. Intrusions in horizontal fissures are called sills. A fine example is the palisade cliffs along the Hudson River.

and certain other properties in common — for instance, characteristic scales of hardness, luster, color, and color variation.

Because we find mineral crystals in granite, and because we know the amount of heat required before they can be produced, we can conclude that granite can be traced back to a hot, plastic magma. As the granite cooled slowly, the crystals took shape and solidified.

Recent discoveries strongly suggest that not all granite is formed from igneous magma. Rather, it seems that hot fluid rock which in turn came from surface sedimentary layers forms certain granites. Thus the history of granite continues as an open and exciting subject.

The size of the crystals (or grains) found in igneous rocks indicates how rapidly or slowly the rocks cooled. The larger crystals, including semiprecious jewels, occur in rocks that cooled slowly.

What size grains would you expect to find in a lava that poured out on the ground and solidified in a few days? No grains at all. There was no time for crystals to form, and the resulting rock is just glassy. It is called *obsidian*. Obsidian was widely used by Indians for arrowheads and spear points (Fig. 3-14).

When a geologist finds coarse-grained igneous rocks at the earth's surface, he looks for traces of a surrounding blanket of overlying rocks that kept the magma from cooling rapidly. If he cannot find such rocks around, he suspects that they have been eroded away during long intervals of time.

Metamorphic Rocks

What would you expect to happen if sedimentary and igneous rocks were subjected to further upheavals and renewed pressure and heat? If you think they would change into other forms, you are right.

Rocks that are changed in this way are known as *metamorphic rocks* (from the Greek words that mean "a shape beyond" the original form). The *slate* formerly used in many school chalkboards is a metamorphic rock. It is a changed form of shale, a sedimentary rock. *Marble* is another rock that is sedimentary in origin — the metamorphic form of limestone.

Two main groups of metamorphic rocks are

American Museum of Natural History

3-14. Obsidian shows the smooth texture characteristic of a quickly cooled igneous rock. It is also known because of its appearance and texture, as volcanic glass.

3-15. Four types of gems are shown in their rough and their polished, or cut, form: top left pair, diamond; top right pair, topaz; bottom left pair, ruby; bottom right pair, emerald. Much work is devoted to synthesizing gems by subjecting their chemical constituents to extreme heat and pressure.

readily identified. One is *gneiss* (NICE), probably a metamorphosed granite. In it, the various light and dark minerals form bands, so that the rock looks striped. The other is *schist* (SHIST), a finer-grained rock than gneiss. It is derived from slate by further metamorphosis. Schists have a brilliant, spangled appearance from the many plates of mica arranged in the same direction.

Metamorphic rocks are often folded and twisted, evidence of great movement of the rocks over long time intervals. Folded downward, or else having become buried deeply under added sedimentary deposits, these rocks have been under great pressure and heat. As a result, many unusual minerals have been formed in them.

Diamonds, garnets, rubies, emeralds, and sapphires occur in metamorphic rock (some of them also occur in igneous rocks). These gems (Fig. 3-15) are crystals, and their value goes up as their purity increases. Of course, value goes up as size increases, also. Lower quality (less expensive) diamonds are widely used in industry because diamonds are the hardest material known. Gems cannot often be identified by color alone — just a trace of impurity can cause the color of a mineral to vary greatly.

Testing for Minerals

Minerals differ from rocks in that minerals are composed either of a single element or a single compound, whereas rocks may be composed of a variety of minerals. We have already seen that granite rock, for example, may contain the minerals quartz, feldspar, mica, and hornblende.

Another important distinction between rocks and minerals is that while rocks may have any shape, the atoms which make up minerals are almost always arranged in definite geometric patterns. As a result, most minerals have a characteristic crystal shape.

Collecting and identifying the many varieties of minerals is a rewarding hobby for many amateurs, especially in the western and southwestern parts of our country. But mineral identification can often be difficult. For one thing, while crystal shape is often a clue, the color of different samples of the same mineral may vary widely due to the presence of slight impurities. Thus, several methods of testing are usually necessary.

One easy test to make with an unknown find is the test of "scratchability." Below is a scale in which ten minerals have been arranged in order of hardness, from the hardest, diamond, to the softest, talc. The surface of each mineral can be scratched by those with higher numbers:

10. Diamond
9. Corundum
8. Topaz
7. Quartz
6. Feldspar
5. Apatite
4. Fluorite
3. Calcite
2. Gypsum
1. Talc

There are, of course, many minerals whose hardness on this scale lies somewhere between these whole numbers.

A mineral can also be identified by its *streak,* the color of the mineral when it is finely powdered. You can obtain the streak of any mineral by rubbing a sample across some unglazed porcelain, like the back of a kitchen tile. The streak is often different from the color of the rock itself. For example, a piece of hematite (an iron ore) may be black, but its streak is always red.

THE INNER EARTH

By direct observation we have learned much about the earth's surface, but how do we find out what it is like beneath its outer crust? We have already referred, for example, to the intense heat deep inside the earth. How can we be so sure it is hot?

Evidence of extreme heat inside the earth comes from many sources. One already cited is the molten lava that erupts from volcanoes. For another, consider the oil wells that man has drilled.

At the bottom of these wells the temperature may go above 300° F.

One source of heat within the earth is the extreme pressures of rock piled upon rock for so great a depth. Anything that is put under increasingly intense pressure gets hot. Once the pressure has built up and become fairly stable, however, additional heat is not generated. Thus, pressure is not a continuing source of heat within the earth.

Today we are aware of another source of internal heat — radioactivity. As uranium, thorium, radium, and many other radioactive elements undergo decay, heat is one of the products given off.

Years ago, many scientists thought that the earth started as a very hot planet indeed, and that it would gradually grow very cold as heat escaped from the earth's crust. Today, there is much doubt that the earth began as a hot planet. As for concern over the heat that escapes through the earth's crust, radioactive decay of elements helps maintain the earth's heat.

It is even possible that the earth gradually is warming up, rather than cooling off. Until scientists find a way to measure or calculate indirectly the temperatures at points inside the earth, we cannot know. At the present time, estimates of the temperature at the earth's center vary from 3000° C. to 6000° C.

Evidence of What the Earth Is Like Inside

Earthquakes provide us with some of our most useful information about the inside of the earth.

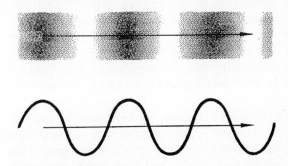

3-16. Earthquakes set up the two kinds of waves shown here. Measurement of their differences in speed and changes in direction helps develop models of the earth's interior.

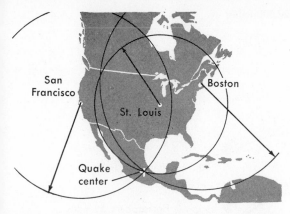

3-17. Can you see from this diagram why only two seismograph stations would not be able to locate a quake center?

When an earthquake occurs, parts of the earth's crust slip violently. Sharp vibrations move out through the earth in all directions from the area of the quake. These vibrations are picked up and recorded on an instrument called a *seismograph* (SIZE-mo-graf).

Vibrations caused by earthquakes are of several kinds — *pressure waves* (or *P-waves* for short), *shear waves* (or *S-waves* for short), and still others. We will concentrate only on the P-waves and S-waves, because only these travel deep into the earth. P-waves travel like sound, compressing whatever is before them at the peak of each vibration, with less compression between these peaks (Fig. 3-16). S-waves travel differently. The direction of wave motion is forward, but the shake of the wave is sideways (Fig. 3-16).

P-waves will travel through solids, liquids, and gases, but S-waves will travel only through solids or very dense, glassy liquids. P-waves also travel faster than S-waves and arrive at a seismographic station first. For this reason, P-waves are also known as the *primary waves,* and S-waves as the *secondary waves.* It is the time lag between the arrival of P-waves and S-waves at seismograph stations that is used as the basis for estimating the distance of the quake center from the station.

When sharp vibrations are recorded by three widely separated seismograph stations, the quake center can be quickly located. A circle is drawn around each station on a map; the size of the circle is based on the estimated distance of the earthquake from the station. Where the three circles meet is the quake center (Fig. 3-17). Rescue services can be alerted at once, in case communications at the quake center have been disrupted.

What do P-waves and S-waves tell us of the interior of the earth? Several things. At certain depths within the earth, the velocities and directions of these waves change. For example, P-waves increase steadily in velocity and change somewhat in direction as they pass downward through the crust. A sudden or abrupt change occurs at a depth of 20 or 30 miles, indicating a definite break in earth structure — a sharply defined change in the density of the earth's interior. At a depth of about 1800 miles or so — almost halfway to the center of the earth — another abrupt change occurs. The P-waves suddenly decrease in velocity and are either reflected back or bent sharply in direction (Fig. 3-18). S-waves are stopped entirely at this point, indicating that the core of the earth from 1800 miles deep on to the center acts like a liquid.

How do we know that P-waves and S-waves undergo changes in velocity and direction deep within the earth? We have been able to calculate

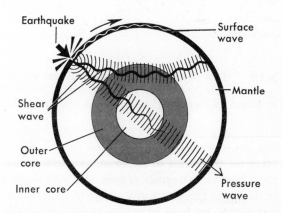

3-18. A stick in the water appears bent because the light reflected from the portion in the water bends as it passes into the less dense air. Similarly, earthquake waves bend as they pass through regions of differing density.

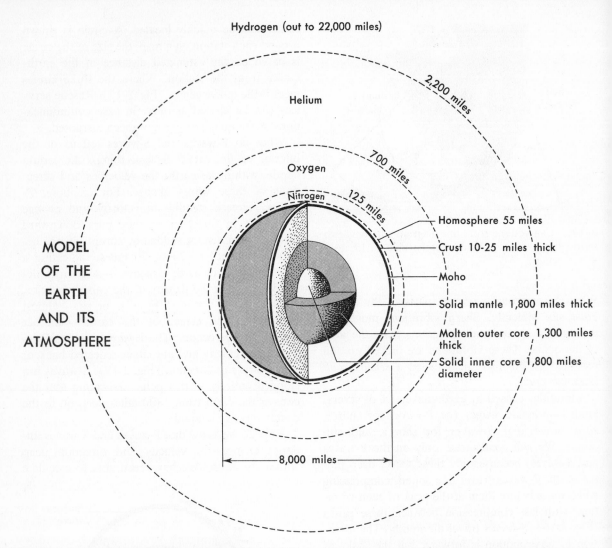

Hydrogen (out to 22,000 miles)

Helium

Oxygen

Nitrogen

2,200 miles

700 miles

125 miles

MODEL

OF THE

EARTH

AND ITS

ATMOSPHERE

Homosphere 55 miles

Crust 10-25 miles thick

Moho

Solid mantle 1,800 miles thick

Molten outer core 1,300 miles thick

Solid inner core 1,800 miles diameter

8,000 miles

3-19. Much research on the earth's interior and atmosphere is summarized here. Above a fairly uniform mixture of gases, now called the homosphere, are relatively separate spheres of nitrogen, oxygen, helium, and hydrogen as " reported " by space satellites in 1961–62.

this information from irregularities in the time it takes for the waves to arrive at seismograph stations from known quake centers. All irregularities in timing of the waves give us *some* information; fortunately, we have been able to find patterns in these irregularities.

Now we can construct a rough model of the earth (Fig. 3-19). On the outside is the atmosphere; next, the crust, primarily sedimentary rock,

granite, and basalt. (P-waves and S-waves also tell us that the granite is missing under the Atlantic Ocean.)

Below the crust, some 20 to 30 miles deep under land areas, another region of the earth begins. This part has been named the *mantle*. We do not know the composition of the mantle, because no samples of it have come to the earth's surface.

The crust and the mantle do not blend with

each other. They are separated from one another by what has been called a *discontinuity* — a change that occurs between layers. This discontinuity is known as the Mohorovičić (moh-hoh-roh-vis-ik) *discontinuity* in honor of its discoverer — *Moho* for short. (We will deal more with the Moho shortly.)

About 1800 or so miles deep, the outer core begins. There is some evidence for a molten outer core and a solid inner core (Fig. 3-19). The inner core may be iron; we do not know for sure.

Here, then, is our model of the earth. We have learned some things, to be sure, but we still know less about the interior of our own earth than we do about the interior of the sun!

Project Mohole

Scientists everywhere are busy thinking of ways to learn more about the earth's interior. Today a major effort is being made to drill a hole down to the Moho!

The crust of the earth is thinner under the oceans, where the granite found in the outer crust of land masses is missing. In some places, the Moho is less than five miles below the ocean bottom. The problems, of course, are many; it isn't easy to operate drilling rigs from the surface of an ocean through thousands of feet of the earth's crust. Oil companies have done it on a modest scale in shallow water, where many oil wells are located today. But *Project Mohole,* as it is called, is quite another thing, dwarfing the oil-drilling operations by comparison.

If Project Mohole could be successful, we would get drilling samples of the entire crust and part of the mantle. Watch the newspapers and magazines to see what happens.

OUR WORLD THROUGH TIME

Looking back over this unit, in which you read of some major features of our earth in space, you must have realized that you were reading, as well, about our earth through time. The land masses, rivers, and mountains were seen to be undergoing ceaseless change due to the forces of wind, erosion,

and the forces behind mountain building. All of these forces are thought to have acted on the earth throughout its history, at least as long as land masses, oceans, and rivers themselves have existed.

We shall, in the last unit of this book, deal with the origin of the earth as but one planet among others in the solar system. But for now, we shall take you on a very brief tour, touching upon some of the methods used and results obtained by geologists as they follow the earth through time.

Exploring the Earth's Past

What are some of the guidelines used by geologists in unraveling the history of the earth? For example, how do they decide, from observation of what seems a complicated rock formation, which geological events occurred before others? Among the most important guidelines is the law of strata, according to which younger rock formations generally lie above the older formations. This guideline is particularly reliable in the case of sedimentary rocks, since they were originally deposited in layer after layer as the product of erosion.

Another clue to uncovering the sequence of events is that rocks (originating from liquid material) that formed dikes, sills, or masses of granite when intruded between gaps in other rocks, are generally younger than the surrounding rocks.

Of very great importance for reconstructing the past is the study of fossils — the remains or imprints of plants and animals trapped in sediments. In some cases original bones or shells have been preserved. In other cases we find, as with petrified wood, that minerals from the surroundings have replaced the original chemical composition of the plants or animals.

Fossils can serve in construction of a " calendar " of earth events. For we find in fossils strong evidence of gradual change in form and complexity. Fossils of simpler plants and animals are found in the deeper, hence older, layers of rock, while younger rock of the higher layers contains fossils of more complex living organisms. Therefore, when one finds a fossil, its complexity is a clue to the relative age of the rock layer in which it was found.

The study of the strata and the fossils they contain tells us the order or sequence of geological events. But by itself this cannot tell us *when* the events occurred. To find the age of the rock formations and of the fossils they contain, geologists can now make use of a powerful tool developed with the help of their fellow scientists in the field of atomic physics.

You may recall from your reading earlier in this chapter, that uranium atoms break up at such a rate that half of any given amount of uranium will result in lead and helium in about 4.5 billion years. From the amount of accumulated lead and helium and the amount of original uranium left, we can, by working backward, reconstruct the age of the rock in which the uranium is found.

The Story in the Rocks

As geologists " read " the story of the rocks, they gradually put together " chapters " — extensive divisions of time related to the complexity or types of life represented by fossils in the rock formations. These divisions are known as eras. Each era, except the first, has, in turn, been divided into shorter spans of time known as periods.

In the oldest rock there is no evidence of life and so the era in which this rock was formed is called the Azoic (a·ZOH·ik) era, from the Greek *a* meaning " no " and *zōē* from " life." The next era, that of the most primitive life forms, is known as the Archeozoic. There follow the Proterozoic, of early life; the Paleozoic, of ancient life; the Mesozoic, of middle life; and finally, the era of recent life — the Cenozoic.

Taken together, the first two eras lasted some 1500 million years, while all the remaining eras of known earth history stretch over less than half of that. The beginning and ending of an era seem to be marked by tremendous upheavals in the earth's crust, which results in the formation of extensive mountain belts. These gigantic disturbances which separate eras are known as revolutions. They generally took a few million years to complete, but these are truly sudden events when measured against the entire sweep of perhaps four billion years of earth history.

The formation of vast mountain ranges has a widespread effect not only on geological but also on biological features of the globe, since weather and climate are affected by the presence or absence of mountain ranges. As you will read in Chapter 20, as water-laden air passes over mountains, the air rises, expands, and cools, dumping much moisture on the slopes. Then the rate of erosion increases sharply as water rushes down the numerous, newly formed slopes. Mountains may also promote the growth of new glaciers, as the snow accumulates year after year on the upper slopes.

Evolving Life

Consider as a case study of the relationship between life and geology a period known as the Carboniferous, or coal, age, some 300 million years ago. Much of the world seems to have been warm and swampy. Plant life flourished, particularly giant ferns and horsetails. As generation after generation of plants was laid down and covered by water, the pressure of accumulated sediments over millions of years turned them to coal. This period, too, saw the flourishing of many insects including the cockroach and huge dragonflies, some of which had two-foot wingspreads. This period was also notable for the appearance of the first boned animals (or vertebrates) which could live in complete independence of a water environment — the reptiles. From these animals, birds and mammals were eventually to develop.

The period following the Carboniferous was the scene of a general lifting of land areas, followed by a drying up of many swampy areas as the water ran off. Many of the swamp plants were wiped out leaving the seed-bearers in dominance. As they altered from the first crude reptiles of the coal age, some types of reptiles developed longer legs and sharper teeth, enabling more activity in search of food and the development of carnivorous eating habits.

As a general rule, some of the animals that existed, at any given time, were able to persist longer under a changing environment than others. Those that survived had opportunities to reproduce; their offspring, in turn, tended to have the needed survival characteristics. But some offspring would be slightly altered, and if the alterations were favorable, they might flourish even more than their parent stock. Thus there was a continual sorting-out of the individual plants and animals into those able to survive and reproduce and those that failed. Carried on through countless generations, many profound changes in the plants and animals would evolve.

Ultimately there developed man. With his large brain and grasping hand, he learned how to make tools to aid in gathering food and how to communicate accumulated experience in the battle for survival. He learned how to utilize natural forces. In the next units you will see further how man has explored nature both close at hand on the earth, and in the depths of space.

Looking Back . . . .

VOCABULARY

Define each of the following key terms to check your understanding of them.

1. folding
2. faulting
3. igneous extrusions
4. igneous intrusions
5. isostasy
6. sedimentary rocks
7. igneous rocks
8. metamorphic rocks
9. fossils
10. radioactive elements
11. uranium-lead dating
12. thorium-lead dating
13. magma
14. earth's crust
15. granite layer
16. basaltic layer
17. Moho
18. earth's mantle
19. earth's core
20. seismograph
21. P-waves
22. S-waves

REVIEW QUESTIONS

1. How do we obtain information about the interior of the earth from the P-waves and S-waves following earthquakes?
2. How might the operators of seismograph stations first have become aware of the possibility of mapping parts of the earth's interior?
3. Do continents float? How does your understand-

ing of isostasy contribute to your answer to the question?
4. What is some of the evidence for high temperatures deep inside the earth?
5. Name at least three kinds of mountains, in terms of their rock structure.
6. What is some of the evidence for a liquid core of the earth?
7. How have studies of radioactive elements enabled scientists to calculate that the earth must be more than three and one-half billion years old?
8. Name several minerals commonly found in rock.
9. How do we know that some of the earth's highest mountains once were part of the bottom of seas?
10. Without which kind of mountain-building activity would the number of states in the United States of America be fewer than it is today?

Going Further . . . .

THOUGHT QUESTIONS

1. In view of man's efforts to discover the age of the earth, what are some of the implications of the oldest known rock formation being metamorphic rock of sedimentary origin?
2. If the situation in question 1 above continues to hold for all old rock formations studied, why might we have to turn to astronomers, rather than geologists, for further calculations of the age of the earth?
3. How many things that you can think of may we hope to learn from Project Mohole, if it can be completed?
4. Do you think the earth will build more mountain ranges in future ages? On what kinds of evidence do you base your opinion?
5. Do you think the shapes, sizes, and locations of the earth's land masses and oceans will change in future ages? Again cite the evidence on which you base your opinion.

THINGS TO DO

Try to arrange a visit (they are not often permitted) to the seismograph station nearest your community. You may write to your own state's Geological Survey for the necessary information about locations of stations.

Going Further (continued)

The study of the life of the past goes on in the field, and at museums and universities throughout the world, directed by a dedicated band of paleontologists.

Finding, uncovering, and coating the fossilized remains with plaster of paris, is the first step. After arrival at the workshop, individual bones are carefully extracted and classified. Each bone is carefully cleaned, if necessary under magnification, so that its exact original form is clear. Finally, the reconstruction is completed — a monument to man's urge to penetrate the past.

All photos American Museum of Natural History

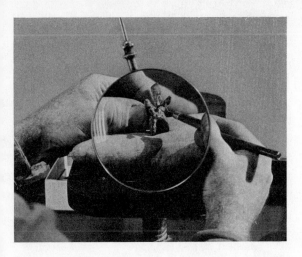

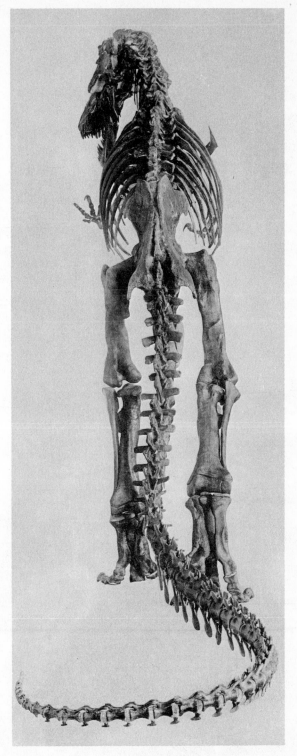

READING FURTHER

The study of the earth's history has been established as a science for but a few hundred years. New discoveries are made almost every day, and it is good to keep in mind that books often lag a few years behind in reporting these discoveries. On the other hand, certain broad outlines of the earth's history, both geological and biological, have been well established. In certain cases a great deal of detailed knowledge has been acquired; for example, there will probably be few changes in our knowledge of the evolution of the horse. Thus, books dealing with certain aspects of earth history may be read without fear that they will soon become outdated.

Introduction to Historical Geology by Raymond C. Moore, McGraw-Hill, 1949, is an interestingly written survey of the earth's past.

The Dinosaur Book by Edwin H. Colbert, McGraw-Hill, 1951. How did dinosaurs develop and why did these creatures, who once ruled the earth, fail in their battle for survival?

The Fossil Book by Carroll and Mildred Fenton, Doubleday, 1958, is noted for its many wonderful illustrations of plant and animal fossils.

Life of the Past by George G. Simpson, Yale Univ. Press, 1953. One of America's greatest students of evolution, especially of the horse, explains his methods of work in reconstructing the past.

America Before Man by Elizabeth C. Baity, Viking Press, 1953, shows how the past of our continent is reconstructed from the fossil evidence.

Man in Search of His Ancestors by André Senet, McGraw-Hill, 1956, traces modern man's link to the various life forms which preceded him.

2

The ABC of Things Around You

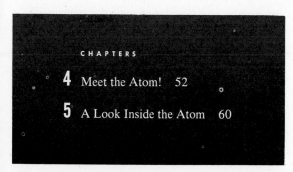

HAVE YOU EVER bumped into the sharp corner of a table? It hurt, didn't it? The table was solid and hard and heavy.

If some friend told you that the table was mostly space — that it consisted only of thinly scattered clouds of tiny electrical particles — you might well think he was joking.

Yet scientists have shown beyond any reasonable doubt that even the most solid table
— *is* mostly space
— *is* made of electricity.
Moreover, they have shown that every object in the world, including your own body and all the things you see around you this very moment, are composed of thinly scattered clouds of electrical particles, far too tiny for anyone to see directly.

Scientists have shown, in other words, that our world is made of atoms.

In this unit we shall look into the atom and study it carefully to get a better idea of how everything from the smallest insect to the earth itself is composed of atoms.

◀ *Atoms are incredibly small. A group of tungsten atoms, enlarged 2,000,000 times, take this pattern.*

Meet the Atom!

You have heard, no doubt, that you are living in an " atomic age "; that you will benefit greatly from " atomic energy "; that we have submarines which are run by " atomic engines." You have heard of " atomic-powered " rockets. The atom is everywhere. And yet, until recently, no one had ever glimpsed its outlines. But scientists had worked with the idea of atoms long before this. What, then, made them think that atoms existed?

WHAT IS AN ATOM?

You are flying in an airplane high above the great Sahara Desert in northern Africa. Far below you a smooth brown ocean of sand stretches as far as your eye can see. Even as you swoop low and stare hard at it through binoculars, the desert still looks like a smooth unbroken sheet. Finally you land, and you find that even when you are only a few feet away from it the desert still looks like a smooth brown sheet. But as you stoop down and take a very careful look, you see that the desert is really made of a vast number of tiny grains of sand.

The desert that looked like a smooth brown sheet is really made of *particles*.

Now look at the room around you and see if you can find some object made of aluminum or iron. Look at it closely. And as you look hard at it from a few inches away, think of yourself as being up in the airplane miles above the Sahara Desert. Think of yourself staring down at the smooth ocean of sand. That aluminum in your hand looks like a smooth unbroken surface, doesn't it? Even if you cut off a chunk and stared hard at it through a powerful microscope it still looks like a continuous sheet. But if you study it as carefully as a scientist does, using some of his interesting tools that we are going to learn about in this unit — then you find that the aluminum really is made of particles, too, although not so completely separated as the grains of sand.

These particles of aluminum are called aluminum *atoms*. They are very, very tiny. Two million of them laid in a row edge to edge would barely span the period at the end of this sentence.

In the same way you can imagine atoms of iron or carbon or tin or oxygen and many others. Altogether there are about 100 different kinds of atoms.

John Dalton's Idea

For hundreds and hundreds of years people had no idea that atoms existed. George Washington, for instance, lived at a time when atoms were unknown.

Then in the early 1800's an English schoolteacher named John Dalton began to study matter very closely.

For clues he had a good deal of information collected by laboratory scientists who had lived before him. For example, he knew that if mercury or lead were heated it gained weight. It gained this weight as it *combined* with the oxygen of the air. Moreover, he knew that the sample *would not go on gaining weight indefinitely*.

For instance, when a sample of lead weighing 207 grams [1] (later on you will see why 207 is used) was heated in air, it gained just 16 grams

---

[1] A gram is the scientist's measure of weight. It is roughly the weight of a small paper clip. More exactly:

28.4 grams = 1 ounce
453.6 grams = 1 pound

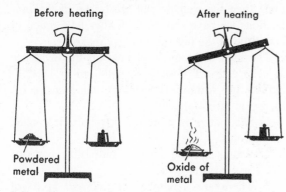

Before heating   After heating

Powdered metal

Oxide of metal

4-1. An oxide of a metal weighs more than the original metal which was heated.

of weight which was due to the oxygen combining with it. It got no heavier *no matter how long it was heated* (Fig. 4-1).

To summarize, here are some figures that will show you the sort of facts Dalton puzzled over in his study of the way matter behaved.

lead + **oxygen** ⟶ **lead oxide**
207 grams   16 grams (produces)   223 grams

mercury + **oxygen** ⟶ **mercuric oxide**
201 g.   16 g.   (produces)   217 g.

zinc + **oxygen** ⟶ **zinc oxide**
65 g.   16 g.   (produces)   81 g.

Of course if a smaller weight of metal were heated, it would combine with less oxygen to make less of the oxide. The important fact Dalton noticed was that the *proportions of the combining substances were always the same.*

Dalton tried to explain why the proportions were always the same. He saw that one possible reason might be that all lead was made of tiny particles, each of *exactly the same weight*. Likewise, the mercury might be made of tiny particles all exactly alike but whose weight differed from the lead particles, and similarly for zinc and oxygen.

Dalton saw that if *one* lead particle always combined with *one* oxygen particle, and if *one* mercury particle always combined with *one* oxygen particle, and *one* zinc particle always combined with *one* oxygen particle then it was easy

to understand why the materials always combined in *definite proportions. One* particle of one substance seemed always to combine with *one* particle of another substance. He called the particles *atoms.*

Example: Suppose a mercury atom has 201 units of weight compared with 16 units of weight for an oxygen atom. Then, no matter how many thousands of mercury atoms pair off with an equal number of oxygen atoms, the mercury and the oxygen will always be in the proportion of 201 to 16 by weight. This will be true even if we combine billions of each so that there are enough of them for us to see in a test tube.

You must be careful to notice that so far Dalton's evidence does not *prove* that atoms exist. So far his idea of atoms is simply a convenient way of explaining his observations.

These figures show us something else, too. When you look at the weights of atoms that were combined you see that they appear to be the same as the weight of the final product. Hence it looks as if no atoms had been made or destroyed when they combined. Even your most careful measurements in your school laboratory will show the same result: the final product appears to weigh the same as the sum of its parts. Similar measurements led Dalton to conclude that *atoms were indestructible.*

A Test for Dalton's Idea

Let us look at a little more laboratory information in order to test Dalton's idea. Here is a list of still more atoms and the weights of each that will combine with another. In examining the laboratory information below, just assume for the time being that one atom of oxygen " weighs " 16, and two " weigh " 32.

Carbon and oxygen can combine in two different ways (Fig. 4-2):

carbon + **oxygen** → **carbon monoxide (mono = one)**
12 g.   16 g.   28 g.

carbon + **oxygen** → **carbon dioxide (di = two)**
12 g.   32 g.   44 g.

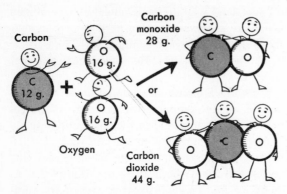

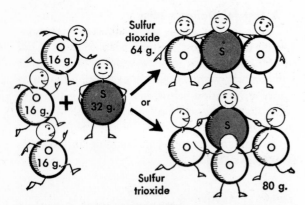

4-2. Carbon can combine under special conditions with one atom of oxygen — or ordinarily with two atoms. How would you write the formula for carbon monoxide?

Sulfur and oxygen can combine in either of two ways (Fig. 4-3):

sulfur + oxygen → sulfur dioxide (di = two)
32 g.   32 g.   64 g.

sulfur + oxygen → sulfur trioxide (tri = three)
32 g.   48 g.   80 g.

Does the idea of atoms help us to understand these weights? Yes indeed! All you need to do is to suppose that one sulfur atom combines either with two or with three atoms of oxygen. Likewise one carbon atom can combine with either one or two oxygen atoms. If carbon and oxygen com-

4-3. Sulfur ordinarily combines with two atoms of oxygen to make sulfur dioxide — or under special conditions with three atoms. How would you write the formula for sulfur trioxide?

bine, then the weights will always be in the proportions we have shown, no matter how much or how little of the final product we make.

The idea of atoms explained all this evidence so clearly that Dalton was finally led in 1808 to publish his Atomic Theory. We can sum up his theory in five statements:

1. All matter is made of tiny particles called atoms.
2. Atoms are the smallest indivisible parts of ordinary matter.
3. There are a number of different kinds of atoms — atoms of iron, of oxygen, of carbon, etc. (Many are listed in Table 5-1 on page 67.)
4. All atoms of iron are exactly alike. All atoms of oxygen are exactly alike, etc. But atoms of iron are different from atoms of oxygen, carbon, etc.
5. Atoms are durable. They cannot be made or destroyed.

Modern scientists have found that Dalton was *very nearly* right. All the experiments they have done since his time tend to support the idea of atoms. No experiments have ever been done that disprove their existence. Therefore, we assume today that atoms exist.

What Dalton's Theory Means

When Dalton proposed that all the atoms in the world were absolutely indestructible, he meant that you could heat them up or pound them with hammers, or try to blow them to pieces in an explosion — all without damaging them in the least! Dalton was sure that his atoms would never wear out. Today, we know that under the right conditions any atom may come apart. But in most ordinary circumstances atoms have a long life ahead of them.

For example, some of the oxygen atoms which help to make up your body were once part of the air floating over, say, Alaska — before the weather carried them to you and you breathed them in. Some of the oxygen atoms of your body were once part of the water of the oceans of the world. Some of the carbon atoms in your body may well have been at one time part of a tree in one of the great forests of Pennsylvania millions of years ago, or a part of the body of Julius Caesar during his campaigns through ancient Gaul, or perhaps part of the body of an elephant in the African jungles only a few years ago. The atoms of which your thumb is made might have been scattered all around the face of the earth. And for millions of years to come, the vast majority of the atoms of which you and the familiar objects around you are built will still exist. But then they will have been scattered, shuffled, and collected again into new objects and living things. These very same atoms probably existed when the earth was first formed and will, except for those atoms that are radioactive, be present at its end.

According to Dalton's Atomic Theory, everything you see or feel — the air you breathe, the earth far beneath your feet, the stars far above you, and even your own body — are all made out of atoms. These tiny building blocks are what all matter in your physical and chemical world is made of. Some kinds of atoms are very rare, however, and if they suddenly disappeared they would hardly be missed. Other kinds of atoms, perhaps 25, are very common (see Table, page 67).

For instance, your body is made mostly out of atoms of carbon, hydrogen, oxygen, and nitrogen. The rocks of the earth are made largely out of atoms of silicon, oxygen, and aluminum. The air you breathe is mostly a mixture of oxygen and nitrogen And water is made out of oxygen and hydrogen.

A material made entirely of just one kind of atom is called an *element*. There are about 100 elements, each made of a different kind of atom. You will find a list of some of the most common elements — or kinds of atoms — on page 67. Most of these were known to John Dalton.

How many different elements can you find in your kitchen, your living room, and your garage? Aluminum? Copper? What others? Refer to Table 5-1.

SIMPLE EXPERIMENTS WITH DALTON'S ATOMS

Let's get acquainted with a few of the elements on our laboratory shelf.

Mixtures

Take down a bottle of sulfur and weigh out 2 grams. If the bottle is marked C.P. (chemically pure), you can be pretty sure that your 2 grams of yellow powder are more than 99.99% sulfur atoms.

Next take down a bottle of iron powder or filings. Weigh out 1 gram of iron and mix it thoroughly with the 2 grams of sulfur. You have made a *mixture* of the two elements, iron and sulfur. Can you separate the iron and sulfur?

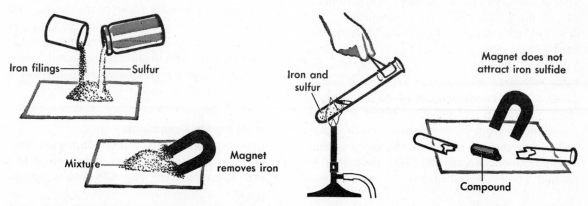

Iron filings — Sulfur

Mixture — Magnet removes iron

Iron and sulfur

Magnet does not attract iron sulfide

Compound

4-4. Iron and sulfur in a mixture can be separated by a magnet. You can do this in your laboratory. What is the difference between a mixture and a compound?

It's easy. Pass a magnet over the mixture several times. The magnet will attract the iron filings and leave the sulfur behind. Once more you have your iron and sulfur in separate piles (Fig. 4-4).

Mixtures are usually fairly easy to separate. For example, sea water is a mixture of pure water and various salty materials. You can separate the water from the salts by boiling off the water. And cow's milk is a mixture of cream and milk that can be separated in a rough way by letting the milk stand; the cream rises to the top.

Chemical Combinations: Making Compounds

Again make a mixture of your iron and sulfur atoms in the same proportions as before, and put it in a test tube. Holding it in a test-tube clamp (Fig. 4-4), heat the test tube over a Bunsen burner.[1] Watch the mixture carefully. You will see a red glow spread through the mixture as you heat the tube. Now remove the tube and when it is cool, crack it open and examine the substance you have made out of iron and sulfur.

Test it with a magnet. You find that it is no longer magnetic. Notice its color. It is neither the yellow of sulfur nor the gray metallic color of the iron. The atoms of iron and sulfur have been joined tightly together to make a new substance with new properties. In other words, they have been *chemically combined*.

A substance made out of one and only one kind of atom is called an *element*. When atoms of two or more different elements combine so that they lose their separate familiar properties, they have formed what the chemist calls a *compound*. You have just combined two elements, iron and sulfur, to make a compound called *iron sulfide*. Table salt is a compound composed of associated atoms of sodium and chlorine. Water is a compound made from hydrogen and oxygen atoms; and carbon dioxide is carbon and oxygen atoms in combination. Recall that John Dalton in his Atomic Theory described how compounds were made from definite proportions of various elements.

We often speak of *molecules of elements* and *molecules of compounds*. For elements and *some* compounds, a *molecule* may be defined as the smallest amount of the particular substance that has all the chemical properties of that substance. Molecules may consist of one, two, three, or more atoms. The molecules of elements such as helium and krypton consist of single atoms.

The element hydrogen, in its usual gaseous form, consists of molecules with two atoms of hydrogen each. And in a compound such as water, we find molecules with two hydrogen and one oxygen atom.

But there are some compounds that do not seem to have a molecular structure at all. In a salt crystal, for example, the sodium and the chlorine atoms, instead of forming separate molecules, are associated together in one giant grouping — the entire salt crystal.

Most of the hundred-odd elements can be combined to form compounds, some of them very complicated. For example, each molecule of hemoglobin, the red compound in your blood, is made of a total of 9512 atoms: 3032 carbon atoms, 4816 of hydrogen, 780 nitrogen atoms, 872 of oxygen, 8 of sulfur, and 4 of iron, for a total of 9512. And if even one of the 4816 hydrogen atoms were missing, the chemical properties of the hemoglobin molecule would be different!

When you combined iron and sulfur, you made a compound. Chemists know of many thousands of compounds. In learning all he can about the properties of compounds, the chemist often makes brand new ones with important and useful properties, and discovers important clues to the way in which the world around us is put together.

Breaking Up Compounds

Let's experiment with taking compounds apart. Place a quarter inch of mercuric oxide in a *Pyrex*[2] test tube, as in Fig. 4-5. Heat it strongly

---

[1] Be sure to follow the safety precautions your teacher will give you for work in the laboratory.

[2] Pyrex is a kind of glass that will usually stand strong heating and quick cooling without cracking.

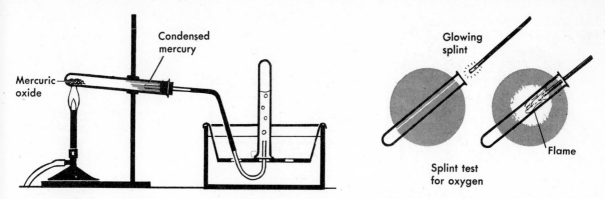

Condensed mercury

Mercuric oxide

Glowing splint

Flame

Splint test for oxygen

4-5. You can prepare oxygen in your laboratory by breaking apart the compound mercuric oxide. What is the test for pure oxygen? (*Caution:* Note the position of the heated test tube.)

over a Bunsen burner. Soon a silvery mirror of mercury forms on the wall of the heated test tube. At this point thrust a glowing splint deep into the collecting tube. It bursts into flame — a test for oxygen. You have formed mercury and oxygen from mercuric oxide. In other words, you have broken up a compound into elements by the use of heat energy. You could write it this way:

mercuric oxide → mercury + oxygen

This is what is called a *word equation*. A chemist uses such equations to describe what is happening to his elements and compounds.

Let's try taking apart another compound, water. From your earlier work in science you no doubt know that water can be written H_2O. This is the *formula* for water. It means that in the compound water two parts of hydrogen (H) are combined with one part of oxygen (O) (Fig. 4-6). Similarly the formula for mercuric oxide is HgO; one atom of mercury (Hg) for each atom of oxygen (O). The formula for carbon dioxide is CO_2, one atom of carbon (C) with two atoms of oxygen (O).

Scientists find it easiest to use electrical energy to take water apart. If you put together the apparatus shown in Fig. 4-7, you will soon see bubbles of gas rising in each tube. You will notice that the volume of gas in one tube is twice the volume of gas in the other.

Lift off the tube with the greater volume of gas

(Fig. 4-7, right). With your thumb over its mouth to prevent air from entering, keep the mouth of the tube down.

If you put a lighted match into the mouth of the test tube, you will hear the "pop" of a small explosion — a test for hydrogen gas. If you test the other tube of gas with a glowing splint, the splint bursts into flame — the test for oxygen.

Thus you have some evidence that you have taken water apart into the hydrogen and oxygen of which it is made. You could write the following word equation for what has happened:

water $\xrightarrow{\text{electrical energy}}$ **hydrogen + oxygen**

When elements combine with one another to form compounds, or when compounds come apart

COMPOUND		FORMULA
Water	H O H	H_2O
Mercuric oxide	Hg O	HgO
Carbon dioxide	O C O	CO_2

4-6. What does a formula tell you about the compound?

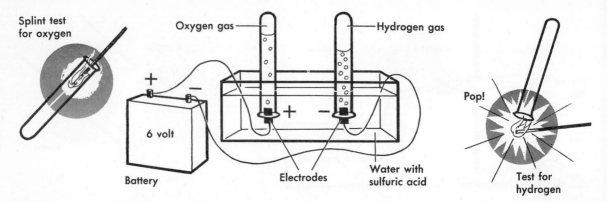

Splint test for oxygen — Oxygen gas — Hydrogen gas — Pop! — 6 volt — Battery — Electrodes — Water with sulfuric acid — Test for hydrogen

4-7. Water can be separated into hydrogen and oxygen by using an electric current. If one ounce (about 28.5 cubic centimeters) of oxygen is produced, how much hydrogen will be produced at the same time?

to form different compounds or elements, the chemist says that a *chemical reaction* has taken place. You have just performed three chemical reactions:

$$\text{iron} + \text{sulfur} \xrightarrow{\text{heat}} \text{iron sulfide}$$

$$\text{mercuric oxide} \xrightarrow{\text{heat}} \text{mercury} + \text{oxygen}$$

$$\text{water} \xrightarrow{\text{electrical energy}} \text{hydrogen} + \text{oxygen}$$

Chemists know of millions of chemical reactions. In a burning match several chemical reactions are going on at once. When you cook your food there is a change in its color and flavor: chemical reactions are taking place. When wood rots, when leaves grow, when pipes rust, when gasoline explodes, chemical reactions are occurring that lead to the formation of new compounds with properties different from those of the original elements or compounds. Your body is a seething mass of chemical reactions, too. Seeing, thinking, digesting your food, growing, moving — each involves many different kinds of chemical reactions going on at the same time. Merely to raise your hand to your mouth requires that over one hundred chemical reactions occur at once in your body. No wonder the working of the human body is still so difficult to understand and is the subject of intense research by many chemists.

Now you see why John Dalton was one of the first great chemists. For he was the first man to understand correctly the existence of invisible atoms and to describe as we have above some of their remarkable behavior.

Two Kinds of Changes

Not all changes are chemical reactions. For example, take a few ice cubes and place them in a jar. Soon, the ice cubes will turn to water. And you could, of course, turn this water back into ice. The water, chemists say, has changed its *state*. The *solid* ice turned to the *liquid* water. And you probably know that the liquid water can also evaporate and turn into water vapor, a *gas*.

Nevertheless the *solid* ice, the *liquid* water, the *gaseous* water vapor, are all chemically the same. They are all water, H_2O; there has been no chemical change. The change from solid to liquid to gas has been a change in physical form, a *physical change*.

On the other hand, when water is broken into hydrogen and oxygen (by electrical energy) we do have a chemical change. So too when iron and sulfur combine to form iron sulfide, we have a chemical change. In a chemical change, a substance is changed into a different substance or substances.

But in both physical and chemical changes, the *amount* of matter doesn't change. Take a liter of water (weighing 1000 grams) and freeze it to form ice. You will get 1000 grams of ice.

Take a liter of water (1000 grams) and break

it up by using electrical energy. The hydrogen and oxygen formed will together weigh 1000 grams — the same amount with which you started. Matter is neither created nor destroyed in ordinary chemical changes. (You may be interested in looking at page 405, Blue Section, for additional investigations into chemical and physical changes of matter.)

Looking Back . . . .

VOCABULARY

The following are key words in chemistry, as well as in understanding the atom. Show that you understand them by defining each term.

1. atom
2. element
3. compound
4. molecule
5. formula
6. chemical equation
7. chemical reaction

REVIEW QUESTIONS

1. About how many different kinds of atoms are there?
2. How are atoms different from molecules?
3. How do atoms of different elements differ from one another?
4. Is the number of atoms in the world about the same today as it was a year ago?
5. Why might a chemist use a word equation?
6. Name six examples of a chemical reaction.
7. For what reasons did Dalton think that atoms existed, even though he couldn't see them?
8. Describe John Dalton's Atomic Theory.
9. Did Dalton *prove* that all matter is made of atoms?
10. What is the difference between a mixture and a compound?
11. What must be done before some elements will enter into chemical combination?

Going Further . . . .

STUDYING ELEMENTS

Collect samples of some of the elements listed in the table on page 67 and bring them to class. Look at them closely, and notice their different properties.

1. Which are metals?
2. Why can't aluminum always be used in place of iron? iron in place of copper? mercury in place of iron?
3. What common elements are gases?
4. Do all the elements that are gases have the same properties? If not, name some differences between them.

CHEMICAL AND PHYSICAL CHANGES

Which of the following are chemical changes, and which are physical changes?

1. A lighted match
2. Water changing to ice
3. An explosion of dynamite
4. Gas burning
5. Gasoline " exploding " in an engine
6. Sugar dissolving in water
7. Rusting of iron
8. Crushing of glass

Which of these are chemical changes?

1. Polish two silver coins with some steel wool until they are bright. Is this a chemical or physical change? Why?
2. Take one of the coins and strike a wooden match against it. Look at the coin. What is the black color? The word equation is:

silver + sulfur → silver sulfide

Is this a physical or chemical change? Why? Where did the sulfur come from?

READING FURTHER

Do you want to do some work in chemistry at home or in the school laboratory?

Experiments in Chemistry by N. F. Beeler and F. M. Branley, Crowell, 1952

The New World of Chemistry by Bernard Jaffe, Silver Burdett, 1955. The first chapters will take you further into chemistry.

CHAPTER 5

A Look Inside the Atom

If you had been in the laboratory of the great English scientist, Lord Rutherford, about the time of the first World War, you might have seen a sketch like the one in Fig. 5-1.

Remember that Dalton's theory stated that an atom was an indivisible particle of matter. Now Rutherford was proposing that the atom had parts.

How did Rutherford develop this idea of the atom? His extraordinary discovery is one of the most important in modern science. In this chapter you will read how scientists found out that the atom is made of electricity — and how they now think the atom is put together.

SIMPLE ELECTRICITY

Let's begin with a few experiments that will show us some of the elementary facts of electricity.

Tear a sheet of newspaper a few inches wide and about 15 inches long. Hold it against a rug or against a woolen suit or coat and rub it gently a few times with your hand. Then place it against the wall. If the weather is *fairly dry,* you will find your piece of newspaper will be attracted to the wall and will stick to it. What you have done is to give it a charge of electricity.

Tear off a second sheet of newspaper the same size as the first. Give both sheets of newspaper an electric charge by rubbing. You will find that your two sheets of paper, charged in exactly the same way, *repel* each other when you hold them up.

Like and Unlike Charges

Here you see that charges of electricity can cause objects to attract one another or to repel one another. You can produce similar effects by rubbing the plastic part of a fountain pen up and down on your suit a few times and then noticing that it will pick up by attraction small bits of paper and sawdust. Or perhaps you have combed your hair briskly on a very dry day and noticed how your hair tended to " stand up " as each hair repelled its neighbors.

In all of these things you did, you notice that the electricity seemed to be produced by rubbing things together. But sometimes the charged objects repel one another, and sometimes they attract. We can find out why by doing some more experiments.

Rub a hard rubber rod briskly with a piece of fur and then hang up the rod by its center, as in Fig. 5-2. Charge a second hard rubber rod in the same way and bring it up close to the first. You will notice that the two rods repel each other; the suspended rod always swings away.

Repeat this experiment using two glass rods rubbed with a piece of silk. You will notice the same result — two charged rods repel one an-

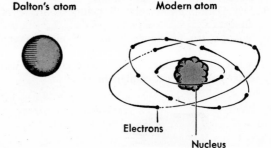

Dalton's atom   Modern atom

Electrons

Nucleus

5-1. What is the difference in Dalton's idea of the atom as compared with Rutherford's?

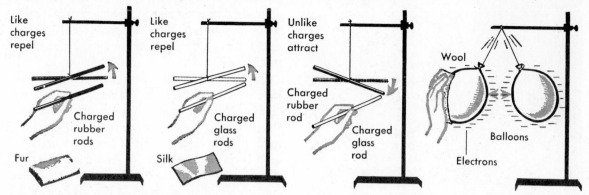

Like charges repel

Charged rubber rods

Fur

Like charges repel

Charged glass rods

Silk

Unlike charges attract

Charged rubber rod

Charged glass rod

Wool

Balloons

Electrons

5-2. Examine the first three illustrations (from left to right). Then check your text to determine the reason for the difference between the first two and the third. Now what is the reason for the two balloons repelling each other in the fourth?

other. You can do this experiment with lots of other materials too.

When two similar objects are rubbed with the same material, it seems reasonable to say that the two objects must be *charged in the same way.* You just saw how they repel one another. So it seems that objects charged in the same way repel each other.

Try bringing together a glass rod rubbed with silk and a rubber rod rubbed with fur, as in Fig. 5-2. What happens? They attract each other. Since similar charges repel each other, it looks as if the charges on these two rods are not similar. The charges must be unlike one another. Scientists have studied experiments like these and many others too and have decided that:

1. There are *two kinds* of electric charges.
2. Objects carrying like charges *repel* each other; objects carrying unlike charges *attract* each other.

Today we call the two kinds of electric charges *positive* (+) and *negative* (−).

One Kind of Electricity?

Very early in the development of science it was thought that positive and negative charges could be explained by supposing there was only *one* kind of electricity. When two objects are rubbed together, some of the electricity rubs off one object and onto the other. One object then has an

extra charge, and the other object lacks its usual charge — that is, it is charged oppositely.

To remember this it may help you to think of a little boy who sees a sign saying " Wet Paint." He touches the paint to make sure it is wet, and sure enough — it is. The paint represents electric charge. When he touches the painted fence, he rubs some of the paint off onto himself (he becomes charged) and the fence loses some of its proper supply of paint (it becomes oppositely charged).

Particles of Electricity

Back in the 1890's it became clear to experimenters that the one kind of electricity they thought existed was really made out of tiny negatively charged particles which were given the name *electrons*. These are the very electrons in the outer regions of the atom in Fig. 5-1.

Apparently there are electrons everywhere, and like the wet paint, they can be easily rubbed off objects. You have experience with this fact nearly every day. As tires rubbing on asphalt roads can give trucks and cars a big charge of electrons, gasoline trucks dangle chains to let this charge leak off. The entrances to highway toll booths have wires projecting upwards from the roadway. In airplanes there are wires at the edge of the wing (Fig. 5-3). After you scuff over a heavy carpet, you get a shock when you shake hands with your friend. As you read previously, this is the same

Trans World Airlines

5-3. Have you ever wondered what the purpose was of the wires at the edge of the wing? When the plane is in flight, the friction of the plane with the air builds up enough electricity to be dangerous. This static electricity must be discharged — and this is one way. How is this done on large trucks?

thing that happens when you comb your hair on a dry day. Your hair and the comb may acquire opposite charges, causing your charged hairs to repel one another and stand on end since they have the same charge.

Lightning is a sudden enormous flow of electrons from or to a cloud. And the electricity that lights our homes is a steady flow of electrons along a wire.

But what have electrons got to do with John Dalton's atoms? In the next few sections you will see.

RADIOACTIVITY

Marie Sklowdowska (sklo-DOF-ska), a Polish chemist working in Paris, had become interested in recently discovered rays given off by the element uranium. Working together with her husband, Pierre Curie, she found that the rays given off by pitchblende — a mineral containing uranium — were more intense than the rays from

pure uranium itself. In 1898 the Curies therefore proposed that pitchblende contained other radioactive elements, hitherto undiscovered. They suggested naming them polonium (puh-LOH-nee-um) and radium.

Only in 1902, after years of painstaking work with tons of pitchblende (from which the uranium had already been removed), were the Curies able to extract a pure enough sample of radium to confirm their discovery of a new element. They were surprised, however, to find that their pure sample, though isolated, was quickly contaminated with other elements. (We shall soon see why.)

The Curies also found that one kind of ray from uranium and radium was *repelled* by a negatively charged plate (see Fig. 5-4). Another kind of ray was *attracted* by the negatively charged plate; a third kind was not bent at all.

The Strange Suicide of Atoms

To scientists this evidence meant that the first kind of ray from radium consisted of positively charged particles. Today we call them *alpha particles*. The second kind of ray must consist of negatively charged particles. We call them *beta particles*. And the last kind of ray apparently was not charged at all. They are what we call *gamma rays,* not gamma *particles* because they are rays much like light rays (Fig. 5-4).

It looked very much as if the radium atoms were busy hurling off pieces of themselves and

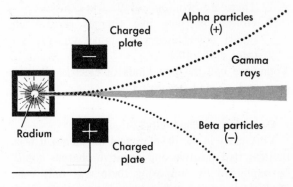

5-4. Why are the beta particles bent toward the (+) plate, the alpha particles to the (−) plate, and the gamma rays not at all?

changing into something else. Further study showed beyond a doubt that the radium atoms were indeed one by one blowing themselves up!

This strange atomic suicide was given the name *radioactivity*.

Radioactivity Unlocks Dalton's Atoms

Within a few years after the Curies discovered the radioactivity of radium, many scientists were hard at work trying to learn what radioactivity could tell them about the insides of the atom.

Quickly a great deal was learned.

It was found that when an atom of radium fired out an alpha particle, the radium turned into an atom of the rare gas, *radon* (RAY-don), and the alpha particle turned into an atom of *helium*.

It was found that radon is radioactive, too. It shoots out an alpha particle and becomes, or is reduced to, the element *polonium*. Then the polonium atom blows up, shooting out beta and gamma rays, and becomes a radioactive kind of lead. On and on the atom goes firing off energy and reducing itself from one element to another until at last it becomes an atom of a nonradioactive kind of lead. It then ceases giving off rays and particles; it remains lead.

These discoveries explained the impurities that Madame Curie had found in her first sample of radium. They were produced by the radium itself.

Would you like to see the explosions of radium atoms for yourself? It's easy! All you need is a strong magnifying glass, a watch with a luminous dial, and a dark room. After a few minutes in the dark room, your eyes will have adjusted themselves to see faint light. Now examine the luminous numbers of your watch through the magnifying glass. Instead of an even glow the numbers will appear as a large number of tiny flashing specks of light.

Each tiny flash is produced by the radioactive explosion of a radium atom in the luminous paint, which is made up of the tiniest amount of radium and a great deal of zinc sulfide. As the radium explodes it fires out an alpha particle at the rate of 10,000 miles a second. When the alpha particle strikes a molecule of zinc sulfide (a molecule

Longines-Wittnauer

5-5. Do you have a clock with a radium dial? What causes it to glow in the dark?

made up of combined zinc and sulfur atoms) in the luminous paint, the collision is marked by a tiny flash of light.

Inside the Atom

When scientists studied the rays that were given off, they were led to even more interesting conclusions. Their reasoning went somewhat like this:

1. Ordinary materials that are unrubbed consist of atoms that neither attract nor repel charged rods.
2. Therefore ordinary materials have atoms that are neither positively nor negatively charged.
3. But the atoms of some materials like uranium and radium blow up and shoot out positively and negatively charged particles.
4. Therefore, even these uncharged atoms must contain within them electric charges.
5. The only way an atom can contain charges and still be *electrically neutral* is for it to have equal quantities of *both positive and negative charges*.

Little by little, experiments began to show that *all* atoms — not just radioactive ones — contained positive and negative charges.

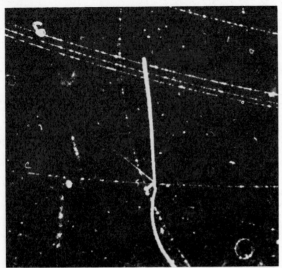

Brookhaven National Laboratory

5-6. This is a photograph taken in a cloud chamber — a device used to detect the paths of atomic particles.

Then it became clear that the negative particles in an atom were nothing but our old friend, the *electron*. And the positive charge turned out to be a new kind of particle called a *proton*. After some years, in 1932 a third kind of particle, the *neutron*, was discovered which oddly had no charge at all! Electrons, protons, neutrons — out of these three kinds of particles, mainly, all atoms are put together. In the center of the atom is its *nucleus*. Around the nucleus are electrons.

It often happens in science that each new discovery raises new questions. Certainly the discovery that atoms contained both positive and negative charges raised a question. For positive and negative charges, as you know, attract one another. Scientists now had to explain why oppositely charged particles do not fall together inside the atom and neutralize each other.

The answer to this question slowly became clearer as further experiments showed scientists how the electrons, protons, and neutrons were arranged inside the atom. Some of the most important experiments with atoms were done by Lord Rutherford, the very scientist with whom we began this chapter.

Lord Rutherford and His Bullets

Rutherford probed invisible atoms with invisible bullets and concluded that the space atoms occupy is mostly *just that* — space!

More precisely, what he did was to aim a very powerful beam of alpha particles (see Fig. 5-7) at a thin sheet of aluminum foil like the wrapper of a candy bar.

Most of the alpha particles went straight through the foil. A few went through but were deflected sideways a bit. And a few were bounced backward. Evidently the particles that bounced backward had hit some heavy part of an aluminum atom. Those that went straight through had generally missed all parts of the aluminum atom completely (Fig. 5-7).

By comparing his numbers of hits and misses, Rutherford figured out how much of his aluminum foil consisted of particles and how much of space.

Rutherford probed many different kinds of atoms with his alpha particle beam. In every case, his small proportion of direct hits told him that atoms have lots of room between their electrical particles. His calculations led to the extraordinary conclusion that the space taken up by the particles inside the atom is similar to the space taken up by a planet moving around the sun. Hence if all the electrons, protons, and neutrons that make the atoms of your body could be squeezed together, until they were touching each other, your body would be a microscopic speck.

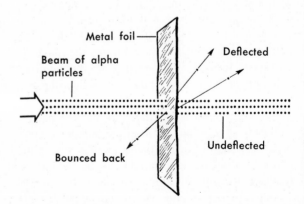

5-7. What did this famous experiment demonstrate?

The experiments of the Curies and Rutherford and many other scientists show us that the atoms of your body — and indeed of the entire world around you — are made entirely of thinly scattered charges of electricity.

Rutherford probed further. He wanted to find out how the positive and negative charges of electricity were arranged inside atoms. His experiments led him to suggest that all the positive charges (protons) were at the center of the atom and the negative charges (electrons) were out around the edges. This led him to make the sketch you saw in Fig. 5-1.

Rutherford's idea of the atom as a kind of miniature solar system with negatively charged electrons whirling around a positively charged center was one of the great steps forward in physics. But it immediately led to equally great difficulties requiring really new and revolutionary ideas about the orbiting electrons. The Danish physicist Niels Bohr supplied them. While somewhat complicated, his major contribution was showing how the orbiting electrons absorb and emit energy without falling into the positively charged center.

Review now for yourself the picture of the atom as these scientists understood it. Notice again that the protons are all closely packed together in the center, the *nucleus*. Notice the electrons whirling around outside. Notice, however, that the number of electrons and protons must be the same if the atom is to be electrically neutral.

This, then, could explain why rubbing glass rods with silk gives the glass a positive charge.

Since the protons (positive charges) remain in the nucleus, they are not rubbed off. Some of the outer electrons, however, are rubbed off. This leaves some atoms in the glass with more positive charge (protons) than negative charge (electrons) (Fig. 5-2). And, of course, the silk, upon which the electrons have been added, will acquire a negative charge.

EVEN ATOMS HAVE WEIGHT

Let's look still more closely at how the parts of an atom are put together.

The Lightest Atom of All

The simplest of all atoms is the atom of hydrogen (Fig. 5-8). Its nucleus consists of a single proton. Outside the nucleus is one electron moving at great speed. That's all. Its size? Two hundred and fifty million of these hydrogen atoms edge to edge barely span one inch.

Hydrogen atoms are not all alike. For example, there is a heavier atom of hydrogen like the others, except that its nucleus also contains one neutron. Thus it has a neutron in addition to a proton (Fig. 5-8). Then there is the heaviest hydrogen atom of all — a hydrogen atom with two neutrons loading its nucleus.

The lightest and simplest hydrogen atom is called *hydrogen one* (or H^1 for short) (Fig. 5-8). Its heavier brothers are called *hydrogen two* (H^2) and *hydrogen three* (H^3) — or more often *deu-*

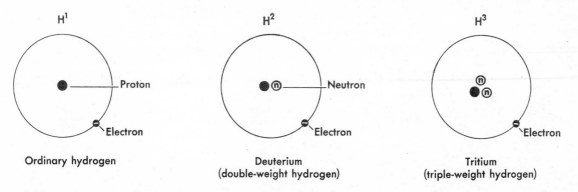

Ordinary hydrogen

Deuterium
(double-weight hydrogen)

Tritium
(triple-weight hydrogen)

5-8. What would be the approximate weight of a deuterium atom? of a tritium atom?

terium (dyoo-TEER-ee-um) and *tritium* (TRIT-ee-um).

Neutrons and protons are about equally heavy. Compared with them the electron is very light. Hence most of the weight of our three hydrogen atoms (and all other atoms, too, for that matter) is in the nucleus.

Since all atoms are so tiny and light, it is inconvenient to talk of the weight of an atom in grams or ounces. For example an atom of H^1 weighs close to 0.000 000 000 000 000 000 000 0003 of an ounce! It is much easier to use a different scale of weights in which we call the weight of H^1 (hydrogen) *approximately* 1 unit of weight. Then, by comparison to it, H^2 (deuterium) and H^3 (tritium) have weights of 2 and 3. These weights are called *atomic weights.*

The " Average " Atom of Hydrogen

The sample of hydrogen you collected from water (page 57) contains all three kinds of hydrogen atoms, but by far the most common of the three is hydrogen one. In fact, everywhere around the world that you find hydrogen atoms, they turn out to be mostly hydrogen one, with a tiny sprinkling of deuterium and tritium. Thus when scientists measure the atomic weight of hydrogen in water and other common compounds, their sample turns out to have an average atomic weight only slightly greater than one. This is one of the reasons for the value 1.008 that you find in the table on page 67. Samples of *pure* hydrogen one

Try These

Here is a table with some figures left out. Copy the table, filling in the blanks as you go. Then compare your figures. On page 68 (don't turn now) you have the table completed.

Atom	No. of protons	No. of neutrons	No. of electrons	Approx. atomic wt.	Atomic number
Sodium	11	12	11	23	11
Chlorine	17	18	17	35	17
Calcium	20	—	—	40	—
Potassium	19	20	—	—	—
Helium	—	2	2	—	—
Uranium	92	—	—	238	—
Oxygen	8	—	—	16	—
Lithium	3	—	3	7	3

or deuterium or tritium are never found in nature; they have to be specially prepared in the laboratory.

These various types of hydrogen atoms (H^1, H^2, and H^3) are called *isotopes* (EYE-suh-tohps) of hydrogen. You will find that the other elements have isotopes, too. All the isotopes of an element have the same number of electrons and protons. They differ from each other only because they have different numbers of neutrons in the nucleus.

Heavier Atoms and Their Numbers

Since Rutherford's sketch of the atom, other scientists have been busy filling in more details. They learned that elements usually have several isotopes, as we have just seen. And they learned

CARBON AND ITS ISOTOPES

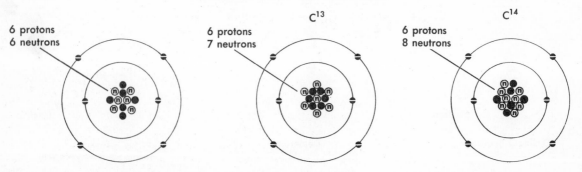

5-9. What makes each of these atoms an atom of carbon? What makes each an isotope of carbon?

how the atoms of one element differ from atoms of another. Let's see now how atoms of other elements are made up.

A carbon atom has six protons and (in its most plentiful isotope) six neutrons in the nucleus and six electrons (Fig. 5-9). A helium atom has two protons in its nucleus. The most common isotope of helium has two neutrons in the nucleus, too, so the atomic weight is four — two neutrons and two protons. Around the outside of the nucleus move two electrons whose charges balance the charges on the two protons. The only other

TABLE **5-1** SOME IMPORTANT ELEMENTS

Element	Symbol	Atomic number	Atomic weight (approximate)	
Hydrogen	H	1	1.008	A colorless inflammable gas lighter than air.
Helium	He	2	4	A colorless inert gas lighter than air.
Carbon	C	6	12	Present in all common living things. By itself—as diamonds, coal, graphite.
Nitrogen	N	7	14	Colorless gas, comprises $\frac{4}{5}$ of the air.
Oxygen	O	8	16	Colorless gas, supports burning. All animals must breathe it.
Sodium	Na	11	23	A very active metal. Reacts with water. A part of many common molecules.
Magnesium	Mg	12	24	A very light metal used in flares and flash bulbs and mixed with aluminum for construction of trains and airplanes.
Aluminum	Al	13	27	A very light metal.
Phosphorus	P	15	31	Inflammable nonmetal. Its compounds are important in small amounts in human muscles and in green plants.
Sulfur	S	16	32	A yellow inflammable solid.
Chlorine	Cl	17	35.5	A yellow-green poisonous gas. Part of the molecule of many common compounds.
Calcium	Ca	20	40	A metal whose compounds are important in forming rocks and strengthening your bones.
Chromium	Cr	24	52	A metal used for plating and hardening steel.
Iron	Fe	26	56	Mixing carbon with iron turns soft, weak iron into hard, strong steel.
Copper	Cu	29	64	One of the best conductors of electricity.
Zinc	Zn	30	65	A metal used to make dry-cell batteries and to coat (galvanize) iron.
Silver	Ag	47	108	Excellent conductor of electricity. Coins and "silverware."
Tin	Sn	50	119	Tin cans are made of steel covered with tin.
Iodine	I	53	127	Dissolved in alcohol to make tincture of iodine.
Platinum	Pt	78	195	Heavy white precious metal.
Gold	Au	79	197	Heavy yellow precious metal.
Mercury	Hg	80	200.6	The heaviest liquid metal.
Lead	Pb	82	207	Used in automobile storage batteries, solder.
Radium	Ra	88	226	Madame Curie's radioactive element.
Uranium	U	92	238	One isotope is used to release atomic power.
Plutonium	Pu	94	239	Also releases atomic power. One of several man-made elements.

known isotope of helium, rarely found, contains but a single neutron. It too bears the helium "trademark"—two electrons, two protons.

The next heavier atom has three protons and three electrons. This is the atom of lithium (LITH-ee-um). How many neutrons does it have? You can find this out by consulting the table on this page.

We can make a still heavier atom out of four protons with four electrons around the outside. This will be an atom of the light metal beryllium (ber-IL-ee-um). How many neutrons has beryllium?

Oxygen's number of protons and electrons is 8, sulfur's 16, iron's 26, and lead's 82. Every one of the elements can be identified by the special number that tells us how many protons it contains in its nucleus. This number is called the *atomic number*. You will find the atomic numbers of some common elements in Table 5-1.

Be careful not to confuse the *atomic number* with the *atomic weight*. Atomic weight tells how heavy the atom is as compared with other atoms.

Example: From Table 4 on page 67 you can now describe how those atoms of iron were put together that you were experimenting with back on page 55. Iron has an atomic number of 26. Hence it has 26 protons in its nucleus — and 26 electrons outside the nucleus. But its atomic weight is 56, which means there are probably 56 particles in the nucleus. Since 26 of them are protons there are therefore 56 − 26 = 30 neutrons. But we should really say "about" 30 neutrons. We must say "about" because there are several isotopes of iron, with a few more or a few less neutrons.

Your World of Atoms

Now at last you know what the atoms in your world are made of. These tiny clusters of electricity and space make up the earth, the atmosphere, the food you eat, your body, and the distant stars. These are our modern atoms.

In the next few chapters we shall learn a little about how the chemist *puts atoms together* in new and surprising combinations to make medicines, fabrics, plastics, fuels, and many other useful materials.

Then in later chapters we shall read the story of

atomic energy — the story of how the scientist is able to *take atoms apart* to release the enormous amounts of energy locked inside the nucleus.

Putting atoms together and taking them apart are two of the most important jobs of the scientist in our chemical and physical world.

Completed Table (from page 66)

Atom	No. of protons	No. of neutrons	No. of electrons	Approx. atomic wt.	Atomic number
Sodium	11	12	11	23	11
Chlorine	17	18	17	35	17
Calcium	20	20	20	40	20
Potassium	19	20	19	39	19
Helium	2	2	2	4	2
Uranium	92	146	92	238	92
Oxygen	8	8	8	16	8
Lithium	3	4	3	7	3

Looking Back . . . .

VOCABULARY

Each of the following terms represents a key idea in chemistry, was well as in the chapter you have just studied. What is the meaning of each?

1. electron
2. alpha particles
3. beta particles
4. gamma rays
5. neutron
6. nucleus
7. radioactivity
8. proton
9. isotope
10. atomic weight
11. atomic number

REVIEW QUESTIONS

1. Describe an experiment that shows there are two kinds of electric charges.
2. What is the law of attraction and repulsion between charged objects?
3. Describe the rays Madame Curie found pouring out of radium.
4. What is radioactivity? Name three elements that are radioactive.
5. How does radioactivity tell us that atoms contain equal quantities of both positive and negative charges?
6. How did Rutherford's experiments with alpha particles show that atoms are mostly empty space?
7. Why isn't a negatively charged electron pulled down into the positively charged nucleus of an atom?

8. Describe the way the isotopes of hydrogen are put together.
9. What is the difference between atomic number and atomic weight?

Going Further . . . .

PUT YOUR IDEAS TO WORK

1. If one atom has 10 neutrons and 12 electrons and a second atom has 10 neutrons and 11 protons, are the two atoms isotopes of the same element?

2. If one atom has 23 neutrons and 22 electrons and another has 24 neutrons and 22 protons, are the two atoms isotopes of the same element?

3. In their atom-smashing experiments, scientists have fired protons and neutrons and alpha particles at the nuclei of various kinds of atoms.

a) Can you explain why it would be difficult to hit the nucleus of an atom with a proton? Why should the proton be fired at the target atoms at high speed?

b) Why would it be easier to hit the nucleus of an atom with a neutron?

c) Why would it be very difficult to hit the nucleus with an electron?

4. Make a diagram of an atom with 6 protons, 6 neutrons, and 6 electrons.

5. Do the same with: (a) an atom with an atomic number of 10 and an atomic weight of 19; (b) an atom with 7 electrons and 8 neutrons.

THINGS TO DO

1. Make some large atom models using wire and balls or marbles of various colors and sizes to represent electrons, protons, and neutrons. Hang them up in your classroom.

2. Read an account of the life of Madame Curie or Lord Rutherford and give a report to your class.

3. Light a fluorescent-lamp tube without wires! In a darkened room on a dry winter day, rub the tube up and down a few times on your coat sleeve and it will light up visibly. Friction with your sleeve has removed electrons from the glass and the charge on the glass causes light-producing surges of electricity in the tube.

READING FURTHER

If you want to read further about atoms, read the chapters which apply in *New World of Chemistry* by B. Jaffe, Silver Burdett, 1955. Also refer daily to your newspapers and magazines in which current discoveries relating to the atom are described.

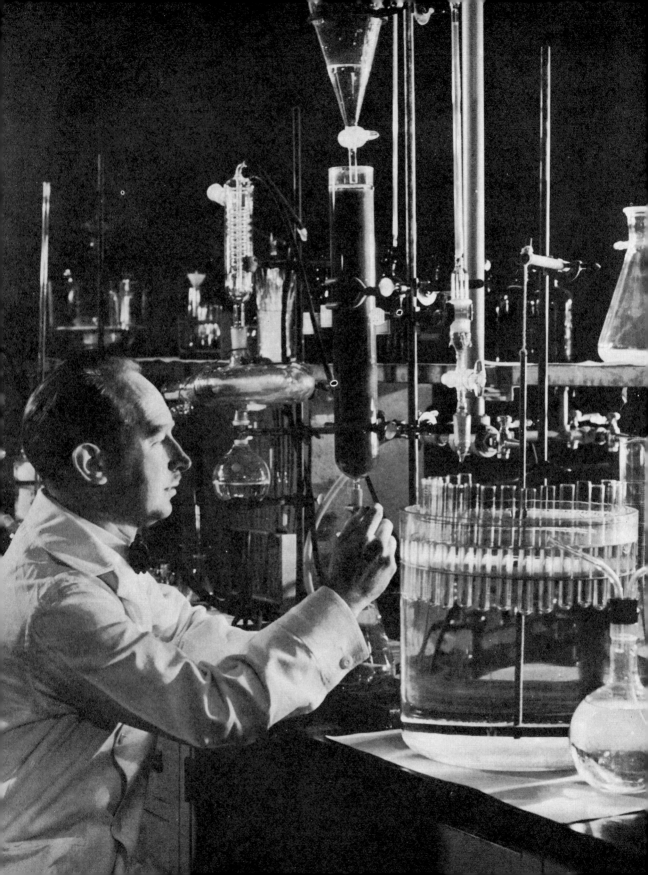

Combining Atoms

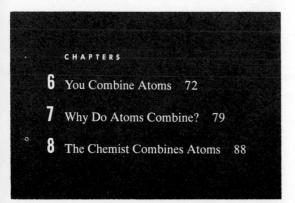

◀ *Chemists, working with a few kinds of atoms, make materials of infinite variety and use.*

HAVE YOU EVER watched a jeweler take apart a small watch or put one back together again? The pieces were hard to handle because they were so tiny, weren't they? Really small watches have to be put together under a microscope.

Now imagine what it would be like to put together a watch so tiny that you couldn't even see the watch under the microscope! Does that sound silly? Yet there are craftsmen in the world today who put together objects so tiny that one million laid end to end can barely be seen.

These craftsmen are chemists, and their tiny products are molecules. Unlike the jeweler, a chemist does not put his molecules together one at a time; he makes numbers of them all at once.

One of his test tubes may contain several thousand billions of billions of molecules all busily arranging themselves in precisely the order that he wishes. Certainly there is something worth learning from a man who can make such enormous numbers of quite invisible objects instantly obey his wishes. In the first two chapters of this unit you will learn enough about molecules to see how he does it.

You will not want to stop there. You will want to go on to learn how the chemist makes some of his most extraordinary molecules — fabrics that surpass silk from the silkworm, metals stronger than steel, drugs that surpass those found in nature, fertilizers to grow food in quantities your grandfather never dreamed of, and fuels that warm you and cook for you and transport you in a style far beyond the means of the richest of ancient kings. In this unit you will learn how the chemist makes a few of these wonders of this, our chemical world.

You Combine Atoms

In the last unit you put a few kinds of elements together to make compounds, and you took a few compounds apart into their separate elements. And then you learned that atoms of different elements are different from each other. How does the chemist use these differences? He may seem like a magician, but once you learn a bit of what he knows, you too can make atoms work for you.

BE YOUR OWN CHEMIST

If you've ever cooked a steak on a hike, or done any cooking whatsoever — or if you've ever struck a match, or lit a fire — you've taken part in a bit of chemistry. In the fire, molecules were put together, torn apart, or rearranged.

In this chapter you will learn how to put elements together into compounds and simple compounds together into more complex compounds. When the chemist puts atoms or molecules together, he calls the process *composition*.

You will also learn how to take compounds apart. When the chemist takes compounds apart, he calls the process *decomposition*.

You have probably looked at something you just finished building, and decided that it wasn't quite what you wanted. You took off a piece or two and replaced it with a different piece. When the chemist takes one element out of a compound and replaces it with another, he calls the process *displacement*. When the chemist exchanges the parts of two *different* compounds in this manner, he calls the process *double displacement*.

Let's go into the laboratory now and try out a few reactions of each process. Along the way we shall become better acquainted with the tools and methods of the chemist.

Composition Experiments

Experiment 1 (Composition). Recall your first composition experiment in which you put together iron and sulfur (page 56). The reaction was

iron + sulfur → iron sulfide

Experiment 2 (Composition). What is burning? Put a few pieces of charcoal in a test tube. Charcoal is almost pure carbon atoms. Heat these carbon atoms strongly and they will glow and slowly disappear. They have combined with the atoms of oxygen in the air to make carbon dioxide. The reaction is

carbon + oxygen → carbon dioxide

If you tip the hot test tube as in Fig. 6-1, the carbon dioxide can flow into a second test tube containing limewater. Put your thumb or a stopper over the second test tube, and shake it. The limewater will turn a milky color. This is a test that proves you have made carbon dioxide; the milky

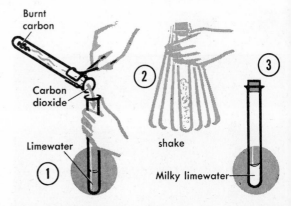

6-1. Which is heavier, carbon dioxide or air? Test a small amount of soda pop with limewater. What will a milky color indicate?

color is due to molecules you have formed, molecules of calcium carbonate.

You might like to try blowing through a glass tube into limewater for a few minutes to see if there is carbon dioxide in your own breath. Is there?

Experiment 3 (Composition). You can watch the oxygen in the air being used up during burning if you do the experiment shown in Fig. 6-2.

Put a few small pieces of red phosphorus in the small floating dish. Obtain a large-mouthed bottle or tall cylinder that will fit over the dish of phosphorus. Now set fire to the phosphorus by lighting it with a burning wooden splint and quickly invert the bottle over it. Be sure that you do this quickly. The fumes of burning phosphorus, if inhaled, may be unpleasant. The heated phosphorus atoms now can react with only the oxygen that is inside the bottle. The reaction is

phosphorus + oxygen → phosphoric oxide

When the phosphorus has burned and the bottle has cooled, notice that the water has risen in the bottle to take the place of the oxygen that has disappeared. The oxygen atoms have now become part of the molecules of that white smoke of phosphoric oxide.

If you have plenty of phosphorus atoms, there should be enough to combine with all the oxygen in the bottle. When the oxygen is all used up the burning has got to stop.

How high has the water risen in your bottle?

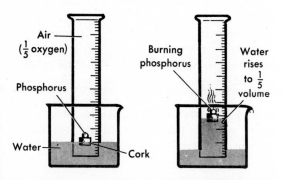

6-2. What does this experiment demonstrate? What compound is formed when phosphorus burns in air?

About one fifth? This shows that one fifth of the air is oxygen.

You have burned carbon atoms, and you have burned phosphorus atoms. What is burning? In both your experiments " burning " meant " atoms combining with oxygen." Usually burning gives off light and lots of heat, too.

Here is another experiment which has to do with burning.

Experiment 4 (Composition). Burning steel. Twist some steel wool into a pencil-shaped bundle and hold one end of it in the flame of your Bunsen burner. There is a shower of tiny sparks as the steel burns. Steel is mostly iron with a small percentage of carbon mixed in so the main reaction is

iron + oxygen → iron oxide

Almost all of the elements will combine with oxygen. If they do it quickly, giving off heat and light, then they are burning. Burning reactions are important examples of composition.

Decomposition Experiments

Experiment 5 (Decomposition). Recall your first work in decomposition when you took apart mercuric oxide into mercury and oxygen (page 57). The equation was

mercuric oxide → mercury + oxygen

Experiment 6 (Decomposition). Recall when you took water apart into hydrogen and oxygen with the help of an electric current (pages 57–58). That was decomposition, too.

water → hydrogen + oxygen
hydrogen hydroxide

Experiment 7 (Decomposition). Making more oxygen. Here is a simple way of making enough pure oxygen so that you can observe its interesting properties. All you need for this decomposition is some hydrogen peroxide from the drugstore and some manganese dioxide. If there is no manganese dioxide on the laboratory shelf, you can break apart an old flashlight battery. The black powdery substance that is inside the battery contains manganese dioxide and can be used instead.

Put one inch of the hydrogen peroxide in a test tube and add a few crumbs of the black powder (manganese dioxide), as in Fig. 6-3. At once oxygen bubbles off furiously from the hydrogen peroxide and quickly fills the tube. The equation for this reaction is

hydrogen peroxide → water + oxygen

You have decomposed hydrogen peroxide. Notice that the manganese dioxide has not taken part in the reaction.

You can tell oxygen is there by thrusting a glowing splint or a glowing piece of string into the test tube. It will burst into flame. This is the chemist's test for oxygen gas.

You will also want to thrust a piece of glowing hot steel wool (for safety's sake hold it in a pair of tongs) into the oxygen you have made and watch the steel burn with a shower of brilliant sparks.

You have noticed that the manganese dioxide did not appear at all in the equation for making oxygen. That is odd, isn't it? Moreover, if you weighed your pinch of manganese dioxide before you dropped it into the test tube and weighed it again after the experiment was over, you would find that it was not used up at all! It looks as if the manganese dioxide did not take part in the reaction. Yet without it the reaction does not seem to occur, or occurs so slowly it is missed.

In this experiment manganese dioxide has been used as a *catalyst*. A catalyst is a substance that helps a reaction to speed up, as in this case, or slow down, without actually taking part in it. Chemists know of many catalysts. They use them to help make gasoline for your car, to make rubber and plastics, and many other essential materials in your modern world. Your own body makes catalysts that help you to see this page, to grow, and to digest your dinner. In this simple experiment you have seen what a catalyst can do.

Experiment 8 (Decomposition). A test for water. Here is an experiment in which you decompose a big molecule into two smaller ones. The big molecule? — copper sulfate with several water molecules attached to it. The chemist calls it hydrated copper sulfate or sometimes blue vitriol.

Put a quarter inch of the blue powder in a dry test tube and heat it gently. It snaps and pops, and if you watch closely you will see a deposit of water collecting on the wall of the test tube up near its mouth (Fig. 6-4). Slowly your blue powder turns pale gray. The reaction is

hydrated copper sulfate →
blue

dry copper sulfate + water
pale gray

You have decomposed a big molecule into smaller ones.

Now the pure, pale gray copper sulfate you have just made has an interesting use. You can use it as a test for water. For example, have you ever wondered if the gasoline or radiator fluid put in your car was 100% pure? You can quickly tell if water has gotten into it. Put some in a bottle. Using a spoon, *not your fingers,* add a pinch or two of your dry copper sulfate. Shake the bottle a few times. If there is any water in the gas or alcohol, the copper sulfate will quickly combine with it and turn blue once more.

Displacement Experiments

Experiment 9 (Displacement). Copper plating. Before you put that bottle of blue copper sul-

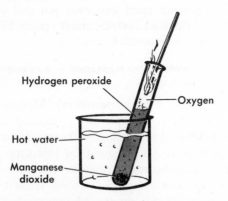

6-3. In this experiment, what is the use of the manganese dioxide? What is the use of the hydrogen peroxide?

fate back on the shelf, try this. Mix some up in water, and into the blue liquid drop a few iron nails or the blade of an old steel knife. After a few minutes fish them out, and you will find they have changed color. They have become copper plated.

The reason is that iron has a stronger tendency to form compounds than copper has. Hence when you put ordinary iron atoms close to the copper sulfate, the iron takes the place of, or *displaces,* the copper from its compound. The iron forces its way into the compound; the copper is set free. In this case the free copper coated, or plated, the iron nail.

iron + copper sulfate → iron sulfate + copper

Experiment 10 (Displacement). A silver tree. You can do even more spectacular displacement experiments as follows. Fill with water an old jar the size of a drinking glass. Dissolve in it about one gram of silver nitrate. Be very careful of silver nitrate. It is poisonous and it stains your skin.

Now from a sheet of tinfoil or aluminum foil cut out the shape of a Christmas tree three or four inches high. Stand it upright in the silver nitrate solution (Fig. 6-5). At once your tree will begin to sprout leaves of real silver! The leaves will continue to grow until the silver in the silver nitrate has been replaced by your tin or aluminum.

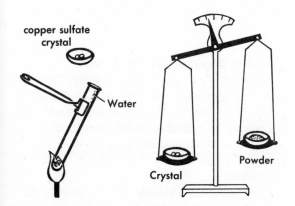

copper sulfate crystal

Water

Crystal

Powder

6-4. Start with two equal weights of copper sulfate crystals. Dehydrate (drive off the water from) one. Why will the crystal weigh more than the powder? Under what conditions will the dry powder regain its original weight?

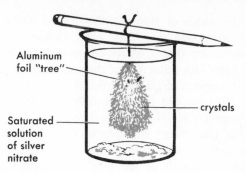

Aluminum foil "tree"

Saturated solution of silver nitrate

crystals

6-5. Explain the reaction when the silver collects on the aluminum foil.

This displacement experiment works for a reason similar to that in Experiment 9. The aluminum or tin atoms have a much stronger tendency to form compounds than does silver. To put this another way, aluminum atoms or tin atoms will attach themselves to the nitrate much more easily than will atoms of silver. Hence the silver atoms get kicked out (or displaced) from their silver nitrate molecules as the aluminum or tin atoms take their place.

tin + silver nitrate → silver + tin nitrate

The dark stain that spoils the appearance of your mother's aluminum pot may be a film of iron atoms that the more active aluminum displaced from oatmeal or some other iron-containing food. The atoms of iron cling to the outside of your aluminum pot.

Experiment 11 (Displacement). You have prepared oxygen by decomposition of two compounds: water (hydrogen oxide) and peroxide (hydrogen peroxide).

Now prepare some hydrogen — but not by decomposing water. Prepare hydrogen by displacing it from a compound such as hydrogen chloride (hydrochloric acid). Zinc will do very nicely for the displacement, so:

zinc + hydrogen chloride (hydrochloric acid) →
zinc chloride + hydrogen

You will need a hydrogen gas generator, as shown in Fig. 6-6. Use diluted hydrochloric acid (1% hydrochloric acid in water). Add the acid to the pieces of zinc (as shown) by pouring it slowly through the thistle tube. Collect the gas under water, that is, fill the collecting test tubes to the brim with water. Cover the collecting test tube with a square of glass and invert them under water. This you did when you collected oxygen (as in page 57, Fig. 4-5).

Put your thumb over one of the tubes, and as you remove your thumb, place a lighted match near the mouth of the tube. You will hear a " pop " as the hydrogen combines with oxygen, in a very, very tiny explosion. The characteristic " pop " of hydrogen as it combines with oxygen is a common test for the gas.

(To stop the action of zinc on the hydrochloric acid, add water through the thistle tube till the bubbling stops. Be sure the delivery tube is drained into the sink.)

Displacement reactions like these are widely used by the chemical industry to obtain materials you use every day. Thus the light metal magnesium is extracted from sea water by processes that include a displacement reaction with lime. Iron and copper and zinc and other metals, too, are displaced from their compounds by mixing their compounds with carbon (coke) and then heating the mixture.

The blast furnace at a steel mill is a big furnace in which carbon atoms (in the form of coke) displace iron from iron oxide (Fig. 6-7).

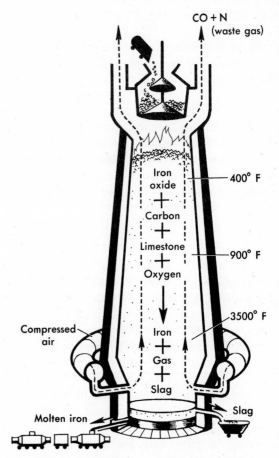

6-7. What is the basic reaction of the blast furnace? Can you see that the reaction is $2Fe_2O_3 + 3C \rightarrow 3CO_2 + 4Fe$?

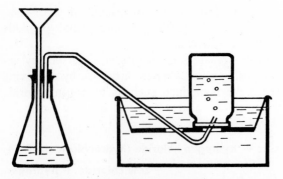

6-6. With this apparatus you can generate hydrogen by displacement rather than by decomposition. (Remember to always use dilute acid and never allow it to come into contact with your body.)

Double Displacement Experiments

Think of a pair of couples dancing. Now and then they exchange partners. The exchange involves both couples; hence, it is a double displacement. In a double displacement reaction, a part of one compound exchanges with a part of another. Let us see how this works in a chemical experiment.

Experiment 12 (Double Displacement). Purifying of water. Put a few drops of ink or a bit of fine dirt in water. This impure water can be cleared by a double displacement reaction.

Add a few grams of alum (aluminum sulfate) to the water and pour in after it a few spoonfuls of ammonia (ammonium hydroxide). These two compounds react to form a sticky cloud of the compound aluminum hydroxide, which slowly settles to the bottom, dragging the impurities with it. The reaction is

**aluminum sulfate + ammonium hydroxide →
aluminum hydroxide + ammonium sulfate**

The aluminum sulfate and ammonium hydroxide exchanged their two parts much as our two couples on the dance floor exchanged partners. This reaction is often used as one of the stages in purifying water supplies.

Experiment 13 (Double Displacement). Here is another double displacement reaction by which you can check up on one of the most important laws of chemistry. The law says that a chemist cannot make or destroy any atoms by performing chemical reactions with them. If atoms *are* made or destroyed, you would expect to notice it by watching for a change in weight during the reaction. Get out a good balance, and let's try it.

In a glass one-quarter full of water dissolve all the washing soda (sodium carbonate) you can. In a second glass one-quarter full of water dissolve all the calcium chloride you can. Calcium chloride is the chemical you may have seen used for drying out damp cellars.

Now find a bottle or chemical flask into which you can fit a small test tube. Fill the test tube almost to the top with the clear calcium chloride solution, and put enough sodium carbonate solution in the flask so that it nearly reaches the top of the test tube. Put together your two solutions and cork the flask tightly.

Now weigh the flask as accurately as you can. Leaving the weights on the balance pan, remove your flask and tip it back and forth until both liquids are mixed. That white cloud you made is calcium carbonate, which you have seen before as the chalk powder used in tooth powder and in cleaning compounds.

The reaction is

**calcium chloride + sodium carbonate →
sodium chloride + calcium carbonate**
chalk

6-8. A ladle of iron from the furnace. The molten iron flows out of the furnace first because it is heavier than the slag. The slag follows next. A bit of a problem: What is being poured from the large ladle into the bucket at the right — slag? or iron?

Do the new molecules seem to weigh the same as those you started with? If so, you are coming close to the idea of *conservation of matter* (see page 58). No one has yet found a chemical reaction in which atoms were destroyed. (Of course, your balance isn't sensitive enough to detect the absence of just a few atoms, but it is a start.)

Experiment 14 (Double Displacement). Invisible ink. Not all double displacements make clouds of solid white particles! Here is one that you can use to make secret writing visible.

In half a test tube of water dissolve as much potassium thiocyanate (thy-oh-sy-uh-nayt) as you can. This colorless liquid is your invisible ink. Try writing with it, using a clean pen.

Now prepare a second liquid by dissolving ferric chloride in half a test tube of water. To reveal your secret message, soak a bit of cotton or a small wad of paper towel in the ferric chloride and wipe it gently across your message.

The reaction is

potassium thiocyanate + ferric chloride →
ferric thiocyanate + potassium chloride
red

Now you have seen examples of four different kinds of chemical reactions. In the hands of a chemist these four kinds of reactions are used to make many useful and important materials.

You have worked with some small molecules. The chemist does similar things with very big molecules, some of them containing hundreds of atoms. As you go on with your study of chemistry, you will find out just how he makes some of the wonderful everyday compounds, about which you will read shortly.

Looking Back . . . .

VOCABULARY
Each of the following terms is a key word in chemistry, as well as in the chapter you have just studied. What is the meaning of each?

1. composition
2. decomposition
3. displacement
4. double displacement
5. catalyst
6. conservation of matter

REVIEW QUESTIONS
1. Describe two composition experiments.
2. Describe two decomposition experiments.

3. Describe three displacement experiments.
4. Describe three double displacement experiments.
5. What is burning?
6. How much of the air is oxygen?
7. What is the chemist's test for oxygen?
8. Name four uses for catalysts.
9. Describe a test for water.
10. How could you copper-plate a piece of iron?
11. What is one cause of dark stains on aluminum cooking pots?
12. What happens inside the blast furnace of a steel mill?
13. Describe a way of clearing muddy water.
14. In a chemical reaction, how would you go about detecting whether large numbers of atoms or molecules were being created or destroyed?

Going Further . . . .

Here are some more chemical reactions. Which ones are compositions? Which ones are decompositions? displacements? double displacements?

1. sulfur + oxygen → sulfur dioxide
2. zinc + copper sulfate → zinc sulfate + copper
3. magnesium chloride + hydrogen phosphate → magnesium phosphate + hydrogen chloride
4. potassium chlorate $\xrightarrow{\text{heat}}$ potassium chloride + oxygen
5. sodium + hydrogen hydroxide (water) → sodium hydroxide + hydrogen
6. hydrogen + chlorine → hydrogen chloride
7. silver + hydrogen sulfide → silver sulfide + hydrogen
8. aluminum + hydrogen chloride → aluminum chloride + hydrogen
9. hydrogen sulfide + copper sulfate → copper sulfide + hydrogen sulfate
10. hydrogen sulfide $\xrightarrow{\text{heat}}$ hydrogen + sulfur

READING FURTHER
If you want to try more chemical reactions (displacement, decomposition, etc.), why not refer to the books listed in Chapter 4, page 59.

Try also *Simple Chemical Experiments,* by Alfred P. Morgan, Appleton, 1941.

CHAPTER 7.

Why Do Atoms Combine?

The title of this chapter is a good question — one that has occupied chemists ever since man noticed that the mixing of two substances in certain ways produced other substances quite different from the original ones. As you may now expect, the answer lies in the structure and behavior of the different kinds of atoms. But why do atoms combine? Will a given atom combine with any other atom? And if not, why not? Let us investigate these questions.

Do you remember the experiment on page 55 in which you combined atoms of iron and sulfur to make molecules of iron sulfide? Let's try now to combine atoms of iron and zinc. Mix two grams of unrusted iron with five grams of zinc powder or shavings, and heat the mixture in a Pyrex test tube. Do you see any signs of a chemical reaction as you did before? Cool the contents of the test tube and hold a magnet over the powder. The iron still acts like iron, and the zinc is still unchanged. Certainly the iron has not combined with the zinc as it did before with sulfur.

Can Any Atom Combine with Any Other Atom?

Why will oxygen, but not iron, combine with zinc?

Why, for that matter, will oxygen combine with hydrogen to make water, though oxygen will not combine at all with helium?

What is it that holds atoms together to make molecules?

Losers and Gainers of Electrons

One answer is this. Iron atoms, like many others, tend to lose a few of their outer electrons (negative charges). You can easily see that when they do so the iron atoms will contain more positive than negative charges, and hence they will be *positively charged*. Sulfur atoms, though (like

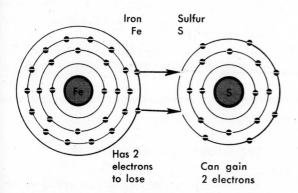

Iron
Fe

Sulfur
S

Has 2
electrons
to lose

Can gain
2 electrons

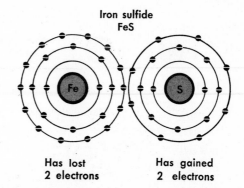

Iron sulfide
FeS

Has lost
2 electrons

Has gained
2 electrons

7-1. Metals are generally elements which lose electrons; nonmetals gain electrons. Can you see how this would lead to the binding together of atoms — in this case, of combining Fe and S?

many other atoms), have a tendency to collect a few extra electrons if any are around. When they gain extra electrons they become *negatively charged.* Study Fig. 7-1 to fix this idea firmly in mind.

When you put some *electron-losing* atoms, such as iron, together with some *electron-gaining* atoms, like sulfur, and use heat energy to speed their combination, the iron gives up some electrons to the sulfur. The iron and sulfur atoms now have opposite charges. You know what this means — they will attract one another very strongly. In fact they " stick " together as molecules of iron sulfide (Fig. 7-1).

This attraction of opposite charges then is one way atoms are held together in molecules.

Which Atoms Combine with Which?

When you try to combine two elements like iron and zinc *both* of which lose electrons, you have no success. Iron and zinc can only become positively charged, and when they both become positively charged they strongly *repel* each other. Thus a molecule made of just iron and zinc will not usually hold together. Likewise two electron-gainers like chlorine and oxygen do not *ordinarily* combine.

If we were to make a list of all the elements that lose electrons when they form compounds, we would find that our list included all the *metals.* Tin, zinc, iron, sodium, aluminum, uranium, silver, and many more metals all lose electrons

when they form compounds. Hydrogen loses its one electron too when it forms compounds, so that chemically hydrogen acts like a metal.

And a list of elements that gain electrons as they go into a compound would include oxygen, chlorine, sulfur, bromine, phosphorus, iodine, and others. These elements are *nonmetals.*

Now you can imagine many different compounds that can be made by combining atoms of metals with atoms of nonmetals.

For example, the tarnish on silver is:

silver + sulfur → silver sulfide.

Rust is: iron + oxygen → iron oxide.
Table salt is: sodium + chlorine →
sodium chloride.
Camera film is: silver + bromine →
silver bromide.
And when a photographer's flash bulb goes off:
magnesium + oxygen → magnesium oxide.

(Notice that the chemist, in naming the compound formed, always writes the metal first and the nonmetal second.)

Sharers of Electrons

Different atoms can also be held together in a molecule by *sharing electrons,* instead of gaining or losing them altogether. By such sharing of electrons, two atoms of hydrogen combine to form one molecule of hydrogen (Fig. 7-2). Molecules made in this way are held together by electrons that are being gripped by two atoms at the same time. In a water molecule, two hydrogen atoms each share their single electrons with an oxygen atom (Fig. 7-3).

In this chapter, most of the compounds discussed are formed by loss and gain of electrons. A few, however — water, for one example — are of the class of compounds formed by electron sharing.

THE SHORTHAND OF CHEMISTRY

You have seen that you cannot combine any atom with just *any* other atom — that you can only combine " electron-gainers " with " electron-

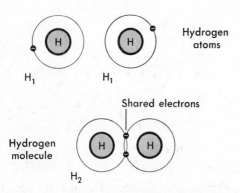

Hydrogen atoms

Shared electrons

Hydrogen molecule

7-2. Why do we say that the electrons are shared?

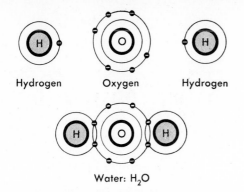

Hydrogen   Oxygen   Hydrogen

Water: H_2O

7-3. How does oxygen combine with hydrogen? How many electrons does each hydrogen atom share with the oxygen atom?

losers," or "electron-sharers" with each other. Now you will want to learn still more about the various kinds of compounds that atoms can make. For you to see most clearly what compounds our atoms can make, we shall need to learn a little of the shorthand of the chemist. Let's begin with symbols.

Symbols

If you had to write the word "nitrogen" ten times, wouldn't you find it easier to shorten the word and just write N? The chemist finds it a lot easier to shorten the names of the elements to one- or two-letter abbreviations which he calls *symbols*. For instance oxygen has the symbol O; zinc has the symbol Zn; chlorine, Cl; sulfur, S; iodine, I; iron, Fe (I is used for iodine); and sodium, Na. You will find these and the symbols for many of the other elements in the table back on page 67.

Symbols are useful for a second reason. When a chemist wants to describe the proportion of each kind of atom in a compound he could use words. But then he would have to write the compound water as "two atoms of hydrogen associated with each atom of oxygen." Isn't it easier to write water as H_2O_1, or simply H_2O?

To form aluminum oxide, two atoms of aluminum combine with three atoms of oxygen. Isn't it easier to write Al_2O_3?

For other compounds the advantage of using symbols is even greater. For example, baking soda is made of this combination of atoms: $NaHCO_3$. This means that one atom of sodium, one of hydrogen, one of carbon, and three of oxygen are all hitched together in baking soda.

H_2O, Al_2O_3, and $NaHCO_3$ are called formulas. The formula of a compound tells the chemist exactly how the atoms of each kind of element are combined proportionately in the compound. Here are the formulas of a few more familiar compounds. Can you read off what each formula says?

water	H_2O (say: " H–two–O ")
carbon dioxide	CO_2
iron sulfide	FeS (say: " F–E–S ")
phosphoric oxide	P_2O_5 (say: " P–two–O– five ")
mercuric oxide	HgO
zinc chloride	$ZnCl_2$ (say: " Z–N–C–L– two ")
potassium bromide	KBr
copper sulfate	$CuSO_4$
silver nitrate	$AgNO_3$
calcium carbonate	$CaCO_3$
aluminum nitrate	$Al(NO_3)_3$ (say: " A–L pa- rentheses N–O–three taken three times ")
ammonium sulfate	$(NH_4)_2SO_4$ (say: " paren- theses N–H–four taken twice, S–O–four ")

Notice that some elements do not start with the first letter of the element as it is known in English. For instance, Na (sodium) is taken from the German *Natrium*, and Fe (iron) is taken from the Latin *ferrum*.

Writing Formulas

When you heated up iron and sulfur in your test tube and saw the glow of their reactions, you could be pretty sure that they had joined together to make molecules of iron and sulfur. But how could you tell *how many* iron atoms and *how many* sulfur atoms were in each molecule? Should the molecule be written FeS or Fe_2S_3 or Fe_3S_2 or even Fe_8S_{17}?

You can answer this question as soon as you know how many electrons an iron atom loses and how many electrons a sulfur atom gains when they combine to form the iron sulfide molecule. The answer: an iron atom loses two electrons and a sulfur atom collects two electrons. Thus, since *one* iron atom provides just the number of electrons needed by *one* sulfur atom, they will combine one-to-one. The formula, Fe_1S_1, or better FeS, shows this fact (Fig. 7-1).

Now look at zinc chloride. Zinc atoms lose two electrons when they go into molecules. Chlorine atoms usually gain one electron. Thus *one* zinc atom will provide enough electrons for *two* chlorine atoms when zinc and chlorine combine. Therefore, the formula for zinc chloride *has to* be $ZnCl_2$ (Fig. 7-4).

The formula cannot be written $Zn_{\frac{1}{2}}Cl$ since the chemist cannot split zinc atoms into halves. Nor is the formula written Zn_2Cl_4, although this would be a correct formula, too. The chemist uses the simplest formula he can express in whole numbers of atoms.

In some cases, however, such a formula does not describe a molecule. For example, a compound such as salt is represented by the formula NaCl. But, as we have mentioned earlier, there are no individual molecules in a salt crystal. In this case, then, the formula NaCl does not represent any actual molecule, but is the simplest description of the relative proportion of elements occurring in the compound salt.

A formula for aluminum oxide is slightly harder to write. Aluminum atoms can give up three electrons and oxygen atoms can each gain two electrons. The only way aluminum atoms can precisely "satisfy" oxygen atoms is for two aluminum atoms to give up their total of six electrons, which is exactly the number that can be gained by three oxygen atoms. Thus aluminum oxide must have the formula Al_2O_3.

Remember that atoms of metals generally lose electrons and atoms of nonmetals generally gain electrons when they form a compound. The secret of compound building is that *the atoms of the metal must lose just the number of electrons that*

zinc chloride

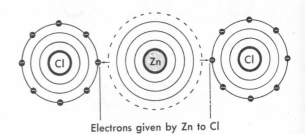

Electrons given by Zn to Cl

7-4. How many electrons does each chlorine atom gain from the zinc atom?

can be gained by the atoms of the nonmetal. Put another way, the number of electrons lost by all the atoms of the metal taken together has to be the same as the number of electrons gained by all the atoms of the nonmetal taken together.

The number of electrons an atom gains or loses or shares when it becomes part of a compound is called its *valence.*

Here is a table showing common valences—numbers of electrons a metal can lose and numbers of electrons a nonmetallic element can gain.

TABLE **7-1** VALENCES OF SOME COMMON ELEMENTS

Metal	Valence	Nonmetal	Valence
aluminum (Al)	3	sulfur (S)	2
zinc (Zn)	2	chlorine (Cl)	1
mercury (Hg)	2	oxygen (O)	2
hydrogen (H)	1	nitrogen (N)	3
(acts like a metal)		iodine (I)	1
copper (Cu)	2	bromine (Br)	1
silver (Ag)	1	phosphorus (P)	3
lead (Pb)	2		
iron (Fe)	2		
magnesium (Mg)	2		
sodium (Na)	1		
potassium (K)	1		
calcium (Ca)	2		

Now you should try your hand at writing some simple formulas. After you have written them check yourself. The answers are given at the bottom of page 84 (1).

a) silver chloride
b) lead oxide
c) sodium bromide
d) zinc bromide
e) potassium sulfide

f) hydrogen chloride
g) copper chloride
h) aluminum sulfide
i) calcium iodide
j) mercuric sulfide

Writing More Difficult Formulas

Lots of common compounds are made of three or four different elements at once. For example, you have seen that baking soda has the formula, $NaHCO_3$ and silver nitrate, $AgNO_3$. How is this possible?

You probably have some classmates whom you see together much of the time. They come to school together, sit together, enter extracurricular activities together, and go together after school. You finally think of them as being nearly inseparable.

Some atoms are like that, too! For example a nitrogen atom is often found with three oxygen atoms. This atom combination is so common that it is given a name — nitrate. It is written NO_3. You never see the nitrate group all by itself though. The nitrate group always carries an extra electron. This negative charge means that it is strongly attracted to atoms of metals and is usually found in compounds with them.

What is the valence of the nitrate group? If you looked at that single extra electron and answered " one," you were right.

There are many common compounds containing the nitrate group. For instance potassium nitrate (also called " saltpeter ") is used to make fireworks; silver nitrate is used as a medicine and in photography; sodium nitrate and calcium nitrate are important fertilizers.

Try writing the formulas for (a) sodium nitrate and (b) potassium nitrate. The answers are at the bottom of page 84 (2).

If you try to write the formula for calcium nitrate, you have to remember that calcium has a valence of 2 and nitrate a valence of 1. Hence you need two nitrate groups for each calcium atom. The formula is written $Ca(NO_3)_2$. The

number 2 means that there are *two* of whatever lies inside the parentheses — in this case, two nitrates.

Aluminum has a valence of 3. Three nitrate groups are needed to give an aluminum atom the three electrons it needs to form an aluminum nitrate molecule. Thus the formula is $Al(NO_3)_3$.

Try writing the formulas for (a) zinc nitrate, (b) magnesium nitrate, (c) iron nitrate. Again the answers are at the bottom of page 84 (3).

Nitrate is not the only common group of atoms. There are many others. Such groups of atoms are called *radicals*. A radical is a combination of atoms acting chemically (to form compounds) as if they were single atoms. Thus, these atoms generally hold together as a group.

Radicals

Many common materials contain radicals. You saw some of them in the table back on page 81. In Table 7-2 you have a list of some of them together with their valences and an example of an important compound.

All of these radicals except ammonium act like nonmetals. Ammonium is the only common radi-

TABLE **7-2**   COMMON RADICALS

Radical	Formula	Valence	A common compound
nitrate	NO_3	1	Silver nitrate is used in photography.
carbonate	CO_3	2	Calcium carbonate is what limestone and chalk are made of.
hydroxide	OH	1	You need sodium hydroxide to make most kinds of soap.
phosphate	PO_4	3	Four or five pounds of calcium phosphate in your body make your bones and teeth hard.
bicarbonate	HCO_3	1	Bread and cake won't "rise" unless the baker uses baking powder (which contains sodium bicarbonate) or yeast.
sulfate	SO_4	2	Calcium sulfate (gypsum) is used in making plaster.
ammonium	NH_4	1	Household ammonia is ammonium hydroxide.

cal that acts like a metal. Notice that the hydroxide radical is made up of O and H (OH). Here are the formulas and names of some compounds containing radicals. Can you fill in the missing ones? Answers are at the bottom of page 86.

sodium hydroxide	NaOH
calcium hydroxide	$Ca(OH)_2$
aluminum hydroxide	(a)
zinc carbonate	$ZnCO_3$
copper nitrate	(b)
ammonium chloride	NH_4Cl
(c)	$(NH_4)_2S$
mercuric bicarbonate	$Hg(HCO_3)_2$
aluminum phosphate	(d)
magnesium phosphate	$Mg_3(PO_4)_2$
zinc phosphate	(e)
ammonium phosphate	(f)
calcium bicarbonate	(g)
(h)	KNO_3
(i)	NH_4HCO_3
(j)	Ag_2SO_4
lead carbonate	(k)

Have you noticed the *endings* of the compounds — *ide, ate?* Study the compounds and see whether you can determine why *ide* is used one time and *ate* another.

EQUATIONS, THE LANGUAGE OF CHEMISTRY

What does a chemist *do* with his formulas? Does he use them as the old alchemists did hundreds of years ago to confuse and mystify anyone who tried to read their secrets?

No, the chemist uses his formulas in much the same way you use words when you write a sen-

(1) *Answers:* (a) AgCl, (b) PbO, (c) NaBr, (d) $ZnBr_2$, (e) K_2S, (f) HCl, (g) $CuCl_2$, (h) Al_2S_3, (i) CaI_2, (j) HgS.

(2) *Answers:* (a) $NaNO_3$, (b) KNO_3.

(3) *Answers:* (a) $Zn(NO_3)_2$, (b) $Mg(NO_3)_2$, (c) $Fe(NO_3)_2$.

tence. The chemist uses formulas instead of words; he puts his formulas together to form what he calls an *equation.* For instance, in combining iron (Fe) with sulfur (S) as you did earlier, he writes Fe + S yields FeS. On the left are the *reacting substances* used in the reaction, on the right is the *product.* He uses an equation to describe a reaction that happens in a test tube just as you would write a sentence to describe an event in your classroom.

Writing Equations

Does that sound complicated? You have already seen something like it back in the preceding chapter, when we wrote *word* equations to describe some of your test tube reactions.

In the experiment back on page 55 you put iron and sulfur atoms together to form iron sulfide. You described the reaction by this word equation

iron + sulfur → iron sulfide

All you need to do to describe this reaction by symbols is to write

Fe + S → FeS

Easy, isn't it?

Look at some of the other reactions you performed back in the last chapter.

In Experiment 2 you wrote,

carbon + oxygen → carbon dioxide

The chemist writes it as

C + O$_2$ → CO$_2$

He writes O_2 instead of 2 O because he has found that the atoms of oxygen in the air travel together in pairs instead of singly. Thus they are in the form of *molecules* of oxygen, not single atoms. Similarly nitrogen atoms in the air as well as atoms of chlorine gas and hydrogen gas seem to travel in pairs. Thus when you write the formulas for these as gases you write O_2, N_2, Cl_2, and H_2. Of course in compounds the atoms may be single, as in MgO and NaCl.

What you have learned to do is to write the chemist's shorthand. But it isn't only a shorthand, is it? It is a whole new language in which every symbol means something. Chemistry is an exact science. The chemist doesn't just mix a bit of one substance with another to get a product. He mixes exact amounts of each. In the next section of this chapter you will see how the chemist uses his knowledge of equations to determine the correct amounts to be used.

Balancing Equations

When you finished one recent experiment (page 58) and put a glowing splint near the mouth of a tube of hydrogen you had collected, there was a loud " pop." If you looked carefully, you found drops of water in the tube. Yes, one way to make water is to burn hydrogen. The chemists might write this equation as follows:

$$H_2 \;+\; O_2 \;\rightarrow\; H_2O$$

| two hydrogen atoms | two oxygen atoms | two hydrogen atoms and one oxygen atom combined as water |

Then he notices an important fact. This simple equation starts out with two hydrogen atoms and ends up with two in the water molecule. But there is only *one* oxygen atom in the water molecule, where he started out with two. He has lost one atom of oxygen! Can this be? Not according to John Dalton's firm belief that atoms are not destroyed!

If you could weigh your hydrogen, oxygen, and water carefully, you would find that what really happens is this:

$$2H_2 + O_2 \rightarrow 2H_2O$$

This says that four hydrogen atoms and two oxygen atoms combine — *not* one atom of each. This is just the right number to make two molecules of water with no extra atoms left over. Count the atoms of hydrogen on both sides of the equation. There are four, aren't there? And how many oxygen atoms are there on each side? If you say " two " you are right.

One of the interesting facts about chemistry is that atoms and molecules always react in *just* the

right numbers so that no atoms are created and none are destroyed in the reaction. When the chemist writes down these numbers in front of his formulas he says he is *balancing* his equation. When he has balanced his equation, he can see at once just how many atoms and molecules take part in his reaction.

As another example look at what happened when you grew your silver tree (Experiment 10, page 75). (CAUTION: compare this equation with the correct equation below.)

$$AgNO_3 + Al \rightarrow Al(NO_3)_3 + Ag$$

Here again you see that silver nitrate and aluminum *cannot* go together in this way, for then we would come out with more nitrates than we started with. Therefore we must find what numbers must be written in front of our formulas in order to make the number of atoms of each element the same on both sides. Try it! With a little experimenting you will probably find that your equation is balanced when you write

$$3AgNO_3 + Al \rightarrow Al(NO_3)_3 + 3Ag$$

Count the atoms of aluminum on each side and see. Aren't there the same number of nitrate radicals on both sides of the equation now? And silver, too?

What's the Use?

" Why does the chemist *bother* to balance an equation? " you may ask. " After all, if he knows what chemicals react and what the final products are, what's the use of writing ' 3 ' in front of the silver nitrate and ' 3 ' in front of the silver in the last equation above? "

You can answer this very reasonable question yourself if you look for a moment at the following recipe for making fudge.

sugar	milk
salt	butter
chocolate	vanilla

Can you make fudge from this recipe? Of course not! What is missing? The *amount* of each ingredient, of course. Let us suppose that you have just ½ of a cup of milk. Is this going to be enough to use up 2 ounces of chocolate? Obviously the recipe is no help at all.

Now look at the complete recipe:

2 ounces chocolate
2 cups sugar
⅛ teaspoon salt
¾ cup milk

Stir together while heating until the sugar dissolves. Cook at 250°F., stirring slowly until it can be formed into balls. Then add 2 tablespoons of butter, cool slightly, and stir until it begins to harden. Add 1 teaspoon of vanilla, pour out onto an oiled plate and cut into squares.

Surely now you can quickly see that you have *not* got enough milk to use up those 2 ounces of chocolate, but that ¾ of a cup will just give you what you need. (A very good recipe, incidentally!)

In the same way a balanced equation tells the chemist how much of each reacting substance he must have to get the product he wants without wasting any of the reacting substances.

Now to a chemist the unbalanced equation $AgNO_3 + Al \rightarrow Al(NO_3)_3 + Ag$ is just like that recipe for fudge without any numbers in it. If you want to deposit 324 grams of silver (that is, displace 324 grams of silver from the silver nitrate) how much aluminum will you need? You cannot possibly answer this, even when you know that each aluminum atom has an atomic weight of 27 and silver atoms have an atomic weight of 108.

But if you write the *balanced* equation you can find the answer.

$$3AgNO_3 + Al \rightarrow Al(NO_3)_3 + 3Ag$$

The balanced equation tells you that each aluminum atom deposits *three* silver atoms. Now one aluminum atom has an atomic weight of 27 (Table 4) and one silver atom has a weight of 108

(Table 4) so the three silver atoms together weigh 3×108 or 324. Hence 27 grams of aluminum atoms will deposit 324 grams of silver.

If you prefer half as much weight of silver then, of course, you use half as much aluminum. How much silver could 54 grams of aluminum displace? 648 grams is the right answer.

When chemists balance their equations, they can calculate the exact weight of the materials they use. They do this in all branches of the chemical industry. For instance: How much liquid oxygen must you put in that rocket motor to use up one ton of alcohol fuel? (A balanced equation will tell the chemist how much he needs.)

How many tons of coke do you need to prepare 1,000 tons of iron from iron oxide in a furnace?

How much sulfur do you need to buy to make 100 tons of sulfuric acid?

These and countless similar questions are asked every day by chemists all over the world. You can see why balancing equations is important when a company must buy coal and iron and other raw materials by the ton. In the next chapter you will see how the chemist uses all his knowledge of atoms, formulas, and chemical compounds to make many familiar materials.

Looking Back . . . .

VOCABULARY

Each of the following terms is a key word in chemistry, as well as in the chapter you have just studied. Show that you understand the meaning by defining each term.

1. electron-losing
2. electron-gaining
3. electron-sharing
4. metals (in terms of gaining or losing electrons)
5. nonmetals (in terms of gaining or losing electrons)
6. symbol
7. formula
8. radical
9. valence
10. balanced equation

Answers: (a) $Al(OH)_3$, (b) $Cu(NO_3)_2$, (c) ammonium sulfide, (d) $AlPO_4$, (e) $Zn_3(PO_4)_2$, (f) $(NH_4)_3PO_4$, (g) $Ca(HCO_3)_2$, (h) potassium nitrate, (i) ammonium bicarbonate, (j) silver sulfate, (k) $PbCO_3$.

Going Further . . . .

BASIC PRINCIPLES

1. Why does iron combine with sulfur and not with zinc?
2. Why will oxygen combine with hydrogen and not with helium?
3. What are the two major ways in which atoms may become chemically associated?
4. Of the following, which are losers of electrons? Which are gainers?

iron	aluminum	zinc
sulfur	copper	nitrogen
oxygen	chlorine	magnesium
hydrogen	iodine	bromine
	helium	

5. How does a symbol differ from a formula?
6. Why must an equation be balanced?
7. State the relative proportions of atoms in each of the compounds listed below:

H_2O	HCl	$Al(NO_3)_3$
NaCl	$KClO_3$	H_2CO_3
Na_2Co_3	MnO_2	$NaHCO_3$
NaOH	$Al_2(CO_3)_3$	Na_2SO_4

8. Balance the following equations that are incorrect:

$$H_2 + O_2 \rightarrow H_2O$$
$$Na + Cl_2 \rightarrow NaCl$$

$$H_2 + Cl_2 \rightarrow HCl$$
$$NaOH + HCl \rightarrow NaCl + H_2O$$
$$Zn + Cl_2 \rightarrow ZnCl_2$$
$$Mg + O_2 \rightarrow MgO$$
$$KClO_3 \rightarrow KCl + O_2$$
$$Fe + S \rightarrow FeS$$
$$Al + S \rightarrow Al_2S_3$$

9. Some of the following equations are wrong. Some are correct. (Their symbols, or formulas, or balancing may be wrong.) Can you detect which are wrong? Explain why.

a) $Mg + Br \rightarrow MgBr$
b) $KOH + HCl \rightarrow KCl + H_2O$
c) $3AlCl_2 + 2NaOH \rightarrow Al(OH)_3 + 2NaCl$
d) $He + Cl_2 \rightarrow HeCl_2$

READING FURTHER

Road to Abundance by Jacob Rosin and Max Eastman, McGraw-Hill, 1953. This is a survey of what has been done by chemists. It is also a non-technical story of the role of the chemist in the future.

Building Blocks of the Universe by Isaac Asimov, Abelard, 1957.

Discovering Chemistry by Elizabeth K. Cooper, Harcourt, Brace & World, 1959.

Elements of the Universe by Glen T. Seaborg and Evans G. Valens, Dutton, 1958. Includes interesting material on elements heavier than uranium which are artificially made. Dr. Seaborg has played a leading role in the investigation of these transuranic elements.

8

The Chemist Combines Atoms

Millions of dollars a day are being spent on scientific research in this country. Tens of thousands of scientists are working to find out things never known before and to make things never before seen. From this enormous expense and labor come new ideas and new products around which whole industries may be built. Some of the most remarkable products — and the most familiar — are the result of chemical research.

SULFURIC ACID — A FOUNDATION STONE OF MODERN LIVING

Many of the products we use today would not exist without the help of sulfuric acid. You will find sulfuric acid in your laboratory in a bottle marked H_2SO_4. It is a colorless oily liquid that chars paper, seriously burns skin, and hisses and splatters dangerously when it touches water. Use it only for experiments under the direction of your teacher. Carelessness may lead to serious injury.

You rarely see sulfuric acid outside the laboratory. Yet without this liquid, the chemical industry would find it impossible to make many of its remarkable products. For example:

Although sulfuric acid is not a plant food, millions of tons a year are needed to make fertilizers to help grow the food you eat.

Although sulfuric acid would destroy your automobile engine, it is used by the millions of tons a year to prepare gasoline.

Sulfuric acid dissolves steel, yet the steel industry needs a million tons of it each year to clean steel sheets before coating and polishing them (Fig. 8-1).

Sulfuric acid is not present in any finished explosive, yet it is absolutely necessary in making most of the explosives used in the construction of roads, tunnels, foundations, and in warfare.

Copper wire, rayon clothing, photographic film, plastics, paints, and paper — all of these require sulfuric acid for their manufacture.

No wonder it has been said that you can judge a nation's standard of living by how much sulfuric acid it uses.

Making Sulfuric Acid

Let us now see how sulfuric acid is made.

We can describe what happens by writing three simple equations:

$$S + O_2 \rightarrow SO_2$$
sulfur   oxygen   sulfur dioxide

$$2SO_2 + O_2 \rightarrow 2SO_3$$
sulfur dioxide   oxygen   sulfur trioxide

$$H_2O + SO_3 \rightarrow H_2SO_4$$
water   sulfur trioxide   sulfuric acid

From these you can see that the materials needed are water, oxygen (oxygen is 20 per cent of the air you breathe), and sulfur (Fig. 8-2). In the sulfuric acid factory the sulfur is first burned. From your experience with " burning " you recognize that to a chemist, the word " burn " means " to combine with oxygen." The reaction is $S + O_2 \rightarrow SO_2$. (See Fig. 8-3, step 1.)

The next step is to combine sulfur dioxide and oxygen. They do not combine very readily. Persuading them to do so is the hardest trick in the whole process of making sulfuric acid. The chemist manages the trick with the help of a catalyst.

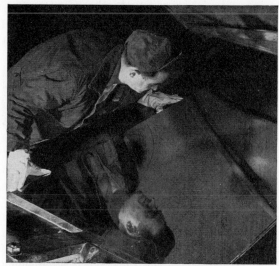

United States Steel Corp.

8-1. One use of sulfuric acid is to clean steel sheets. What other uses can you suggest?

You will remember (page 74) how manganese dioxide acted as a catalyst, helping your hydrogen peroxide to fall apart into water and oxygen. It has been found that platinum metal is one of the best catalysts for helping along the reaction $2SO_2 + O_2 \rightarrow 2SO_3$. The reaction takes place in a tower several stories high filled with perforated trays of durable asbestos fiber coated with platinum. A stream of hot SO_2 and air flows upwards over the trays, and SO_3 emerges at the top of the tower (Fig. 8-3, step 3).

Sulfur trioxide does not dissolve in water very readily. Hence, to make the last step in the process work the chemist is faced with another problem. He has found, however, that sulfur trioxide does dissolve very readily in concentrated sulfuric acid. Thus it is only necessary to bubble the gas through concentrated sulfuric acid. To the resulting solution he then adds enough water to combine with the dissolved SO_3 (Fig. 8-3, step 4).

Every year, millions of tons of sulfuric acid are made by this method. It is called the *contact process*. The contact process is a good example of forming compounds by composition (see experiment 1–4, pages 72–74).

The acid is shipped in specially lined tank cars

to factories where it is used to prepare fertilizers, gasoline, steel, explosives, dyes, and a host of other familiar and useful products.

NITROGEN — YOUR LIFE DEPENDS ON IT

If you weigh 130 pounds, there are about 4 pounds of nitrogen in your body. Atoms of nitrogen, combined mainly in important compounds, are a part of every cell of your body. No animal or human can possibly live without nitrogen atoms to build into the chemicals which make up flesh and bone and blood.

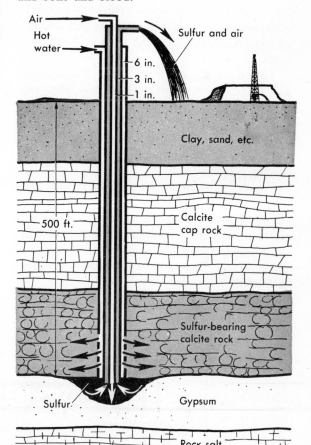

8-2. The best place to obtain sulfur is 500 feet or so underground along the shores of Texas and Louisiana. Here it is mined by drilling a hole down to the sulfur, melting it with steam, and pumping it out of the ground as a liquid.

You get your precious nitrogen atoms by eating proteins such as meat, eggs, and milk. You get your nitrogen atoms also from the chemicals contained in fruits and vegetables. In fact it is hard *not* to eat some nitrogen-containing compounds every time you take a bite at the dinner table.

Where do the nitrogen atoms in your food come from? The nitrogen atoms in the fruits and vegetables you eat all come from the soil. For that matter all the nitrogen atoms in your meat and eggs come from the soil too, since cows, pigs, and chickens all eat grain and hay and other plant food. The nitrogen atoms in your body right now were once part of the soil of farms and orchards all over North America and even of some other lands.

You might suppose that growing wheat or apples or beans on the same land year after year would finally draw from the soil most of the nitrogen atoms it contained. This is exactly what can happen. And when it does, the plants die and the farm is no longer able to supply enough food to keep people alive.

Clearly, nitrogen atoms have to be put back into the soil to replace the ones that have been harvested and carried off to market. Otherwise all the world's farmlands slowly lose their fertility, and all the people and animals on earth starve to death. Where, then, are more nitrogen atoms to be found?

You probably know that 80 per cent of the air you breathe is nitrogen. Here is a convenient and endless supply to replenish exhausted fields. But here also is a very serious difficulty.

The difficulty is this: plants cannot take in nitrogen gas directly out of the air. The nitrogen has to be combined with other atoms to form molecules that can be absorbed through the roots of the plant. Moreover, to make matters much worse, nitrogen atoms will not combine with other atoms except in very unusual circumstances. It looks then as if farmlands must surely lose their fertility after a few years of use.

The human race would have starved to death long ago if the problem had not been solved somehow. One of the important ways of solving it is to add to the soil such nitrogen-containing material as manure and other dead plant and animal matter. The nitrogen that once came from the soil thus goes back to it. Another way is to turn a nitrogen-poor field over for a year to alfalfa or clover. These plants have special bacteria clustered about their roots that can capture the nitrogen of the air and cause it to combine with other elements to make plant-sustaining compounds (Fig. 8-4).

But these two ways cannot possibly put enough nitrogen into plants to feed our nation of 170 million people three meals every day. Years ago we turned to the chemist to invent a way of capturing nitrogen from the air and turning it into

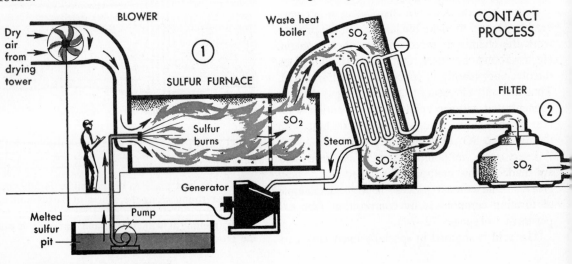

plant food on an enormous scale. Your health — indeed, your very life — depends on his success.

Capturing Nitrogen Atoms

Nitrogen is hard to force into compounds. And when you have finally persuaded it to combine with other elements, you sometimes find that it will suddenly break out again, and the result is an explosion. Many nitrogen compounds are explosive. *Nitro*glycerine, tri*nitro*toluene (TNT), and *nitro*cellulose (guncotton) are widely used explosives. These names of explosives remind you that nitrogen atoms do not "like" to be in compounds. They prefer to be alone.

Ammonia (NH_3) is more stable. Chemists have found a way of making this nitrogen compound on a large scale and building it into plant food. Millions of tons of ammonia compounds are spread on America's fields every year.

Ammonia is made by combining nitrogen gas and hydrogen gas.

$$N_3 \ + \ 3H_3 \ \rightarrow \ 2NH_2$$
nitrogen   hydrogen   ammonia

If you try to do this by mixing the two gases in a bottle in your laboratory, they will not combine. For years chemists tried to find some way of forcing these molecules into partnership.

The secret was finally discovered by the German chemist Fritz Haber in 1912. He found that you have to squeeze the gases with a pressure at least 200 times greater than the ordinary pressure of the air in the room around you. At the same time you have to heat the mixture up to about 500° C. (You remember that water boils at 100° C.) And even then the two reluctant gases do not combine to make much ammonia unless you help them along with a catalyst. Haber found that the best catalyst for this reaction is finely divided iron. Perhaps you can see why it took years of experiment to discover this complicated process.

Nowadays there are many factories in this country busily making ammonia by the *Haber process* (Fig. 8-5). Ammonia (NH_3) is a gas,

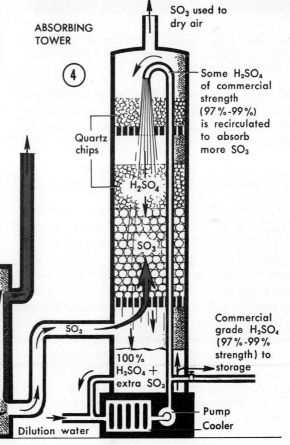

8-3. Why is this called the contact process? What is the equation for the conversion of sulfur (S) into sulfuric acid (H_2SO_4)?

Hugh Spencer

8-4. This is the root of a pea, a legume. Notice the bumps, or nodules. In the nodules are bacteria which fix nitrogen for use by the plants.

and for most of its uses the chemist combines it with other compounds. For instance, as a fertilizer it is commonly combined with sulfuric acid as follows:

$$2NH_3 + H_2SO_4 \rightarrow (NH_4)_2SO_4$$
ammonia   sulfuric acid   ammonium sulfate

Ammonium sulfate is one of the most widely used fertilizers. Thus, as a result of the work of the chemist, nitrogen is restored to the soil so that plants can use it in making food. Many of the nitrogen atoms in your body right now were forced into ammonia molecules in a Haber process factory, thence made into ammonium sulfate and spread in the right amounts on farmland where they were built into your food. Every meal you eat contains the handiwork of the chemist.

Ammonia has other uses, too. One of them is in making explosives, those touchy molecules from which nitrogen atoms suddenly separate with such destructive force.

Still another use is in making household ammonia. This useful household cleaner is really ammonium hydroxide, made by dissolving ammonia in water.

$$NH_3 + H_2O \leftrightarrows NH_4OH$$
ammonia   water   ammonium
hydroxide

We have written this reaction with arrows in both directions to indicate continual composition and decomposition. There is evidence of this when you cautiously sniff at a bottle of household ammonia. The choking odor is the free gas NH_3.

There is a fourth important use for this versatile nitrogen compound which we shall examine in the next section — the manufacture of sodium carbonate.

SALT IN DAILY LIFE

You probably use salt to season your food, but did you realize that salt is present in most foods you eat? Your food would hardly taste right without it. Moreover most people need to eat about 16 pounds of salt a year for health.

But the usefulness of salt at mealtimes does not stop there. The next time you sit down to dinner look about you at some of the other objects that are made with the help of salt. For example:

Your drinking glass is made from sand and sodium carbonate. Salt is used in making sodium carbonate.

The water you drink and wash the dishes in may have been purified with sodium carbonate, made from salt.

If you are using a paper napkin it was probably made (as most paper is) with the help of sodium hydroxide. Salt went into the making of sodium hydroxide.

If you have a tablecloth, it was probably mercerized (as many of your clothes are, too) with the help of sodium hydroxide to give it sheen and durability. If it is rayon, sodium hydroxide was used in making it.

The soap you wash the dishes with was probably made with sodium hydroxide.

The baking powder used to make your bread and cake is made with sodium bicarbonate, which in turn is a result of reactions in which salt has been used.

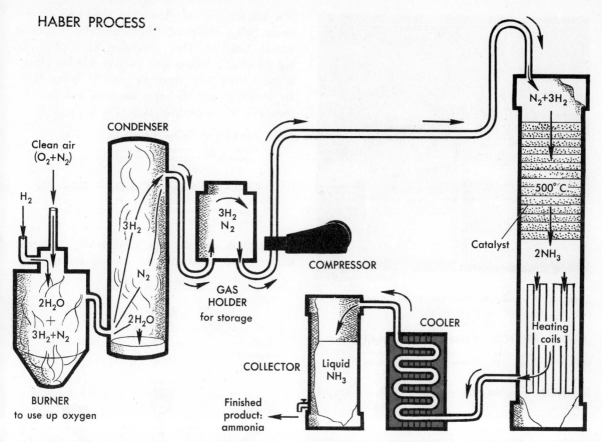

Clean air
(O_2+N_2)

H_2

CONDENSER

$3H_2$

N_2

$2H_2O$

$2H_2O$
+
$3H_2$+N_2

BURNER
to use up oxygen

GAS
HOLDER
for storage

$3H_2$
N_2

COMPRESSOR

N_2+$3H_2$

500°C

Catalyst

$2NH_3$

COOLER

Heating
coils

COLLECTOR

Liquid
NH_3

Finished
product:
ammonia

8-5. The Haber process. Simplified, it is $N_2 + 3H_2 \rightarrow 2NH_3$.

Glass, paper, soap, cloth — all these everyday materials owe their existence in large part to the use of chemicals made in reactions in which salt played a great part. What would your life be like without them? Salt is clearly one of the important materials in your chemical world.

Putting Salt to Work

Salt (NaCl, sodium chloride) is found in large underground deposits in many parts of the United States and in many other countries as well.

Sodium chloride is used for preserving fish and other foods as well as for flavoring food, but most of it is used to make sodium carbonate. In the preceding section you saw how useful sodium carbonate is. It is made from sodium chloride by a very ingenious chemical process.

First of all, limestone, which is calcium carbonate, is strongly heated to drive off carbon dioxide gas. This reaction of decomposition is

$$CaCO_3 \rightarrow \quad CaO \quad + \quad CO_2 \quad (\textit{step 1})$$
calcium   calcium   carbon
carbonate   oxide   dioxide
           (quick lime)

The carbon dioxide is then combined with ammonium hydroxide (see page 92).

$$CO_2 + NH_4OH \rightarrow NH_4HCO \quad (\textit{step 2})$$
carbon   ammonium   ammonium
dioxide   hydroxide   bicarbonate

Now the ammonium bicarbonate and sodium chloride "switch partners" in a double displacement reaction which results in sodium bicarbonate.

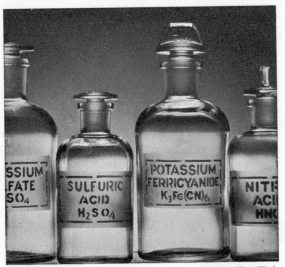

Corning Glass Works

you will see piles of pure white sand (silicon dioxide, SiO_2) and piles of limestone (calcium carbonate, $CaCO_3$). There are many kinds of glass, but the most common kind of glass, window glass, is made from these three compounds. When they are mixed in just the right amounts and heated, these two reactions take place (Fig. 8-8).

$$Na_2CO_3 + SiO_2 \rightarrow Na_2SiO_3 + CO_2$$
sodium carbonate   silicon dioxide (sand)   sodium silicate   carbon dioxide

$$CaCO_3 + SiO_2 \rightarrow CaSiO_3 + CO_2$$
calcium carbonate (limestone)   silicon dioxide (sand)   calcium silicate   carbon dioxide

The carbon dioxide gas bubbles off, and the molten glass, a mixture of sodium silicate and

8-6. Did you know that salt (NaCl) was used in making the glass for these bottles?

$$NaCl + NH_4HCO_3 \rightarrow NaHCO_3 + NH_4Cl$$ (step 3)
sodium chloride   ammonium bicarbonate   sodium bicarbonate   ammonium chloride

$$2NaHCO_3 \xrightarrow{heat} Na_2CO_3 + H_2O + CO_2$$ (step 4)
sodium bicarbonate   sodium carbonate   water   carbon dioxide

Most of the sodium bicarbonate is heated at once in the factory to make sodium carbonate by the last reaction above. This long series of reactions is called the *Solvay process*. Over three million tons of sodium carbonate are made by the Solvay process in this country every year and sent to the industries that make glass, paper, soap, water softeners, rayon, and even gasoline. Some of the sodium bicarbonate (baking soda) is used in making baking powders. In baking bread its molecules fall apart to form carbon dioxide and other compounds. The CO_2 gas makes the bread " rise."

Putting Sodium Carbonate to Work

Before leaving our study of sodium carbonate we should see how some of these industries put it to work.

If you ever take a tour through a glass factory, you will see great storage piles of sodium carbonate near the glass-making furnaces. Likewise

GLASS FURNACE

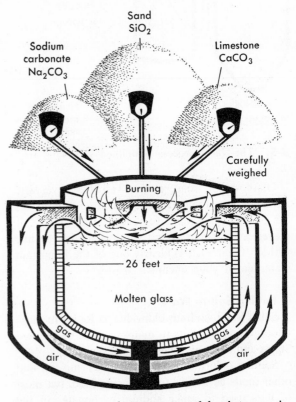

8-7. Glass, one of our most useful substances, is made from sand (SiO_2), washing soda (Na_2CO_3), and limestone ($CaCO_3$). What is the formula for glass?

Campbell-Hays, from Monkmeyer

8-8. Here are some of the chemist's remarkable (yet common) products that have come out of his work. How many can you identify?

calcium silicate, is poured from the furnace and molded into bottles, window glass, and other products.

Thus, as you look out the window you peer through molecules that the chemist assembled out of air, limestone, salt, and sand.

A great deal of sodium carbonate is turned into sodium hydroxide (lye) for use in making paper and soap. One way is by a double displacement reaction of the sodium carbonate with calcium hydroxide (slaked lime, $Ca(OH)_2$).

$$Na_2CO_3 + Ca(OH)_2 \rightarrow 2NaOH + CaCO_3$$

sodium   calcium   sodium   calcium
carbonate hydroxide hydroxide carbonate
                      (lye)

Making Paper

Paper is made out of wood.

Wood is made of long fine wood fibers glued tightly together by gums and resins secreted by the growing tree. Paper-making is a complex process, but what follows is an outline of the important steps.

Crown Zellerbach Corp.

8-9. What do you think is being made here? This is a paper pulp digester — one stage in the making of paper from wood pulp.

To make paper you must grind and crush the wood until the fibers are torn apart. Mixed with water and certain other substances the result is wood pulp. You can make wood pulp directly into paper by spreading it out into a thin sheet and drying it. Newspaper is made in this way. It is inexpensive, but it soon becomes discolored and weakened with age.

To make better grades of paper you must remove the gums and resins from the wood pulp.

This is done by cooking the wood pulp in a paper pulp digester with sodium hydroxide until the gums and resins are dissolved and can be washed away (Fig. 8-9). The pure wood fibers can now be pressed into high grade white paper. With further processing such as bleaching the result is the paper of this page.

Making Soap

You can make soap at home or in the laboratory by the same process that the chemist uses in industry. To make a simple soap all you will need is some sodium hydroxide (lye) and some lard or other kind of fat (Fig. 8-10).

Warm the lard (just a few tablespoons) in a beaker or small pot and add the ten per cent solution of sodium hydroxide (a ten per cent solution means 10 grams in 100 cc of water) so that it covers the lard with about an inch of solution. Boil gently for ten minutes stirring it with a glass rod. Be careful that the mixture does not spatter. If it gets on your skin, wash it off with water immediately.

Let the mixture stand for ten more minutes. Then add a tablespoonful of salt to the mixture and stir. The soap is insoluble (will not dissolve) in salt water and will rise to the top. Filter this through a funnel as shown in Fig. 8-10. Wash the soap by pouring some cold water on the filter paper. This will get rid of some more of the sodium hydroxide as well as the salt.

Show the soap to your teacher before you use some of it to wash your hands.

Now what really happened is this:

$$C_3H_5(C_{18}H_{35}O_2)_3 + 3NaOH \rightarrow$$

fat   lye

$$3NaC_{18}H_{35}O_2 + C_3H_5(OH)_3$$

soap   glycerine
(sodium
stearate)

That equation may look very complicated until you see that it is really a double displacement reaction. The Na from the NaOH has replaced the C_3H_5 in the fat. Over 2 billion pounds of soap are made every year in the United States and 200 million pounds of glycerine.

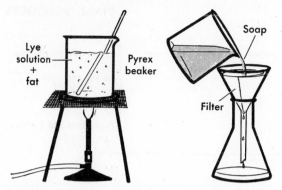

8-10. Making soap. Compare with Fig. 8-11. If you do not have NaOH, try Na_2CO_3 (washing soda).

Soap-making is the most important source of glycerine. The glycerine that is made along with the soap is sent off to be made into nitroglycerine, dynamite, rayon, cellophane, ink, cosmetics, and antifreeze for your car.

By now you should begin to see that the chemical industry is very large and complex. You should notice how various *branches of the industry depend on one another*. Can you trace the manufacture of soap back to the original raw materials found in the air and in the ground? See Fig. 8-12 for the answer.

Can you trace the path of the atoms that finally end up in molecules of glass? Perhaps you can see also how a *very few chemical processes are basic to the manufacture of a great variety of useful everyday things*. Can you name the processes?

How many of the objects in the room around you are made with the help of the Haber process? the contact process? the Solvay process? See Fig. 8-12.

MAKING AN ALLOY

It has been said that without alloys we would not have our present civilization — no factories, no airplanes, no television sets, no cars — none of the things we take for granted. One of the best ways to find out what alloys are is to make one.

Solder

First examine a piece of lead and a piece of tin. How do they differ? Now weigh out about five grams of lead and five grams of tin. Place both metals in a crucible and sprinkle a little sodium carbonate on top of them. (This helps the action along by lowering the temperature at which melting the metals takes place.) Now heat the metals until they are both melted together. Allow the melted material to cool. When it is cool, examine it.

You have made a solder (SOD-er) — a very useful alloy. How is it different from lead or tin? For one thing, its melting point is lower than either lead or tin. Second, it is stronger than either lead or tin. There is nothing easier to use if you want to fuse two copper wires together. Try it.

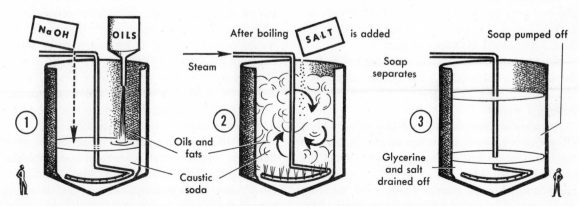

8-11. Soap made from lye and fat is cooked commercially in giant steam-heated kettles.

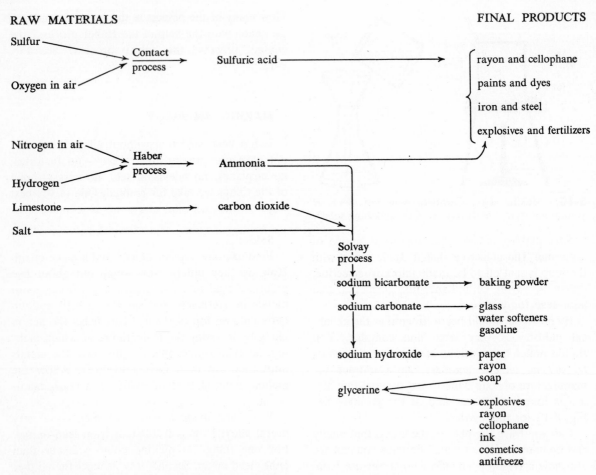

8-12. Trace the manufacture of paper back to the original raw materials.

Melt some of the solder in your crucible and dip two very clean copper wires, held closely together, into it. Let the solder cool. Note how the solder has joined the copper wires.

Next time you look into a radio set notice how the wires are soldered to their connections. They are soldered with an alloy similar to the one you have just made.

An alloy is a combination of two metals. Most alloys are not merely a mixture of metals, because the combination has different properties from the original metals. Also, it is clear that alloys are *not* compounds, for the metals which make them up can be mixed in many different proportions. (Re-

member Dalton, page 53; the atoms of a compound always combine in definite proportions.) Moreover if an alloy were a true compound, we would expect most of its properties to be different from the metals it was made of.

Thus an alloy is a very peculiar kind of material. It is neither a mixture nor a compound. There is a lot that chemists do not know about how metals combine to form an alloy.

Nevertheless alloys are so common in your daily life that it would be next to impossible for you to get along without them. Study Table 8-1. How many of these alloys can you find in use in your home?

TABLE **8-1** COMMON ALLOYS

Alloy	Metals
bronze	copper and tin
brass	copper and zinc
duralumin	aluminum, magnesium, copper, and manganese
magnalium	aluminum and magnesium
steel	iron, carbon, and manganese
monel	nickel and copper
pennies	bronze and copper
alnico	nickel, cobalt, aluminum, and iron

PETROLEUM — BLACK GOLD

When Colonel Drake drilled the first oil well near Titusville, Pennsylvania, in 1859, it produced about 20 barrels of petroleum a day — not enough to supply the fuel oil needed to heat a large modern apartment house for a day. (Oil is simply a common term for petroleum.)

From petroleum we make gasoline. Within the last 50 years men have learned how to use gasoline engines to propel themselves all over the earth, the sea, and the sky. Indeed, taken altogether the power of the gasoline engines built *in one day* in this country far exceeds that of all the power generators installed at Niagara Falls. To run these engines Americans are using up, on the average, nearly 5,000,000 gallons of gasoline every hour, mostly for transportation.

Your family car uses up about two gallons of " gas " every hour it is run, a big airplane uses a hundred times as much, and big ocean liners may use up a thousand gallons of fuel an hour — all obtained from petroleum.

No wonder that drilling for oil and refining and distributing it is a very big business indeed. Let us see how the chemist obtains gasoline and other useful materials from petroleum.

Refining Petroleum

Petroleum, as it is pumped out of the ground (Fig. 8-14), is usually, though not always, a thick,

black, sticky mixture that is quite useless until it has been *refined*. Refining is the process of separating the petroleum mixture into its various parts.

If we are to see how a petroleum refinery works, we had better first write down a list of some of the compounds that have to be separated from each other, as in Table 8-2.

Isn't it odd that all the formulas should be so similar? You will notice that in the examples given, the number of hydrogen atoms is always two more than double the number of carbon atoms.

And you have probably noticed that the more carbon atoms the molecules contain, the higher is the boiling temperature of the substances which contain them. Indeed the first four boil at so low a temperature that they are gases at ordinary " room temperatures." Hence petroleum contains only a little dissolved methane, ethane, propane, and butane. Most oil wells produce great quantities of them as gases, however. Methane and ethane (called *natural gas*) are carried all over the United States in pipelines and widely used for heating and cooking (Fig. 8-15). Propane and

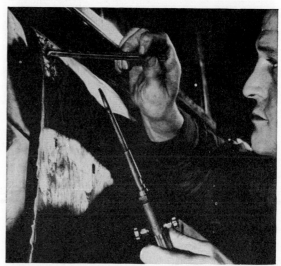

American Smelting & Refining Co.

8-13. This worker is using a solder, a mixture of tin and lead, for fusing electrical connections in an automobile.

away first, and has condensed as a liquid in the container which collects the gas. After a while no more pentane would collect. You would have *distilled* out all of it from the petroleum.

Now change collecting bottles and warm the petroleum up to 75° C. What will boil away now? Presently you will have distilled off all the hexane.

Since it is not safe for you to use an open flame to heat the petroleum any higher, you cannot distill off any of the remaining compounds. But at a refinery there are ways of heating petroleum enough to separate each of the compounds in this way. The process of separating a mixture by boiling off its ingredients at different temperatures is called *fractional distillation.* Fig. 8-16 is a diagram of a fractionating tower where all the ingredients are separated in one operation. In Fig. 8-17 you see fractionating towers at work in a large modern petroleum refinery.

What Is Gasoline?

Ordinary gasoline is mostly a mixture of hexane, heptane, and octane. The mixture varies for different uses. Pentane or nonane may be added too, along with special compounds such as tetra-

8-14. Oil drillers call this a "Christmas tree." The gauges and valves in the "tree" control the flow of oil from oil-bearing rock below.

butane are compressed into steel tanks and marketed as *bottled gas,* commonly used in rural areas for heating and cooking.

Imagine that you have a bottle of petroleum. It contains all the compounds on our list beginning with pentane. Suppose you warmed the mixture up to 40° C. Would anything boil away? If you were to distill petroleum as shown in Fig. 8-16, you would find that at 40° pentane has boiled

8-15. This natural-gas pipeline, thirty-six inches in diameter, serves New York City, New Jersey, Philadelphia, Wilmington, and the Southern Piedmont.

TABLE 8-2 PETROLEUM REFINERY PRODUCTS

Name	Formula	Boiling point	Use
methane	CH_4	–161° C.	natural gas
ethane	C_2H_6	– 88° C.	natural gas
propane	C_3H_8	– 42° C.	bottled gas
butane	C_4H_{10}	0° C.	bottled gas
pentane	C_5H_{12}	36° C.	gasoline
hexane	C_6H_{14}	69° C.	"
heptane	C_7H_{16}	99° C.	"
octane	C_8H_{18}	125° C.	"
nonane	C_9H_{20}	150° C.	"
decane	$C_{10}H_{22}$	174° C.	kerosene
etc., all the way up to:			
$C_{20}H_{42}$ to $C_{35}H_{72}$		about 700° C	lubricating oil
$C_{23}H_{48}$ to $C_{29}H_{60}$		"	vaseline and paraffin

ethyl lead to reduce knocking or " ping " in your engine. Ethylene dibromide is usually put in (remember bromine, page 11) to protect the spark plugs from being fouled. Indeed, by the time the chemist has finished adding improvements to the gasoline it is nearly as complicated a mixture as the petroleum from which it is obtained.

Gasoline is so useful because it is easily evaporated and very inflammable. Inside the engine of your car it is mixed with just the right amount of air (by the carburetor), led into the cylinders, and set on fire by an electric spark. The burning is a fast chemical reaction that produces carbon dioxide and water vapor and lots of heat. Hexane for instance burns like this:

$$2C_6H_{14} + 19O_2 \rightarrow 12CO_2 + 14H_2O$$
hexane   oxygen   carbon   water
                  dioxide   vapor

The heat produced expands the CO_2 and water vapor and forces the piston down the cylinder, thereby moving your car.

Not Enough Gasoline

The gasoline-making molecules make up less than one third of petroleum. But gasoline is need-ed in *far* larger amounts than all the rest of the petroleum compounds put together. Of course the heavier petroleum molecules are needed for fuel oil, lubricating oil, paraffin, and asphalt. In petroleum there is more than enough oil, paraffin, and asphalt, but nowhere nearly enough gasoline. This shortage of gasoline has been solved by the chemist. He has found a way of changing the unwanted surplus of heavy molecules into more gasoline molecules.

You will notice that a molecule like $C_{16}H_{34}$ is just about twice as big as octane. $C_{16}H_{34}$ is not

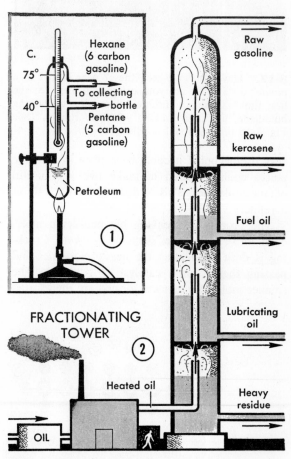

FRACTIONATING TOWER

8-16. You can repeat in a small way the work of the fractionating tower in (2) with the apparatus in (1). What products are produced through the fractionating of oil? Which is the lightest fraction? the heaviest?

8-17. Have you ever seen these? near home? in a movie? on TV? Or are you seeing them here for the first time? These are fractionating units containing butadiene, useful in making synthetic rubber. (See Fig. 8-16 for fractional distillation.)

very useful, but if it could be broken in half, the pieces could be used to make two very useful octane molecules. This is done on a big scale at a refinery.

The process of breaking big petroleum molecules into smaller ones is called *cracking*. Cracking is done by heating the heavy molecules and passing them over a catalyst (Fig. 8-19). The smaller molecules that are formed are then sorted

out in the same way as before — by fractional distillation. Almost half the gasoline used in the United States today is made by the *cracking process*.

Thus by taking petroleum apart and reassembling and altering the pieces, the chemist has been able to create fuels that heat our houses, cook our food, and drive us over land and sea. If you drive up to the gasoline station and say, " Fill her up," will you know what you are getting?

PLASTICS — BIG MOLECULES FROM LITTLE ONES

You have seen how the chemist can take apart large molecules found in petroleum in order to make the more useful smaller molecules of gasoline. Chemists can also string small molecules together to make big ones. In fact they can hitch molecules together in long chains to produce giant molecules called *polymers* (POL-ih-merz). A polymer, which is built rather like a freight train, is a long string of similar molecules. The molecules in rubber join together in a zigzag chain. That's why rubber is so elastic.

You see and use polymers every day. Rubber is a polymer, nylon is a polymer, most plastics are polymers. Nature produces polymers too. Wood fibers are mostly cellulose, a polymer made of hundreds of the molecules, $C_6H_{10}O_5$, strung end-to-end. At every meal you eat countless numbers of starch molecules, which are also polymers.

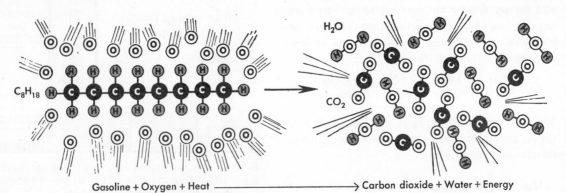

Gasoline + Oxygen + Heat ⟶ Carbon dioxide + Water + Energy

8-18. This happens when gasoline is burned in the air. Do you know what happens when it is burned in a limited amount of air in your gasoline engine? What poisonous gas is produced?

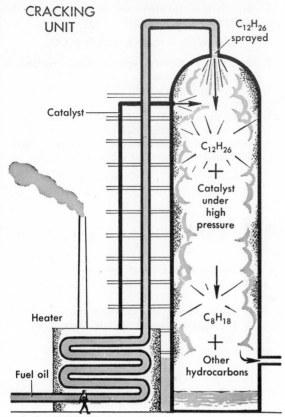

CRACKING UNIT

C₁₂H₂₆ sprayed

Catalyst

$C_{12}H_{26}$

$+$

Catalyst under high pressure

$\downarrow$

C_8H_{18}

$+$

Other hydrocarbons

Heater

Fuel oil

8-19. What is the difference between cracking and fractionating? Compare with Fig. 8-16. Why is a catalyst used in cracking and not in fractionating?

Making a Polymer

You can easily make a polymer yourself.

Put about one inch of powdered sulfur in a test tube and heat it gently over a low flame. Soon the sulfur will melt into a watery straw-colored liquid. You can easily pour it out into a jar of water where it will quickly harden.

Repeat the experiment, but this time when the sulfur has melted continue to heat it gently. Watch for a change in color. Soon it will turn a deep reddish-brown color and you will discover that it no longer pours easily out of the test tube. It is thick and rubbery. Indeed you can stretch a piece of it like a rubber band and it will snap back to its original shape. By heating the sulfur atoms,

you have made them string together by the hundreds forming long chains. You have made a polymer.

Your sulfur polymer is rubbery because the chains of atoms are kinky. When you stretch a lump of sulfur polymer, you are pulling the chains out straight; when you let go, the chain-like molecules snap back to their kinky form.

A rubber band is made of kinky chains of another polymer that are pulled out straight as you stretch it.

Everyday Plastics

A *plastic* is any substance that we can form or shape by molding.

Of course not all polymers are rubbery. For example, the Bakelite (BAYK-uh-lyte) your telephone is made of is a polymer. Bakelite is made by heating phenol and formaldehyde together under rather special conditions. It has the convenient property that it can be molded into useful shapes and made to " set " in a hard rigid mass.

Celluloid is another common plastic that is used in making piano keys and photographic film. This plastic is a polymer too, made from formaldehyde and phenol.

Standard Oil Co. (N.J.)

8-20. This synthetic rubber from a vinyl compound is a polymer made of hundreds of molecules.

Still another is lucite, the transparent glass-like plastic used for small boxes, for toilet articles, for novelties, and even for the noses of bombing planes.

Other plastics are used to cement plywood together, to make drugstore table tops, to make fabrics creaseproof, to make wrapping and packaging material, to strengthen paper, to make bottles and for an almost endless number of everyday uses.

In creating plastics the chemist has had an important effect on your everyday life. Plastics can be molded cheaply into complicated shapes in a minute or two — shapes that would take a trained machinist hours to make of metal. Thus the price of many familiar objects has been brought within the range of your pocketbook.

Moreover plastics can be made to have a great variety of special properties: they can be made strong, transparent, brightly colored, resistant to acids or water. Some are suitable as good electrical insulators, and are fireproof.

Looking Back . . . .

VOCABULARY
The following terms are some of the key words in this chapter. What is the meaning of each?

1. catalyst
2. contact process
3. natural gas
4. cracking
5. polymer
6. plastic
7. Haber process
8. Solvay process
9. soap
10. alloy
11. petroleum
12. fractional distillation

REVIEW QUESTIONS
1. Name at least five substances which did not exist in large quantities twenty years ago.
2. What are three common uses of sulfuric acid?
3. Describe the contact process. What is the catalyst used?
4. How do we depend upon nitrogen? Give at least four examples.
5. How are nitrogen atoms captured?
6. What use do you find for salts in your daily living? Give at least five examples.

7. How is this equation used in preparing an important food in your life?

$$2NaHCO_3 \rightarrow Na_2CO_3 + H_2O + CO_2$$

8. Describe the Solvay process. What use does it have in modern life?
9. How is paper made?
10. How is soap made?
11. Name three alloys found in your home.
12. How is gasoline prepared?
13. Name at least three uses for plastics as you have discovered them used at school or at home.

Going Further . . . .

BE YOUR OWN MANUFACTURING CHEMIST
a) Making Talcum Powder (or after-shave powder)
Add about 6 drops of a perfume you particularly like to 1 pound of powdered talc. Mix it so that the talc has the odor of the perfume. Now sift the powder through a fine cloth (silk, for instance).
b) Making Tooth Powder
1. A simple tooth powder often suggested by dentists is made up of 1 ounce powdered table salt and 2 ounces baking soda. If less is desired, use one half of each quantity but use one part of the salt to two parts of the baking soda. (Ask your dentist whether he recommends your using it.)
2. Another type of tooth powder has precipitated chalk ($CaCO_3$) in it. You may purchase such a flavored tooth powder from your druggist. Or you may make it by mixing a few drops (5 or 6) of oil of wintergreen with about two ounces of precipitated chalk.
c) Making Cheese
Pour about a half quart of skim, or dried milk (dissolved in water) into a pan. Take a rennet tablet and dissolve it in about 10 cubic centimeters of warm water. Heat the milk slowly to about 65–70° C. As the milk begins to heat, add the rennet solution. Allow to stand for fifteen minutes off the flame. Stir to separate the " curds " into casein and whey. Pour (filter) the mixture through cheesecloth. Press out the whey. What you have is *cottage cheese.*

A PIECE OF RESEARCH
Study the following table. When you don't know the meaning of a term (for example, *silicones*) look for it in the dictionary of scientific terms at the

end of this book. Or you may want to refer to a chemistry text such as: *Modern Chemistry* by Charles E. Dull, William O. Brooks, and H. Clark Metcalfe, Holt, 1954, or *New World of Chemistry* by Bernard Jaffe, Silver Burdett, 1955.

What aspects of your life has the chemist touched? What new chemical inventions have been produced since this book was printed?

FURTHER READING AND EXPERIMENTING

Man and the Chemical Elements, from Stone-Age Hearth to the Cyclotron by J. A. N. Friend, Scribner, 1953, is an interesting history of chemistry and shows how chemistry has changed our lives.

Are you interested in experiments you can do at home? *The Chemistry We Use* by B. L. Hawk, Science Service, 1954, will be useful to you.

CHEMICAL RESEARCH INCREASINGLY SERVES BASIC HUMAN NEEDS

Year	Food	Clothing	Shelter	Health	Transportation, communication	Tools and equipment
1931 to 1940	mineral supplements synthetic flavors nitrogen fertilizer solutions	nylon synthetic tanning agents water repellents crease-resistant finishes flame-retardant finishes	wood preservatives resin-adhesives for plywood fire-retardant paints	sulfa drugs synthetic detergents synthetic vitamins	gasoline antioxidants plastics magnesium	magnesium rust preventives
1941 to Present	selective and pre-emergent weed killers defoliants insecticides fungicides soil conditioners mold inhibitors resin linings for cans high-analysis fertilizers	shrink-proofing chemicals newer synthetic fibers permanent "starch" inherent colors in man-made textile fibers	silicones vinyl floor tiles glass fibers room deodorants resin-emulsion and latex-base paints insulation	antimalarials antibiotics antihistamines synthetic hormones cortisone antituberculars amino acids radioisotopes tranquilizing drugs	more powerful gasolines extreme-pressure lubricants non-flammable hydraulic fluid synthetic rubbers plastic car bodies lubricating oil additives	titanium silicones plastic dies for moiding

Hundreds of new products of chemical industry research are introduced commercially each year.

Chemical Manufacturers' Association

Splitting

Atoms

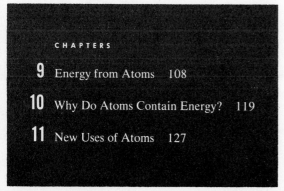

◀ *At Shippingport, Pennsylvania, the nation's first commercial atomic "furnace" is lowered into position.*

HAVE YOU EVER asked yourself what are the most important front-page news items of the last few years? What would you put on your list? You would probably include the beginning and the end of World War II. And you would be very likely to list the beginning of the Atomic Age announced in the headlines.

Since 1945, the atom has been continually in the headlines. Even if you had not already studied the atom in this book, you would know a great deal about it. You would know that:

Atoms contain a lot of energy.

Scientists have found ways to release this energy.

This energy has been used to destroy cities full of people and tamed to drive submarines and generate electricity for heating houses.

Atoms are so important to us that our government is spending billions of dollars of tax money each year in order to learn more ways to use the energy locked in them.

As the earth's stock of chemical fuel dwindles, we turn hopefully to the atom.

In this unit we shall learn how this energy can be released. We shall see how the energy of these mighty mites, the atoms, can be turned to new uses — to heal disease, to provide us with abundant power and the tools for richer and more abundant lives for all of us if only we are wise enough to avoid the destruction it can also bring.

CHAPTER

9

Energy from Atoms

There are several ways of releasing the energy locked up in atoms. Let's begin our story with the fastest way to release energy — in a bomb.

In this chapter we shall deal with one kind of bomb called the atomic bomb, or A-bomb. In the next chapter you will study the hydrogen bomb, or H-bomb, which works in an entirely different way.

DESTRUCTIVE POWER FROM ATOMS

To prepare one kind of atomic bomb the most important thing needed is a pure supply of one isotope of uranium. To make the bomb go off, all that is necessary is to bring a few pounds of this isotope together in one place (Fig. 9-1). That's all there is to it! The result may be an explosion as great as that of 20,000 tons of TNT and a temperature close to one million degrees Centigrade.

All atomic bombs work in this simple way. The reason *why* so much energy is released when a few pounds of a certain uranium isotope are brought together is the next thing to consider. The story of " why " is longer but not any more difficult.

Ingredients for an Atomic Bomb

An atomic bomb will *not* work if it is made with *ordinary* uranium. After all, large blocks of ordinary uranium have been lying about in laboratories for years without blowing up. The atomic-bomb uranium is something very special.

Ordinary uranium is really a mixture of two kinds of uranium atoms — two isotopes (see page 66). One kind has a nucleus containing 92 protons and 146 neutrons, which make a total of 238 particles. This one is called uranium 238, or U 238 for short. The other kind of uranium atom is a bit lighter. It also has 92 protons, of course, but only 143 neutrons. Thus this atom is a trifle lighter than U 238. It contains only 235 particles in its nucleus and is called U 235 (Fig. 9-2).

Both of these atoms are uranium because they have 92 protons. They are different isotopes of uranium because their atomic weights are different.

A mountain of U 238 atoms will not explode, but a few pounds of pure U 235 will blow up im-

Several thousand degrees C.

One million degrees C.

TNT
20,000 tons

Atomic bomb
22 lbs.

9-1. Compare the explosion of an atomic bomb with that of TNT.

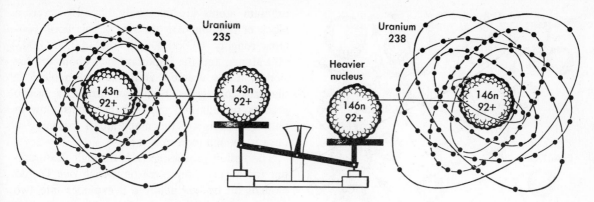

9-2. Why is uranium 238 heavier than uranium 235?

mediately. Obviously, U 235 atoms are not easy to handle. What makes them so strangely and terribly sensitive?

It turns out that a neutron hitting a U 235 nucleus can cause the nucleus to split apart. We call this *nuclear fission*. It is the fission of the nucleus which releases atomic energy (Fig. 9-3).

The U 235 nucleus will split whether the incoming neutron moves with slow or high speed. In fact, the chances for fission of U 235 are even better if the neutron moves in slowly.

Can the nucleus of U 238 be split by neutrons? Yes — but not nearly so easily. The incoming neutron would have to be moving at high speed. And even so the U 238 nucleus may not undergo fission. Instead the nucleus may bounce the incoming neutron away.

Or there is still another possibility. The U 238 nucleus may absorb the incoming neutron and, as a result, throw off a few atomic particles — that is, it becomes radioactive. When this happens the U 238 will start changing into another element (just as radium eventually changes into lead). In this case U 238 changes into a new element called plutonium.

Plutonium is just as sensitive to incoming neutrons as U 235 is and undergoes fission as easily. It can also, then, be used in atomic bombs.

Since U 238 is unlikely to undergo fission while U 235 splits so easily, A-bombs use U 235. But more often, A-bombs employ the plutonium made from U 238 in nuclear reactors.

Atom Splitting — Fission

The fission of U 235 is not like an ordinary explosion of, say, gunpowder or dynamite. The explosion of dynamite is merely a rapid chemical reaction in which atoms exchange partners suddenly and form new compounds. During this process, they release a great deal of energy very quickly. No atoms are damaged by such an explosion. They are merely rearranged.

The fission of U 235 is not even like radioactivity (see page 63). In radioactivity a *small* piece of a nucleus is blown off, and a different kind of atom is produced.

The fission of a U 235 or plutonium atom is far more violent than radioactivity. It is as violent as the explosion of ten million dynamite molecules, and the atom is split almost in halves.

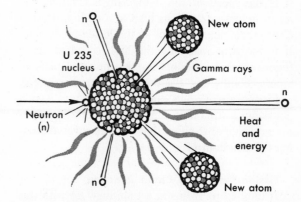

9-3. What happens when a neutron strikes a U 235 nucleus?

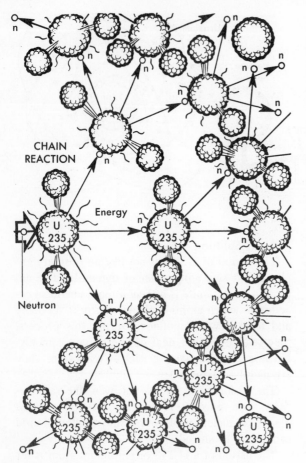

CHAIN REACTION

Energy

U 235

Neutron

U 235

U 235

U 235

U 235

U 235

U 235

U 235

9-4. What happens during a chain reaction?

The two pieces fly apart with tremendous force. It is the speed of the flying fragments that can result in temperatures as high as a million degrees Centigrade, nearly as hot as the inside of the sun. It is the heat made by the high speed of these fragments that accounts for the immense blast of atomic bombs and the power of atomic engines.

Fission also throws out more neutrons. And it pours out a stream of dangerous penetrating gamma rays similar to those that were discovered coming from radium (Fig. 9-3).

Fission May Be a Chain Reaction

If only a few atoms at a time blew up with this extraordinary violence, you would neither see it nor feel it even in the palm of your hand, for uranium atoms are extremely tiny. However, a block of uranium 235 the size of this book contains roughly 10,000,000,000,000,000,000,000,000 atoms, and the important fact about the fission of a few uranium atoms in such a block is that it is contagious! Within an instant the fission process spreads and most of the atoms blow in half. The energy of this many atoms fissioning at once is enough to destroy a city.

The fission process spreads through the uranium for a very simple reason. When *one* U 235 atom is hit by *one* neutron, it explodes into two pieces and also hurls out *two* or *three* neutrons. These neutrons can then explode more U 235 atoms, whose neutrons fly about and explode still more atoms, and so on, until a large number of the uranium atoms have split (Fig. 9-4). This process is called a *chain reaction*.

You know other examples of chain reactions. If one tree in a dry forest is set afire, a chain reaction occurs which you call a "forest fire." And if one boy or girl in your class comes to school with measles and gives the disease to others who pass it on to still more boys and girls, you may have a chain reaction called an "epidemic."

Thus the explosion of an atomic bomb is a chain reaction which is started when a neutron causes the first U 235 atom to fission.

What Sets Off the Bomb?

You probably wonder how the first neutron is produced that starts the chain reaction. Actually

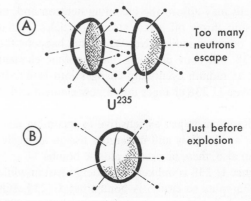

(A) Too many neutrons escape

U²³⁵

(B) Just before explosion

9-5. Atomic bombs blow up only if there is more than a certain critical mass of U 235 or plutonium.

there is no problem finding enough neutrons. There are lots whizzing about your room right now, hitting your body from all directions, produced by the mysterious cosmic rays from outer space. The really difficult problem is to *prevent* these neutrons from starting the chain reaction in the uranium — to prevent the bomb from going off the moment it has been built!

This danger is avoided in a clever way. The uranium is made into two small pieces instead of one big one. Each of the small pieces is so small that fission-causing neutrons are more likely to escape into the air than they are to hit other uranium atoms. Thus the chain reaction cannot " get up steam." But when the two blocks are pushed together, there are so many atoms together in one lump that neutrons are now more likely to hit uranium atoms than to escape (Fig. 9-5).

Thus the bomb is made to go off by rapidly bringing together two small harmless pieces of U 235 to make one big piece. Instantly fission neutrons shoot about at speeds of thousands of miles a second, splitting one atom after another. The whole explosion takes less than one-millionth of a second. Fortunately, this is not the only use for the atom's energy. The atom's energy is not only a curse; it is also a blessing.

CONSTRUCTIVE POWER FROM ATOMS

One way the atom's energy is being used for man's benefit is for the controlled production of power. The fission of one pound of uranium 235 atoms produces as much energy as burning three million pounds of coal or 200,000 gallons of gasoline. Scientists have found ways of letting all this atomic energy trickle out of uranium slowly.

Atomic Piles or Reactors

To see how uranium fission can be tamed and harnessed for useful work, imagine that you have a large number of bars of ordinary uranium and numerous graphite blocks (graphite is a form of carbon). If the uranium bars were simply heaped together, without the graphite blocks, a chain

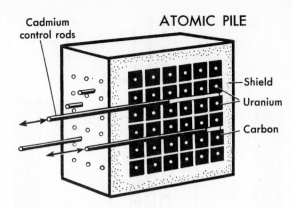

ATOMIC PILE

Cadmium control rods

Shield
Uranium
Carbon

9-6. A model of a pile. What is the function of the cadmium control rods? of the shield? of the carbon?

reaction could not get started. For in ordinary uranium there is much more of the U 238 isotope than there is U 235 and, as you know, U 238 will not undergo fission easily. So the neutrons whizzing among the uranium bars would more likely be absorbed by the numerous U 238 atoms than hit and split the relatively few U 235 atoms.

But here is where the graphite blocks come in. Recall that U 235 is specially sensitive to fission from slow neutrons. If the uranium bars are separated by the graphite blocks, the circulating neutrons will be slowed down by the graphite (which was chosen because it rarely absorbs neutrons). Now many of the neutrons are moving too slowly to be captured by U 238 nuclei but at just the right speed to split U 235!

Each U 235 nucleus that splits will now, on the average, cause only one other U 235 to fission rather than three as in the atomic bomb. The chain reaction keeps going but does not multiply explosively because some neutrons will still be captured by U 238 rather than split more U 235. Thus, by proper arrangement of ordinary uranium and graphite blocks in an *atomic pile* or *reactor* (Fig. 9-6) we can control fission.

But suppose that the chain reaction inside the reactor begins to go too fast. The heat it makes may be enough to melt the reactor or burst it apart. Therefore, some means of controlling the atom-splitting that produces this heat must be found. The chain reaction can be slowed down

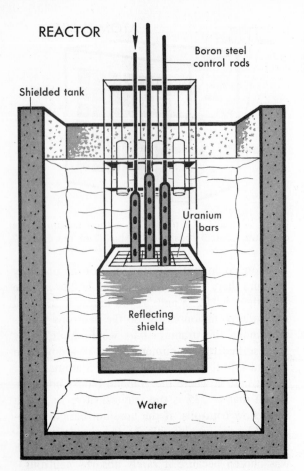

REACTOR

Boron steel control rods

Shielded tank

Uranium bars

Reflecting shield

Water

9-7. The "swimming pool" reactor is a shielded tank of ordinary water. Uranium rods at the bottom release energy in a chain reaction. The control rods control the reaction.

safely by rods of the metal cadmium inserted in the reactor. Cadmium rods soak up the neutrons that keep the chain reaction going. Starved for neutrons, the reaction stops. If the rods are withdrawn once more, the scientist can control the rate of the reaction at any speed he pleases.

Getting Atomic Power Out of the Reactor

To get power out of the reactor in a useful form, the scientist must now criss-cross its inside with pipes filled with a suitable gas or liquid; this liquid may even be a molten metal such as sodium. The liquid metal becomes intensely hot from the hail

Brookhaven National Laboratory

9-8. In a research reactor, of which this is a wooden model, are numerous rows of holes through which pure uranium metal must be loaded before uranium atoms can fission in a chain reaction. The reaction releases neutrons for use in experiments and for production of isotopes.

of atomic fragments. As the pipes come out of the reactor, they can be led to an ordinary steam engine boiler. As you see in Fig. 9-9, the steam made in the boiler can then be used to make electricity or turn wheels, as you will learn in Unit 5.

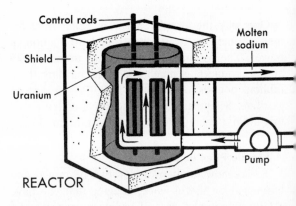

Control rods

Molten sodium

Shield

Uranium

Pump

REACTOR

9-9. You can figure out this "complex" device for yourself. The only thing you really need to know is that molten sodium takes the great heat from the reactor, and its internal heat causes water (under

Let's suppose you are using atomic power for making electricity.

Operating instructions for an atomic engine (Fig. 9-9):

1. Slowly withdraw cadmium control rods from the reactor, to allow chain reaction to begin.
2. When the chain reaction is going steadily, stop pulling out the rods. Important!
3. When the fission has made the inside of the reactor hot enough, start pumping liquid through the pipes.
4. When hot liquid from the reactor is turning boiler water to steam, feed the steam to steam turbine which operates electric generator.
5. The electric generator, turned by steam, will produce electric power.

Applying Atomic Energy

Atomic power plants like this one are already in use. They are still rather expensive, however, compared to ordinary coal- and oil-burning power plants. Many scientists are hard at work trying to make atomic-power plants less expensive. There is no doubt that they are succeeding and when they do it may become as economical to light a city or run a factory by energy from the atom as from burning coal or oil. You may know of Calder Hall, in England (Fig. 9-16), one of the first power plants using the energy of atomic reactors

to produce electricity. Several American cities also are or soon will be using the energy of such reactors as those located at Shippingport, Pennsylvania (see unit photograph), Chicago, New York, and elsewhere.

Don't get your hopes up too high, though! It is very unlikely that the atom's energy will soon drive your family automobile, and it will certainly be many years before it is driving many airplanes. One reason is that reactors are dangerous. They work only when there is a fiery storm of neutrons raging inside them, and some of the neutrons are always leaking out, too. If too many neutrons strike you, they will make you very sick or even kill you. Therefore, they must be walled in with thick layers of some heavy material like concrete — more weight than cars and airplanes could afford to carry. There is always the danger, too, that the controls might fail and the reactor burst from the resulting heat. How, too, shall we get rid of the radioactive wastes from the reactors? There are still problems to be solved.

These are the reasons that the first use of atomic power is in big central power stations and on ships big enough to carry the necessary heavy shielding and elaborate safety controls. Later it may become possible to put atomic-power plants into railroad locomotives and extra-large airplanes.

When these uses of the atom become common,

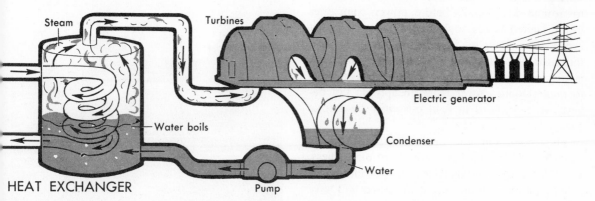

HEAT EXCHANGER

pressure) to change into steam in the heat exchanger. Otherwise you can follow the process from what you have read in the text.

What is the source of energy? How is the heat carried to the heat exchanger? How is the heat used to push the wheels of a turbine? In what form does the energy eventually come out of the device?

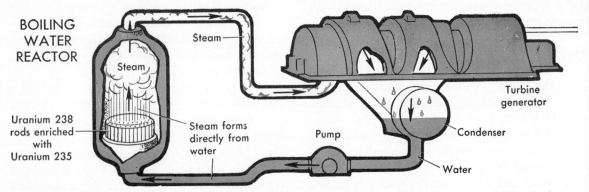

BOILING WATER REACTOR

Steam

Steam

Uranium 238 rods enriched with Uranium 235

Steam forms directly from water

Pump

Turbine generator

Condenser

Water

9-10. Follow the route of the transformation of energy. What is the source of the energy? How is the energy carried? How is it converted into electrical energy (electricity)?

you may expect to see tiny weights of uranium doing enormous jobs. For example, a block of pure uranium 235 the size of this book would weigh 50 pounds. How much more convenient this is than the 75,000 tons of coal or 10 million gallons of gasoline you would need to do the same amount of work!

As you grow older you can expect to see the atom being used more and more as a source of power. But you must not expect atomic power to reduce your present gas or electricity bills very much. Atomic fuel takes up very little space, but it is also amazingly expensive stuff. The cost of that book-sized block of pure uranium 235 we were just talking about would have to come *down* to around $1,250,000 before power companies in the United States could afford to start using it instead of coal or oil for making power. Even a thin mixture of uranium 235 in ordinary uranium is still too expensive. Engineers working on ways to make atomic power more cheaply do not believe we can afford to light our cities by atomic energy before about 1975.

They point out, too, that atomic energy will never put oil and coal companies out of business. For, by the time atomic power comes into widespread use, our nation's needs for power will have grown so immense that we will need all the power we can possibly get from the atom and from coal and oil, too. Thus you will see atomic energy being added to other sources of power, not displac-

ing them. At least that is what we think at the moment.

Certainly a very important use for atomic power will be in parts of the world where oil, gas, coal, and water power are all scarce and too expensive to use. In such power-hungry lands people are poor, and life is full of hardships. Atomic power may well help them to a better life by providing them with industries, with jobs, and with the means to happier, healthier, more productive lives. The promise that atomic energy holds

9-11. Two of the Navy's atomic-powered submarines, the U.S.S. *Sea Wolf* and the U.S.S. *Nautilus*.

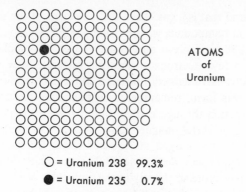

ATOMS
of
Uranium

○ = Uranium 238   99.3%
● = Uranium 235   0.7%

9-12. Problem: How much uranium 235 in proportion will be found in 100 tons of uranium ore?

for millions of people in some of the world's undeveloped areas is one of the most exciting results of our having learned how to split the atom.

SOURCES OF FISSIONABLE ATOMS

All over the world there is a new rush on, not for gold or oil, but for rocks containing uranium. For this is the source of our splitting atoms. Uranium is what is called *fissionable* material. Without it there can be no atomic bombs or hydrogen bombs (see Chapter 10) or atomic piles or atomic submarines.

Uranium Rock

Pure uranium is a white metal even heavier, size for size, than is lead. Rocks containing uranium are surprisingly common. In fact, the metal is almost as common as the familiar metals lead and zinc. Unfortunately, although uranium-bearing rocks are found all over the earth, the uranium in most of them is so thinly scattered that it is very difficult to extract. In all the United States almost the only rocks that contain a useful amount of uranium are in Utah and Colorado, and this is not nearly enough for our needs. We depend on rock brought to us from far northwestern Canada and from the Republic of the Congo in central Africa for the rest of our supply of uranium.

These rocks contain rich supplies of uranium compounds which are easy to extract. From these

compounds pure uranium is easy to obtain, too.

But the uranium first obtained may not be suitable for practical use. Ordinary uranium has much more of the U 238 isotope than of the easily fissionable U 235. As it occurs in nature the useful U 235 makes up about .7% of the raw mixture — one out of every 142 atoms of uranium (Fig. 9–12). For use in atomic bombs some method had to be found for separating out the two isotopes.

And for peaceful purposes a supply of uranium *enriched* to a higher percentage of U 235 may be needed. We may, for example, want a supply of uranium with 5% U 235 instead of only .7%. We then need a separate supply of U 235 to blend in with the natural mixture to bring it up to the desired richness.

Sorting Out U 235 and U 238

No chemical reactions can possibly sort out U 235 atoms from U 238 atoms. You will remember John Dalton's statement that all the atoms of an element are identical. Even today this is still true as far as their chemical reactions with other atoms are concerned. Both isotopes of uranium act exactly the same way in a chemistry laboratory, for they are identical twins, except for their small differences in weight.

There is another important fact that helps us determine how U 235 may be sorted out from U 238. When two cars turn a corner at high speed, the heavier one is not able to swerve quite so sharply as the lighter one. Have you noticed

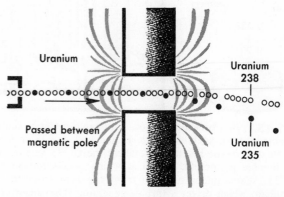

Uranium

Uranium
238

Passed between
magnetic poles

Uranium
235

9-13. How may U 235 be separated from U 238?

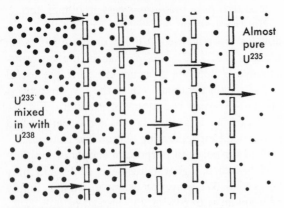

9-14. In the actual separation of uranium isotopes by the diffusion process there would be many more separate stages than are shown here. Eventually the lighter isotope drifts ahead of the heavier. This process is then repeated using the gas now enriched in U 235. With each repetition of the cycle, the ratio of U 235 to U 238 gets greater and greater until the desired degree of enrichment is obtained. The enriched gas is then drawn off for chemical treatment.

how the family automobile turns a corner when only the driver is in it and how it turns the corner when full of people? One way of sorting out uranium isotopes depends upon this last effect. First the uranium atoms are changed into a com-

pound that is a gas. Then the molecules of the uranium compounds we are dealing with (U 235 and U 238) are given an electric charge by knocking off a few electrons outside the nucleus. Now the electrically charged molecules of these compounds (in gas form, remember) are pulled by electrical attraction through a small hole between the poles of a powerful magnet (Fig. 9-13). The magnet makes the charged molecules swerve. But as you should expect, the heavier U 238 molecules do not swerve quite so sharply as the molecules of U 235. The result is that in the gas two separate beams of molecules are formed; these shoot into separate boxes. U 235 is separated from U 238. Notice carefully that this separation of isotopes does not depend on any differences in their chemistry.

There is a second way of separating the isotopes from each other. Little boys can generally run faster and climb through fences more quickly than their fathers. If you built an obstacle course with many rail fences to be climbed through, you might expect one small boy to finish before 140 heavier, more sedate fathers. Scientists have devised a similar obstacle course in such a way that molecules of U 235 are favored to win over the slightly heavier molecules containing U 238. These obstacles are porous plates through whose

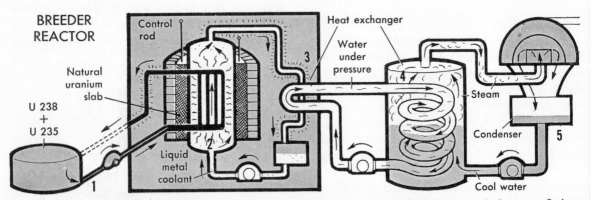

9-15. In a breeder reactor, fissionable material such as plutonium is constantly being made from nonfissionable material such as U 238. Liquid fuel, U 238 enriched with U 235 (or plutonium), is pumped from (1) into the core of the reactor (2). There the U 235 acts on a slab of U 238 to convert it (or " breed " it) into fissionable plutonium. The heat which results is transferred to a liquid metal coolant — in this case, sodium (3). Water under pressure takes the heat from the sodium in the heat exchanger (4); the water becomes steam, which drives a turbine-generator. The steam condenses (5) and is pumped back as water into the heat exchanger. The fissionable material (plutonium) " bred " in the reactor can be recovered for use elsewhere.

tiny holes the lighter molecules move with slightly greater speed. By the time the race has passed through many thousands of porous plates, almost pure U 235 compound is out in front (Fig. 9-14).

Both of these processes are used for preparing pure uranium 235. But for separation of large amounts of U 235 from U 238 the process of trickling uranium gas through porous plates is much more economical than is magnetic separation. The large government plants at Oak Ridge, Tennessee, are used mainly for this purpose.

The Government Enters

The methods you have just read about were perfected during World War II by a large team of some of the world's greatest scientists and engineers. The factories for performing the separation are so big and expensive to run that no single company could afford to build them or operate them. Hence the urgency of war forced the government to spend the billions of dollars needed. For this purpose a branch of the government called the Atomic Energy Commission (or AEC) was set up. Now, in peacetime, it continues to spend many millions of dollars of taxpayers' money preparing atoms for the release of energy, making atomic bombs, and searching for new ways of turning the power of the atom to the benefit of mankind instead of its destruction. You will read about these new uses of atoms in Chapter 11.

British Information Service

9-16. Britain's Calder Hall, the first large-scale atomic power station in the world. Built in just over three years, the Calder Hall station uses atomic energy to produce electricity for homes and factories in Britain. On the left are shown two cooling towers.

ENERGY FROM ATOMS **117**

Looking Back . . . .

VOCABULARY

The following are some of the key words in the chapter you have just studied. Give a definition for each one.

1. fission
2. atomic pile
3. reactor
4. chain reaction
5. plutonium
6. Atomic Energy Commission

REVIEW QUESTIONS

1. What would be your instructions for operating a small atomic engine? State them in order.
2. What was the problem faced by scientists in separating U 235 from U 238? How was it solved?
3. How is an atomic bomb set off?
4. How is the fission of uranium different from radioactivity? Name as many differences as you can.
5. Why will atomic power probably not be used to drive your family automobile, even when such power becomes less expensive to produce?
6. In what ways will atomic power probably be most useful to mankind?
7. Which isotope of uranium is the more plentiful?
8. Which of the two isotopes fissions easily?
9. What is a chain reaction?
10. How is the chain reaction in an atomic bomb different from the chain reaction in a reactor?
11. How is the chain reaction in a reactor kept under control?
12. In what parts of the world is atomic power most likely to be used?
13. In what ways is a reactor apt to be dangerous?

Going Further . . . .

THINGS TO DO

1. Observe atomic breakdowns. Examine a luminous clock or watch dial with a powerful magnifying glass or microscope in the dark. After your eyes have become accustomed to the dark, you can see the sparkling that is the result of the passage of particles shot out from the radioactive material in the paint.

2. Show the penetrating powers of radioactive rays. With a piece of radioactive uranium ore (pitchblende), you can repeat the experiment that led to the discovery of radioactivity. Place the ore on a sheet of photographic paper wrapped in black opaque paper. Develop the photographic paper after a day or more and note that it is exposed. A shadow picture of a key or coin can be made by placing it under the radioactive material.

3. Build a small model of an atomic pile. Use Fig. 9-8 for ideas of what it should look like.

4. Build a model of an atomic engine. Use Fig. 9-9 to help you. Also write to General Electric Company, Schenectady, N.Y., for a poster or drawing of the engine in the atomic submarine.

5. Write an article for your school paper on " The New Age — the Age of the Atom."

6. Set up an exhibit on atomic energy in the school lobby. Purpose: to bring before the school recent advances in atomic energy. Organize a committee to do the various jobs needed. You might want to get pictures, pamphlets, and posters from: a) School Service, Westinghouse Electric Corporation, 306 Fourth Avenue, P.O. Box 1017, Pittsburgh 30, Pa.; b) General Electric Company, Schenectady, N.Y.; c) Division of Education, Atomic Energy Commission, Washington, D.C.

7. Using the reading material suggested below, find out more about the fissionable element plutonium. How is it made? Is it as hard to obtain as uranium 235? Is it as useful as uranium 235? Give a ten-minute report to your class on what you have been able to find.

READING FURTHER

Inside the Atom by Isaac Asimov, Abelard, 1958.

About Atomic Power for People by Edward and Ruth Radlauer, Melmont, 1960, gives many details on how an atomic-power plant is built and operated.

Atomic Experiments for Boys (girls can do them, too) by Raymond F. Yates, Harper, 1952.

Write to the Superintendent of Documents, Government Printing Office, Washington, D.C., for a catalogue of free or low-cost materials. Among them you will find certain materials on atomic energy.

CHAPTER
10

Why Do Atoms Contain Energy?

How is it that splitting atoms release such tremendous amounts of energy?

You have seen that the nucleus of an atom is a piled-together bundle of neutrons and protons. Single neutrons and protons do not seem to have any remarkable energy, any more than a marble or a bar magnet seems to. How is it that they possess such tremendous energy when they are lumped together in their tight bundle in the center of the atom?

To get some idea of where all the energy comes from, take two strong bar magnets and lay them on the table in front of you. Slowly slide them toward one another. If you have aimed the proper ends together, they will suddenly snap together by themselves with a " click " (Fig. 10-1). Such pep as this is one example of what the scientist calls *energy*. In this experiment you heard and saw and felt magnets release energy as they snapped together.

To make a louder collision that releases more energy, you might try arranging four magnets so that they all snap together at once — or on a really grand scale 238 of them (Fig. 10-1).

Now imagine that you have a supply of magically big protons and neutrons, and you are going to let them snap together in a similar way to make the nucleus of an atom.

Let's suppose that you could bring one proton and one neutron close together on your table top. They would release a *lot* of energy as they roll together. As they join they make a nucleus of heavy hydrogen (deuterium). Suppose that you try making a bigger nucleus. The protons and neutrons all rush together with an even bigger crash. If you could put together 92 protons and 146 neutrons all at once to make the nucleus of a uranium-238 atom, you would be forced to agree that there is a lot of energy released by atom building.

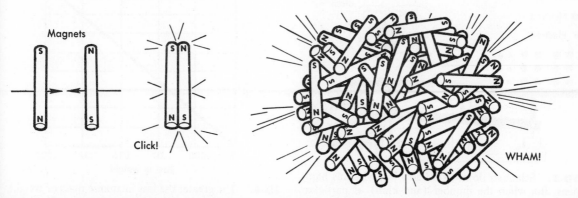

10-1. Magnets snapping together release energy. So do protons and neutrons joining together in the nucleus of an atom. (However, don't mistake magnets for protons or neutrons.)

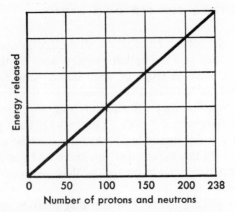

10-2. As bigger atoms are assembled from more and more protons and neutrons, the amount of energy released increases, as is shown by the rising line of the graph.

If you had kept a record of the energy with which each nucleus crashed together, your figures on a graph would look something like Fig. 10-2.

Where Did the " Pep " Come From?

Now that you have put together a make-believe collection of nuclei, you will want to try a very surprising make-believe experiment with them. The experiment is very simple. All you must do is to weigh each nucleus you have put together.

Perhaps you think this is silly. " After all," you may say, " if I put together exactly 6 protons and 6 neutrons to make a nucleus of carbon, I expect

it will weigh exactly 12 units on my atomic-weight scale."

When you try it, though, you are surprised to find that the carbon nucleus weighs less than the weight of its 12 particles when they were separate. When those 12 particles came together, they seem to have lost weight (Fig. 10-3).

You will probably want to weigh your other atoms, too. With every one you will find that *the whole nucleus weighs less than the sum of its separate parts!* It looks as if matter had been destroyed. Indeed, John Dalton would have been astounded, for he believed, you remember, that matter could not be created or destroyed.

The weight missing from each nucleus is extremely small. In fact, only the most sensitive kinds of instruments can reveal it. But there is no doubt that it is missing.

Again it will be a good idea to keep a record of the weight that seems to have disappeared from each nucleus we've put together in our make-believe experiment. Again it will be a good idea to arrange our record on a graph.

Graphs often reveal very interesting things. Your new graph looks something like Fig. 10-4. Do you notice its surprising similarity to the previous graph, Fig. 10-2? If you compare them, you will see that they have identical shapes.

When two different graphs from the same ex-

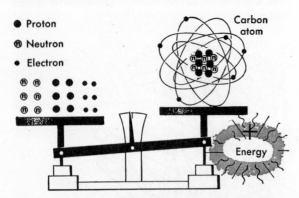

10-3. Scientists do not yet know just why this happens. But when the number (and kind) of particles at the left combine to form the atom at the right, the combined atom weighs less and energy is given off.

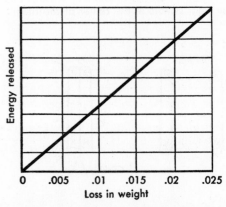

10-4. The greater the loss in atomic mass or weight, the greater the amount of atomic energy that is released. How does this graph compare with Fig. 10-2?

periments have the same shape, it suggests to the scientist that there is some connection between the things the graphs describe. In your graphs it looks as if there were some connection between the energy released when your nuclei snapped together and the mass (the amount of matter) that vanished at the same time.

A great many scientists have actually done real experiments like your make-believe ones and studied the results very carefully. These experiments and others similar show that when you put together some nuclei, *weight (mass) really is destroyed and turned into energy* — the energy of the crash! The more weight that is destroyed, the more energy is released, as you have already seen.

Tiny Mass into Tremendous Energy

What is almost as surprising is the vast amount of energy given out when only a tiny bit of weight is destroyed. If you could put together exactly one pound of protons and neutrons to make helium nuclei (2 protons and 2 neutrons in each nucleus), you would end up 0.12 ounce short of a pound of helium nuclei. That 0.12 ounce of vanished mass or weight — about the weight of a penny — is turned into as much energy as Boulder Dam generates in 2½ days!

Write your name on a piece of paper. That ink or pencil mark probably weighs about $\frac{1}{10,000}$ of a gram (Fig. 10-5). That's not much mass, is it? Now suppose the tiny mass, m, of your signature (0.0001 gram) were totally destroyed and hence turned into energy, E. You can find the energy that is produced by multiplying 0.001 gram by an enormous number, the speed of light (186,000 miles per second) squared. The symbol for this is c^2 ($c \times c$). That is:

$$E = m \times c^2$$

$$E = 0.0001 \times c^2$$

for   tiny mass   the speed
energy   of your   of light,
    signature   squared

$$E = 0.0001 \times 900,000,000,000,000,000,000.[1]$$

This energy is in units called *ergs*. In more common units E turns out to be 2500 kilowatt-hours.

How much energy is 2500 kilowatt-hours?

It is enough energy to run 2500 100-watt light bulbs for a 10-hour day or to lift a 100,000-ton ocean liner from its drydock 35 feet into the air!

This is the amount of energy equivalent to the

[1] The speed of light is about 186,000 miles per second. However, it can also be considered as 30,000,000,000 centimeters per second. The formula is $E = mc^2$; hence, $c^2 = 30,000,000,000 \times 30,000,000,000 = 900,000,000,000,000,000,000$. You do not need to remember the calculations, only the formula.

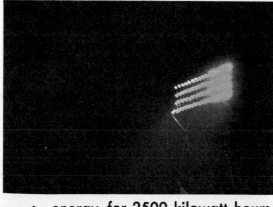

Ink

0.0001 gram of matter × (speed of light)^2 ——→ energy for 2500 kilowatt hours

10-5. Physicists have calculated that 0.0001 of a gram of matter (say ink) if completely destroyed can release 2500 kilowatt-hours of electricity.

tiny weight of your signature. Thus when matter, even in small amounts, is destroyed tremendous amounts of energy can be produced. This energy is what is released in the tremendous hydrogen bomb explosion experiments carried on in the Pacific.

The formula $E = mc^2$ was first suggested by Albert Einstein back in 1905, long before anyone had seen mass turned into energy in a laboratory. Nowadays scientists agree that this useful formula must be right. It means that if the air you exhale in your next breath could all be " destroyed," it would provide enough energy to drive an ocean liner for several years. It means that if we could destroy just 25 pounds of matter, it would turn into enough energy to supply the entire world's need for electrical power for one year. It means that John Dalton's indestructible atoms *can* be destroyed, but when they are, an equivalent amount of energy is produced.

Einstein's famous formula says that energy can be converted back into matter, too. You can easily see how this is so if you will *imagine* that you have your magically big uranium nucleus sitting on the table in front of you once more. Suppose you take a screwdriver and start to pry the protons and neutrons apart once more. You will have to work very hard, but by the time you have finished, perhaps those 238 balls (neutrons and protons) are once more scattered about the table. As separate particles they now weigh more than they did as a uranium nucleus.

That lost weight is restored as a result of all the energy you used up in prying the protons and neutrons apart. In this *imaginary* experiment *your energy was turned back into weight.* In a laboratory, sensitive measurements show that this sort of thing actually does happen when real atoms are pulled apart.

You will notice that this is not a job a chemist can do. A chemist cannot destroy atoms. In all of his work the chemist only joins atoms to one another in various combinations, never doing anything more violent than removing a few of their lightweight outermost electrons (see p. 79). He does not usually tinker with the nucleus of the atom, where nearly all of the atom's weight is concentrated.

Taking atoms apart is the job of a *physicist*. A physicist is a scientist who is interested in what matter is made of. He is also interested in finding out all he can about energy — what it is and how it behaves. You can see why the release of energy from atoms is a problem that has physicists today very excited.

EXPLAINING FISSION ENERGY

How does the physicist explain all the energy that is released by the fission of uranium and plutonium?

We can see the answer to this most simply by doing a little bookkeeping. The entries on our balance sheet will be weight and energy though, instead of dollars and cents.

Einstein Explains Fission Energy

The exact weight of 92 protons and 143 neutrons in a uranium 235 nucleus is

Atomic weight of uranium 235 nucleus	= 235.124
Atomic weight of neutron causing fission	= 1.009
Total atomic weight to start with	= 236.133

When the uranium atom splits (by fission), two lighter elements are formed, like lanthanum (LAN-thuh-num), and molybdenum (muh-LIB-deh-num), and two neutrons. If we add up the weight of all these pieces we have the following results:

Atomic weight of molybdenum nucleus	= 94.945
Atomic weight of lanthanum nucleus	= 138.955
Atomic weight of 2 neutrons	= 2.018
Total atomic weight after fission is over	= 235.918

Here you can see that we end up with less weight than when we started. To be precise we have lost: $236.133 - 235.918 = 0.215$ atomic weight units.

Mass has been converted into energy! Here is the secret of atomic energy! This tiny speck of mass that is lost after fission is multiplied by Dr. Einstein's fabulous number, c^2, to represent an enormous amount of energy.

A uranium 235 atom can split apart into many other kinds of atoms, too. In every case, though, there is a little bit of weight lost that shows up as a lot of energy.

Fusion Energy

Whenever it is possible to rearrange protons and neutrons to make a nucleus that weighs less than before, then you may expect energy to be released. You have just seen that this accounts for the energy of fission. But nuclear particles can be rearranged not only by separating them, as in fission, but also by joining them together. The process of joining nuclear particles together is called *fusion* — the opposite of fission. And we now know that it is this process of nuclear fusion which accounts for the production of energy in the sun and all the other stars in the universe.

The Sun's Energy

The fuel that keeps the sun hot is hydrogen.

Does the hydrogen burn in the sun? Far from it. If hydrogen were merely burning the way gas does in a stove, the sun should have burned itself to a dead cinder millions of years ago. Nor could ordinary burning heat the sun to its temperature of over a million degrees.

Yet that is how hot it is down in the center of the sun where hydrogen nuclei are building up into helium nuclei (see Fig. 10-6). Four hydrogen nuclei go together to make each helium nucleus with a little bit of mass left over. It's that left-over mass that all the energy comes from. Here is the balance sheet.

Atomic weight of 4 hydrogen nuclei	= 4.032
Atomic weight of 1 helium nucleus	= 4.004
Weight left over	= 0.028 units

Convert that tiny surplus mass into energy (remember $E = mc^2$), and you have the source of

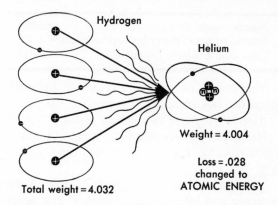

10-6. When four hydrogen atoms fuse to form an atom of helium, weight is lost. The lost matter is released as atomic energy. This happens in the hydrogen bomb.

the energy of the sun and stars. Convert four million tons of such surplus mass every second and you have the sun's heat that keeps you warm here on the earth and is responsible for the weather, and you have the sun's light that enables trees and all the food you eat to grow.

Even the most primitive cave men depended on atomic energy for their warmth and food and shelter! Today in just the same way your very life depends on the steady hour-by-hour release of atomic energy on a gigantic scale deep down inside the sun.

The Hydrogen Bomb

Scientists have learned how to imitate the sun's method of releasing energy. Moreover, they can do it on a large scale in what you know of as the hydrogen bomb (or H-bomb).

Building hydrogen atoms up into helium is only one kind of fusion. Several kinds of lightweight atoms have a little weight left over when they are joined by fusion, and all of them release enormous amounts of energy, just as in fission.

In the hydrogen bomb, energy is released by fusion. Because they are the easiest nuclei to fuse together, atoms of the light metal lithium may be combined with atoms of heavy hydrogen (deuterium), to make two helium atoms. The balance sheet looks like this:

Atomic weight of lithium nucleus	= 6.017
Atomic weight of heavy hydrogen nucleus	= 2.017
Total atomic weight to start with	= 8.034

The fusion of lithium and heavy hydrogen forms two helium nuclei. The result is this:

Atomic weight of two helium nuclei = 8.008.

Hence you can see that some weight (8.034 − 8.008 = .026) has to be turned into energy (Fig. 10-7).

The bomb is made to explode by forcing the hydrogen and lithium nuclei together. This never happens at ordinary temperatures. Thus you cannot release energy yourself by the fusion of light-weight atoms from your laboratory shelf.

Ordinarily the hydrogen and lithium nuclei are held apart by their shells of outer electrons. But a temperature of several million degrees will make the atoms move so fast that their collisions crush the electron shells and drive the nuclei together. As soon as the fusion of nuclei begins it releases tremendous energy in the form of heat which drives more nuclei together and keeps the process going until all the hydrogen and lithium are used up.

One possible way of making the high temperature needed to start the fusion is by setting off a fission bomb. Thus the fission bomb can act as a kind of trigger for the hydrogen fusion bomb.

A hydrogen bomb could be given almost unlimited explosive power, for unlike the fission bomb, a hydrogen bomb can be made of any size at all. Bombs thousands of times more powerful than the original atomic bombs have been constructed.

TAMING THE H–BOMB

Widespread efforts are underway in the United States, England, and the Soviet Union to control fusion energy. The difficulties are very great. But the possible reward is even greater — the permanent solution to mankind's search for energy. For hydrogen, particularly its heavy isotope — deuterium — can serve as the fuel in fusion reactions. And from each gallon of ordinary sea water enough heavy hydrogen can be separated to provide the energy equivalent of 35 gallons of gasoline.

In addition to the great abundance of deuterium compared to the rarity of uranium used in fission power, there is another advantage to fusion power — fusion reactors, unlike atomic piles, would produce no dangerously radioactive " ashes." The end product of hydrogen fusion is simply helium.

Yes, controlling fusion would be a great victory — but is there really any practical hope of achieving it? After all, isn't it necessary to raise the temperature of heavy hydrogen to millions of degrees before fusion can occur? In the hydrogen bomb this is done by using a fission-bomb " trigger," but

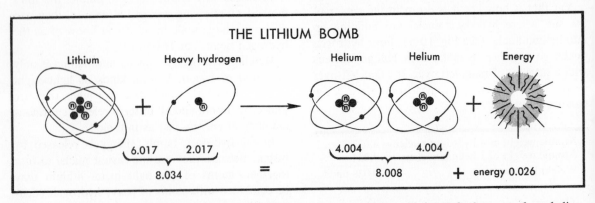

THE LITHIUM BOMB

Lithium   Heavy hydrogen   Helium   Helium   Energy

6.017   2.017   4.004   4.004

8.034   =   8.008   +   energy 0.026

10-7. In one version of the hydrogen bomb, lithium is used to combine with heavy hydrogen to form helium and release nuclear energy. Compare with Fig. 10-6.

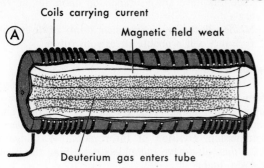

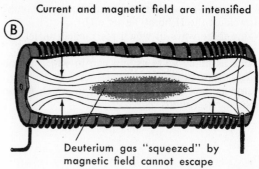

Ⓐ Coils carrying current

Magnetic field weak

Deuterium gas enters tube

Ⓑ Current and magnetic field are intensified

Deuterium gas "squeezed" by magnetic field cannot escape

Adapted from Amasa S. Bishop *Project Sherwood*, 1958, Addison-Wesley, Reading, Mass.

10-8. A simplified diagram of a device for containing ionized deuterium (heavy hydrogen) while raising its temperature. (Ionized hydrogen has separated nuclei and electrons.) Containment is accomplished by a magnetic " bottle " across whose magnetic lines of force charged nuclei cannot move. As the magnetic field is altered (right) the ionized gas is squeezed and its temperature rises.

such a method would hardly do for peaceful purposes.

Achieving Controlled Fusion

What is wanted is some nonexplosive means for raising the temperature of small amounts of deuterium particles to the point where they will be in violent collision and, moreover, containing this reaction in some vessel. Once we could accomplish this, fusion may start and the fusion energy then produced will keep the temperature high. The reaction can be kept going as more deuterium is introduced into the reactor vessel.

But to start with, it is absolutely necessary to prevent the deuterium from contacting the walls of the reactor vessel. Otherwise the deuterium particles will rapidly transfer their energy of motion to these walls, the deuterium's temperature will drop and the fusion reaction will not be kindled.

Designing vessels to contain the fusion reaction and finding methods for raising the enormous temperatures necessary involve a great deal of very complicated physics. And many problems are still unsolved.

But with the goal of an almost limitless source of energy ahead of them, scientists are continuing their work on control of fusion reactions (Fig. 10-8). Within your lifetime the power we can

now release from atoms can easily destroy our civilization at one stroke; or it can improve people's welfare beyond our dreams. Faced with this choice, your wisdom will have to rise to the challenge of these scientific achievements, for certainly the choice will be partly yours to make.

Looking Back . . . .

VOCABULARY

Each of the following terms is a key word in the chapter you have just studied. What is the meaning of each?

1. energy
2. physicist
3. fusion
4. fission
5. mass
6. erg
7. deuterium
8. kilowatt-hours

REVIEW QUESTIONS

1. Where does the energy come from that holds an atom's nucleus together?
2. Why would John Dalton be surprised by our modern knowledge of the nucleus?
3. What do the letters and numbers mean in the formula $E = mc^2$? Who was the first man to suggest this formula?

4. How does $E = mc^2$ help to explain why the sun stays hot?
5. What materials are needed to make an H-bomb?
6. How must the H-bomb be set off?
7. Name three ways in which rearranged nuclei can release atomic energy.
8. Name as many ways as you can in which fission differs from fusion.
9. Name as many ways as you can in which fission is similar to fusion.

Going Further . . . .

1. Hydrogen atoms (atomic weight, 1.008) and atoms of the element lithium (atomic weight, 6.017) can be combined by physicists into two helium atoms. The atomic weight of one helium atom is 4.004. How much matter is turned into energy?

2. Explain how your life and the lives of all your ancestors have always depended upon atomic energy.
3. Name all the ways you can think of in which $E = mc^2$ will probably affect your future.

THINGS TO DO
1. Make a model of a power plant that uses energy from the atom. Write to General Electric Company, Schenectady, New York, for posters and diagrams dealing with an atomic plant. The Atomic Energy Commission, Division of Information, Washington, D.C., may also have pamphlets describing the plant at Arco, Idaho.
2. Make an outline for a five- or ten-minute speech you might make on "Why Do Atoms Contain Energy?"

READING FURTHER
Sourcebook on Atomic Energy by Samuel Glasstone, D. Van Nostrand, 1958, gives the basic facts of atomic science, clearly written and carefully organized.
The Atom Story by J. G. Feinberg, Philosophical Library, 1953, is a book which everyone can read with appreciation. It gives, in a highly interesting manner, the story of the atom from Democritus to the present day.

CHAPTER

11

New Uses of Atoms

One of the earliest uses of atomic energy, the atomic bomb, resulted in the destruction of life. But since then, the use of new products of atomic fission has saved or prolonged the lives of many times the number of those who were killed at Hiroshima. Moreover, by using the energy of the atom we are daily gaining new knowledge about the world in which we live that is certain to enrich our lives in ways undreamed of 20 years ago. Atomic energy began by destroying life, but as we shall see in this chapter scientists are industriously harnessing the atom in ways that will make our lives happier and healthier if we are wise enough to control its destructive power.

MAN–MADE ATOMS

When uranium and plutonium atoms split and release their energy either in a reactor or in a bomb, you will remember, several kinds of pieces fly out.

First there are several neutrons that may set off the fission of more atoms.

Then there are very intense and penetrating gamma rays.

Third there are the two pieces of the split atom. As you might suppose, the two pieces of the split atom are atoms themselves —

usually atoms about half as heavy as the original uranium or plutonium atom.

Making " New " Isotopes

Scientists had some surprises when they studied this atomic wreckage. Some of the fragments were atoms of very rare elements (Fig. 11-1). This was exciting in itself for it meant that useful amounts of rare and unobtainable elements might now be made to order!

Even more exciting, however, was the discovery that many of the fragments were radioactive (see page 63). This meant that, like radium, they gave off large amounts of alpha rays, beta rays, or gamma rays, as they turned themselves into still other elements. Here was a whole new collection of atoms to explore, and who could guess what hidden secrets of nature they might reveal?

The atoms made by fission are not *new* elements. They are familiar elements. They are so special because they often have more neutrons or fewer neutrons than usual in their nuclei. Thus they are often new isotopes of familiar elements.

A good example is iodine. You put iodine atoms dissolved in alcohol on cuts to prevent infections. Each iodine atom has 53 protons and

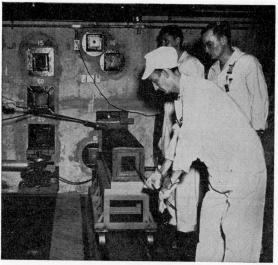

U.S. Army Photograph

11-1. These technicians are removing isotopes manufactured in an atomic pile by absorption of neutrons.

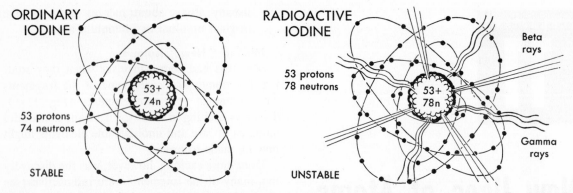

ORDINARY
IODINE

53 protons
74 neutrons

53+
74n

STABLE

RADIOACTIVE
IODINE

53 protons
78 neutrons

53+
78n

Beta
rays

Gamma
rays

UNSTABLE

11-2. Radioactive iodine releases atomic energy because of its unstable nucleus. In giving off a beta ray, the iodine atom turns from an unstable atom into a stable one.

74 neutrons in its nucleus. If you put in a few extra neutrons or take out a few, you can make some new isotopes of iodine. These isotopes are all too unstable to hold together, though; they throw out beta or gamma rays as the atom settles down to something more stable (Fig. 11-2). Thus we say that these isotopes of iodine are radioactive.

Iodine has 17 different isotopes, all of them radioactive except the one with an atomic weight of 127. You don't find the radioactive ones lying about in the earth's rocks because they all fall apart too quickly. If they were ever in the earth's rocks they fell apart long ago into more stable forms.

However, when uranium and plutonium break apart, a number of radioactive isotopes of iodine are produced.

The ordinary tin on a tin can is a mixture of ten isotopes, none of them radioactive. Fission produces all these isotopes of tin, and eight more besides which are radioactive and all new to science. The isotopes of many other elements are also found in the wreckage of fission.

Moreover, additional isotopes of familiar elements can be made simply by holding them *near* uranium or plutonium as it fissions. A good way to make phosphorus radioactive, for example, is to push pieces of it into the center of a reactor. Inside the reactor an ordinary phosphorus atom with a total of 31 neutrons and protons in its nucleus gets sprayed by a hail of neutrons. Eventually it captures one neutron to become phosphorus 32, which is radioactive (Fig. 11-3).

Thus many new isotopes have been obtained by spraying common atoms with neutrons in a

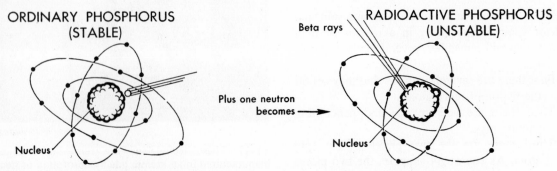

ORDINARY PHOSPHORUS
(STABLE)

Nucleus

Plus one neutron
becomes →

Beta rays

RADIOACTIVE PHOSPHORUS
(UNSTABLE)

Nucleus

11-3. Radioactive phosphorus contains one extra neutron in its nucleus. This makes it unstable.

reactor or by searching through the wreckage of fission. Altogether scientists now know of over 2000 different isotopes of the known chemical elements, and can make a supply of almost any one of them when it is needed for study.

What a rich supply of new material has been made available by the splitting of the atom! We should look at some of the uses these new isotopes have been put to — uses which have resulted in the saving of many lives.

USES OF MAN–MADE ATOMS

When the penetrating gamma rays from radium and other radioactive materials penetrate your flesh, you do not see them or feel them in any way. Spending an afternoon at the beach in the hot sun may not be uncomfortable either, but you probably know that painful burns can show up later, after you get home. In the same way the damage done by a strong dose of gamma rays does not show up until much later. Moreover, because the gamma rays are so much more penetrating than sunlight, the damage they do is often concealed

Cities Service Company by Fritz Henle

11-4. The cave in which the radioactive cobalt is stored here has walls 42 inches thick made of dense concrete. The sensitive manipulators shown can pick up a pin from the floor or paint from the wall.

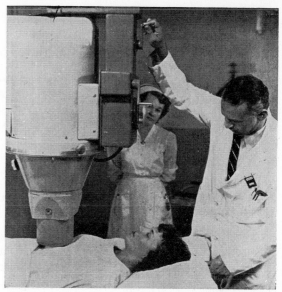

Atomic Energy Commission

11-5. Radioactive cobalt is replacing the use of powerful X rays in cancer treatment.

deep inside the body — one might say it is a sort of internal sunburn.

Radioisotopes and Longer Life

Doctors have found that gamma rays (when carefully applied) do not damage healthy flesh and bone as much as they damage some kinds of diseased flesh and bone. Some kinds of cancer tissue are particularly sensitive to gamma rays. Thus for many years it has been possible to treat some forms of cancer successfully by burning it with the penetrating gamma rays from radium.

The dose has to be very carefully controlled so that the patient's healthy tissue is not destroyed too. Overdoses of gamma rays injured many early experimenters with radium.

For many years in their fight against cancer, doctors have needed a cheaper and more plentiful source of gamma rays even stronger than those from radium. Scientists have provided them with just what they needed from among the fission fragments in reactors. The ordinary element, cobalt, used in making some kinds of steel, has a radioactive isotope whose gamma rays are more

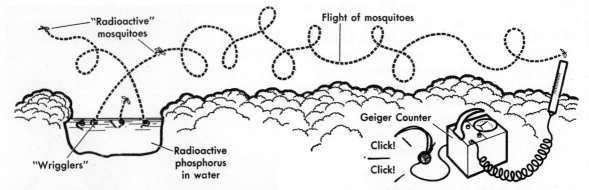

11-6. The distances mosquitoes travel from their breeding grounds can be traced if the mosquito " wrigglers " (larvae) feed in water to which radioactive phosphorus has been added.

satisfactory than those of radium. Moreover, it can be obtained much more cheaply and in larger quantities. This isotope, produced in the big reactors of the government's Atomic Energy Commission, is already in use in hospitals all over the world (Fig. 11-5).

The healing powers of other radioisotopes are being applied to human diseases, too. A radioisotope of iodine is used in treatment of thyroid gland diseases and of brain tumors. Radioactive sodium is helping doctors diagnose diseases of blood vessels, and radioactive phosphorus is used extensively in treating the blood disease, *leukemia*. More uses for these new weapons against disease are being tried out all the time. One of the most important uses of isotopes is as tracers, for they can be followed as they move about the body of a living thing.

Isotopes As Tracers

The United States is full of sparrows. As you watch them come and go with the changing seasons you may wonder where they go to, whether the same ones come back year after year, or how fast they can travel. You cannot answer these questions by trying to follow just one sparrow; you cannot tell him apart from his companions as they fly. However, people interested in the travels of birds have answered these questions by marking some of them with numbered bands. Then as the birds are recaptured elsewhere at a

later time something is learned about their travels. The bird band is a kind of " tracer " that makes it possible to follow one bird in a flock of many thousands.

It isn't as easy to band mosquitoes. But mosquitoes *have* been marked in order to study how far and in what directions they fly. They have been marked by adding a radioisotope of phosphorus to a breeding pool. Then by collecting mosquitoes at a number of points nearby and testing them for radioactivity it is easy to identify which mosquitoes came from the marked pond. In this way the travel habits of these little pests can be charted (Fig. 11-6). In this work the tracer was radioactive phosphorus.

Radioactive atoms are extraordinarily useful as tracers, and the variety of their uses is quite amazing.

For example, your body has lots of iron atoms in it, many of them in the red part of your blood. How quickly does red blood use up iron, and where does the iron go after it has been used? Until recently there was no way of knowing the answers to these questions because the iron atoms all over your body look just alike (remember Dalton!). Who could say which atoms had taken part in forming red blood?

Nowadays it's easy to answer the question. An experimental animal is fed food that contains a harmless amount of radioactive iron. With ray-detecting equipment the progress of the iron through its body can be checked at every stage. As the radioactive iron becomes a part of the different chemicals in the body, these chemicals (now with radioactive iron in them) can be spotted. The moment the iron arrives in the experimental animal's blood it is signaled by the blood's becoming radioactive. The length of time that iron stays in the blood is marked by the blood beginning to lose its radioactivity. Finally the path iron takes out of the body is marked at each step in the same way. Such a study of the path of iron atoms through the blood is quite impossible in a body full of iron atoms that *all* look alike. You can see why tracers are sometimes called " tagged atoms."

By means of such studies with iron tracers, medical scientists have learned a great deal about the disease *anemia.* Their knowledge promises in time to lead to more effective cures. You may remember from your earlier studies in science that anemia is caused by the lack of the substance *hemoglobin* (the red coloring matter in the red cells). Hemoglobin combines with the oxygen you breathe; without it, your cells would not get sufficient oxygen. What has this to do with iron? The hemoglobin is made up partly of iron. Hence, without enough iron there is not enough hemoglobin. Without enough hemoglobin there is not enough oxygen for the body's cells. Hence, anemia. Thus by studying the way the body uses iron, scientists are discovering the cause of anemia.

Tracers have also been used to study diet. From what food, for example, does the body most quickly digest fat? Scientists tagged a number of different kinds of fat with radioactive carbon atoms and fed one kind to each rat in a laboratory colony. The first rat to exhale radioactive carbon dioxide was declared the winner, and the kind of fat it was fed is now made part of the diet of people who cannot digest fat properly; in this respect, it is of especial value in the treatment of diabetes.

Because their radiation can usually be followed so easily these tagged carbon atoms are being used to trace the most complicated chemical reactions in the human body, and the medical discoveries made with their help are saving an increasing number of lives every week.

The use of tracers is not limited to medicine. Biologists are using tagged atoms to trace the processes of life itself. For instance, where do the elements come from that make up certain vitamins the body needs? How does the body build new bone cells? These and other questions are being attacked by the use of tracer atoms. Biologists are so excited by what they are learning with the help of radioisotopes that they have called them their most valuable new tool since the invention of the microscope.

Tracers in Industry

Industry is finding endless uses for tracers, too.

The fertilizer industry " tags " its fertilizers to find out which ones plants can take in fastest.

Auto makers put radioactive metal in piston rings and then test the efficiency of lubricating oil by measuring how much radioactive metal is scraped off into the oil (Fig. 11-8).

11-7. In this airtight chamber, scientists culture and study the radioactive forms of various plants under safe conditions. Studies are then made of the degrees to which plant-growth processes are affected by radiation.

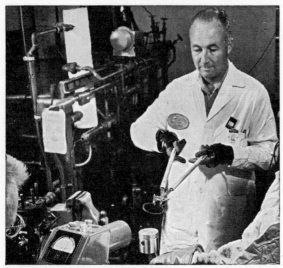

Standard Oil Co. (N.J.)

11-8. This research scientist is placing a radioactive piston ring on a piston of a test engine. The piston's wear is measured by the amount of radioactive material found in the oil.

The durability of floor waxes is tested by making them radioactive and measuring how many tagged atoms rub off onto passing shoes.

Weed killers are tagged and their progress into vital parts of weeds is charted.

The action of soapsuds, the rusting of iron, the manufacture of food by green plants are all better understood today thanks to these very useful atoms.

Over 100 varieties of radioisotopes are now being made in the reactors of the Atomic Energy Commission for anyone trained to use them. They are being sent to laboratories not only in America but all over the world. The steady flow of new knowledge they are making possible affects human welfare everywhere. The atoms first formed by fission for purposes of war are busy right now improving your life in times of peace.

Isotopes Help Explore the Past

One radioisotope that is *not* man-made can be used to tell us the age of ancient objects.

Cloth from an Indian burial mound is very faintly radioactive. Modern cloth is more radio-active. Why is this so?

In the air there is always a small amount of radioactive carbon (carbon of atomic weight 14). This isotope is being made all the time by the action of certain rays, called cosmic rays, on the atoms of the air. Plants, animals, and people are always taking it up in the form of carbon dioxide. Hence cloth and food and wood and animal bodies (including yours!) are all very slightly radioactive.

When a plant is made into cloth, though, or when an animal dies, or a tree falls down, it stops absorbing carbon 14 atoms. The carbon 14 atoms it already contains continue to give off particles and change to nitrogen atoms. In approximately 5760 years half of the carbon 14 has been changed. (Sometimes we say the half-life of carbon is 5760 years.) Thus the cloth from an old Indian burial mound is less radioactive than modern cloth. By measuring the loss of radioactivity, scientists can figure out the age of the burial mound quite accurately.

You can see one way it has been possible to measure the ages of mummies from Egyptian tombs, timbers from ancient sunken ships, firewood from the caves of prehistoric men, and flesh from frozen mammoths and saber-toothed tigers.

Our knowledge of radioactive atoms has opened up a great new tool for studying the ages of the distant past.

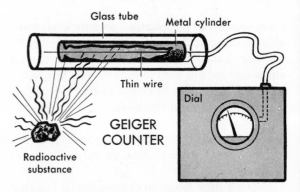

11-9. The Geiger Counter is a useful device for the detection and counting of particles given off during radioactivity. The particles detected per minute are indicated on the dial.

Looking Back . . . .

1. When uranium or plutonium atoms " fission," what are the pieces that fly about?
2. Name two ways of producing new isotopes. Name at least two examples of new isotopes that can now be man-made.
3. Why aren't many of the new radioisotopes found in the rocks of the earth?
4. What do gamma rays do to living flesh and bone?
5. Why are gamma rays from radium and other isotopes useful in treating cancer?
6. Name some other diseases that can be treated with the rays from radioisotopes.
7. What is a " tracer "? Name four problems that tracers have helped to solve.
8. What isotope has been helpful in telling us the ages of ancient objects? Explain how it is used in " dating " the age of a mummy from an Egyptian tomb.

Going Further . . . .

THOUGHT QUESTIONS

1. The heaviest atom that you can find in nature is uranium 238. It has 92 protons in its nucleus, and 146 neutrons. How would you go about *making* even heavier atoms? Atoms containing up to 102 protons have been prepared artificially.
2. The gamma rays given out by radioactive cobalt can pass through thick steel plates. Describe a way of using radioactive cobalt for finding hidden cracks and holes inside steel rails and boiler plates.
3. If you had a bottle of radioactive phosphorus and equipment for measuring radioactivity, how would you go about finding out: (a) what part of a tree uses phosphorus; and (b) how quickly the phosphorus is carried through the tree to where it is needed?
4. Nearly all the iodine atoms in your body are in the thyroid glands in your neck on each side of your windpipe. Explain how you might prove this fact if you had ray-detecting equipment and a harmlessly small amount of radioactive iodine.
5. Serious frostbite or disease can destroy the circulation of blood in part of an arm or a leg, and it may become necessary to amputate the affected part. The element sodium is carried all over your body by the circulation of your blood. Explain how a surgeon might use harmlessly small doses of radioactive sodium to locate the precise spot beyond which the circulation of blood is blocked. Surgeons use this technique so that they may cut off as little of the arm or leg as possible.

THINGS TO DO

1. With the help of your classmates prepare a bulletin board with a title like " The Atomic Age Advances." On it place all the clippings and pictures you can get from newspapers and magazines to show the new uses to which atomic energy is being put.
2. Only ten short years ago this chapter could not have been written. Why? Write a short (250-word) statement on the topic " A New Age Opens."

READING FURTHER

Atoms at Work by John Mander, Transatlantic, 1957, describes how radioisotopes are prepared in reactors.

5

Easing Work with Machines

◀ *Machines multiply muscle power a thousandfold, making bridges sturdy for modern loads.*

IN ALL man's history no one ever lived with machines as you do. We have invented and produced machines and made them part of our everyday lives. *We live with machines.* In eating, sleeping, working, playing, we are constantly surrounded by machines and with things made by machines. We even die by machines.

Machines have shortened our working hours and lengthened our play hours. They have helped us to make many things for many people — instead of for just a few people. They have bettered our health and lengthened our lives. They have relieved us of drudgery and given us time for education. They entertain us, help instruct us, feed us, clothe us.

Indeed, machines have become so much a part of our lives that we take them for granted. We find it hard to realize that only a short time ago many of them did not even exist. But, in fact, *living with machines* as we do is something very new in man's history. It is a great adventure — in which you are taking part.

In this unit we shall explore some of the most powerful machines that are a part of our world. We shall learn some of the principles on which they work and we'll see what new uses they may soon be put to. For the machines you see around you are rapidly creating a new world full of problems and full of promise — problems and promise that will shortly be yours.

CHAPTER 12

What Is a Machine?

You probably use the word "machine" for many different devices: phonographs, autos, lawnmowers, alarm clocks, typewriters, snowplows, mousetraps, gyrocompasses, dishwashers, turbines, eggbeaters, and hair dryers. Did you know that a pencil sharpener and the pulley that pulls up your window shade, a nutcracker and scissors are also machines? And that even your arm acts as a machine? Let us begin finding out what a machine is.

A SIMPLE MACHINE

Have you ever pried up the lid of a paint can with a screwdriver? If you have, you were making use of what the physicist calls a *simple machine* — in this case, the *lever*. Probably you did not give the matter much thought at the time: you just put one end of the lever under the lid, pushed down on the other end, and up came the lid.

Prying Up a Lid

Let's look at just what does happen when you try to pry up that lid. When you discover that you can't get the lid off with your fingers, you call in a machine to help you do the job.

First, you set up the machine as shown in Fig. 12-1 tip of screwdriver under rim of lid, blade of

screwdriver resting on edge of can, and your hand on the handle.

Then you push down gently but firmly on the handle, and the machine goes into action, with these results

1. the handle (A) goes down two or three inches
2. the blade of your screwdriver-lever turns about its resting place (C) on the edge of the can
3. the lid rises a fraction of an inch at B, enough to free it from the can.

Your small *force* — which wasn't strong enough to lift the lid unaided — is multiplied by the lever so that the lid is raised.

All of this happens in less time than it takes to tell about it. Yet by closely observing the action of the lever, we are able to see one of its advantages: it can multiply force. A lever can easily change a 10-pound push into a 100-pound push, for example, multiplying the original force by 10. Reasonably enough, this *multiplying of force* is called the machine's *mechanical advantage*. A lever in the hands of a man (Fig. 12-2) might change a 70-pound push to, say, 840 pounds. The mechanical advantage of the bar would then be 840 divided by 70, or 12, since it multiplies the original force that many times.

Mechanical advantage is an important feature of the lever, and of other simple machines too, as we shall see. But isn't there something suspicious about this trick of getting a large force for a small

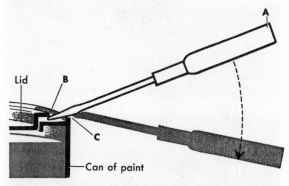

12-1. When you pry up this lid with a screwdriver, you are using a machine — the lever.

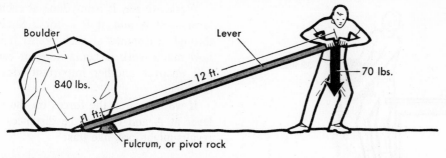

Boulder

Lever

840 lbs.

12 ft.

70 lbs.

1 ft.

Fulcrum, or pivot rock

12-2. This simple machine, the lever, multiplies force many times. But what happens to the distance the weight is lifted as compared with the distance through which the force is exerted?

one? Aren't you getting something for nothing? To find out, we must know what is meant by *work*.

WORK

The physicist's idea of work is probably different from your idea of work. For instance, you may think that as you sit reading these words you are working — but the physicist does not agree with you. He defines work in a special way.

The Meaning of Work

Work is done, says the physicist, when a force — a push or a pull — *moves through some distance.*

The boy in Fig. 12-3 is certainly exerting a force as he pushes against the door (marked " Pull "). But nothing moves, no matter how hard

he pushes; his force is not exerted through any distance. " No work is being done," says the physicist.

The girl exerts a force too, as she pulls on the door. But as the door opens, the force she is exerting *moves* through a distance. " Work *is* being done," says the physicist.

As the boy in Fig. 12-4 lifts the film projector from the floor, the force he uses to lift the projector moves up through the height he raises the machine — 3 feet. Work is done. But if he has to hold the projector for a moment, is he doing any work? Although he certainly is exerting a force to prevent the projector from falling to the floor, that force is not being moved through any distance. Therefore, no work is being done. If he has to hold the machine motionless for several minutes, he probably will grow very tired, yet he is doing no work at all, according to the physicist.

No work done

Work done

12-3. He's not working but she is, according to the physicist. Do you know why?

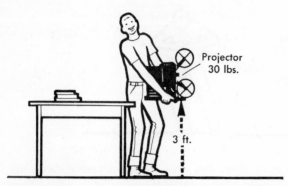

Projector
30 lbs.

3 ft.

12-4. How much work? Multiply force times distance moved.

Words met in everyday life sometimes take on special meanings in science. But you soon get used to this and no confusion results.

Measuring Work

Work is measured in this way. Suppose the projector in Fig. 12-4 weighs 30 pounds, and the boy lifts it 3 feet from the floor to the table. To find the work he does, multiply the force exerted, 30 pounds, by the distance it moved, 3 feet. 30 pounds × 3 feet gives 90 foot-pounds. (A *foot-pound* is one unit in which physicists measure work.) Thus, the boy has done 90 foot-pounds of work by raising a 30 pound weight 3 feet.

If we keep in mind that " distance " here means always the distance through which the force moves, we can shorten all this to a formula.

Work equals force times distance the force moves or,

Work = Force × Distance

Now that we have a scientific definition of work, let's take another look at the paint can and screwdriver. The screwdriver-lever, we saw, multiplied the force exerted by the hand. We also noticed (Fig. 12-1) that the force applied by the hand, at A, moved through a much greater distance than did the force lifting the lid, at the tip of the lever, B.

Work, we see, is being done at each end of the lever — at A and at B — for a force is moving through a distance at each point. If we find out how much work is being done at each end, we will uncover another important idea about the machine.

If we measured the forces on the screwdriver-lever at A and B, and the distances moved, the results might look like this:

Force at A = 20 pounds
Force at B = 160 pounds

Distance moved by force at A = 3 inches
Distance moved by force at B = ¼ inch

Now, by using our formula, let us find the work done at each end of our lever (Fig. 12-1):

input

Work = Force × Distance
Work at A = Force at A × Distance moved
= 20 pounds × 3 inches
= 60 inch-pounds

(Since we have measured the distances in inches in this case, our unit of work is inch-pounds. This is just as correct as the foot-pounds used earlier.)

output

Work at B = Force at B × Distance moved
= 160 pounds × ¼ inch
= 40 inch-pounds

Input is the work put in a machine.
Output is the work done by the machine.

So we put 60 inch-pounds of work into our machine — the lever — by moving a small force through a large distance, at A. In return we got a large force at B, at the price of having it move through only a small distance. Something is not being given away for nothing, after all. The physicist's definition of work shows us that a fair exchange of work is going on.

But 20 inch-pounds of work are missing! We put in 60 inch-pounds at one end of our simple machine: we got out only 40 inch-pounds at the other end.

Where have the missing inch-pounds of work gone?

The Case of the Lost Inch-Pounds

The lid of the paint can fits tightly. As it is pried up, it rubs against the edge of the can. Thus some of our missing work went into *overcoming friction*. Can you see other points at which friction might use up some of the input work?

Timken Co.

12-5. The roller bearings greatly reduce friction, but cannot remove it altogether.

The wheel shown in Fig. 12-5 is so finely balanced and so well mounted on bearings that a gentle push will make it spin. But sooner or later it comes to a stop, because friction uses up the supply of work put into the machine by the push. Lubricants, such as oil or powdered graphite, and bearings like the roller or ball bearings in roller skates, can reduce friction to an amazingly small force. But no machine is frictionless.

This hard fact is the one that brings inventors of " perpetual motion " machines down to earth at last. Where there is motion in a machine, there is friction. Where there is friction, the supply of energy (the ability to do work) put into the machine is being used up; and when the energy is all used up, the machine stops.

Friction, then, swallowed up a part of the work that was put into our lever to raise the lid of the can. It took 20 of our 60 inch-pounds of work, in fact.

Is friction always a disadvantage? Imagine what would happen if the soles of your shoes should suddenly become frictionless — or friction disappeared from the brakes of automobiles — or the cover of this book became perfectly slippery and frictionless. Friction is necessary.

If we used a lubricant, it might be possible to cut down the amount of useless friction and get more useful work out of a machine. You probably begin to suspect that we could never get more work out of the machine than we put into it. Experiments, done many times, have shown that this is the case — and that it is true of machines in general. In fact, *if the work spent on friction is counted in with the useful work,* then *the total work output of a simple machine equals the work put in.* No less — no more.

To do work, you need energy. In science, energy is defined as *the ability to do work.* A machine is designed to take in energy and to give it out in a more useful form, as when it multiplies a small *force* many times. But the *work* itself is never multiplied.

ALL LEVERS ARE MACHINES

You are now pretty well equipped for the job of opening a paint can with a screwdriver. But you probably were opening paint cans with ease when you knew nothing scientific about this simple machine. Why have we been studying this? We're looking for an answer to our question: What is a machine?

Now that we have spent so much time studying this simple machine — our well-worn screwdriver applied to the can lid — we are coming to a point where we can look next at *all levers,* and then, *all simple machines.* And, from there, we'll begin to see answers to our question.

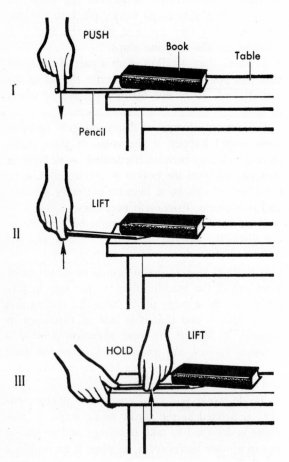

12-6. There are only three kinds — or classes — of levers. Here they are.

All Levers

If you have a pencil and a book at hand, you may want to try this for yourself. Put the pencil under the end of the book at a table's edge as shown in Fig. 12-6. Without letting the book slide away, push down as in I. Pull up, as in II. Now, holding the end of the pencil firmly against the table, as in III, lift it in the middle. Can you feel the difference in force needed to do these three things?

Look at the different ways you used your pencil lever. Notice that in all three cases your lever had a *load,* sometimes called a *resistance* (the book), an *effort* force (your hand), and the pivot or *fulcrum* around which the lever turns. This is true of every lever in the world.

You will also notice that there are just three different ways in which these three things — load, effort, fulcrum — can be arranged (Fig. 12-7). This you will also find true of every lever in the world.

Mechanical Disadvantage

Multiplying a force is probably what we think of at once as the lever's job. An auto jack, for instance, may multiply by 30 the force of 50 pounds applied to its handle. This produces a force of 1500 pounds, which is enough to lift one end of the car. The jack's mechanical advantage, then, is 30. Producing mechanical advantage is one of the lever's jobs.

But some levers are different.

If you will try again the experiment shown in part III of Fig. 12-6 you may find something you did not notice before. This time when you lift the book by means of the pencil, as shown, be careful to keep the fulcrum close to the hand holding down the end of the pencil. When you do this, what do you observe about the force needed to lift the book with the pencil?

Now lift the book with your hand alone. Isn't the force needed to lift the book using this lever arrangement greater than the force needed to lift the book without the lever? If you do this experiment carefully, you will see that this is so.

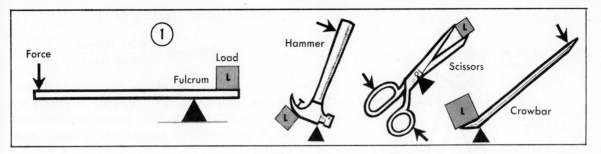

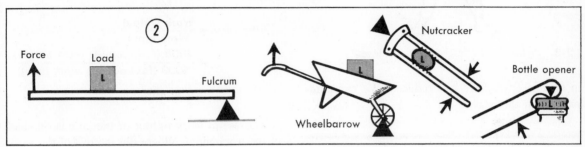

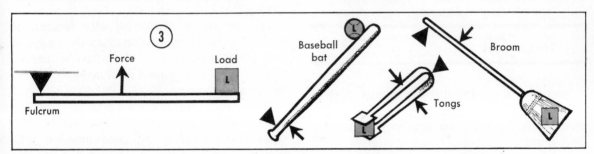

12-7. These are only a few of the levers we live with. How many more can you see around you?

This kind of lever does not increase force. In fact, it *reduces* the force you put into it.

But what use is a lever that doesn't multiply force? Isn't that a mechanical *dis*advantage?

Gaining Distance and Speed

When you use a hammer to drive a nail, you are using a lever of this kind. When you swing a bat or a racket or a golf club to hit a ball, you use such a lever. All these levers reduce the force you put into them. Why use them?

When you swing that bat as the ball comes across the plate, your object is to get the end of the bat moving as fast as possible. Luckily, you don't have to stop to figure this out: experience has told you that the faster the end of the bat is

moving, the farther the ball will go — other things being right. And this is where the lever comes in: to gain speed. As you can see in Fig. 12-8, the handle of the bat — where you apply the effort force — does not move very far. The tip of the bat moves much farther in the same time — which means more speed.

So here we have a *large effort* force moving through a *small distance* (at the bat handle) to make a *small load* force move through a *large distance*. Force is reduced; distance is multiplied. This is just the opposite of the action of the lever with which we began: the screwdriver lifting the lid. There a *small effort* moved through a *large distance,* you remember, to move a *large load* through a *small distance*. Force was multiplied

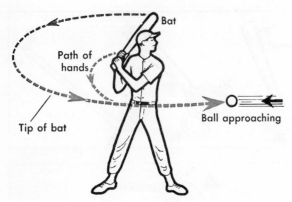

Bat

Path of hands

Tip of bat

Ball approaching

12-8. Where is the fulcrum for this lever?

in that case; distance was reduced. We can compare them this way:

	Effort Force	Effort Distance	Load Force	Load Distance
Bat	large	small	small	large
Lidlifter	small	large	large	small

Now we can see that although we may think of levers at first as multipliers of force, they may be used to reduce force and thus to gain distance (and speed).

In fact, as Fig. 12-7 shows, levers are used for still other purposes than gaining force or distance. A lever may be used just to change the direction of a force, or to transfer a force to another place. Which kind of lever you use depends on what you want to do with it.

Efficiency and Work

"She's a very efficient secretary," you may have heard someone say. By that he probably meant that she is a highly capable worker. If you say "efficiency" to a half-a-dozen different people, it can mean many different things.

But say "efficiency" to half-a-dozen physicists or engineers and you will bring to each one's mind the same precise idea: *efficiency* means comparing the useful work output of a machine with its work input.

Mathematically speaking, that is,

$$\text{Efficiency} = \frac{\text{Work Output}}{\text{Work Input}}$$

An auto jack, for example, may take 4000 foot-pounds of your work — pumping its handle up and down — to raise 2000 pounds one foot; that is, to produce 2000 foot-pounds of useful work output.

$$\begin{aligned}\text{Efficiency} &= \frac{\text{Work Output}}{\text{Work Input}} \\ &= \frac{2000 \text{ (foot-pounds work output)}}{4000 \text{ (foot-pounds work input)}} \\ &= \frac{1}{2} \text{ or } 50\%\end{aligned}$$

The useful work output of the jack is one-half of the work input. Where did the rest of the work input go?

Perhaps you are wondering what becomes of the energy taken by friction. Rub the palms of your hands together, hard. You have friction — and feel *heat*. Energy used in overcoming friction becomes heat energy.

It may strike you that it's a poor machine that will return as useful work only one-half or 50% of the work put into it, and spends the other 50% producing noises and heat. In that case you will be startled to find what the efficiency ratings of some common machines are as listed in Table 9. As you can see, there is good reason for using oil and other lubricants to reduce friction.

Since there is always friction in any moving machine, the work output will always be less than the work input. We can state this important principle in another way:

Efficiency can never reach 100% in any machine; it is always less.

Why?

OTHER SIMPLE MACHINES

These scientific principles about work which we have described for levers help you to understand what's going on in the other simple machines, shown in Fig. 12-9. Notice that we are leaving friction out of the picture here — "neglecting friction" — to make it clearer. But we have put beside each machine, for your information, a way in which you can figure its mechanical advantage — again, neglecting friction.

Back on page 137 we suggested that the physicist's definition of *work* was odd — but useful. Perhaps you can now see how useful his definition is.

"Work is done," says the physicist, "when a force moves through a distance." Multiplying the force by the distance gives a measure of the amount of work done (page 138). In mathematical shorthand, W = F × D.

In other words: if a *large force* is wanted from a certain amount of work, then the distance through which that force moves will be *small*. Or, if a *large distance* is what is needed (from a given amount of work), then the force will be correspondingly *small*. For in every case *force* times *distance* must equal the quantity of *work* put into the machine and also gotten out of it.

There are, to be sure, some very complex combinations of machines which are not understood at a glance. And there is a good deal more to the lever than we have looked at here.[1] But every lever big or small — the escapement lever in a tiny wristwatch or the 80-foot boom of a dockyard crane — behaves according to the basic principles you have been examining.

What are these basic principles or rules which all the world's machines follow? Let's sum them up:

1. *Machines must have work (or energy) put into them.*

2. *Machines convert work input into more useful work output:* gaining force, or distance and speed, or changing direction.

3. *Machines give out only as much work as is put into them:* counting in work used to overcome friction.

[1] For example, there is the mathematics of levers which allows us to predict how big a lever will be needed to do a given job. High school physics continues the lever story. And engineering schools do, too.

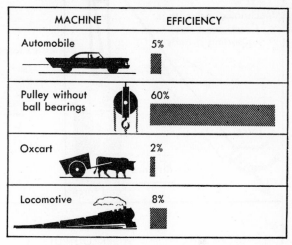

TABLE **12-1** EFFICIENCY RATINGS

MACHINE	EFFICIENCY
Automobile	5%
Pulley without ball bearings	60%
Oxcart	2%
Locomotive	8%

Thus these basic work principles bring all the simple machines — lever, wheel and axle, inclined plane, pulley — together for us. Indeed, these principles apply to not-so-simple machines too — for example, the power shovel in Fig. 12-10.

It may seem to you now that scientists know everything about simple machines. To be sure, their basic principles are known as well as anything can be known in science. But the applications of these principles are very far from finished. People are inventing new combinations of simple machines all the time, from can openers to construction machines. There is plenty of room — and plenty of need — for new applications of simple machines.

What Are Some Machines You Commonly Use?

In your mind, look back over these simple machines — the lever, pulley, inclined plane, wedge, screw, and wheel and axle. Not all of these are really different machines. For instance, a *wheel and axle* acts like a rotating lever. When you use an egg beater, the pedals on your bicycle, a steering wheel, or a doorknob, you are using a wheel and axle.

The wedge and the screw are forms of the *in-*

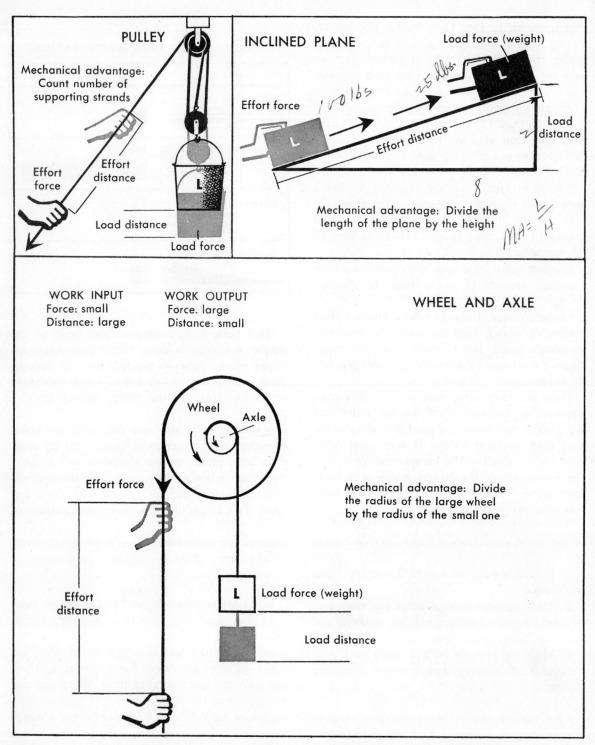

12-9. Some other simple machines — how they work, and how to figure their mechanical advantages (not counting friction).

Kennecott Copper Corp.

12-10. This power shovel is a combination of simple machines. How many can you detect?

clined plane, another useful machine. The knife and ax are also examples of the inclined plane. Do you know any others?

Many of the machines you use around the house are *compound machines.* Compound machines are made up of two or more simple machines. The typewriter, carpet sweeper, and water faucet are all examples. So is the automobile jack.

What Are Machines?

They are *energy converters.* They convert " raw " energy — work input — into some kind of more useful energy — work output.

A simple answer, to be sure. You may wonder now why we took so long to reach it! But perhaps it looks simple because you understand it.

And — take another look at that " simple " answer. It settles one question — and at the same time raises two more.

Machines are energy converters, but:
Where does the energy come from?
Machines help us to do work, but:
What sort of work?

Answering these will take us into the next chapter of man's adventures with machines — his quest for more powerful energy converters.

Looking Back . . . .

Going Further . . . .

Encyclopædia Britannica Films, Inc.

Jones and Laughlin Steel Corp.

Evaporated Milk Association

12-11. Find and identify a simple machine in each of these illustrations. For what purpose is each of them used?

5. Which would you find easier to lift: a 625-pound rock with a lever whose mechanical advantage is 5, or a 960-pound rock with a lever whose mechanical advantage is 8? Explain your answer.

6. In theory a gallon of gasoline has enough energy to do about 100 million foot-pounds of work. If a 2000-pound car climbs a mountain 5000 feet high using a gallon of gasoline, what is the efficiency of the car?

7. Consider a pulley with 3 supporting strands (as in Fig. 12–9) used to lift a 120-pound weight. Find the mechanical advantage and the effort force needed to lift the weight (neglecting friction).

8. You are told that using a pulley with 8 supporting strands, an effort of 12 pounds lifted a load of 300 pounds. Is this possible? If you say "no," what is your reasoning?

9. Find the mechanical advantage of an inclined plane 24-feet long that rises 4 feet.
10. What effort is needed to move a 360-pound weight all the way up the plane in problem 9?

PERPETUAL MOTION

Many inventors have tried to win fame and fortune by inventing a perpetual motion machine — a machine which, once started, would run forever, without using up any fuel or other source of energy. What a wonderful idea! But so far all such attempts have failed. Scientists are certain that it is impossible to make such a machine — because there is always friction.

As you know, even in the most efficient machine there is friction, and so the useful work output is always less than the work input. Some of the input work is used up in overcoming friction.

From a perpetual motion machine, however, the inventor hopes to get out more work than he puts in. The efficiency of such a machine would be more than 100%! Scientists feel sure that it is impossible for any machine to do this.

Look up "perpetual motion" in an encyclopedia or in your library's card index There are many strange stories connected with this tantalizing idea.

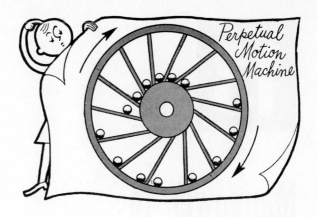

READING FURTHER

March of the Iron Men and *Engines of Democracy,* both by Roger Burlingame (Scribner), hold many interesting tales of machines, inventors, and their effects on how we live.

A high school physics textbook, like *Exploring Physics* (1952) by Ruchlis and Lemon (Harcourt), will tell you still more about simple machines.

Work = force x distance

Power = $\dfrac{\text{Work}}{\text{time}}$

CHAPTER

13

Manpower to Horsepower

Have you ever raced up a flight of stairs as fast as you could go — and found yourself gasping for breath when you got to the top, your heart pounding? That's " hard work," isn't it?

Yet if you walk leisurely up the same stairs, *taking your time*, you do just the same amount of work — according to the scientific definition of work. The same force (your weight) is moved through the same distance (the height of the stairs) each time, whether you walk or run up the stairs.

What makes one trip hard work, the other easy? *Time* has something to do with it, certainly. But just what?

MEASURING POWER

If you look into the simple question of walking and running upstairs, you will uncover another important principle about machines.

What Are the Facts?

If you are to tackle this problem scientifically you will need to make some measurements. You need a stop watch for measuring time, a tape or ruler for measuring distance, and scales for measuring your weight. Can you see, before reading on, how these instruments are to be used to measure work and time?

1. Measure the height (not the length) of the stairs (Fig. 13-1).
2. Time yourself running upstairs, from bottom step to top.
3. Time yourself walking upstairs.
4. Measure your weight.

To keep measurements in order, a careful worker might write them down in the form of a table. Here are some typical measurements as one student put them down.

	Jim's weight	Stair height	Time
Running	120 pounds	10 feet	3 seconds
Walking	120 pounds	10 feet	8 seconds

Of course the height of the stairs and Jim's weight haven't changed. Why put them down

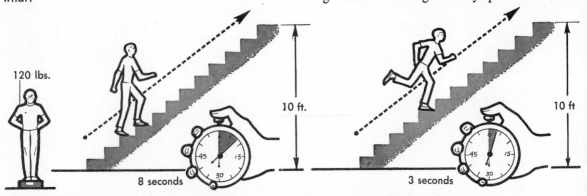

13-1. Running or walking, the boy does the same amount of work. What is not the same?

twice? "Careful workmanship," the scientist would say. This double entry makes it plain that the height and weight have not changed.

How much work is done in each case? You may be able to figure it out in your head. So may the scientist, but he would write down all the numbers just the same so that nothing is hidden and any mistakes can be found quickly.

	Force (Jim's weight)	×	Distance (stair height)	=	Work
Running	120 pounds	×	10 feet	=	1200 foot-pounds
Walking	120 pounds	×	10 feet	=	1200 foot-pounds

The work done in each case, running or walking, turns out to be the same: 1200 foot-pounds. But we see that Jim did 1200 foot-pounds in 8 seconds walking upstairs — and in only 3 seconds when running. Let us find out the work he did per second in each case.

	Work	Time	Work/Time	=	Work per second
Running	1200 foot-pounds	3 seconds	1200/3		= 400 foot-pounds per second
Walking	1200 foot-pounds	8 seconds	1200/8		= 150 foot-pounds per second

We see that the rate at which Jim was working is different in the two cases. What matters is not just how much work Jim did, but how long he took to do it.

Working Against Time
In Jim's stair-climbing "working harder" really means "working faster." *The amount of work that is done in a given time,* such as a minute or a second, is an important and useful idea.

The amount of work done in a certain time is exactly what is meant by *power.* A child shoveling sand into a pail day after day might do as much work as a bulldozer, but the difference between the two rates of working is tremendous. Because the bulldozer can work so much faster than the child, we say that the bulldozer has more power.

In everyday speech, you'll notice, people sometimes use the word "power" as if it meant "force." But in scientific language *power* has just one meaning: *rate of doing work.* Or, in shorthand:

$$\text{Power} = \frac{\textbf{Work done}}{\textbf{Time needed to do it}}$$

Strong Man
The muscular man shown in Fig. 13-2 has a fine set of muscles. In doing a "snatch" he achieves an extraordinary burst of *power* — in fact, about the maximum power a man can deliver. Let us see what his muscles can do.

Height bar bell is raised	6 feet
Weight of bar bell	300 pounds
Time taken to raise bar bell	3 seconds

How much work does this man do?

Work = Force × Distance force moves
= 300 pounds × 6 feet
Work = 1800 foot-pounds

This is hardly an extraordinary amount of work. Probably you do as much whenever you walk up a couple of flights of stairs. But let's look at the *power* produced:

Power = Work per unit of time
= Work/seconds
= 1800 foot-pounds/3 seconds
Power = 600 foot-pounds in one second

6 ft. in 3 seconds

300 lbs. Bar bell

13-2. How much work is this man doing?

The best way to appreciate what 600 foot-pounds per second means is to try generating some power *yourself*. For example, chin yourself as rapidly as you can for a certain length of time, and figure out the power you've developed. Or, try for yourself the stair-climbing power test described at the beginning of this chapter, and figure out your power. It is very likely that you will respect the power of that bar bell snatch thereafter.

Average Man

How much power can an average man develop day after day at a muscular job like shoveling coal?

Experiments have been done to answer this question. During a year of 2400 working hours, the muscle power output of an average man comes to about 46 foot-pounds per second. When it comes to shoveling coal, for example, this makes quite a pile of coal, as you can see.

There is, however, a drawback to this muscle power.

It is not nearly enough.

© 1955 Warner Bros. Pictures, Inc.

13-3. For centuries power meant manpower, and manpower meant slavepower.

Weak Man

The picture in Fig. 13-3 shows man's dissatisfaction with his own power and his determination to find ways of producing *more power* to serve his needs.

One way of getting more power, of course, was to get more men — more men to prepare the fields, plant crops and harvest them; more men to build fortifying walls, monuments, cities; more men to transport goods and people.

The practice of using slaves seemed to answer this demand for more power for a time. Thousands of slaves hauled on the ropes to drag the enormous stone blocks of the Pyramids up an inclined plane into place. The Roman galley was rowed by 138 slaves. It was capable of short bursts of speed — when trying to ram an enemy ship, for instance — but its average speed over any distance was very low. Men looked about for other means of getting more power.

HORSEPOWER

It must have been a brave and desperate man who first tried the experiment of using wild oxen as load-pullers, as an addition to his own muscle-power. How the experiment went at first we can only imagine.

The horse too was first kept for food and only later tried as a source of power. Horses turned out to be very useful power sources. They could pull heavy loads (especially after wheels, axles, and lubricants were developed), and for centuries horses were the fastest form of transportation short of going over a waterfall in a boat. They were easily trained to harness and not particularly hard to feed. Moreover, they were intelligent as well as companionable, and soon established " horse sense " as a standard envied by men.

One Horse's Power

So common was the horse as power source, for fast transport or heavy hauling, that back in 1770 when James Watt needed a way of measuring the power produced by his invention, the steam engine, he picked the horse as the best standard for comparison. First he set about discovering how much work in a given length of time the familiar source of power — the horse — could do.

Watt collected data from millers who used horses to turn the heavy millstones which ground the grain to flour. He found that a horse could pull with a force of 180 pounds around a circle about 23 feet in diameter and make about 2½ round trips per minute (Fig. 13-4). The distance the horse marched in one minute, then, was the circumference of the circle — 72 feet, times 2½, or 180 feet. The force (exerted by the horse) was 180 pounds. Since

Work = Force times Distance
Work = 180 pounds × 180 feet
Work = 32,400 foot-pounds

And since power is the work done in a given time, or

Power = Work/Time

then

Power of one horse =
32,400 foot-pounds/1 minute

This is the rate at which Watt's horse did work. Watt later rounded off the figure to get the definition of horsepower used to this day:

ONE HORSEPOWER = 33,000 FOOT-POUNDS OF WORK PER MINUTE

A strong man can produce for a very short time as much as 600 foot-pounds of work in a second, as we have seen; or an average man for a long time can do about 46 foot-pounds of work per second. How does this compare with one horsepower? Let's change our horsepower definition from work *per minute* to work *per second*:

1 horsepower = 33,000 foot-pounds/1 minute
= 33,000 foot-pounds/60 seconds
= 550 foot-pounds per second

The weight lifter's power is 600 foot-pounds per second. When his power is compared with one horsepower we find:

$$\frac{\textbf{600 foot-pounds per second}}{\textbf{550 foot-pounds per second}} =$$

1.1 horsepower used to lift the bar bell.

Average manpower is 46 foot-pounds per second.

$$\frac{\textbf{46 foot-pounds per second}}{\textbf{550 foot-pounds per second}} =$$

0.084 horsepower

Not very much, is it?

" Get a Horse! "

We may find it hard to imagine, but the horse was to people a hundred years ago what the car is to people today (Fig. 13-5). Men went on as usual inventing machines that called for more and more power, which in those days meant more horses. But probably the upper limit of sheer horsepower was achieved with the horsedrawn

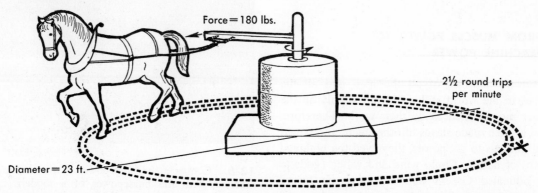

Force = 180 lbs.

2½ round trips per minute

Diameter = 23 ft.

13-4. How much work does a horse do in a minute? This is how James Watt defined " horsepower."

U.S. Dept. of Agriculture

13-5. The horseless carriage is not yet in sight, but even so, horsepower was the thing.

combine shown in Fig. 13-6. You can see, however, that all this musclepower needed something like the Great Plains of the West to maneuver in.

There were also impatient people like Thomas Edison, who pointed out that a horse ate up about ten pounds of food for every hour of work. Edison calculated that as a machine the horse's efficiency was only 2 per cent and that about 3½ acres of land were needed to raise the food for a single horse, compared with only 2½ acres for one human being. Yet for a long time the horse, donkey, and mule reigned supreme as power suppliers to man.

FROM MUSCLE POWER TO MACHINE POWER

But the muscles of all the men and all the horses in the world still could not supply all the power men wanted to do their work. Therefore, even as men made slaves of other men, and tamed wild animals to get power, they eyed the untamed forces of nature. Could wind and water (gods to the educated Greeks and Romans) be forced into giving some of their power to do man's work?

Sails on Land: Windmills

We can imagine that the first windmill came into its inventor's mind as he watched the sail of a boat fill with the breeze and begin to pull.

As far as it goes, the windmill is a remarkable machine, the work of many inventors. The earliest windmills faced in one direction only, and stopped turning whenever the wind changed direction. Then — in Germany — the whole windmill was perched on a single post, on which it could turn to face into the wind. The Dutch take credit for the next change in design. Just the top of the windmill carrying the sails swung around. The rest of the tower stood firm. This allowed the construction of larger and heavier windmills. For some time the job of turning the dome so that the sails faced the wind had to be done by the miller or his apprentice. Then an unknown inventor fixed the windmill to turn itself as shown in Fig. 13-7. When the wind changed course, it turned the small vanes, which were geared to swing the dome around into the wind again. This is one of the earliest *automatic* machines we know of.

How much power could a first-class windmill develop under favorable conditions? About 8

International Harvester Co.

13-6. Compare the horsepower of this harvesting machine with the horsepower of a modern automobile.

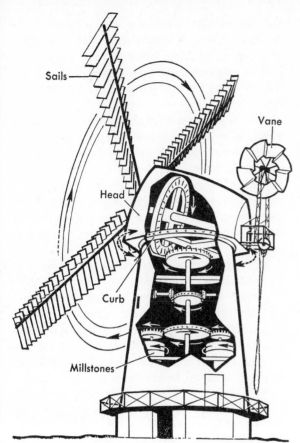

Sails

Vane

Head

Curb

Millstones

13-7. Power from the wind: this windmill automatically swung 'round to face the breeze.

horsepower. You can see that men were making progress in this quest for power. And in the business of grinding grain into flour between millstones, or pumping water out of places where it was not wanted, which were the two main jobs of windmills, some ups and downs in power output did not matter. If the wind failed sometimes, or at other times blew the sails off the arms, the interruption was not necessarily fatal to business.

But to drive other kinds of machinery, such as spinning and weaving machines, a steadier flow of power was needed. This the windmill could not supply, for it had no way of storing up energy when the wind was blowing in order to dole it out when the wind failed. The windmill was powerful but unreliable. Men looked elsewhere again for the power to meet their growing needs.

Water Wheels

The water wheel was more reliable. Fig. 13-8 shows a typical one. Where it could be set up, with dam and millstream to turn the wheel, it could deliver a good deal of horsepower. Some designs of water wheels had a surprisingly high efficiency. They could catch as much as 90 per cent of the energy from the flowing water. Connected to a system of shafts, belts, and pulleys, water wheels could turn the new machines being invented during the late 1700's and early 1800's. Of course this meant that the machines had to be gathered in one place near the water wheel, and the workers had to come to the "factory" to work, instead of working in their homes. You can see that the invention of the water wheel had an

WATER WHEEL

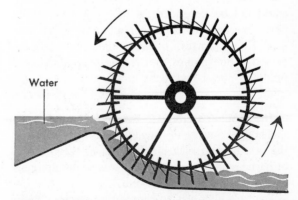

Water

13-8. The water wheel changes the energy of falling water into mechanical energy that can be used for running machines.

important effect on the lives of people in the manufacturing business. It forced many of them to live close together in factory towns.

At times the millpond ran dry, or the wheel clogged with ice. The trouble with the water wheel was that it needed water. Though it was more reliable than the windmill, it also had limits in power and speed. Men needed not only more power, but more convenient power — power to run new machines, to carry more goods and people on land and water, and power to pump water.

MORE HORSEPOWER — STEAM ENGINES

You might think that the first problem the owner of a coal mine faces is how to get the coal out of the ground. This is not so. The main problem in many mines is to keep the mine dry enough so that it can be worked at all. For as soon as you dig a deep hole in the ground, water is likely to seep into it, if the underground water table is high enough. You may even strike an underground stream. Miners have always had to use pumps and have called desperately for better ones.

With the growing demand for coal in England in the late 1700's, there were more mines, larger mines, deeper mines — and more water to be pumped out, day and night, without stopping, if the miners were to work at all. The windmill could not be depended on to supply the steady power needed, of course. The water wheel was used. Men, horses, ponies, donkeys were harnessed to the pumps, but it was plain that more pumping power had to be found somehow.

The " Miner's Friend ": Steam Power

Thomas Savery of England was certainly not the first man to rack his brains over the problem of harnessing steam. But there was something new in Savery's idea — it worked.

Savery's idea was so simple that we may wonder if it deserves to be called a steam engine at all. Except for valves which were turned by hand, it

had no moving parts — a goal engineers still strive for today. It simply used cooling steam to draw up water from below it into a tank, then pushed that water out up above. Savery called it the " Miner's Friend " (Fig. 13-9). It worked in this way.

First, a good pressure of steam is raised in the boiler, all valves being shut. Then the steam valve is opened and steam trapped in the tank is cooled by turning on the cold water spray. This causes the steam to condense and creates a vacuum in the tank. Now the water-inlet valve is opened, and water from the mine rises into the vacuum — pushed into the tank by atmospheric pressure, of course.

When as much water as possible is in the tank, the water-inlet valve is shut. Now the steam valve is opened and steam from the boiler enters the tank and presses against the water. The water-outlet valve is now opened, and the steam pressure pushes the water in the tank up to the surface of the ground. The tank, now filled with steam, is ready to repeat the process.

As you see, the flow of water from this engine was not steady. To make it more steady Savery put two of his tanks side by side (drawing steam from the same boiler), and as one tank filled with water the other emptied. This made a fairly steady stream, if all the valves were opened and closed on schedule.

The " Miner's Friend " worked. However, it took a tremendous quantity of steam to do its job, which meant a great deal of fuel.

Moreover, the " Friend " worked by steam *pressure*. Boilers and tanks that could safely stand high pressure were rare in those days, when the art of boilermaking was just beginning.

And — still further — the " Miner's Friend " could do nothing but pump water.

The " Friendlier Engine ": Newcomen's Engine

If a modern advertising man were given the job of selling Thomas Newcomen's engine, he would probably call it " the *friendlier* engine," bearing in mind the competition from Savery's " Miner's Friend." For Newcomen's engine was

THE "MINER'S FRIEND"

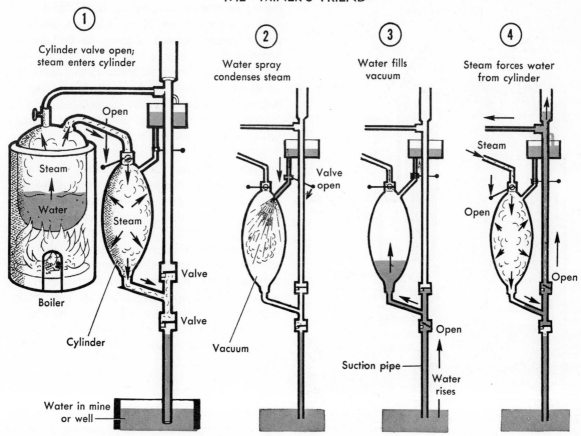

13-9. The "Miner's Friend," Savery's steam engine, pumped water.

safer. It did not use the huge steam pressure that had to be so carefully watched lest the "Miner's Friend" burst and become the miner's executioner.

How could a steam engine be made to work on next to no steam pressure? Newcomen showed that the pressure of the *atmosphere* could be made to do the work. By this time experiments by Torricelli (tohr-eh-CHEL-lee), von Guericke (GAY-ri-keh), and others had proved that the ocean of air under which we live exerts pressure on all our surroundings. Here's how Newcomen's engine used the pressure of the atmosphere (Fig. 13-10).

When the *piston* is at the bottom of the *cylinder*, the *steam valve* is opened. Very low-pressure steam flows into the cylinder and raises the piston. It is able to lift the piston because the piston's weight is almost exactly balanced by the *counterweight* on the other side of the beam. Therefore, very little force is needed to raise the piston.

The piston rises. When it reaches the top, the cylinder is full of steam. Now the steam valve is closed and the cold water *spray valve* is opened. The steam in the cylinder condenses, creating a vacuum beneath the piston. At once the piston is forced down by the pressure of the atmosphere on the top of the piston. As it goes down it gives a strong stroke to the *water pump* at the other end of the beam. When the piston reaches the bottom of the cylinder, the process begins again.

In the early Newcomen models the valves were

NEWCOMEN'S ENGINE
(Down stroke)

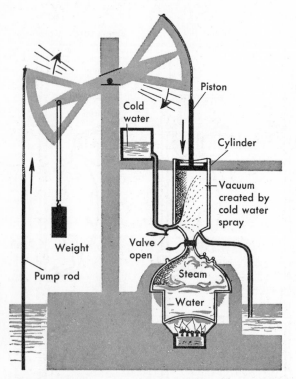

Piston

Cold water

Cylinder

Vacuum created by cold water spray

Weight

Valve open

Steam

Pump rod

Water

13-10. Thomas Newcomen's steam engine really used atmospheric pressure to do the work.

worked on schedule by hand, as with Savery's engine. It was not long before a way was found to open and close them at the right times by levers and rods connected to the beam.

Safe, Strong, Heavy, Greedy

The Newcomen engine was safer, even if it was slow and made only a few strokes in a minute. Moreover, it could deliver a strong stroke, for the bigger the area of its piston, the more atmospheric force was brought to bear. It could lift a large amount of water at a single stroke.

On the other hand it had drawbacks. The engine was enormously heavy with its big cylinder and piston (sometimes four or five feet across), to say nothing of the boiler and beam. It ate up a lot of fuel. Of course the piston did not fit very

well in the cylinder either, for the problem of boring a true cylinder had not yet been solved.

Like Savery's contraption, moreover, the Newcomen engine seemed able to do nothing but pump water. It is true that it was set to work pumping water into a millpond so that the water wheel would have a steady supply for turning the mill machines. But this was a roundabout and remarkably inefficient way of using the engine's power. It never became popular.

Just the same, Newcomen's engine was an improvement over the " Miner's Friend." In its ponderous, slow, reliable way it did its work for over half a century before any better engine was invented. While it was wheezing and creaking and pumping in England, James Watt, a " dull and inept " boy (so some of his teachers called him) was growing up in Scotland. He tried his hand at various jobs: mathematical-instrument maker, surveyor, shopkeeper, organ builder. His meeting with Newcomen's engine was almost by chance. That meeting changed not only James Watt's life and the shape of the steam engine: it changed the shape of the world.

Watt's Engine

The Newcomen engine that James Watt saw was a working model, used in science classes at Glasgow College. But it worked for a few strokes only, then stopped. It was sent to London to be repaired. It returned. Then it worked for a few strokes and stopped. It was finally handed over to Watt — the mathematical-instrument maker for the college.

Watt found the trouble. The boiler of the engine was too small and could not supply enough steam. A bigger boiler was needed.

With another man, the matter might have ended there. But Watt started to wonder how Newcomen's engine might be improved so that it would not need so much steam to begin with. He had already figured out why it ate up so much fuel. It was because the whole cylinder was cooled off by the water spray that condensed the steam. This meant that the whole cylinder had to be heated up again by fresh steam before the piston could go to work again. Experimenting, he had discovered that this took four times as much steam as the cylinder held. This was why the Newcomen engine needed so much steam, and used so much fuel.

Walking on the Glasgow green one afternoon, Watt had an idea. The job of condensing the steam could be done *outside the big cylinder*. If the steam were fed into a second chamber connected to the cylinder, the spray of water could then condense the steam — without cooling off the big cylinder (Fig. 13-11). Result: a great saving in steam and fuel, and a startling improvement in the Newcomen engine.

James Watt, Revolutionist

What did Watt do to the steam engine? Before he was through with it there were:
1. separate condensation of steam
2. use of high pressure steam (instead of atmospheric pressure) to move the piston
3. double-acting steam pressure on the piston, pushing it first one way then the other
4. rotary power (the engine could turn a wheel)
5. a governor to regulate engine speed *automatically*

and a number of other improvements.

What did Watt do to the steam engine? He changed it from a slow, heavy, very inefficient machine for pumping water to a more powerful, lighter, faster, more efficient engine that could *turn wheels* as well as pump water.

" All very fine, but hardly sensational," you may be thinking. But look at what followed. Some men had been dreaming of an engine that somehow could make a boat move. Or one that would take the place of horses to draw cars along rails. Or one that would even fit into some kind of wagon or carriage and propel it along the road. A look at Newcomen's big heavy engine dampened such dreams. But Watt's smaller, lighter, faster engine — that was something else again. Inventors and designers of all kinds of machinery had been crying for this sort of power all along.

The revolution was on: the revolution in power, in transportation, in manufacturing. It changed our world.

Watt Plus Other Men Plus Science

Of course Watt did not do all this single-handed. In fact, if he had not had help from people who believed in his ideas — like Matthew Boulton, a brilliant manufacturer — he might never have been heard of. Many inventors have failed to find successful uses for their ideas, to their disappointment. Later their ideas are re-invented by others. Watt was lucky. Later, too, he had inventive helpers who contributed their ideas. One of them, for instance — a man named Murdock — wanted to put the Watt engine into a cart to make it go. It might have been the first automobile, but Watt saw no future in that sort of thing, and discouraged him!

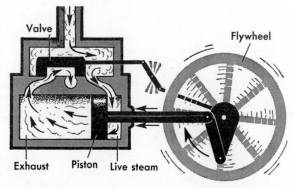

13-11. Lighter, more powerful, more efficient, James Watt's steam engine put power in men's hands to change the face of the earth.

Valve
Flywheel
Exhaust   Piston   Live steam

Looking Back . . . .

VOCABULARY

Define the following expressions to show that you understand their meaning in this chapter.

1. rate of work
2. power
3. horsepower
4. atmospheric pressure
5. steam pressure
6. vacuum
7. condensation
8. cylinder
9. piston
10. foot-pound

- You need a watch, a ruler, and a scale to measure the power you produce when running upstairs.
- Horsepower is more convenient than manpower for rating engines.
- Windmills and water wheels are not satisfactory sources of power.
- Savery's steam engine was dangerous.
- Watt's engine was more efficient and more powerful than Newcomen's engine.
- The piston of Newcomen's engine was very large.
- *Cold* water was squirted into the cylinder to condense the steam.
- Watt's engine started a revolution.

Going Further . . . .

TRY THESE PROBLEMS

1. The average muscle power output of a man is 46 foot-pounds per second. At this rate, about how many men are needed to produce one horsepower?
2. What power are you producing if you weigh 130 pounds and climb a ladder 12 feet in 4 seconds into a hayloft?
3. How long will it take a hoist that produces 3 horsepower to lift an 1100-pound bale up into the same hayloft?

4. An electric motor turning a fan may be rated on its nameplate as one-fifth horsepower. How many foot-pounds of work does it do in one minute? in one hour?
5. A load of 5 steel girders, each weighing 3 tons, is hoisted up 110 feet. Calculate the number of foot-pounds of work done. Then compute the power developed if this work was performed in 1 minute and 45 seconds.
6. For the same time as in problem 5, what is the horsepower developed if the weight is halved but the height is doubled?
7. Find the horsepower developed by an airplane that weighs 40 tons if it climbs from 2000 to 3500 feet, in 2 minutes and 10 seconds.

THINGS TO DO

1. With your teacher's permission, and under his supervision, demonstrate how to " pop the cork." Watch the force of steam. Boil some water in a Pyrex test tube corked at the top. The expanding steam causes the cork to shoot out and hit the ceiling. Stand far away from the test tube as it is heated and point it upward at an angle in a safe direction.

2. Make a model water wheel. Show the different ways in which a stream of water can turn the wheel.

READING FURTHER

From Man to Machine by Agnes Rogers, Little, Brown, 1941. This book, with its many illustrations, contains, among others, interesting stories of Watt's steam engine and Fulton's steamboat.

1st
tar bĭn (bīn)
2nd

Engines—Complex to Simple

The steam engine was a milestone in man's quest for power. It led to powered boats, locomotives, land vehicles, and industrial power of all sorts. Under the combined efforts of engineers, scientists, and industrialists it has become a wonderfully useful source of power. Even today steam piston engines are still making a considerable part of the world's power.

As the demand for more powerful steam engines grew, more and more improvements were made. One invention stimulated other inventions. Out of these improvements to the steam engine grew a new addition to man's power tools, the *turbine.*

THE TURBINE — MORE POWER

As Fig. 14-1 shows, the idea of using the energy of a rushing jet of steam to turn a wheel — to get power — is an old one. But, as sometimes happens in science, the simplest-looking idea is not the easiest to carry out.

The little steam turbine in Fig. 14-2, which you can easily make, will demonstrate some of the difficulties in the way of making a steam turbine that works. These difficulties prevented the turbine from being a practical power supply for many

centuries. You may want to figure out some of the practical difficulties for yourself before reading on. It will be a good test of your foresight. As steam begins to spurt from the small hole in the model and the little bladed wheel begins to twirl, see how many difficulties you can find in the way of getting that spurt of steam to do some useful work.

Designing a Turbine

For instance, the little bladed wheel will spin quite rapidly — probably several hundred revolutions per minute. This is impressive speed compared with a water wheel. But if you touch the spinning blades with a strip of light paper, you will see that the wheel is exerting a very small force. Even though it is being exerted over a considerable distance due to the rapid revolutions of the wheel, it is a small force. Of course gears could convert this *small force-large distance* work system to a *large force-small distance* system. But some of these gears, those close to the turbine, will have to turn at high speed, and pass on the energy with high efficiency. A hundred years ago gears could be made strong but they were not efficient at high speed. Here was one difficulty in the way of developing the simple-looking steam turbine idea.

There is another difficulty with the simple-looking turbine idea, suggested by our model; the blades of the turbine wheel get hot. In a real working turbine the hotter the steam entering the

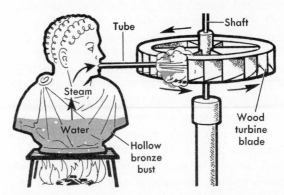

14-1. Why wasn't this ancient idea of a steam engine successful?

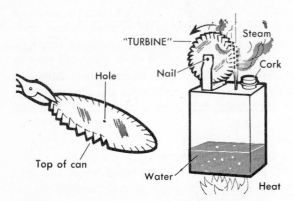

14-2. By making this simple model turbine, you can learn a great deal about the real thing.

turbine, the more efficient the turbine becomes. Thus high temperature steam is used — even up to 1100° F. But high temperatures weaken metal. The steam must not be so hot as to melt the turbine blades. The steam entering the modern turbine heats the blades in Fig. 14-3 to a dull red.

There is still a third difficulty in building an efficient turbine. As a turbine spins, huge adhesive forces are needed to keep the blades in the sockets, else they detach like mud from a spinning car wheel. Moreover, this force increases by four times when the speed of the blades only doubles. You can begin to see the tough problem that a metallurgist faces when looking for a turbine blade metal to stand higher and higher turbine speeds.

A fourth difficulty is shown by our model turbine. You can see that much of the steam jet is wasted. Some steam hits the blades sideways, and some misses them entirely. So the steam jet must be aimed at the blades in such a way that little of its energy is wasted. The blades must be so shaped that they take from the steam blast every possible pound of force. Also when the steam has done its work, it must leave the blade without interfering with the fresh steam entering.

This doesn't by any means end the list of problems that mechanical engineers had to solve as they designed a practical, reliable, and efficient steam turbine. However, it may give you an idea of the kinds of problems on which an engineer spends his time.

Late Model

Only after much brain-wracking, reasoning and guessing, experimenting, " accidental " discoveries, frustrations and satisfactions have engineers solved these tough problems.

1. The gears are efficient power conductors. They turn at 3600 revolutions per minute.

2. Steam shoots into the turbine at a pressure of about one ton on each square inch of surface it touches, and at a temperature of about 1100° F. Under the impact of this screaming stream of heat energy, the first row of turbine blades moves at about 600 miles per hour. At this speed the force trying to wrench loose each of these blades is about 90,000 pounds.

3. Each moving blade is curved so as to take some energy from the rushing steam and then pass the steam on efficiently to a set of fixed blades. These are curved to direct the steam against the next set of moving blades, where still more energy will be given up by the steam.

4. As the steam works its way along from one set of blades to the next, it is allowed to expand, as the diameter of the turbine wheels gets bigger. In expanding, it does still more work on the blades.

14-3. Turbine blades must be very strong and precisely made to withstand high speed.

5. The horsepower generated in the turbine shown in Fig. 14-3 is about 108,000, with an efficiency of 75 per cent.

There is of course much more to turbine design, as some of the books listed at the end of this chapter can show you. But there is enough in this short section to show you that the turbine is another great advance in *man's quest for power*.

Turbines are well suited to driving electric generators, which they can do without gears. And they are used in large ships such as ocean liners and aircraft carriers, where smooth control of great power is important. About 75 per cent of all the world's engine power is generated by steam turbines.

Nowadays the *water turbine* is more powerful and efficient too, compared with the old water wheel. Its blades have been scientifically designed to take from the moving water the greatest possible number of foot-pounds of energy. Using mathematics, engineers have applied the laws of physics, as well as tinkering on a " try it and see if it works " plan. Careful scientific study of how water behaves in motion (*hydrodynamics*) and at rest (*hydrostatics*) has resulted in the information and general principles for designing such huge water-power plants as the Grand Coulee Dam.

INSIDE JOB: INTERNAL COMBUSTION

Although the steam engine kept becoming more efficient, and more powerful for every pound of its weight, it did not satisfy the dreams of some men for still more power, more efficient power, lighter power, more portable power. " The inventor is a fault-finder, a discontented fellow," says an inventor who has studied other inventors,[1] and there were some men who looked at the faults of steam engines, rather than at their merits, and tried to invent a still better engine.

One of the biggest faults of a steam engine is that it wastes a lot of heat energy. Steam is made by a fire burning *outside* the boiler. The fire heats

[1] H. Stafford Hatfield, in *The Inventor and His World*.

HEAT ENERGY WASTED

14-4. Wasted heat energy pours from a steam locomotive.

the boiler, but it also heats all the surrounding air (Fig. 14-4) and everybody standing nearby. A steam engine wastes heat energy in about the same way you waste water when you are washing yourself under a strong shower bath.

Wouldn't it be a big improvement if the fire supplying heat to the engine could burn *inside the cylinder,* where it is needed? Then much less heat energy would be lost.

In order to put this very attractive idea to work, several questions had to be answered first.

What Is Heat?

For one thing, there was the question, " What is heat? "

If you look back over the last two or three paragraphs, you will see that we have spoken about *heat energy* several times. To speak about heat as energy may seem right enough to you, especially if you have studied general science in school. But the idea that heat is a kind of energy did not look right to anybody until around 1800, when the development of the steam engine was in full swing.

Until 1800, you see, people thought heat was a kind of fluid. They thought something got hot when heat fluid ran into it from something else. When something grew cold, it was because the heat fluid — called *caloric* (cal-OHR-ic) — left it and went somewhere else. If you will recall some of your own everyday experiences with heat — such as putting your warm hand on a cold piece of ice, or boiling water over a flame — it may seem to you that this old theory of heat fluid works pretty well. So it does — up to a point. There were some facts that it did not explain very well, especially in the growing science of chemistry. However, in general, with a bit of pulling and stretching, the caloric theory about heat explained a lot of the facts known before 1800.

But if you rub your hands together, you can generate quite a lot of heat. Where do you think the heat comes from? The heat is even greater if you take two wooden blocks and rub them violently together; they will not only become hot, *they will continue to produce heat — a lot of it — as long as you continue to rub them* (Fig. 14-5).

Where does all this heat come from? Count Rumford, watching metal cannon being bored and noting the tremendous quantity of heat produced by the rubbing drill, asked the same question. For the metal of the cannon, the wooden blocks, and the palms of your hands seem to hold an endless supply of heat fluid. If heat is a fluid, it must be flowing into the bored cannon and the wooden blocks and the palms of your hands, from something else — something which must be getting cold, of course, as heat fluid leaves it. Do your arms get cold as the palms of your hands get warm? No — the mystery of where all the heat comes from cannot be answered in this way; heat is *not* really a fluid. It had to be explained in some other way.

As you perhaps know, the new explanation was the *molecular theory* of heat. The molecular theory suggests that heat is due to the motion of the molecules in a substance. Rubbing the wooden blocks together, for instance, made the molecules they are made of dance about more rapidly.

The faster their molecules dance about, the hotter the blocks become (Fig. 14-5). The energy of this molecular dance is heat energy.

The heat energy of a flame is the energy of motion of its molecules, and when the flame sears your fingers or boils water its speeding molecules are simply passing along to you or the water some of their energy of motion. In a cold object, such as an ice cube, the molecules are moving more slowly and therefore have less energy to pass along to nearby objects. In fact if the liquid surrounding an ice cube is warmer than the cube, the liquid gives heat energy to the cube and melts it.

The heat energy in an object is the same thing as the energy of motion of its molecules.

With this new molecular theory of the nature of heat, the development of heat engines such as the steam engine and the internal combustion engine was able to go ahead more rapidly.

The Problem of Fuel

Before the notion of internal combustion (fire inside the engine cylinder) could be made to work, there was a second question that had to be answered — the question of what fuel to use. It was

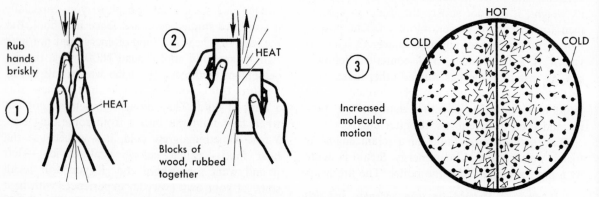

14-5. The faster the molecules dance, the hotter the substance. Heat is energy of molecular motion.

soon clear to experimenters that coal would not do.

Soon after gunpowder appeared in Europe, an inventor appeared with the idea that gunpowder was the fuel for internal-combustion engines. As you may imagine, however, nothing came of the gunpowder engine, in spite of the efforts of several inventors.

But with the discovery, in England in 1792, of the process of making " illuminating gas " from coal, a new fuel appeared. Coal gas, made by heating coal without burning it, could be stored in tanks near an engine. Then the gas could be fed into the engine cylinder through pipes as it was needed. Practical " gas " engines were not long in developing.

A big problem was how to *slow down* the explosion of the mixture of coal gas and air in the cylinder, so that the explosion would drive the piston down smoothly and efficiently. This was soon solved by compressing the gas/air mixture before lighting it. It then exploded more slowly. Now *internal combustion* — burning inside a cylinder — was a reality.

Explosion in Four Strokes

Inside the cylinder, the whole process of supplying, burning, and exhausting the gas takes *four* strokes of the piston to complete. During these four strokes of the piston, the *flywheel* to which it is connected makes two complete turns. The complete process is called a *four-stroke cycle*. You can see now why the heavy spinning flywheel is there in Fig. 14-6. Using energy given it by the single power stroke, it spins the piston through its three powerless strokes: intake, compression, and exhaust.

You must be careful not to confuse such a *gas* engine with the modern *gasoline* engine, which uses liquid fuel rather than a gas as its fuel.

The first use of these gas engines was in factories, where they were connected to a system of shafts, belts, and pulleys. Today the gas engine is still being used. For example, engines used in some sewage treatment plants run on gas (methane) produced by the treated sewage and supply power for the plant. And the pumps used to drive natural gas long distances through pipelines are run on gas taken from the pipelines.

Substitute for Gas

In 1859 petroleum was discovered in Pennsylvania. Almost at once uses were found for it. At first petroleum took the place of whale oil in lamps and put many of the whalers to doing other things. Then chemists and chemical engineers found that petroleum was really a mixture of many different substances which could be separated from one another (see Chapter 8). One of the substances in the petroleum mixture is kerosene, which proved to be a much better lamp fuel than crude petroleum. Another was petroleum jelly, which you may have met under the

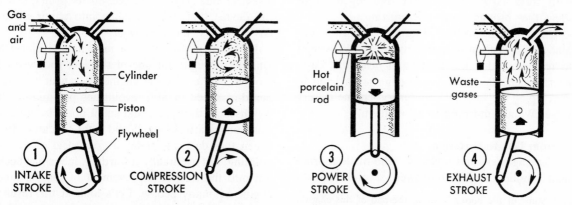

14-6. The four-stroke cycle: early engines which ran on illuminating gas used it, too.

14-7. This engine in a sewage treatment plant runs not on gasoline, but on a gas (methane principally) produced in the digestion of sludge resulting from sewage treatment.

name of Vaseline. Still another substance was axle grease that was better than the old tallow. Chemists sorted out a multitude of other products from the petroleum mixture among which were some (like benzine) that looked good as engine fuels.

Out of black sticky petroleum, inventors and engineers began to use liquid fuels for a practical internal-combustion engine. These liquid fuels held more energy per pound than coal gas, and unlike coal gas plenty could be carried in a tank ready to use. Engineers and inventors worked away at improving internal-combustion engines with fresh vigor. The variety and ingenuity of ideas they brought forth are amazing.[1]

Our modern gasoline internal-combustion engine is a collection of many inventions. We ought to remember that the number of inventors, engineers, scientists, businessmen who had a hand in developing the internal-combustion engine is very large. We are indebted to all of them.

From Gas to Gasoline

The engineers and inventors who made a practical gasoline engine borrowed several features

[1] Some of the books listed at the end of this chapter tell that story.

from the old gas engine: the four-stroke cycle, compression of the explosive mixture before burning, ignition by electric spark, and water-cooled cylinders, for example.

Liquid fuels made from petroleum can easily be evaporated into a gaseous *vapor* without using the heat of a roaring fire. And just like coal gas, the vapor burns readily inside the engine — explosively, in fact — when mixed with the right amount of air.

Charles Duryea, an American, is supposed to have seen his wife spraying perfume from an atomizer one day and seized on its principle for the device that turns gasoline into vapor in today's engines: the *carburetor*.

In 1883, in Germany, a man named Gottlieb Daimler brought out one of the first widely used models of the gasoline engine. It ran at the unheard-of speed of 800 revolutions per minute. It was used to drive cars and small boats because it was comparatively small and light to carry. Between that date and today a great deal of disappointing, but eventually rewarding, labor has been put into the further improvement of the gasoline engine by many people. Let's look at the result: today's gasoline engine.

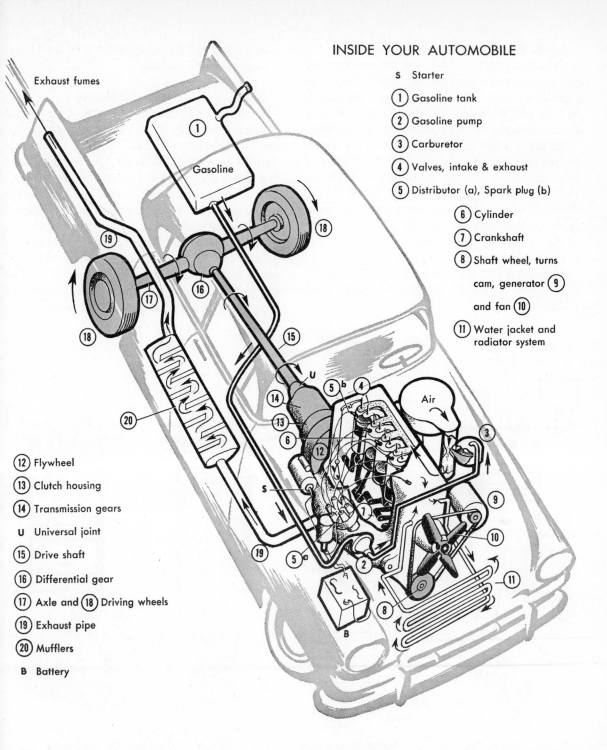

INSIDE YOUR AUTOMOBILE

Exhaust fumes

Gasoline

Air

S Starter
1 Gasoline tank
2 Gasoline pump
3 Carburetor
4 Valves, intake & exhaust
5 Distributor (a), Spark plug (b)
6 Cylinder
7 Crankshaft
8 Shaft wheel, turns cam, generator 9 and fan 10
11 Water jacket and radiator system
12 Flywheel
13 Clutch housing
14 Transmission gears
U Universal joint
15 Drive shaft
16 Differential gear
17 Axle and 18 Driving wheels
19 Exhaust pipe
20 Mufflers
B Battery

14-8. The modern automobile is a collection of inventions. Start with the tank of gasoline (1) and follow the number of operations that are performed until the burned gases are expelled through the exhaust pipe.

Inside the Gasoline Engine

Look back at Fig. 14-6, the four-stroke cycle gas engine, and substitute for "gas" the words "gasoline vapor." You will then have the picture of what goes on inside the cylinders of most modern gasoline engines such as those in automobiles.

Filling in some of the more important details of that general picture is Fig. 14-9. Not shown in this illustration are the thousands of problems that had to be solved by engineers, inventors, and scientists before the whole contraption became as remarkably reliable as it is today. Here are some of the things they had to invent:

Forced lubrication to every moving part

Lubricants that work in all kinds of weather

A battery source of electricity for sparks, light, horn

A cooling system to keep the engine from overheating and melting

Efficiency — and Higher Efficiency

Even with all their refinements, today's best gasoline engines reach an efficiency of 25–30 per cent — sometimes. Do you think this is very efficient? The wasted 70–75 per cent is heat energy that either goes out the exhaust pipe or stays inside to heat up the engine. A cooling system has to be put in to prevent the engine from melting itself with its own waste heat.

But compare this efficiency and the power it creates for each pound of its weight with the steam engine and the gas engine. You will see that the gasoline engine's 25 per cent efficiency is a long step forward in man's quest for power.

GASOLINE ENGINE
(4-stroke cycle)

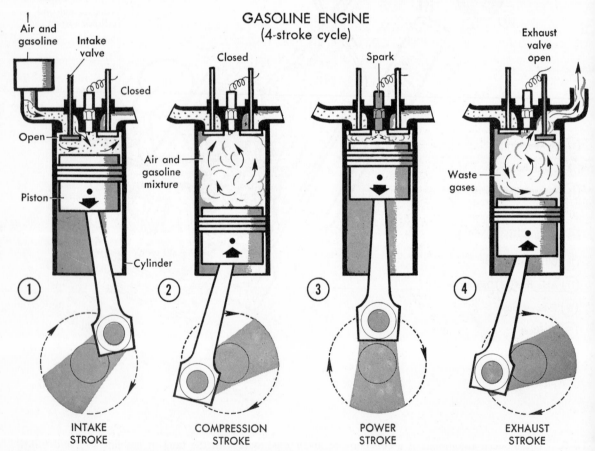

14-9. Modern automobile engines use the four-stroke cycle.

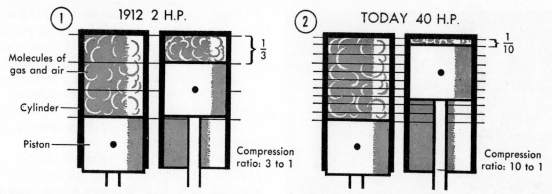

14-10. The more the fuel mixture is compressed, the more useful energy is produced.

Oddly enough, the way to make gasoline engines still more efficient has been known to engineers for over 75 years. All that time engineers knew that the greater the pressure of the fuel/air mixture in the cylinder just before it was exploded, the higher the efficiency of the engine. In other words, the more the compression stroke of the piston squeezed the fuel mixture, the greater the kicking energy of the burning, expanding gas (Fig. 14-10).

But as you might guess, getting this *high compression* raises some tough practical problems, such as making pistons and valves fit perfectly in cylinders. Also when the pressure on a gas is suddenly increased by a piston, the gas gets hot — as you may have noticed when pumping up a bicycle tire. Indeed, under high compression the fuel mixture gets hot enough to explode before the spark ignites it. Such badly timed explosions are what make engines " knock." Perhaps you have heard the " ping, ping, ping " sound of a knocking engine as your car starts up a hill. Chemists had to develop a gasoline that could be highly compressed without exploding too soon. Today you buy it at filling stations under the name of " high-octane " gasoline. When your engine is properly adjusted to use it, high-octane gasoline makes your engine more efficient, and gives you more miles to the gallon.

Using high-octane gasoline, today's auto engines may work at a compression ratio of about 10 to 1 — that is, the fuel/air mixture is squeezed by the piston into one-tenth of the space it had on

entering the cylinder. (Back in 1912 auto engines had a compression ratio of around 3 to 1.) But if engineers can reach the still higher compression ratio, say, of 12 to 1, then a greater efficiency will result. What is the compression ratio of the engine in your family car?

It may well be that the gasoline piston engine of the future will be smaller, lighter, and more efficient. It is not likely, however, that anything bigger and more powerful than the 14-cylinder, 3500 horsepower giant shown in Fig. 14-11 will be built.

Still Higher Compression: Diesel Engines

Highly compressed air in an engine cylinder can get hot enough to explode the fuel too soon. Rudolf Diesel — a German engineer — considered this fact and wondered if he could take advantage of it. If he could only make the hot gas explode all by itself at the proper moment in the cycle, perhaps an engine could be made to run without spark plugs.

His first engine blew up; but Diesel survived, and eventually worked out the scheme used in diesel engines all over the world. First, air alone enters the cylinder. It is compressed to about one-eighteenth of its former volume, and its temperature soars — to around 1000° F. Next, the fuel is squirted into the cylinder. It burns on contact with the hot air. The burning expanding gases deliver the power stroke of the familiar four-stroke cycle (Fig. 14-12).

Not only does the diesel engine have an effi-

14-11. Gasoline piston engines probably will not get much more powerful than this 3500-horsepower model. Do you know why?

ciency as high as 40 per cent, with its high compression ratio of 18 to 1, it burns low-cost fuel oil which won't ignite at much lower compression ratios. On the other hand, its very high compression ratio and the high pressure needed to force the fuel oil into the cylinder require rugged, heavy construction. This, plus the large starting motor needed to get high compression, makes it considerably heavier than gasoline engines of equal power. Diesel engines are used in ships, trucks, tractors, and other power installations where the weight of the engine is not very important. (Because the price of coal has gone up and the efficiency of the steam locomotive has not, the diesel locomotive is replacing it.)

Piston Limit

The giant piston engine in Fig. 14-11 may be the biggest that will ever be built. To understand why, put your hand near any running piston engine. What do you feel? Vibration and heat are signs of wasted energy.

Inside the cylinders, the pistons are flashing up and down. As each piston suddenly changes its direction of motion it shakes the whole engine. In doing so it uses up energy to no good purpose. Moreover, each explosion in the cylinders shakes the engine. In fact, energy is being produced in a series of separate kicks, not in a smooth continuous flow. Only by using several cylinders, by careful timing of the explosions, and by ingenious balancing of moving parts, can engineers make a piston engine deliver smooth power.

However, as the piston engine has become more powerful and efficient, a limit has appeared. Beyond this limit, fresh designing efforts, improvements, and refinements will not give very much more power and efficiency — not enough of it, at any rate, to make the efforts worthwhile. The engine in Fig. 14-11 has just about reached the power limit of the piston type. This does not mean that the piston engine has no future, for more uses and new uses as well as new engines will certainly continue to appear. But it looks as if the piston engine's growth in sheer power has stopped. The piston engine is what the social scientist calls a " mature invention."

Moreover, a different sort of heat engine has appeared recently. It is a rival of great promise — a young squirt, in fact.

JET ENGINES

The first time you hear the tearing sound of a jet plane as it rips across the sky you don't have to be told that you're hearing a new voice in the chorus of man's machines.

Amid the muffled roar of gasoline and diesel engines, the whine of steam turbines, the hum of electric motors, and the puffing of steam engines, the voice of the jet engine is just beginning to be heard. But it is getting louder. You need no crystal ball to see that this howl of power has a future. To glimpse that future — on land and sea as well as in the air — you need to see how the jet engine works, and how it is being improved month by month by teams of physicists, chemists, metallurgists, ceramicists, mathematicians, and assorted engineers.

DIESEL ENGINE

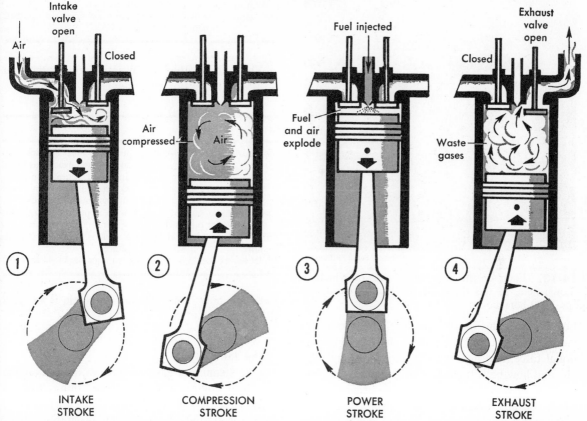

① INTAKE STROKE — Intake valve open, Air, Closed

② COMPRESSION STROKE — Air compressed, Air

③ POWER STROKE — Fuel injected, Fuel and air explode

④ EXHAUST STROKE — Exhaust valve open, Closed, Waste gases

14-12. The diesel engine is very much like the gasoline engine shown in Fig. 14-9. But what ignites the fuel for the power stroke?

Kicking Yourself Backwards: Action (Force) and Reaction (Equal and Opposite Force)

The jet engine works on a very simple principle. If you happen to be sitting in a sturdy chair that can slide across the floor fairly easily, you can demonstrate the principle of jet propulsion right now.

Put the chair on a clear space on the floor. Sit on it. Lift your feet off the floor, knees bent. Now kick your feet away, sharply and straight out. Your chair — and you — will slide backwards. Only a little, to be sure. But it does move. Why?

What did you kick against? Not air, certainly, for air is too thin for you to push against it very hard.

This curious force that pushes you and your chair back an inch or two is the very same kind of force that pushes a jet plane through the air. What is this mysterious push?

The backward push you have just experimented with was first explained by a shy scholarly Englishman, Isaac Newton, over 200 years ago. He was not thinking of jet planes. He was wondering about what made the moon or a falling apple or a cannon ball or a planet move in its particular path.

Newton's Third Law

One result of his thinking was his three Laws of Motion. Newton's Laws of Motion describe the way objects move when forces push against them.

Santa Fe Railway

14-13. Each of the four units, one of which is shown here, of this diesel-electric locomotive develops 1500 horsepower.

For instance his laws describe how the earth moves as a result of the pull of the sun's gravitational force, and how a bullet moves through the air, and how balls bounce after colliding with one another, or why it is hard to turn a corner sharply when you are traveling at high speed.

Newton's Third Law of Motion concerns any two bodies that exert forces on each other. It states that *for every action there will be an equal and oppositely directed reaction.* This is why your chair (and the jet plane) jump.

Action: you push your feet away from you.
Reaction: your feet push you and the chair in the opposite direction.

You can see this law in action all around you — if you look. For example:

Action	Reaction
You push against the wall	The wall pushes backward against you exactly as hard. In fact if you are on roller skates this reaction force moves you backwards.
Lawn sprinkler nozzle throws water outward	Nozzle is pushed away from water, and revolves.
Girl steps from rowboat to shore	Rowboat is pushed away from shore.
Bullet leaves gun	Gun jumps back — "kicks."

Let's see now how Newton's principle is used in the jet engine.

The Jet Engine

Like steam and gasoline engines, the jet engine is a heat engine. The same basic things happen in all three. A gas is compressed and then heated, so that it expands. Let's see how these things happen in a jet engine.

Air enters the long tube in Fig. 14-15. It is immediately crammed into a small space by the high-speed fan called the *compressor*. Next, fuel

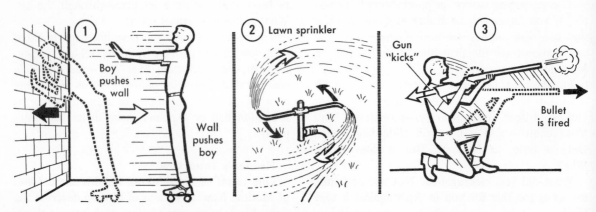

14-14. How does each of these drawings illustrate Newton's Third Law of Motion?

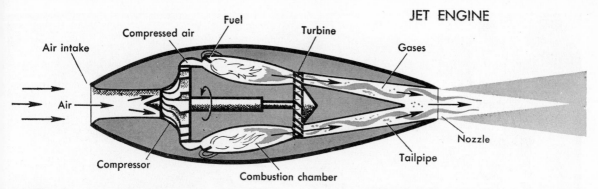

Air intake

Air

Compressor

Compressed air

Fuel

Turbine

Combustion chamber

Gases

Tailpipe

Nozzle

14-15. In a jet engine, the hot gases that push out of the rear of the engine drive the plane forward. What are some advantages of jet propulsion?

is squirted into the compressed air, and ignited. Heated by the burning fuel, air molecules dance about, bustling with heat energy. They cannot get out by the way they came in because the compressor is hard at work there, blocking that end of the tube. But the other end of the tube, the *tailpipe,* is open. There air molecules roar out at tremendous speed — as fast as 3600 miles per hour. As they drive out to the rear (action), the engine is driven forward (reaction), much as you kicked yourself along in your sliding chair.

On the way out, the flaming gas molecules give up a little of their energy to spin the fan — called a *turbine* — that spins the compressor. This kind of engine is called a *turbojet.*

Since this compression, heating, and expansion go on continuously, a steady flow of smooth power pours from the jet tailpipe. There are no separate explosions of energy to be smoothed over by a heavy flywheel, as in the piston engine, and no thumping pistons to set up vibrations.

Why are jet engines worth all the tremendous scientific, engineering, and business effort that is now being made to improve them? One answer is that they can develop more power for their size and weight than any other engine in sight. In other words, man's quest for power is still in full swing. Another important reason is that the jet engine has special advantages for aircraft uses. It can work in thin air at high altitudes, where propellers lose their grip, and gasoline-driven piston engines gasp and die for lack of air.

Performance

The principle of the jet engine is quite simple. Building large numbers of dependable jet motors, however, is quite a difficult job.

What it means to put Newton's Third Law of Motion into practical form is shown in Fig. 14-16. That jet motor — or " jet " for short — shown in the picture can exert a force of 10,000 pounds. At a speed of 375 miles per hour, this is equal to 10,000 horsepower, and even more at higher speed.[1] At cruising speed this jet gulps down about 7000 pounds of fuel in an hour. Compare this amount with your family automobile engine that uses about 20 pounds of fuel per hour, when cruising at 45 miles per hour. Even though the jet can use low-cost kerosene, its high fuel consumption is a drawback. Engineers are trying hard to find other ways of feeding this hungry monster or reducing its appetite.

At cruising speed the compressor and turbine of the engine in Fig. 14-15 spin at about 6100 turns per minute. At this speed the compressor stuffs 20 cubic feet of air into one cubic foot of space inside the combustion chamber — a compression ratio of 20 to 1. Kerosene squirted into this compressed air burns violently, and even at cruising speed the hot burning gases roar out of the tailpipe at a speed much faster than that of a

[1] One pound of thrust is equal to one horsepower at 375 miles per hour. Can you see how this follows from the definition: one horsepower = 33,000 foot-pounds per minute?

14-16. This shows what engineers have done with the jet-engine principle shown in Fig. 14-15.

bullet. Spinning in this man-made volcano at 1200° F. the turbine blades are prevented from disintegrating by cooling air flowing inside them. The whole turbojet engine weighs about a ton; but this is only about one-quarter the weight of a piston engine of the same output.

The Windmill of the Future

The future of the jet engine is not only up in the sky driving airplanes. With a few small changes, jet engines can be made to do many other jobs.

The turbine in the airplane jet engine is de-signed to take from the stream of hot gases only as much energy as is needed to spin the compressor. All the rest of the energy streams back out the tailpipe to thrust the airplane ahead. But suppose we design the turbine to capture *all* possible energy from the jet stream? Then the power of the jet can be harnessed to spin the turbine shaft and anything connected to it. We would have a new kind of engine that could turn factory wheels, drive cars and locomotives, or spin electric generators. Connected to an airplane propeller, this engine is called a *turboprop engine* (Fig. 14-17).

Would this kind of power be better in any way

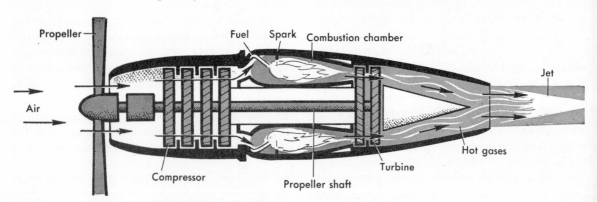

14-17. How is the turboprop engine different from the turbojet engine?

than the more familiar engines we already have? When we add up fuel consumption, engine weight, efficiency, cost of manufacture, and all the other matters that engineers and businessmen must consider, the answer is yes. In fact, the future for this *gas turbine engine* looks very bright. It looks as if it could be made to produce great power for its weight and still be inexpensive to run. You may expect to hear more news of this promising new power-producer during the next few years as swiftly spinning turbine shafts are connected to pumps, propellers, electric generators, helicopter motors, and even automobile driveshafts.

Fire in a Stovepipe

There is an even simpler kind of jet engine than the one we began with on page 170. It is hardly more than a fire burning in a length of stovepipe. But unlike most engines, which must start before they can move, this kind must be moving before it can start!

The air entering any jet engine must be compressed, of course. The more compressed it is, the better. In the jet engine we have been describing, this job is done by the compressor and its turbine, an expensive and precise piece of hardware. But the *ram-jet engine* has no compressor and no turbine (Fig. 14-18). Air is compressed in a very simple way — just by pushing the engine swiftly through the air.

As the ram-jet engine moves, air is being rammed down its throat. Since the throat narrows, the air is compressed. Then — as in the gas turbine — fuel is squirted into the compressed air

Fairchild Engine & Airplane Corp.

14-19. A ram-jet engine at the tip of each rotor blade powers these helicopters.

and ignited. Tremendous expansion takes place, and the flaming gases roar out the tailpipe because the rammed air entering the tube prevents them from going out the front way. Lacking a compressor and turbine, the ram-jet engine is light, simple, and powerful. But it is not very efficient, for there is a limit to the compression ratio that can be reached by ramming. Just the same, a bright future is certainly ahead of it.

The helicopter in Fig. 14-19, for instance, has a small ram jet at the tip of each rotor blade — a very convenient way to spin a rotor. To start the ram jets, an extra motor spins the rotor until its blades are moving fast enough for the ram effect to take hold; then the ignition sparks are turned on and the ram-jet engines take over.

ROCKET ENGINES

Have you ever watched a Fourth of July rocket suddenly soar with a hiss up into the night sky, leaving a trail of sparks behind it? Rockets like it have already gone farther away from this earth than any other kind of engine. Rockets are cer-

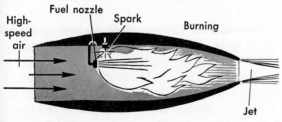

RAM-JET, or "Flying Stovepipe"

High-speed air

Fuel nozzle

Spark

Burning

Jet

14-18. At last a simple engine: the ram-jet. Fire in a stovepipe!

tain to soar still further into the incredible cold and silence of interplanetary space.

Rockets and Jets

The rocket is a jet engine with an important difference. It doesn't need to take in air as the jet engine does. It carries its own air supply. More accurately speaking, it carries its own oxygen which is, as you know, the part of the air that engines need to support the burning of their fuel. The rocket may carry its oxygen supply either in pure liquid form, or bound up in some chemical combination with other elements. In any case, no air compressor or ramming is required.

Hence the rocket engine is as self-sufficient as an engine can be. When it comes to space travel, for instance, the rocket engine has no competition. There is no air in space. Other engines, needing air to breathe (like the turbojet) or even air to grip (with a propeller), have to stay near the ground where there is plenty of air. But rocket engines carrying their own oxygen supply thrive in the airless reaches above our atmosphere. Kicking themselves along by spitting high-speed streams of exhaust gases out behind them, rockets move most easily up where there is little or no air resistance.

Big Kick

Moreover when it comes to sheer *power,* the rocket leaves all other engines far behind. The engine in Fig. 14-20, for example, develops about 600,000 horsepower.

It is true that it pours out this appalling number of foot-pounds per second for a brief time only — in a matter of minutes. It is also true that it squirts such a roaring, flaming inferno of heat from its tail that it is inconvenient to have around, and not easy to control. It wears out very quickly, too. Like a Fourth of July skyrocket, once used it has little trade-in value. But when you need sheer power, such as for getting away from this earth into space, here is where you will find it. As in any jet engine, the driving force is produced as the engine forces molecules out from its tailpipe in one direction (action) and is forced at the same time in the opposite direction (reaction).

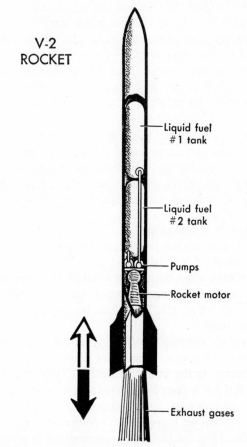

V-2 ROCKET

Liquid fuel #1 tank

Liquid fuel #2 tank

Pumps

Rocket motor

Exhaust gases

14-20. A rocket engine: tops for sheer power and independence.

The rocket engine's future is not all out in cold space, however. Simpler models — more closely related to that Fourth of July model than the one shown here — have plenty to do on earth in spite of the unnecessary air surrounding them. Rockets are already assisting heavy-laden planes to take off, and starting turbojet and ram-jet motors.

Although the Chinese made rockets centuries ago, it is the development of the molecular theory of heat and the pioneering rocket experiments by an American, Robert H. Goddard, that started this type of jet engine on the way to practical use.

There is another important engine in our quest for power. It is not a heat engine — like the gasoline motor, the steam engine, or the turbojet. Nor does it use a fluid, like steam or water or hot gases, to create its driving force. It differs so remarkably from every other engine or power-producing machine that it — and the stuff it runs on — needs a whole unit in this book to describe it properly. It is the electric motor.

HARNESSED LIGHTING

We shall deal with electricity in Unit 7. Here we will only mention the electric motor, to complete our list of power-producing machines. Unlike most power-producing machines, electric motors come in a great range of sizes, from a tiny fraction of a horsepower (as an electric clock motor) to as much as 20,000 horsepower (for driving a wind tunnel fan). They are efficient, clean, make little noise, and give off little heat. Although the fuel energy, electricity, must be specially produced by an expensive and elaborate plant, it is easy to send electricity over wires to drive motors many miles away from the power plant. These special features and advantages of the electric motor have had a good deal to do with making the world you live in different from the one your grandfathers and grandmothers lived in — so different that they would have a hard time recognizing it. But more about the electric motor later.

More Power — to You

In Revolutionary days the power supply outside of a man's own muscles — or a woman's, for that matter — was to be found only in horses, donkeys, oxen, water wheels, and a few steam engines. If this meager power supply had been equally divided among all the citizens of early America, each person would have had about $\frac{1}{33}$ of a horsepower for his share — about one small dogpower, you might say.

But in 1959 our engines and turbines turned out 500 billion horsepower. And as you look at the graph in Fig. 14-21, you will see that our power supply is rising steadily. What does this graph have to say about the world you and your

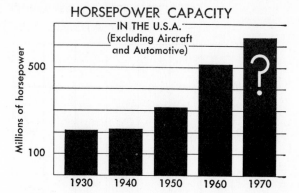

14-21. More power to you — and your children. Can you glimpse the future with this graph?

children will live in? More power to *you!*

Forty-five per cent of the world's horsepower was developed in America, which has only *seven* per cent of all the world's people. In many parts of the world, even as you read this, donkeys are still trudging in dusty circles around millstones; men are still stepping tiredly, slowly on the spokes of water-lifting wheels; women are pounding a little grain into flour, with clubs; children are searching for fuel for tomorrow's fire. All over the world millions of people still live today much as your forefathers did in 1776, for lack of power and machines.

Fuel

All engines need fuel. Coal, oil, natural gas, and water are the most important fuels that drive our engines. Fig. 14-22 shows how much of each fuel we have used up in the past, and how much we are likely to need in our future.

You can see that there are limits to our fuel reserves. New reserves are being found all the time, and new and more efficient ways of getting and using fuels are being invented. But the earth's resources are not inexhaustible; and we are using up our fuel reserves faster and faster.

We would be very foolish to burn up our coal. gas, oil — or even atoms — without giving a thought to conserving our supplies. If the world's enormous needs for fuel are to be met, we shall need all our resources, and need to use them carefully and wisely. The problems of conserving the

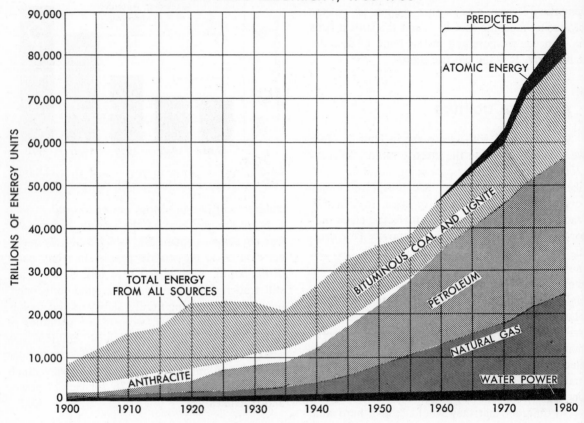

ENERGY SUPPLIED BY MINERAL FUELS, WATER POWER, AND ATOMIC ELECTRICITY, 1900-1980

14-22. Do we have enough fuel for our power needs? Look to the future!

world's fuel resources — protecting and using them efficiently, with an eye to the future — will have to be solved by engineers, scientists, and citizens like yourself, if our power-producing engines are to keep on running.

Engines of the Future

Atomic power — as described in Chapter 9 — has opened up a new source of energy which will be used more and more as a source of heat to drive various kinds of heat engines. It is also possible that out of the energy released from the atom new kinds of engines will appear — for instance, one that produces electric power directly from splitting and uniting atoms.

There is, however, an even more inviting pow-

er prospect, some scientists and engineers say. Any insignificant blade of growing green grass is turning the energy of the sun's rays directly into useful energy. Why can't man capture the energy of sunlight directly? The idea of using the energy of sunlight directly, instead of getting it at second or third hand out of coal, oil, natural gas, and water, is the more tantalizing because the sun pours 126 trillion horsepower on the earth — free of charge. Under good conditions each square yard of sunlit earth receives almost one horsepower of solar energy.

So far, attempts to change solar energy into heat or mechanical energy have failed to develop very efficient engines (Fig. 14-23). However, solar energy has successfully been turned into electrical energy (Fig. 14-24). And, while you read this, solar batteries attached to space satellites convert sunlight into the electrical energy needed to operate space instruments.

The *solar battery* in Fig. 14-24 is turning the energy of the sun's rays into electric power in a different way — by way of a special chemical. While it develops only about 0.015 horsepower for each square foot of its surface, this is much more than the photocell in a photographer's exposure meter can produce. Perhaps the solar engine of the future here on earth will depend on such a device as this.

14-24. This solar power plant converts sunlight into electricity, to power telephones.

Looking Back . . . .

VOCABULARY

The following expressions are some of the key words in this chapter. Define each term.

1. turbine
2. internal combustion
3. caloric
4. molecular theory of heat
5. four-stroke cycle
6. carburetor
7. high compression
8. diesel engine
9. compressor
10. tailpipe
11. turbojet engine
12. ram-jet engine
13. gas turbine engine
14. rocket engine
15. solar battery
16. turboprop engine

EXPLAIN WHY
- It is difficult to build an efficient steam turbine.
- A rapidly spinning wheel tends to break and fly apart.

- Scientists believe that heat is a form of energy.
- Today's most efficient gasoline engines waste three fourths of the energy in the fuel.
- Diesel engines are used in trucks and ships but not in your family automobile.
- Jet engines are better than propellers for some aircraft uses.
- Rocket engines are the only known type of engine that will work in airless space.
- An internal-combustion engine, such as a gasoline engine, is more efficient than an external-combustion engine, such as the steam engine.
- Diesel engines do not need spark plugs.
- Sunlight is a very promising source of power.

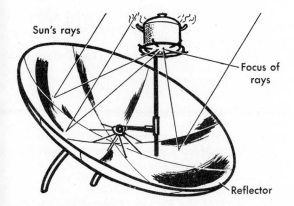

Sun's rays

Focus of rays

Reflector

14-23. This solar engine converts the sun's rays to heat for power.

Going Further . . . .

APPLYING PRINCIPLES
1. Show how the power of a jet of steam is harnessed by a turbine.
2. Try to build a model to explain how the four-stroke cycle works in an internal-combustion engine.

3. Describe the use of the following parts of a modern gasoline engine.

a) valves   e) lubricants
b) spark plugs   f) battery
c) carburetor   g) cooling system
d) radiator   h) drive shaft

4. Explain how the efficiency of a piston engine depends upon the compression ratio.
5. State Newton's Third Law of Motion and give several examples of its operation in everyday life.
6. Explain how Newton's Third Law of Motion is applied to the operation of jet engines and rockets.
7. Using simplified diagrams, explain the operation of turbojet, ram-jet, and rocket engines.
8. Make a list of all the kinds of engines you can. Beside each one write down the kind of fuel it uses. Beside each one write down the uses to which it is put.
9. Explain why it is important for us to conserve our world's supply of coal, oil, natural gas, and water.
10. Show how Newton's Third Law is illustrated in walking, jumping, rowing, driving a boat, accelerating a car, and flying an airplane.

THINGS TO DO

1. A balloon driven by rocket power. You can show the principle of a rocket ship using a toy balloon. Blow up a balloon and let go of it. The air is forced out of the open neck in one direction like the hot gases of a rocket engine. The action and reaction send the balloon flying in the opposite direction.

2. A jet-propelled automobile. Fasten a carbon dioxide or Jetex cartridge to a toy car to serve as a rocket motor. When the cartridge is punctured, the carbon dioxide is forced out the back at high speed. The action and reaction drive the car forward at speeds as great as 50 miles an hour. Be sure to have someone show you how to handle such a jet-propelled car properly before you try this demonstration.

TRY THESE

1. Explain why you find it hard to run on ice.
2. Explain why the rocket shown in Fig. 14-25 won't work. An explosive charge forces a heavy weight (W) down the tube (T) toward a shock-absorbing pad (P). The opposite force (recoil) sends the rocket ship forward. Then the weight is brought back slowly to the front end of the rocket and the process is repeated over and over again. What is wrong with this scheme?

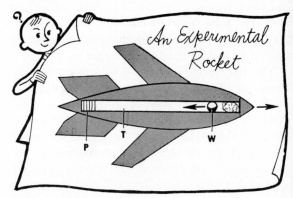

An Experimental Rocket

14-25. What is wrong with this design of a propelling mechanism for a rocket in space?

3. Why do large guns have a recoil mechanism that lets the gun move back several feet as it is fired?
4. Describe five changes that have occurred in our lives as a result of the development of engines in the past hundred years.

MORE THINGS TO DO

1. Make a model turbine as shown in Fig. 14-2. Don't omit the cork " safety valve "!
2. Bring a one-cylinder model airplane engine to class and explain its two-stroke cycle.
3. Demonstrate a Jetex engine as a form of jet or rocket propulsion.
4. One pound of thrust in a jet engine is equal to one horsepower, at 375 miles per hour speed. Can you see why this follows from the definition of one horsepower as 33,000 foot-pounds per minute? Clues: Change 375 miles per hour to feet per minute; how many foot-pounds of work are done by a pound of thrust force in a minute at this speed?

READING FURTHER

Model Jets and Rockets for Boys by Raymond Yates, Harper, 1952. Simple experiments clearly illustrated and described.

Science Looks Ahead by A. M. Low, Oxford University Press. In the section called " Power " special mention is made of the diesel engine.

Rockets, Jets, Guided Missiles, and Space Ships by J. Coggins and F. Pratt, Random House, 1951. Large exciting color pictures and cutaway drawings. An amazing story clearly and simply told.

Diesel, the Modern Power, General Motors Educational Service, Detroit, Michigan. An illustrated free booklet containing further details on this important source of power.

The Story of the Turbine, General Electric Co., Schenectady, New York. A pamphlet that explains the working of the steam turbine and its uses.

CHAPTER 15

Engines on Land and Sea

Before the first horseless carriage, sometime in the late 1800's, ways of traveling were very limited. Consider how the development of the automobile has changed our lives. It influences where we live, the food we eat, the places we visit, and the kind of people we are. Just think, in a little more than half a century all these changes have come about.

THE AUTOMOBILE

One day the head of an automobile manufacturing company walked into a room where his assistants were gathered, and made an announcement. It took them all by surprise.

"From now on," he said, "we are going to make just one kind of car."

They did. They called it "Model T." It was rugged, simple — it had no streamlined elegance, as you see in Fig. 15-1 — and cheap. By concentrating on this one model, by using mass-production methods, by picking first-rate men to do the job, and by being himself a fine engineer, Henry Ford, and his men, brought the Model T into the world.

Revolutionists

Doing so, they brought about a revolution.

They changed the idea that each car had to be a hand-made project. They showed that autos made in large quantities were cheaper to make and hence cheaper to buy.

They changed the people's idea that the automobile was a rich man's expensive toy into the idea that the auto was something the farmer, the

Ford Motor Co.

15-1. Henry Ford's famous Model T, an early example of which is shown here, caused a revolution in our way of living.

doctor, the merchant, the salesman, and a lot of other people needed and could afford.

Doing so, they changed the way people lived more drastically than the revolutionists of 1776.

Today there are more than 70,000,000 motor vehicles in the world. No wonder we can be referred to as a nation on wheels. The United States alone uses five out of every seven of the world's automobiles.

" Model T "

Here's how you ran a Model T.

You reached in over the door, and pulled down the *spark lever* (Fig. 15-2). This " retarded " the spark timing. (Some of the car-minded boys in class can explain what this means.) You pushed the *gas lever* down a few notches to give the engine some fuel.

Then you went around to the front of the car, and you cranked. " You " in this case means men only. It took a good strong arm. Women waited until the self-starter was invented.

You cranked. If you had forgotten to pull down the spark lever, however, the crank " kicked " back against your arm as a cylinder fired at the wrong time. It could break your arm. You wouldn't forget often to " retard the spark."

But if all went well, the engine started. You dropped the crank and dashed around to adjust the spark and gas levers before the engine stopped. Then you climbed in behind the steering wheel,

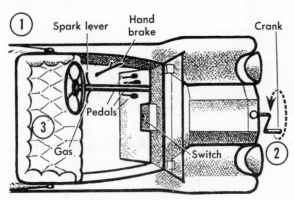

15-2. In starting the Model T, you almost had to be in two places at the same time: at the crank and at the gas lever.

and pushed the left-hand pedal down to the floor. You took a look, reached down and released the hand brake — and the car moved off, in low gear, for the hand brake worked the clutch. When you got up speed, you let up on the pedal and thus went into high gear. You were on your way.

Does this seem primitive in these days of automatic chokes and gearshifts, self-starters, and so forth? Consider the Model T's advantages. Mechanically it was wondrously simple. It could be kept in order by its owner. None of the adjustments that had to be made were difficult. Special tools were not needed. Parts were easy to get. You could, really, fix it yourself. And it was cheap enough to be within the reach of people who could *use* an automobile.

The Model T started us on automobile-buying. Today the auto industry is one of the largest in the land.

Before — and after — Ford

Henry Ford did not invent the automobile. No one man did. It is a collection of many inventions. But Ford first applied mass production methods to bring automobiles within reach. Before Ford were men like Benz and Daimler in Germany; like Panhard (pa-NAR) and Levassor (le-vah-SOHR) in France (where the good roads laid down for bicyclists were a help); like Todd and Napier in England (where laws that limited the appearance of these disturbing vehicles on the public roads were no help); like Duryea and Olds in this country (where inventors seemed to think that the more closely the new vehicle looked like the familiar carriage — without the horse — the better). These are just a few of the people who worked on the idea of the automobile.

You can see what their efforts led to in Fig. 15-3. If you are a good observer, you may be able to spot some of the important changes in design that eventually made autos what they are today. For instance, when did glass windows appear? When did the running board disappear? From what did the hood ornament on cars today evolve? By studying this illustration you may even be able to see the shape of things to come: the automo-

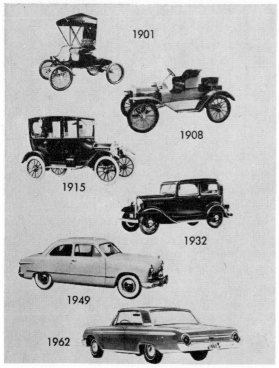

15-3. Can you imagine what the car of your future will be like?

bile of the future, for of course the evolution of the automobile is still going on.

After Ford — and with him — the auto industry grew at a tremendous rate. It brought together engineers, scientists, inventors, designers, artists, businessmen, workers. It demanded steel, rubber, glass, and a thousand other things; then it demanded a new kind of steel, a different kind of rubber, a new sort of glass, and ten thousand other things including better understanding of how these things could be made cheaply and in large quantities. Research and development went ahead too.

TODAY'S CAR

Let's look at some of the important features of today's automobiles — features that shape the car you see today — and the kind of car you will see in your future.

Fluid Drive

It used to be that when you saw a car start off in a series of rabbit-like jumps, you were fairly sure that someone was learning to drive — and having trouble with the *clutch pedal*. Since that pedal controls the connection between the running engine and the stationary rear wheels, it has to be eased up smoothly and gently. Then the transfer of energy from engine to wheels will increase gradually and the car will start off smoothly. It usually took the learner a little time to get the knack of using the clutch pedal. Meanwhile the car started with a hop.

Many people learning to drive today never see a clutch pedal at all. In many car models the clutch has disappeared. It is giving way to *fluid drive* (sometimes called *fluid flywheel* or *hydraulic coupling*).

If you place two electric fans so that they face each other (as in Fig. 15-4) and start one turning very slowly, the blades of the other fan will not move — at first. But if you speed up the first fan a bit, its air stream will begin to turn the second fan. Energy is being transferred. And as you continue to speed up the *driving* fan, the *driven* fan turns faster, too. But you may be able to notice that its blades never spin quite as fast as those of the driving fan.

Here we have energy transferred from one

15-4. Fluid drive in principle: the flow from one fan spins the other. But what about efficiency?

FLUID DRIVE

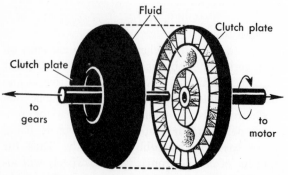

15-5. Fluid drive in practice: oil is the fluid used to transfer energy, and the efficiency is good, thanks to untold man-hours of engineering.

place to another, the first fan driving the second, by means of a fluid — air. This is fluid drive. *Disadvantage:* there is some loss of energy during transfer. *Advantage:* the transfer of energy is smooth, not jerky.

The same sort of thing happens in the fluid-drive unit shown in Fig. 15-5. The fluid-drive unit transfers energy from the engine to the rear wheels. It does this in a rather complex way, as you can see, but the principle is the same. Oil is used as the energy-transferring fluid, instead of air (which is too compressible).

The spinning blades are cleverly designed. The driving blade set forces maximum energy into the oil flow, and the driven set takes as much energy as possible from the oil flow. (If it occurs to you that this might be called a turbine, you are right.) Both sets of blades are sealed in a case that is shaped to allow the oil to circulate from driving blades to driven blades and back to driving blades with the least loss to friction.

Can you now imagine what happens when you start a car with fluid drive? As the engine turns over, the driving blades begin to spin. The oil between the blades is thrown against the driven blades, but does not have enough force to move them yet — the car is still at rest. You give the engine more gas. As it speeds up, the driving blades spin faster, and the oil is thrust with more force against the driven blades. As that force becomes great enough to overcome the inertia and

friction of the car at rest, the car begins to move smoothly.

There is always some "slip" between the two sets of blades. The driven blades run more slowly than the drivers. However, at ordinary driving speeds the loss of power may be as little as one per cent.

Torque Converter

With even more complex design, the fluid drive becomes what is called a *torque* (TORK) *converter* (Fig. 15-6). *Torque* is the technical word that describes the tendency to cause rotation.

A running automobile engine produces a twist — nothing more. It is this twist, carried to the rear wheels by gears and shafts, that makes the wheels turn and the car move. Fluid drive simply passes along smoothly the twist produced by the running engine. But the torque converter is able to change or convert that twist while passing it along to the rear wheels. It is able to convert the force in the twist to the most convenient size for the work to be done, just as you do when you shift gears.

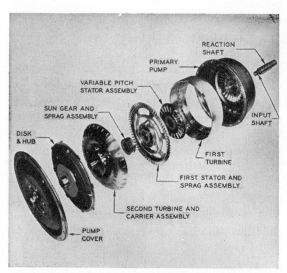

General Motors Corp., Buick Division

15-6. Still more complex is the torque converter. Its many parts fit into the "primary pump" case; they combine the advantages of fluid drive with variable force to rear wheels.

Does this idea of changing a force to a more useful size sound familiar? If you'll glance back at pages 136–37, you will see why. The job of the first simple machine there — the lever — was to convert the force of the hand in Fig. 12-1 to a size that would conveniently lift the lid off the paint can. Like that lever, the torque converter combines force conversion and transfer of energy in one package.

To get some idea of how a torque converter works, set up the two fans again, as in Fig. 15-4. This time, though, imagine that the blades of the second fan — the driven one — can be turned at any angle to the air stream. If the blades are set edge-on to the air stream, the fan won't turn at all, of course. But as the angle of the blades to the rushing stream of air is increased, the fan will begin to turn. Will it turn more slowly or more quickly as the angle of the blade is increased? Will the strength of the twist of the fan grow?

The torque converter takes the place of some of the gears, doing their job at the cost of some loss in efficiency but with far more convenience to the driver. Can gears be done away with entirely? Not quite. The torque converter operates with lower efficiency at high speed. Therefore, a combination of gears, fluid drive, and torque conversion is used, with each carrying energy to the rear wheels of the car when it can do so most efficiently.

Power Steering and Power Brakes

Power steering, as you know, takes most of the work out of steering a car. "Work" is the right word, too, because power steering actually reduces the foot-pounds of work the driver does in turning the steering wheel.

Here's how it's done. The long-used mechanical steering system simply converts your work in turning the steering wheel into a force turning the front wheels through some distance. As with any simple machine or combination of simple machines, the work done depends on how much work you put in, with something lost to friction of course.

But power steering lets the driver draw on a supply of energy that can do the work of turning the front wheels for him. This energy is stored, ready for action, in the form of oil under pressure. By this arrangement the stored-up energy can be released by the driver to do the work of turning the front wheels. All the work the driver has to do is the small amount needed to control the release of this stored energy. Released, it becomes power; hence this is called *power steering*.

What if the power-steering system should fail somehow? It is so designed that it becomes a mechanical-steering system at once, so that the driver still has control of the car. The power-steering system "fails safe," as engineers say.

Where does the stored energy come from? A pump attached to the engine builds up the supply of energy in the form of oil pressure.

The same plan is used in power brakes. Large trucks and buses have had power brakes for years. The brake-operating energy is stored as compressed air, usually. One of the most important instruments on the panel under the eyes of the truck or bus driver is the air pressure gauge. It tells him that the air supply for working the brakes is up to the necessary pressure. Since ordinary automobile power brakes are designed to "fail safe" — like power steering — no pressure gauge is supplied.

Can you see why this power-controlling idea used in power steering and power brakes is important? It means that the driver has less work to do. But it means even more than that. Car designers are no longer limited in their plans by the amount of work the driver can do, personally, on the brake pedal or the steering wheel. With these powered controls, cars can be made bigger and heavier. Can you think of other possible developments?

Automatic Gearshifts or Transmissions

Of all the machinery collected in today's cars, the *automatic gearshift* is a very high point in engineering skill. It is a very complicated machine.

As you know, an automatic gearshift or transmission shifts gears without help from the driver. Note the word "automatic." It means "self-

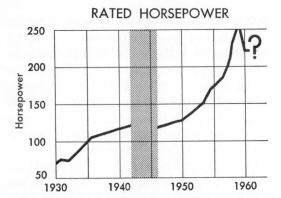

RATED HORSEPOWER

15-7. Look to the future: what's happening to auto-engine power? (The shaded area represents the war years when production was interrupted.)

acting, self-regulating," according to the dictionary. You will find the word turning up more and more often in this book. In fact, you will probably find it turning up more and more often in your life.

Note what has happened: an automatic machine has entered the automobile. It has taken off the driver's hands what used to be an important part of his job.

Radar-controlled brakes are being tested. How automatic do you think the automobile can get?

High compression-ratio engine, fluid drive, torque converter, and automatic transmission are just a few of the new developments in today's cars.

As a result today's cars
— require less work to drive,
— are more automatic,
— and more complex.

The auto mechanic's shelf of service manuals gets longer year by year.

CHANGE

With new features added to the automobile almost yearly, the auto is changing under your very eyes. It is changing in appearance, in performance, in materials, in what it's used for. There are no signs that such changes are slowing down, either. The auto is going right on changing.

What will the car of your future be like?

Car of the Future

Look at the "changing auto" in Fig. 15-3 again. Can you imagine what pictures will be added to it ten or twenty years from now? Can you glimpse the car of the future? Let's try by stretching the following graphs into the future.

Power is important in an automobile. It is one of the factors that influence design (Duryea's first self-propelled buggy had a two-horsepower engine). Fig. 15-7 shows, in a graph, the average horsepower of automobile engines from 1930 to 1960. To bring the graph up to the minute, you may get the latest power figures from auto dealers. What is the trend in engine power? Can it go on, into the future, as it has been going? What effect can the invention of the gas turbine have on auto engines? Are there other factors that may affect this power trend besides technical and engineering ones?

Speed affects automobile design. Fig. 15-8 graphs maximum car speeds. What is the trend here? — increasing speed.

Economy — measured in miles per gallon — is another important feature, graphed in Fig. 15-9. What do you predict for the car of the future in economy? Are other trends in power and speed working with this one or against it?

These are but a few of many trends in automobile development. Watch for new inventions and

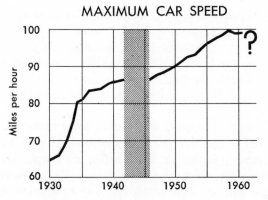

MAXIMUM CAR SPEED

15-8. Look to the future: what will auto speeds be like 20 years from now?

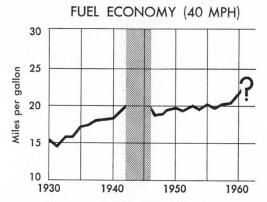

FUEL ECONOMY (40 MPH)

15-9. Are power and speed trends working with or against the automobile economy trend?

technical developments, and you will see the cars of the future taking shape.

The Changing Auto — and the Changing World You Live In

What Fig. 15-3 — "the changing auto" — does *not* show is what happened to America as a result of the development of the automobile. Here are some of the results: more roads becoming highways and superhighways; more and bigger trucks, helping to carry the country's goods; more and bigger buses; more cars. All these help to tie together farms, towns, villages, and cities into "one nation, indivisible."

More gas stations, more auto factories, more auto parts factories; more oil and gasoline, more refineries. More oil wells. More rubber. More metal. More drive-ins. All these help to create more jobs and provide a living for more people.

More people going places. More policemen. More laws. More lawbreakers. More accidents.

Are Drivers Developing?

The automobile is being improved, as you have seen. Are drivers improving too?

Anthropologists say that the human brain hasn't changed in design since the time of the cave man. This fact poses problems for auto designers, accident ward surgeons, pedestrians, and all others connected with the automobile.

But until the coming of the completely auto-

matic car — into which you will step, perhaps, and simply say, "Take me to the shopping center," and watch a television program until you are automatically ejected at the stores — until then we have to do the best driving we can, with our old-model brains. Meanwhile the auto is still developing.

A "NATION ON WHEELS"

Now let's look at some other important applications of the internal-combustion engine — uses that are changing still further the way we live. Nearly four-fifths of all power used in the United States comes from internal-combustion engines in the automobile, truck, bus, ship, and tractor.

Buses and Trucks

At the moment you are reading these words, a good part of our population is on the move, by one means or another. Buses carry a large share of these restless citizens — to town, to school, to the other end of the country, to work and play. Buses have changed and developed too.

Today's model bus is 40 feet long and weighs, loaded, 40,000 pounds. Two four-cylinder, 150 horsepower diesel engines push all this as fast as 75 miles per hour — and drive two air compressors (for power braking), air-conditioning apparatus, a power-steering pump, and a large electric generator besides.

A trailer truck is also diesel powered. It may carry a small gasoline engine on the trailer for refrigeration power. This means, for example, that there is very little time and money lost between the freezing of fresh fish and vegetables and their appearance in your local supermarket. The diesel engine develops 150 horsepower. Compared with a passenger automobile's power, for a much smaller load, this may seem surprisingly small. But remember that much of the passenger car's power is not used most of the time.

Tractors

Fifty years ago one farmer produced enough to feed about seven people besides himself and his

Caterpillar Tractor Co.

15-10. Do you know why a diesel engine is used in this tractor, but not in a pleasure car?

family. Today he can produce enough for about twenty people. A good part of this increase is due to tractor power, which started off with a gigantic and inefficient steam engine. The diesel-powered modern tractor in Fig. 15-10 is many times more efficient, more powerful — and more reliable.

Locomotives

Why is the picturesque steam locomotive fading out of sight? Because the efficiency of the oil-burning diesel locomotive is much greater. Each unit in Fig. 14-13 has a 1500 horsepower engine which drives an electric generator, which powers compact electric motors in the engine "trucks." The reason for this triple-play — diesel to generator to motor — is that electrical power is more easily regulated than mechanical. But the fluid drive used in cars is making for changes here, too. Already, in European diesels, the smooth transfer of energy by fluid drive is replacing the generator and motor links.

Construction Machinery

The earth mover and power shovel in Fig. 12-10 use — again — diesel engines, since rugged but heavy structure is no disadvantage in such

machines. The power shovel can move more earth in one day than a large gang of workmen could move in one week. Note here (as well as in the other machines shown) the combination of simple machines — levers, pulleys, and wheel and a... for example.

Ships

The tugboat shown in Fig. 15-11 is a tractor, and uses a diesel engine of ... power. Gears reduce the speed of the crankshaft to the best propeller speed. Like tractors, tugs are not designed for speed but for force.

The vessel shown in Fig. 15-12 is an internal-combustion engine powered ship. Its diesel engines develop 21,000 horsepower.

Doing Our Work with Engines

In this chapter we have seen a few of the most important applications of a major energy converter — the internal-combustion engine. On land and sea we count on it to do the world's work.

But man and his engines are not bound to land and sea — they also fly. In the next chapter we look at engines in the air — and beyond.

Standard Oil Co. (N.J.)

15-11. Harbor tugboats must be powerful enough to tow large ocean liners and freight barges into port.

Official U.S. Navy Photograph

15-12. The engines of this specially designed vessel are so powerful that it can force its way through ice.

Looking Back . . . .

VOCABULARY

The following expressions are some of the key words in this chapter. What is the meaning of each?

1. fluid drive
2. torque converter
3. hydraulic coupling
4. power steering
5. automatic gearshift
6. power brakes
7. transmission

EXPLAIN WHY:

- Fluid drive delivers smooth power.
- The Model T was a great success.
- No one man is the inventor of the automobile.
- The invention of the self-starter made women drivers.
- The auto industry uses scientists and research.
- Oil is better than air for transferring energy in a fluid drive.
- The torque converter differs from fluid drive.
- Power steering is desirable.
- Power steering must " fail safe."
- The air pressure gauge on the panel in front of the bus or truck driver is very important.
- The automatic gearshift means less work for the driver.
- Cars are getting more complex.

- Car design changes.
- Good drivers are important.
- Diesel engines are used in trucks, buses, and ships.

Going Further . . . .

THINGS TO DO

1. Draw your impression of how an automobile of the future might look. Use what you know about present trends in power, size, speed, etc., needed improvements and safety devices, along with imagination. The car of your future will surely be different from today's car. What will it be like? Perhaps you will want to make a model of it.

2. Find out from an experienced automobile mechanic how cars have changed from his point of view.

3. Interview an experienced police officer as to how car drivers have changed — if they have — over the years. Ask how the automobile has affected the policeman's job. What does he think of today's trends in automobile design?

4. Make a large (poster-size) diagram of a bus (or some other internal-combustion-engined machine) that you use. Show the location of engine, controls, etc. Note horsepower, fuel, fuel consumption, and so forth.

5. Interview the driver of a large truck. How far does he travel? What sort of engine is used? How much does the truck carry? What is the fuel consumption, mileage? How often does the engine need an overhaul? What are the driving conditions and problems?

READING FURTHER

A Power Primer, General Motors Educational Service, Detroit, Michigan. An excellent free booklet, clearly and colorfully illustrated, explaining the working of internal-combustion engines.

Power Goes To Work, another General Motors Educational Service Booklet you can get free. It shows how gears, transmissions, propellers work in cars, boats, and planes.

Write to the American Trucking Association, 1424 Sixteenth Street, Washington 5, D.C., for a list of free publications on trucks, and to the Automobile Manufacturers Association, Detroit, Michigan, for information on autos.

Machines That Built America by Roger Burlingame, Harcourt, 1953. The final chapter tells of Henry Ford and his works. But there is nothing to prevent you from reading about the six-shooter, the bicycle, and the clock, for instance, in other chapters.

16

Engines in the Air

a too-sensitive elevator control. Suddenly, on a low dip, it touched ground — and slid to a stop, a hundred feet from where it left the launching rail. The Wright brothers had achieved, for the first time, controlled, powered flight.

John Daniels, coastguardsman, at the camera, had remembered to snap the shutter, so this historic photograph (Fig. 16-1) was taken on December 17, 1903, among the sand dunes of Kitty Hawk, North Carolina.

How did two brothers who ran a bicycle shop in Dayton, Ohio, manage to succeed where others — scientists and engineers among them — had failed?

The invention of the airplane has made great changes in our everyday living. Fresh fruit can be flown from California to New York in time for dinner. Farmers use airplanes to dust and spray their crops. Many diseases can be conquered and lives saved by flying drugs to far distant places that were impossible to penetrate before.

The development of the airplane took many years and the experiments of many men. As early as 1500, Leonardo da Vinci tried to make a flying machine. However, it was not until 1903 that the first successful powered flight was made.

" Knowledge and Skill "

Wilbur and Orville Wright *were* scientists and engineers even though neither had gone to college. They were able to read — and learn — for themselves. What physics and mathematics they needed, they taught themselves on the good foundation of what they had learned in high school. The knowledge about flight that men like Cayley, Lilienthal, Langley, and Chanute had painstaking-

16-1. For the first time, controlled, sustained, powered flight — caught by John Daniels, coastguardsman, with Orville Wright's camera.

THE AIRPLANE

It was Orville Wright's turn. He planted his camera on its tripod and aimed it at the end of the launching rail. Then he walked across the sand and lay down on the lower wing of the " Flyer." It quivered under him as the motor roared, and the propellers thrashed the cold air. Orville's brother, Wilbur, took hold of the wing tip to steady the plane and released the anchor wire. The " Flyer " moved down the rail, then rose from it into the chilly wind. For twelve long seconds it skimmed uncertainly and slowly across the sand, weaving up and down as Orville struggled with

ly obtained and written down, the brothers read and discussed by the hour.

Being in the bicycle business, the Wright brothers appreciated the sort of balancing skill needed to control an airplane in restless, invisible air. As Wilbur wrote in a letter to the Smithsonian Institution, " It is only a question of knowledge and skill, just as in all acrobatic feats." They set themselves to get that knowledge and skill.

When they needed new knowledge, they found it by experimenting. For instance, they obtained accurate knowledge about the efficiencies of various wing shapes from a homemade wind tunnel of their own design. They watched buzzards circling in the sky, and saw how they twisted their wing-tip feathers for control.

Control in Flight

Men had flown on wings before the Wrights, but only in engineless gliders. Lilienthal, the German engineer, jumping from a hillside sometimes glided a hundred yards. But it was risky. He was at the mercy of the wind, for no one had found a reliable way to control a glider's quick, dangerous tilt in a gust of wind. See how Lilienthal is holding his legs forward in Fig. 16-2. When his glider nosed up on meeting a puff of wind, he swung his legs ahead. Thus he brought weight forward to pull the nose of the glider down to level flight again. This gave him some lengthwise or

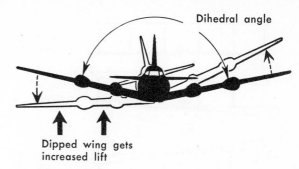

Dihedral angle

Dipped wing gets increased lift

16-3. The dipped wing has more lifting area at work than the high wing, which tends to level the plane.

longitudinal control. When a gust suddenly tilted the wings to one side, he had to swing his legs quickly toward the high wing to bear it down. This sidewise weight-shifting gave him some *lateral* control.

Can you see in this same picture that the wings are tilted at an angle to each other, making a very shallow " V "? This *dihedral* (dy-HEE-drul) *angle,* as it is called, gives some *automatic* lateral control. How it acts to return a tilted wing to the level is shown in Fig. 16-3. Dihedral angle works, as model airplane builders know. But it acts slowly, and is not under the pilot's direct control. (The Wrights rejected dihedral angle, as you can see in the " first-flight " photograph.)

Lilienthal's lateral control was an unsatisfactory combination of the weight-shifting and dihedral angle.

His longitudinal control improved when he invented a movable elevator. He worked it by means of a harness which he wore on his head. But this did nothing to prevent the frightening falling-off to one side that happened when a wing tilted too steeply.

Lilienthal's control system was not good enough. He crashed out of control in 1896.

However, he left behind him valuable information about the lifting force of various shapes of wings. He left as well an example of enthusiasm, perseverance, courage, and achievement in flight that greatly encouraged men like the Wright brothers who eagerly read his writings and studied his photographs and plans.

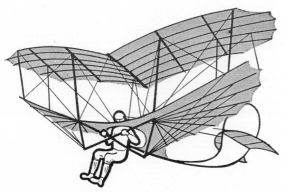

16-2. About 1890 Otto Lilienthal controlled his glider by swinging his legs from side to side or forward and backward. But such control wasn't reliable.

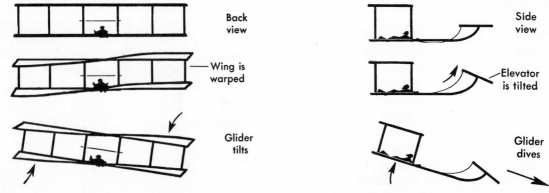

16-4. This wing-warping idea gave the Wright brothers lateral control of their " Flyer " that was dependable.

Control in Flight: Achievement

In 1899, when the Wright brothers took up gliding for the fun of it, the problem of controlling an airplane in flight — especially lateral control — was serious.

While studying the way buzzards twisted their wing tips when flying, the brothers had an idea: why not twist or warp the glider wing tips for control in flight (Fig. 16-4)? They built their first glider in 1900, flying it kite-fashion to begin with. The wing-warping system worked well. They added a movable elevator out in front of the main wing for longitudinal control as well. Soon they were able to glide *in control* in straightaway flight over the Kitty Hawk sand dunes.

By the time they had built glider Number 3, in 1902, they could turn corners in control. The Wright control system was a success. They patented its features, which are the basis of most flight controls used today.

With this reliable control system, plus their knowledge and flying skill, the brothers felt sure that powered flight was now only a matter of adding an engine and propellers to their glider. With a light engine — which they had to make themselves — and efficient propellers — which they had to design — they felt confident, now, that they could rise off the ground and fly. They did.

Out of their work, and the work of the pioneers of flight before them, and the work of those who came after them, have grown the airplanes you see and sometimes only hear today.

Newton on the Bottom, Bernoulli on the Top

Wings lift today's planes in much the same way that they lifted the Wright " Flyer " more than half a century ago. But today's aircraft engineers know a good deal more than the Wrights did about what happens as air flows around a wing. They know more because of thousands of experiments, and because of discoveries that scientists have made which explain why the experiments turn out as they do.

As you know, a wing cutting through air, as in Fig. 16-5, is forced up. It has *lift*. It gets this lift force in two different ways.

One part of the lift is caused as you would expect. Air moves over the tilted lower surface of the wing. Bouncing off that surface, the air is shoved down. But — as Newton pointed out —

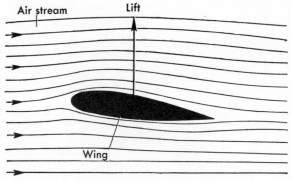

16-5. The air stream has farther to travel over the top of this wing section than under the bottom. Do you know why this produces lift?

where there is a shove down there must be an equal and opposite shove up (see page 170). The bottom surface of the wing forces the air *down:* action. Reaction: the wing is forced *up* by the air. In other words, it has lift.

The other part of the lift comes about differently. The top of the wing is gracefully curved, as you can see in Fig. 16-5. This is not done for beauty's sake. It is done so that the air flowing over the top of the wing has farther to travel than the air flowing under the wing.

If the air that goes *over* the wing is to arrive at the rear edge at the same time as the air going *under* the wing — and it does — it has to travel faster over its lengthy detour than the air along the bottom. *When air is speeded up in this way, its pressure drops.* As a result the pressure on top of the wing is less than the pressure on the bottom. The difference in pressures produces an upward force. The upward forces on a wing are called *lift.*

It was a mathematician named Daniel Bernoulli (behr-NOOL-ee) who showed that *as a moving fluid speeds up, the pressure it exerts on its surroundings decreases.* In his honor, this is called Bernoulli's Principle.

Does it seem odd to you that making a fluid, such as air, flow faster lowers its pressure? Try the simple experiment shown in Fig. 16-7. If you can explain why the sides of the folded-paper passage collapse as you blow through it, without Bernoulli's Principle, you're extraordinary.

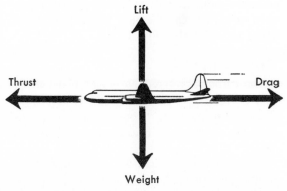

16-6. These four forces act on an airplane in flight.

16-7. Speeding up the air flow beneath the paper lowers the air pressure there and pulls the paper down, demonstrating Bernoulli's Principle.

An airplane wing may get as much as two-thirds of its lift by way of Bernoulli on top, and the remaining one-third by way of Newton on the bottom.

Development

Winged flight is simply a matter of pushing or pulling a wing through the air. For convenience some controls are added to point the wing in the right direction and keep it on an even keel. To do the pushing or pulling, an engine is hitched to a propeller, which is able to force a large amount of air to the rear. Hence the engine and everything else attached (including the wing) is forced *forward.*

Spurred by the First World War, airplanes developed rapidly. More efficient wings were designed, along with more powerful engines and better propellers. Air friction or *drag* was reduced by careful streamlining, worked out with models and man-made winds in wind tunnels. Speed, range, size of aircraft increased. By the 1930's a military plane in a steep dive might touch a speed of more than 700 miles per hour.

At that speed something unexpected happened.

Change of Air

Pilots who invaded this 700 miles-per-hour speed zone — by accident or otherwise — reported that usually well-behaved planes changed at about this speed. They began to shake violently,

as if being struck giant blows. The controls became almost useless. The planes threatened to
fall apart — and sometimes did.

In other words, at about 700 miles per hour the
air that bore an airplane smoothly enough at ordinary speeds behaved in a different way. Why
this sudden change?

When a wing slices through air, it shoves the
air molecules out of the way, to one side or the
other. Air molecules that have been shoved aside
bump those molecules next to them — and so on
down the line. Thus the bump is passed along
from air molecule to air molecule.

This passing-along of energy by air molecules
is exactly what happens as a *sound wave* travels
through the air.

Now sound, as we know from many experiments, travels through air at a speed of about
1100 feet per second — or *about 750 miles per
hour,* about the speed at which airplanes get into
trouble. This can hardly be just a coincidence.
But what is the connection between the speed of
sound and a disintegrating airplane?

The Sound Barrier

A wing slicing through the air bumps into the
air molecules, as we've said, and the bump is
passed along from molecule to molecule at the
speed of sound. By this bumping and passing-
along process, the wing signals to air molecules
ahead that it is approaching. This advance warn-
ing is passed along to molecules farther ahead at
the speed of sound. Thus a wing traveling at *less
than the speed of sound* is preceded by its air-
wave signals, and the *air molecules are already
moving aside when it arrives.*

Can you see what happens, however, when a
wing travels with the speed of sound? The air-
wave signal that it is coming no longer runs out
ahead of it, for the wing is already traveling as
fast as the signal can go. As a result the *air molecules are not moving aside when the wing arrives.*
The wing smashes into the air, which behaves
like a comparatively solid mass and sets up *shock
waves.* Enormous strains twist and batter the airplane. This is the " sound barrier."

16-8. At supersonic speeds the most careful streamlining is needed to cut down air drag. Each of these
planes can exceed the speed of sound in level flight.

Through the Barrier

Once a plane is through the sound barrier —
that is, traveling faster than sound — the batter-
ing ceases and smooth flight returns, because the
shock waves are left behind. This is *supersonic
flight,* swift and almost silent, for engine and air
noise is left behind. But to overcome the extraordinary resistance the air exerts on a plane going
through the sound barrier and beyond, great power is needed. This is where the jet engine takes
over, for present day propellers cannot drive an
airplane faster than about 600 miles per hour. To
make the enormous air resistance as low as possible, thin wings and the most painstaking streamlining are necessary (Fig. 16-8).

Today's Jet Planes

The turbojet-powered passenger plane in Fig.
16-9 is very highly streamlined. Note that the engines are hanging in " pods " beneath the thin
wings which are swept back toward the tail of the
plane.

Other passenger planes are powered by turboprop engines, which are connected to the propeller. A diagram of this engine is shown in Fig. 14-17.

Douglas Aircraft Co.

16-9. Four turbojet engines produce the tremendous thrust needed to lift this plane into, and drive it through, thin air at 500 miles per hour.

Swept-back Wings

Shock waves, you may recall, are set up as a wing pierces the " sound barrier " — that is, moves through the air at about the speed of sound. If the leading edge of a wing is swept back as shown, the shock waves do not form as soon as the wing reaches the speed of sound, but are delayed until some higher speed is reached. For an airplane which flies near or at the speed of sound, in the 600–700 miles-per-hour zone, this delaying of shock waves makes flight practical. For aircraft which fly above the speed of sound, however, leaving their shock waves behind them, swept-back wings may have no advantage.

Delta Wings

The airplane in Fig. 16-10 has wings shaped like a triangle. Since the Greek letter " delta " is triangle-shaped, such wings are called *delta wings*. High-speed jet planes have them for two reasons.

For one reason, they provide a good sweepback, as you can see. Another reason for this wing form is connected with air resistance or drag. A great part of the drag of an airplane flying near or at the speed of sound is wing drag. In order to reduce this drag, the thickness of the wing must be reduced. The thinner the wing, *compared with its width,* the weaker the shock waves it sets up.

If the wing is not wide to begin with, then the desired thinness may make it so weak as to be impractical: the necessary strength can't be built into so small a space.

But if the wing is wide (and short), its thickness may be much greater. There will be plenty of room for building in the necessary strength, and even space to put the jet engines inside the wing, too.

Flight Without Wings: the Rocket

The airplane is an engine on wings; the car is an engine on wheels; the ship is an engine on water. The rocket is simply an engine! And what an engine it is, as we saw in Chapter 14. It may well carry adventurous men away from Earth completely, out into interplanetary space. To what sort of machine must this engine be hitched if it is to take men so far?

The many successes in launching earth satel-

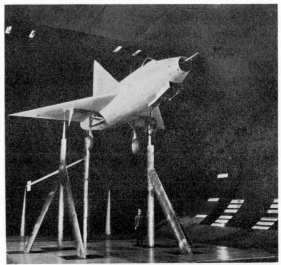

National Advisory Committee for Aeronautics

16-10. The delta-winged plane and the paper dart are close relatives. This actual plane is being tested in a 40 x 80 foot wind tunnel.

lites, carried aloft by rocket engines, may give the impression that such tasks are almost simple. Nothing could be further from the truth. Despite the combined skills of engineers, mathematicians, and technicians, occasional failures show that rocketry has only recently left infancy.

There is the problem of fuel, for example. For a long time — rockets were known to the Chinese hundreds of years ago, you know — rockets were propelled by powder fuels, such as gunpowder. It was when scientists found that *liquid fuels* for the rocket engine held much greater promise that things began to happen. But fuel is, of course, incapable of burning unless oxygen, or some similar combining element, is present. Often the burning, or combustion, element used is liquefied oxygen. The preparation of liquid oxygen, which involves first cooling oxygen gas to about −216° F., has become a little industry in itself.

While liquid fuel and oxygen provide a great amount of energy per pound, their use also poses several problems. Among these are how to keep huge supplies of liquids running to the rocket engines and how to mix them smoothly at the same time. New pumps have been designed to solve this problem.

There is the problem of control, too. How is a rocket to be steered and kept on its course? An arrow's flight is directed by the feathers at the end of its shaft. But such *vanes* are of no use where there is little or no atmosphere for them to work against. Moreover they can make the flight of an arrow — or a rocket — very unsteady when there are cross-winds. A bullet from a rifle spins like a top: this spin steadies the bullet on its course. But rockets tend to be much longer for their width than bullets, and much more difficult to steady by spinning. Spin won't do for control, either. But there are other possible systems. For one, vanes may be placed in the jet stream of the rocket engine to deflect it to one side or another, and so change the rocket's course. As you can imagine, this system demands special material for the vane.

For another control system, additional small rocket engines may be placed so as to squirt jet streams to the side and maneuver the rocket on course. And for a third solution, the jet engine itself may be mounted so that it can be turned from side to side, thus steering the rocket in the same way as an outboard motor may be used to steer a boat.

Among the major problems in getting a rocket into outer space is that of attaining the *escape velocity*. By escape velocity we mean the least velocity with which an object must be thrown straight up so that it never comes down again. Suppose you wanted to do this with a tennis ball. What velocity would it need? It turns out that you would have to throw it with a velocity of 25,000 miles per hour or a little less than 7 miles per second. And this velocity must be attained for escape whether you are dealing with a two-ounce tennis ball or a many-ton rocket.

Of course, the heavier an object is, the more energy is needed for it to reach the escape velocity. You should not, therefore, be surprised to learn that over three quarters of a rocket is taken up in fuel tanks and their pumps. You can see, then, how foolish it would be to have a rocket that had to drag along the useless weight of emptied fuel tanks. This problem is solved by constructing a rocket in stages (Fig. 16-11). By mounting rockets in stages that burn out before the next rocket motor begins its sprint, the velocity of 25,000 miles per hour is finally achieved. It takes some clever engineering to adjust these stages so that they separate cleanly and start operating at just the right moment. And, even so, it is difficult to reserve enough weight out of the total for the final stage or payload. It is this final stage that will one day take human explorers to other planets.

In the last chapter of this book you can read more about this great new frontier.

Heat Barrier

One especially large obstacle stands in the way of high-speed flight, whether with wings or without.

A machine flying in the stratosphere at, say, 2500 miles per hour gets hot — because of the friction of the air through which it is boring.

"Thin" as air is in the stratosphere, it can rub the surface of a rocket or a plane up to a temperature of 350° C. (100° C. is the temperature at which water boils, as you know.)

And this "heat barrier" isn't an obstacle that can be passed through and left behind, like the "sound barrier." As the speed of a machine going through the atmosphere gets higher, things continue to get hotter and hotter.

So aircraft of the future will probably carry cooling equipment, and not just for passenger comfort. At high temperatures some aircraft metals are affected — in an undesirable way. The strength of aluminum alloy, for instance, drops sharply when its temperature goes above 200° C. And a metal may "creep," or stretch, to a point where it suddenly snaps, at a higher temperature. At lower temperatures it may stretch but return elastically to its original length.

But with the help of insulation and refrigeration even the heat barrier can be pushed back, so that men may fly at speeds measured in thousands of miles per hour rather than hundreds. The fuel of the craft may be used as a source of "cold" to offset the heat from friction. New metals and alloys, better able to stand high temperatures, are being developed — such as stainless steel and titanium, for example. It will be interesting to see how scientists and engineers will overcome the obstacle of the heat barrier.

Flight — in Your Future

In one lifetime the airplane has gone from a few feet above the dunes of Kitty Hawk to altitudes of over 100,000 feet, in the case of rocket planes, and to speeds of over 2,000 miles per hour.

But high speeds and altitudes are not all airplane designers are working on. They also look to new kinds of airplanes, and new ways of driving them through the sky.

Here are some developments:

Helicopters get lift by whirling their wings — the rotor blades — through the air. They go forward by tilting the rotor. Control is achieved by adjusting the angle of each rotor blade as it spins. However, plenty of power is needed to lift a plane straight up off the ground. When landing space is small and the trip is short, the helicopter is a useful airplane. But its speed in level flight may never be as great as the speed of conventional planes.

Designers have tried for years to invent a plane that can take off straight up like a helicopter, yet travel as fast as more conventional planes. One of their solutions is the convertiplane.

Convertiplanes take off as helicopters, rising vertically. But once they are airborne, part or all of the load is shifted from rotors to wings. Thus

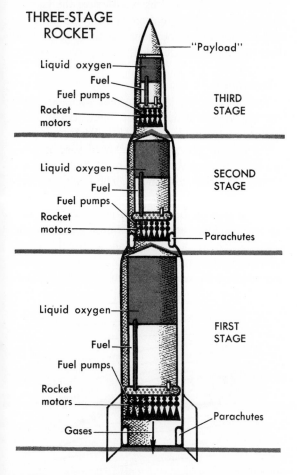

THREE-STAGE ROCKET

"Payload"

Liquid oxygen
Fuel
Fuel pumps
Rocket motors

THIRD STAGE

Liquid oxygen
Fuel
Fuel pumps
Rocket motors

SECOND STAGE

Parachutes

Liquid oxygen
Fuel
Fuel pumps
Rocket motors

FIRST STAGE

Parachutes

Gases

16-11. This simplified version of a three-stage rocket omits the complex control devices. The small, separate rocket motors in each stage can be adjusted in flight.

16-12. The convertiplane takes off like a helicopter, flies like an airplane.

the helicopter converts to an airplane. The rotors may fold away to reduce drag, or swivel to become propellers (Fig. 16-12).

Rockets can assist the take-off of almost any aircraft. And, as power sources that need no air, they can travel out into space.

Powered lift through wings is a promising development. Instead of using jet power to drive the airplane along an expensive runway at take-off — so as to get enough air flowing around the wing — the jet engine can blow or pull air through slots across the wing to get vertical lift. The jet engine is after all nothing more than a machine for sucking and blowing air (Fig. 16-13).

Low-drag wings are the latest attempt to reduce the constant enemy of efficiency in all machines — friction. With the airplane, friction occurs not only between the moving parts of the engine, but also between the wings and the air. And, despite their best efforts at streamlining, airplane designers have long been troubled by the frictional drag set up in the thin layer of air flowing just next to the airplane's " skin."

This so-called boundary layer of air has the nasty habit of breaking into tiny, but violent, eddies and whorls as it flows back over the wing

surface. The resultant frictional drag must, of course, be overcome by the engines, which wastes some of their fuel.

Now, however, there seems to be hope that this boundary layer can be kept flowing without turbulence by using a specially designed wing. As shown in Fig. 16-14, this wing has many slots (much finer than is drawn) through which boundary-layer air may be " inhaled " under suction from a pump within the wing structure. Such inhalation, if carried on gently and smoothly, prevents the turbulence from getting started.

If applied to the wings alone, it is estimated that the reduction in drag would save the engines enough fuel to increase their range by 50 per cent, and if employed throughout the fuselage as well, their range may be doubled.

Ignorance

You may think, by now, that there are men who know a great deal about flight, and that our mastery of the air is remarkable. Perhaps it is.

But men in gliders have followed soaring birds and have studied their mastery of flight with accurate measuring instruments. The results are perplexing. The air friction of some birds is far less than half that of the best man-made aircraft, taking size, weight, and other things into account. Just how the bird's structure allows for this is not yet known. But there is some evidence that the fine pores of the feathers act much as do the slots

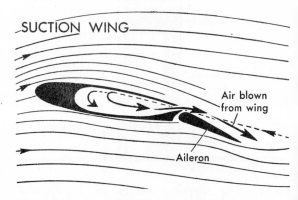

16-13. A plane's jet engine arranged so that it sucks air into the wing and out over it produces greater lift. It may shorten airport runways.

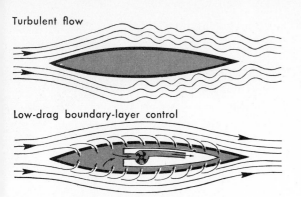

Turbulent flow

Low-drag boundary-layer control

16-14. A recent effort in the fight against friction uses slotted wings to reduce turbulent drag.

in low-drag wings. Indeed, it was partly through study of the bird that the possibility of low-drag wings was suggested.

Thus, despite our advanced technology, we can still learn much from the birds — flying " machines " produced by millions of years of natural, selective evolution.

Looking Back . . . .

VOCABULARY

The following expressions are important in understanding this chapter. Show that you know their meaning by defining each one.

1. Bernoulli's Principle
2. convertiplane
3. delta wing
4. helicopter
5. shock waves
6. sound barrier
7. lift
8. drag
9. dihedral angle
10. lateral control
11. longitudinal control
12. streamlining
13. heat barrier

EXPLAIN WHY

- Air flowing over an airplane wing gives it lift.
- Dihedral angle keeps an airplane from tipping over sideways.
- Airplanes are shaken and strained as they fly through the sound barrier.
- Propellers cannot drive planes through the sound barrier.

Going Further . . . .

APPLYING PRINCIPLES

1. A plane is flying level at a certain speed. The propeller is speeded up to make the plane fly faster. What adjustment must the pilot now make to keep the plane in level flight? Explain your answer.

2. Can you use Bernoulli's Principle to explain how a baseball can be thrown in a curve?

3. How is Bernoulli's Principle applied to a spray gun?

TRY THESE

1. Arrange an upward jet of water or of air (from a vacuum cleaner). Place a ping-pong ball on the jet and it will stay on top without falling off. Explain why this happens.

2. A pin is pushed through a card and then inserted into the hole of a spool. Challenge your friends to blow the card off by blowing in at the other end. The harder they blow, the harder the card " sticks " to the spool. Rapidly moving air in the space between the card and the spool creates a low pressure. The air outside then holds the card in place. The same effect can be obtained by blowing downward into a funnel containing a ping-pong ball.

UNIT 6

Controlling Temperature

◀ *Delicate instruments sent aloft relay useful information about temperature and weather conditions.*

ON WHAT will you spend most of the money you ever earn?

It surprises most people to realize that they will spend most of their money trying to control temperature. Think about it for a moment and you will see that this is true.

Some of the money you will earn will be spent for food. The food will be burned in your body to make heat. This heat will be used to keep the temperature inside of your body at 98.6° F.

Some of your money will go for clothing. In the winter it will be used to hold in your body heat. Without warm clothes the temperature at the surface of your body will fall and you will be too cold. For summer wear you will need to buy light clothing so that your body heat may leave your skin easily. Otherwise you will be too hot.

Some of your money will go for a house or apartment which you will heat in winter and try to keep cool in summer.

Yes, you will spend most of your money to try to control temperature. It may mean your life if you do not. Certainly, whether you know how to use heat for better living may mean the difference between living a comfortable or an uncomfortable life.

And so the purpose of this unit is to show you how you can control temperatures for healthful and comfortable living.

CHAPTER 17

Measuring Temperature

Pour some liquid ether into a dish at one end of the room. In just a moment you will be able to smell ether everywhere in the room. At the same time the ether seems to disappear from the dish (Fig. 17-1).

You may have noticed how solid mothballs in a closet slowly disappear in the same way, filling the whole closet with their odor. Certainly you have seen a lump of sugar dissolve in a hot drink, making the entire liquid taste sweet. What is happening in all of these examples?

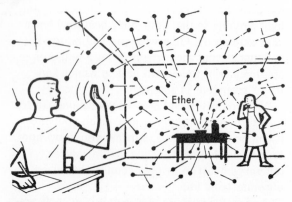

17-1. As the liquid ether evaporates, there is a noticeable odor of ether in all parts of the room. Why?

MOVING MOLECULES

In every case, matter seems to be disappearing from one spot and scattering itself throughout a larger space. All matter, including ether, mothballs, and sugar, is made of molecules, as you remember from your earlier reading. Therefore, it must be the molecules that have scattered. Of course molecules can only scatter about like this if they are moving. Whenever its molecules are scattering, a substance dissolves or evaporates.

You may ask whether the molecules of ether, mothballs, and sugar are moving *all* the time. The answer is " Yes, they are. And so are the molecules of *all* substances."

It is possible to see direct evidence of this molecular motion by watching smoke particles through a microscope (Fig. 17-2). The particles of smoke are very tiny. Through the microscope they seem to vibrate and zigzag about in a wild dance. The only explanation scientists have been able to give is that this motion of the smoke particles results from the particles being struck from all sides by speeding molecules of air. This effect is called *Brownian motion*.

Like the molecules of air, all the molecules of the things you see around you are moving, some at speeds as high as several miles a second.

Even the molecules your own body is made of are all busily dancing and jiggling about. Of course, the molecules a solid material is made of

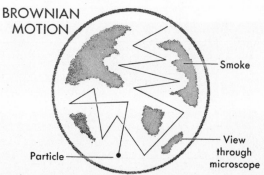

BROWNIAN MOTION

Smoke

Particle

View through microscope

17-2. You can observe smoke particles under the microscope. The smoke particles show a peculiar zigzag motion. Their directions change when they are hit by the molecules in the air.

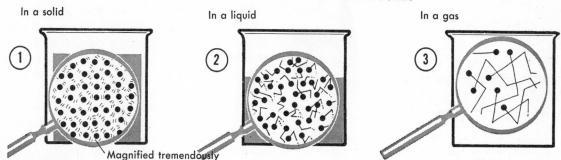

RELATIVE MOTION OF MOLECULES

In a solid   In a liquid   In a gas

Magnified tremendously

17-3. Molecules in solids vibrate in one spot, whereas molecules in a liquid are free to travel within the liquid. Molecules in gases have almost no cohesion and move about freely in all directions.

do not travel very far. They dance and quiver about the same spot, much as you do when you jump up and down excitedly cheering at a ball game. Since the molecules are tightly confined, their back and forth jiggling is too tiny for you to see. A solid object is solid because its molecules cannot travel away (Fig. 17-3).

Molecules of a liquid are more free to travel about than those of a solid. *You* act like a molecule of a liquid as soon as the ball game is over and you leave your place in the grandstand. No longer held close to your seat (like a molecule of a solid), you begin to travel (like a molecule of a liquid).

Molecules of gases travel even more freely than those of liquids. An air molecule bouncing off your nose as you read the word " now " may be across the room by the time you finish reading the end of this column.

When you first think of this extraordinary motion of molecules, you may wonder why the world does not dissolve into a shapeless whirling gas. You may wonder what holds the molecules of this book together in a fixed shape. Why doesn't a piece of iron evaporate, just as the ether did? Why don't *you* evaporate?

What Holds Molecules Together?

Dip a piece of glass, or a pencil, or a spoon into water. When you pull the spoon or pencil out of the water, some drops of water come with

it. Ordinarily a drop of water should fall downward since the force of gravity acts to pull it down. Therefore, if some of the water still clings, there must be a force of attraction between the pencil and the water. This force of attraction, which holds molecules of *different* materials together — in this case, water and wood — is called *adhesion*. As you will see, the force of adhesion is sometimes very strong.

You have also seen water drip from a faucet. The water is always in the form of drops. Apparently there is also a force holding *similar* molecules together. We call the force which holds molecules of the same material together — in this case, those of water — *cohesion*.

If the forces of adhesion and cohesion did not exist, nothing would hold together. All materials would fly apart. The world and everything in it would be changed into gas.

Cohesion Plus

Have you ever tried to pull a copper wire apart? You would need a powerful machine because the force which holds the molecules of copper together is very strong. Chemists think that forces greater than cohesion hold molecules of copper together; some call these " bonding forces."

Suppose we want to separate the molecules of copper from one another; that is, to make a vapor of the metal. We could do so by heating it (Fig. 17-4). However, it will take lots of heat to break the force holding the molecules of copper together, and

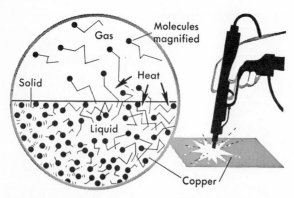

17-4. If molecules of a metal, like copper, are heated sufficiently (as by the hot iron above), their vibrating motion overcomes the forces that hold them together. Could copper be turned into a gas?

scatter them about like the molecules of ether. The force that holds the molecules of a solid together is very great.

You know from experience that many liquids can be evaporated, some of them very easily. For instance, water evaporates easily in an ordinary room. When heat is added, evaporation is speeded up. This fact shows that the force of cohesion between molecules in liquids is not so great as that in solids.

You might guess from the foregoing that the cohesion between molecules of a gas, like oxygen or nitrogen, is less than that in a liquid. In gases, the molecules are flying wildly about with almost no force of cohesion between them (Fig. 17-3).

Summing up, we can say then that *molecules of a substance ordinarily are attracted to each other by the force of cohesion.* Cohesion prevents molecules from moving about freely. In a solid, cohesion keeps the molecules tightly fastened to one another. In a liquid, cohesion is less and the molecules move more freely; and, in a gas, they are freest of all.

In addition, we know that *heat speeds up the movement of molecules,* and may even wrench them loose from one another. As heat tears molecules apart, the spaces between the molecules grow larger (Fig. 17-4). This is what happens when solids melt and liquids evaporate.

More about Adhesion

Fill a glass with water and then pour the water off. Do some drops remain? There are nearly always some adhering to the glass. It is the force of adhesion which keeps water and glass together.

It seems that the force of adhesion between water and glass is greater than the force of cohesion pulling the water together into a separate drop. However, if we put grease on the glass, the water no longer adheres to it. We have reduced the force of adhesion. The force of cohesion pulling water molecules into a drop is now greater than the adhesion between grease and water.

On the other hand, soap and chemicals called *wetting agents* reduce the *co*hesion of water droplets and increase their *ad*hesion to a surface that is to be cleaned. Soap and wetting agents help us keep things clean because they change the forces of adhesion and cohesion. This allows water to surround the particles of dirt and float them away (Fig. 17-5).

You know that to remove grease from your hands or from the dishes, you need not only soap but lots of *hot* water. The heat reduces the forces of both adhesion and cohesion. Heat makes the

17-5. Notice how the soapy water on the left clings to the material (wets it), while water (without soap) merely forms spherical drops.

molecules of grease move faster, bouncing them to and fro until they are wrenched loose.

You can compare the action of molecules on grease and dirt to the action of a strong wind on ripe apples on a tree. In fact, if the wind becomes a tornado even the tree is shaken to pieces. Similarly, very high temperatures can melt the greasy frying pan or burn your hand.

Heat and Moving Molecules

It should be clear then that we can separate molecules or atoms by heating them. As soon as we allow them to cool off, the forces of attraction (cohesion and adhesion) between molecules pull them together once more. When we heat water, it becomes steam. As the steam cools, cohesion pulls it back into drops of water again.

What then is heat? We have been talking about heat as if it had something to do with moving molecules. We have been saying that we add heat to make molecules move. What we should have said is that an object is hot because its molecules are moving. *Heat is the energy of motion of molecules.*

In hot water the molecules are rushing about at very high speeds. They have lots of energy. Their heat *is* their energy of motion.

"Cooling off" means "molecules are losing their energy of motion." As the water cools off, its molecules move more slowly. In ice, molecules are moving still more slowly. That is why ice is colder than cool water (Fig. 17-6).

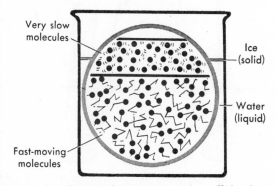

Very slow molecules

Ice (solid)

Water (liquid)

Fast-moving molecules

17-6. Ice forms when water cools sufficiently to reduce the speed of the water molecules.

The colder an object is the more slowly its molecules move. The hotter an object gets the faster its molecules move.

There are many ways of making objects hotter — of making their molecules move with more energy.

When we hammer a nail so hard it gets hot, rub our hands together briskly, rub one metal against another, strike a match, light gas, we are speeding up the motion of molecules. We are turning the energy of the hammer, or our hands, or the energy in chemicals into the energy of motion of molecules, making the molecules move faster. We are turning other forms of energy into heat energy.

Heat Can Travel

Next time you go to the kitchen, place a small pan of cold water in a pan of hot water. Within a short time, both pans will be warm. The pan of hot water has given up some of its heat to the pan of cold water. How did this happen?

The hot pan is hot because its molecules are moving rapidly. The cold pan is cold because the molecules of the pan are moving more slowly. When they are put close together, the rapidly moving molecules of the hot pan knock hard against the slower molecules of the cold pan. The molecules of the cold pan, knocked by rapidly moving molecules, speed up. Therefore, the water warms up. Thus heat — the movement of molecules — is transferred from a warm object to a cold one.

In exactly the same way, the heat of your body — the movement of its molecules — is transferred to a cold object, the mercury in a fever thermometer, for example. The molecules of mercury speed up, and thus the mercury gains heat. Heat expands it, and its expansion is a measure of the temperature of your body.

We have seen that all the objects in the world around you are made of moving molecules, and that their molecular motion is heat. Even very cold objects like ice contain some heat. This can be tested by an experiment.

Air, as you have learned from your earlier

reading, can become a liquid. It is then extremely cold, some 200° below 0° C. A cake of ice may be at 0° C. Yet when a flask of liquid air is placed on a cake of ice, it will boil. Yes, actually boil. The energy of motion, that is the heat, of the molecules in the ice has been transferred to the even slower-moving molecules of liquid air. The molecules of liquid air are speeded up and begin to leave the liquid. In other words, the liquid air boils.

In all three of these cases you have seen how heat flows from one object to another. Notice that the *heat always flows from a warmer object to a cooler one* — never from a cool object to a hot one.

When a pan of boiling water is left to cool, heat always flows from the pot into the cooler air of the room. Even though there is some heat in the air of the room, it never flows into the pan to make the pan hotter.

If you sit down in a tub of ice water, though there is still some heat in the ice water, it does not warm you up at all. The heat all flows from the warmer " you " to the cooler ice water.

How many other examples can you give to illustrate the fact that heat flows from hot objects to cold ones, not from cold to hot?

TEMPERATURE AND THERMOMETERS

Which has a higher temperature, a red hot nail or a bathtub full of cold water? You would no doubt say that the red hot nail has a higher temperature. And you would be right. But suppose we asked which has more heat, the hot nail or the bathtub full of cold water? Would you have answered that the bathtub had more heat? If you had, you would be right. Why?

The bathtub water has trillions upon trillions upon trillions more molecules than the nail has. Although each of these water molecules has only a little energy of motion, there are so many of them that their *total* energy far exceeds the heat energy in the molecules of the nail. Thus we say

that the bathtub water contains more heat than the nail.

We can put the matter another way. The nail has far, far fewer molecules than the bathtub water. There are so few that their total amount of energy is not so great as the total amount in the water despite the great amount of energy of each single molecule in the nail.

Each molecule in the nail has more energy than each water molecule. Thus the nail has the higher *temperature*.

Apparently a thermometer reads the temperature, not the total amount of heat in a body.

Making a Simple Thermometer

If you make a simple thermometer in the laboratory, it will help you to understand these principles. Take a flask or bottle such as the one in Fig. 17-7. Fill half of it with water colored with red or blue ink. Then put a glass tube about two feet long through a one-hole rubber stopper as shown in the diagram.

Now place your hands over the upper part of the bottle. The heat of your hands will be transmitted through the glass to the air. (Remember: heat flows from warmer objects to cooler ones.) The molecules in the air will get hotter, that is they will be set in more rapid motion. The spaces between them will grow larger. The air will thus expand and push on the water. And the water will rise in the tube.

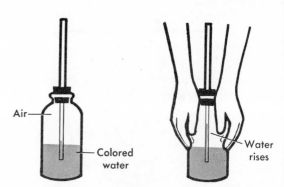

17-7. The air thermometer. Air expands when heated and pushes the liquid down. It can move only up the tube. What happens when the air cools?

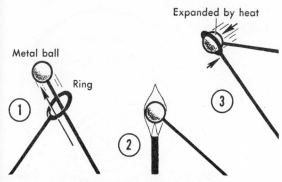

17-8. The ball and ring experiment. Why do most objects expand when heated and contract when cool?

If you placed regular, evenly spaced marks on the tube and called each one a degree, you would have a simple thermometer. Your thermometer measures an effect that depends on the speed of movement of air molecules.

Expansion

Have you ever seen the ball and ring experiment shown in Fig. 17-8? You may have one in your school laboratory.

Take the ball and try to slip it through the ring. It goes through quite easily. Now heat the ball for a minute or so in the flame of a Bunsen burner, and try again to slip it through the ring. It won't go through. Why? In heating the ball, its molecules were set into more rapid motion. This increased the distances between the molecules. As the ball is heated, each molecule hits its neighbors and pushes them harder. The distances between them get larger. The material expands.

The working of a thermometer depends on the regular expansion of material. Alcohol, mercury, or even gases expand inside the tube of the thermometer as they are heated.

Suppose you used a liquid in the thermometer like water which expands irregularly. For instance, at 4° C. water expands at a different rate than it does at 20° C. As you add equal amounts of heat to water, it expands a small amount at one temperature, a large amount at another. The divisions on a water-filled thermometer would therefore have to be irregularly spaced. That is one reason why water is not used in thermometers.

Let us make a water thermometer to see this. Use the same thermometer as you made before (Fig. 17-7). This time, however, fill the flask to the top and put it in a mixture of ice and salt. From your earlier reading you know that such a mixture has a temperature below the freezing point of water. After an hour, remove the salt and ice mixture. You will find the water has frozen. Did water continue to contract as it froze? No, the flask is cracked.

When water *cools* it contracts until just before it freezes. Down to 4° C. it contracts; at 0° C. it freezes and then it expands greatly. Therefore, if water were used in a thermometer, it would break the glass when temperatures went below freezing. Similarly, if the temperature went above the boiling point of water, the water would expand into steam and break the thermometer. Water is, therefore, useless for most thermometers.

Different materials expand and contract at different rates as their temperatures change. For instance, in your home or in your schoolroom you may have a device which makes use of the different rates of expansion of two metals. Are you acquainted with your thermostat?

Thermostats

If you were to weld two strips of metal such as brass and iron together, as in Fig. 17-9A, you would have a simple *thermostat*. Let us see how it works. If you heated each one of the strips separately, you would find that they both increase in length. But you would also find that the brass expands more than the iron. Now what happens when you heat the welded strip with brass on one side and iron on the other? As you would expect, the brass expands more than the iron. Therefore, the bar bends. It bends toward the iron since the brass expands more than the iron (Fig. 17-9A). When the bar is cooled, it must bend in the other direction; the brass now contracts more than the iron, and the iron is on the outer side. Usually, an alloy like Invar is used rather than iron since it expands less than iron does for the same change in temperature.

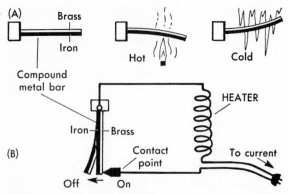

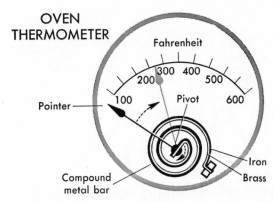

17-9. (A) The thermostat makes use of the fact that the brass expands more than the iron, thus bending the iron. (B) Explain how a compound metal bar works in shutting a heater off; in turning it on.

17-10. In an oven thermometer, the thin coiled compound bar expands when heated and moves the coil. Where will the pointer move when the oven is turned off? Why?

Controlling Temperatures with Thermostats

Let us see how a bar type thermostat such as the one we have been studying could help us control the temperature in a room. We will use an electric heater to heat the room. We move the bar as is shown in Fig. 17-9B so that it completes the circuit with the wiring going into the heater. You can see that as the heater warms up, the thermostat bar will also warm up. The brass side expands and the bar bends away from the contact point (Fig. 17-9B). This breaks the circuit, the current is shut off, and the heater goes off. Now as the heater and bar cool off, the bar returns to its original position. Why? The brass contracts and bends toward the contact point, touches it, and the current goes on again. As you see, the distance the bar is placed from the contact point determines the temperature at which the heat will be shut off and put on.

In much the same way, a thermostat can control the current which is responsible for putting on or shutting off oil or gas burners and refrigerators. In an automobile a thermostat controls the flow of water through the radiator. Thus the temperature of the water is kept fairly constant. Nevertheless you should keep watch on the temperature meter of your car, for sometimes the temperature may go above the danger point — the point when your motor may be harmed.

Thermostats may also be used to control the temperatures of freezers, automatic irons, ovens, waffle irons, and other devices.

As you can see, the principle behind most thermometers is that *heated material in the thermometer expands.* You may have a simple thermometer in your oven — a dial type that contains a two-metal bar like the one in a thermostat. The heat in the oven causes the bar to turn or twist (Fig. 17-10). As the bar twists it turns a pointer which shows the temperature on the dial.

Standards for Measuring Temperature

All your life you have tried to set certain standards for measuring temperature. For instance, you have probably said, " It's warmer today than it was yesterday." You were using yesterday's temperature as a standard for comparison. But you can see how unsatisfactory that is because the standard changes from day to day, and differs with different people.

You probably know that the standards widely accepted for measuring temperature are the freezing and boiling points of water. Our two common scales in use are the Fahrenheit and Centigrade [1] scales (Fig. 17-11). Compare the two in the following table. Then study Fig. 17-11 carefully.

[1] Sometimes you will find the word *Celsius* used instead of Centigrade.

	Centigrade	Fahrenheit
Freezing point of water	0°	32°
Boiling point of water	100°	212°

In melting ice, a Fahrenheit thermometer would read 32° F.; a Centigrade thermometer would read 0° C. In boiling water, the Centigrade thermometer would read 100° C.; the Fahrenheit would read 212° F. But what would a Fahrenheit thermometer read if it were placed in a room whose temperature measures 20° C.? By reading

the Fahrenheit scale in Fig. 17-11, you find that it is 68° F.

Many thermometers have a scale like the one in the drawing you have just examined. However, if you didn't have such a thermometer, and if you found it necessary, you could still change one scale to the other by using a simple formula.

F.° to C.° and C.° to F.°

As you saw above, ordinary room temperature is about 20° C. or 68° F. Check your room now. Is it about that temperature?

But let us change a higher temperature, say 122° F., to Centigrade. To change Fahrenheit to Centigrade you use this formula:

$$C = \tfrac{5}{9} (F - 32)$$

As you can see you must first subtract 32 from the temperature in degrees Fahrenheit.

Therefore,

$$C = \tfrac{5}{9} (122-32)$$
$$C = \tfrac{5}{9} (90)$$
$$C = 50$$

Another formula, really the same one written in reverse, is used to change Centigrade to Fahrenheit:

$$F = \frac{9C}{5} + 32$$

Let us change 50° C. back to Fahrenheit, just to see if we get the same number we started with.

$$F = \tfrac{9}{5} (50) + 32$$
$$F = 90 + 32$$
$$F = 122$$

As you can see, you must first take $\tfrac{9}{5}$ of the Centigrade temperature and then add 32.

Now try these. Change 98.6° F. (your body temperature) to Centigrade. Change 60° C. to Fahrenheit. Do you get the same answers you see on page 208?

Gas Thermometers

On page 204 you read of a thermometer which used the expansion of air, a gas, as a means of recording temperature. Unlike solids and liquids, a gas expands by the same amount for each de-

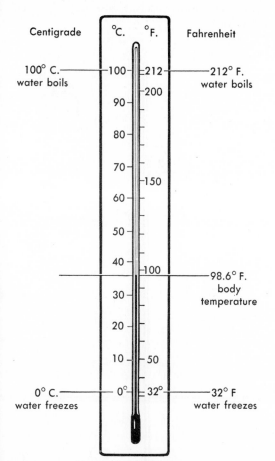

17-11. Compare the Fahrenheit and Centigrade scales. Is a Centigrade degree larger or smaller than a Fahrenheit degree? How much? What is the approximate equivalent in Fahrenheit degrees of room temperature (20° C.)?

gree when it is heated. Thus a thermometer filled with hydrogen gas will have evenly spaced temperature markings. Moreover all kinds of gases expand alike as they are heated. If the hydrogen were all removed and replaced with oxygen, the markings would not need to be changed.

Galileo invented a gas thermometer which was very similar to the one you made. But it was the French scientist Jacques Charles who first prepared a really accurate gas-filled thermometer.

Suppose we take 273 cubic centimeters of a colored gas and put it in a bulb at the bottom of a long tube at 0° C. For each cubic centimeter up the tube, we will place a mark. Now we will heat the tube to 1° C. We find that the gas will rise to the mark of 1. Hence it has expanded $\frac{1}{273}$ of its original volume (Fig. 17-12). If the gas were heated one more Centigrade degree, it would rise to $\frac{2}{273}$ of its original volume — to the mark 2. If we now heated the gas to 100° C., it would go up to $\frac{100}{273}$ of its original volume.

Put it another way. If we heated this gas to 273° C., it would double its volume. If a liter (1000 cc.) of a gas at 0° C. were heated to 273° C., it would double its volume to 2 liters. If the liter were heated 2 × 273° C. (546° C.), it would triple its volume.

What would happen if we were to cool the gas to 273° C. below 0° C.? If the gas contracted $\frac{1}{273}$ of its volume for each degree, then it would contract $\frac{273}{273}$ of its volume. In other words, it would disappear. Could this happen? Actually, before this temperature is reached, all known gases have become liquids and most of them solids.

But from this calculation you can see that the lowest temperature a substance can ever reach is −273° C. or −459.4° F., or, as it is called, *absolute zero*. At the temperature of absolute zero the substance would have lost all its heat. An interesting question: at absolute zero, would molecules still move?

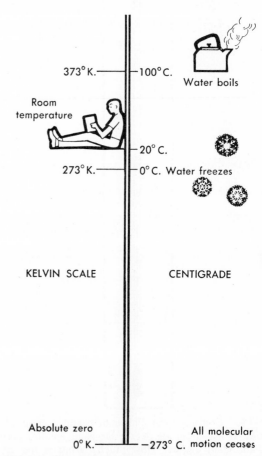

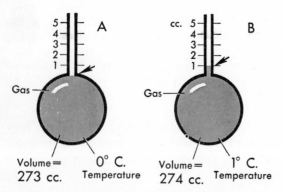

17-12. If any gas at 0° C. is heated 1 degree, it will expand $\frac{1}{273}$ of its volume. What would happen if the gas were heated to 5° C.?

98.6° F. = 36.7° C.; 60° C. = 140° F.

17-13. The Kelvin scale starts at absolute zero. What is the equivalent in Kelvin degrees of 20° C.?

A New Temperature Scale

Absolute zero is the starting point for a temperature scale called the *Kelvin scale* often used by scientists. The Kelvin scale is the same as the Centigrade scale, except that it starts at absolute zero. Thus 0° C. is 273° above absolute zero and is written as 273° Kelvin (or 273° K.). On the Kelvin scale, 100° C. is another 100° higher or 373° K. To get Kelvin temperatures you simply add 273 to the Centigrade reading. Thus 10° C. = 10 + 273 or 283° K., and −40° C. = −40 + 273 or 233° K.

Suppose we cooled the gas after it had reached 373° K. to 0° C. Do you see it would go down 100 degrees to 273° K. (or 0° C.)? See Fig. 17-13 to check on your understanding of the Kelvin scale.

Looking Back . . . .

VOCABULARY

The following terms are keys to the main ideas in this chapter. Show that you understand their meanings by using each one in a complete sentence.

1. adhesion
2. Centigrade scale
3. cohesion
4. Fahrenheit scale
5. heat
6. molecule
7. temperature
8. thermostat
9. wetting agent

REVIEW QUESTIONS

1. Explain the principle of Brownian motion.
2. Why is a solid object solid?
3. Why is a drop of water round in shape?
4. Do molecules move faster in cold objects or in warm objects?
5. Why does heat help remove grease?
6. How does soap remove dirt from your hands?
7. How can you prove that heat travels?
8. Distinguish between heat and temperature.
9. How does a thermostat control temperature?
10. What are the freezing and boiling points of water on the Centigrade and Fahrenheit scales?
11. Why is mercury or alcohol, rather than water, used in a thermometer?
12. What is meant by absolute zero?
13. What reading would 37° C. be on a Fahrenheit thermometer?

Going Further . . . .

APPLYING PRINCIPLES

1. When you touch a cold doorknob, your hand feels cold. Is this because cold is transferred to your hand or because heat is transferred away from your hand? Explain your answer.
2. What is the use of a thermostat in an automobile? List as many appliances in your home as you can which go on or off automatically because a thermostat is in use.

THINGS TO DO

1. Demonstrate heat from motion. Bend a piece of thin copper or other metal back and forth rapidly until it breaks. Touch the point of the break. It has become hot from the motion of bending. Try pounding a nail with a hammer when the nail is lying flat. The nail becomes very hot.
2. Make a camphor boat. Fasten a small piece of camphor to one edge of a wooden match and float it in water. The wood moves away from the camphor. As the camphor dissolves, the molecules of camphor weaken the surface tension of the water. The surface tension of the water on the other side of the boat then pulls the boat forward.
3. Float a boat with holes in it. Make a small boat out of copper screening. Despite the fact that the boat is full of holes, it does not sink if carefully placed on the water. The boat does not break through the surface tension of the water.
4. Blow up a balloon with hot air. Fasten a balloon to the top of a tall soda bottle. Place the bottle in a pan of hot water. The expanded air in the bottle will blow up the balloon slightly.
5. Show the expansion of water. Fill a narrow-necked bottle, such as a soda bottle, with hot water. Then place the bottle of hot water in a pan of cold water. The hot water will contract in a short while, and you will note a space at the top of the bottle. How could you show that this loss of volume was not just the result of evaporation of the hot water?

18

Keeping Warm

In cold winter weather a bear curls up and hibernates for months at a time. When the warmer spring and summer months come, he wakes up and sets out in search of food. Thus a bear's activity is determined by the warmth of his surroundings. You can probably name other animals that are inactive in cold weather and are full of pep when summer comes.

Man is different. He can control the temperature of his surroundings. He adjusts a thermostat or fires up the stove and manages to be active and comfortable even during the coldest weather. His home is a capsule of almost perfect weather because he knows how to control the temperature of his surroundings.

What principles are used in heating a home? We shall study several of them in this chapter.

FROM MOLECULE TO MOLECULE

You know better than to put one end of a needle in a flame and hold on to the other end. You would soon drop the needle or be burned. Heat flows easily from the hot end of the needle to the cooler end. We say heat is *conducted* along the needle.

Yet if you stuck the needle in a piece of wood, say a pencil, and used the pencil as a handle you could hold the needle in the flame a long time. That is because wood is a poor conductor of heat.

Some materials are good conductors and other materials are poor conductors of heat (Fig. 18-1).

Good Conductors of Heat

Go into the kitchen and look at the cooking utensils your mother uses. Most of them will be made of aluminum, stainless steel, or copper. When water is boiling in one of them, touch the metal handle if the pot has one. Hot, isn't it? The metal is a good conductor.

Now if you wanted to grasp the handle you would take a cloth, a pot holder, and put it around the handle. Or perhaps the pot has a wooden handle. Why? The cloth or wood does not conduct heat as well as the metal does.

Study the list of conductors in Table 10. Which material is the best conductor? Which is the poorest? (In the study of conductors air is taken as standard and assigned the value 1.0. Thus, the table tells you that a piece of copper will conduct 17,400 times as much heat as an equal quantity of air at 0° C.)

Comparing Conductors

Examine Fig. 18-2. Boiling water was poured into each container. But the thermometer in one of them now reads only 80° C. and the other still

TABLE **18-1**   COMPARING CONDUCTORS

Material	Conductivity
silver	19,300
copper	17,400
aluminum	8,800
iron	2,900
glass	44
concrete	35
water	25
wood	7
asbestos	4.8
linen	3.8
glass wool	2.6
cotton	2.4
rock wool	1.8
air at 0° C	1.0

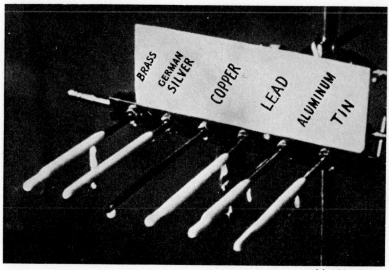

Johns-Manville Co.

18-1. Note the different rates at which the wax melts on these various metal rods. Which metals would you say are the best heat conductors? Which have the least heat conductivity?

reads nearly 100° C. The temperature is different because one container is wrapped in asbestos. Apparently the asbestos keeps the heat from passing out of the container. In the same way, when asbestos is wrapped around steam or hot-water pipes, it keeps them from losing heat. A material that is a poor conductor of heat is called an *insulator*. Name some other good insulators.

As you study Table 18-1, you will begin to see why rock wool and glass wool are placed inside the walls of houses as insulators. In winter they keep the indoor heat from escaping. In summer they keep the outdoor heat from being conducted indoors.

Is it wintertime? If it is, then you are probably wearing some good insulators — woolen clothing that keeps your body heat from escaping.

Why Do Materials Conduct Heat?

You know that heat is the energy of motion of molecules. You know that all materials are made of molecules. When we heat one end of a good conductor, the molecules at the heated end begin to move more rapidly. They bombard the slower moving molecules near them and set these to moving faster, too. They in turn hit their neighbors

and so on. This transfer of motion takes place down the whole length of the conductor till it is heated throughout. Good conductors transfer heat easily in this way.

Good conductors of heat are poor insulators, and poor conductors of heat are good insulators.

Gases as Insulators

What is the best insulator of all? Of all materials, gases are the best insulators — better than

18-2. Asbestos is used as a heat insulator because it is a poor conductor of heat. Boiling water was poured into the containers a few minutes ago. What has happened?

Johns-Manville Co.

18-3. Insulating materials like asbestos placed around these pipes prevent the loss of heat and save a large part of the fuel bill.

liquids or solids. Look at Table 18-1 again and see if this is not so.

Why is air such a good insulator? From your earlier reading you know that in a gas the moving molecules are much farther apart than the molecules of a solid or liquid. In a gas there is less chance for moving molecules to hit one another than there is in a liquid or solid. Thus in a gas the molecules cannot pass along their energy of motion or heat from one to another as easily as molecules of a liquid or a solid do.

Now if we could remove some of the molecules from a gas, we could have a still better insulator — or poorer conductor. We can get rid of some molecules of a gas with a powerful pump and thus create a vacuum. A partial *vacuum* is a space that has very few molecules in it.

Since the conduction of heat depends on molecules colliding with each other, a vacuum is the best insulator of all. This is the principle upon which the thermos bottle works (Fig. 18-4). There is a vacuum between the double walls of glass which means there are few molecules to conduct heat in or out. Next time you use a thermos bottle, examine it.

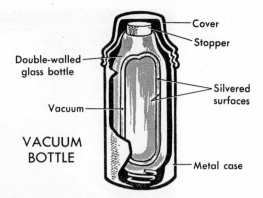

VACUUM BOTTLE

18-4. A thermos bottle keeps things hot or cold because the vacuum space does not conduct heat. In addition, the silvered surfaces reflect heat. How does reflection prevent heat from entering or leaving the bottle?

FROM CURRENT TO CURRENT

If you have any apparatus like that shown in Fig. 18-5, you can do an interesting experiment with heat. All you need is a pinwheel and a Bunsen burner, or another source of heat. If you hold the pinwheel above the burner as is shown in the diagram, the pinwheel will begin to turn. Why?

Convection Currents

The air above the burner is heated. As it warms up it expands — just as most solids and liquids expand when they are heated. As the

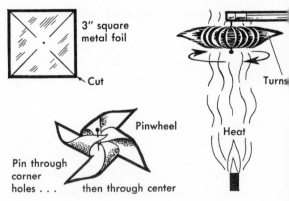

18-5. The spinning of a pinwheel above a flame indicates that rising air currents are present.

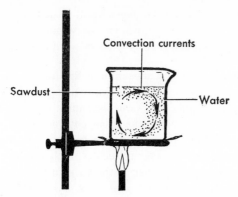

18-6. As this demonstration shows, heat is transferred in liquids by convection. In what direction does the hot water move? the cooler water?

heated air expands, it becomes lighter and lighter because there are fewer molecules of gases in a body of heated air than in the same volume of cool air. Thus the warm air is pushed up by the cool air which is heavier. It is the warm rising air which turns your pinwheel.

The warm rising air is called a *convection current*. A convection current is caused by some gas or liquid becoming warmer than its surroundings and therefore rising — or cooler than its surroundings and therefore contracting and sinking downward.

Wind is caused by a convection current in the atmosphere. What usually heats up the air? The sun, of course, is one source of heat.

You can watch convection currents in a liquid by warming one end of a beaker of water similar to the one in Fig. 18-6. Put in some sawdust shortly after you start heating the water. The sawdust, carried along by the convection currents, will show you how the warmer water rises and the cooler water settles. Does your sawdust move around and around in the direction of the arrows in Fig. 18-6?

In just the same way, in a room heated by a radiator, the heated air will rise and the cooler air will sink. If someone is smoking in a heated room, you can watch the smoke being carried about by convection currents much like the sawdust in your heated liquid. The heating systems of your house and school probably depend upon convection currents to carry heat from the radiators to the rest of the room.

Conduction and convection both play an important part in keeping you comfortably warm in winter and cool in summer. But there is also a third important way of transferring heat.

HEAT WAVES

Have you ever used a magnifying glass to burn a hole in a piece of paper? To do so, place the glass in the path of the sun's rays and focus it on the paper. Soon the paper burns as in Fig. 18-7. You have used the sun's light to make heat — heat great enough to start a fire.

This is nothing new to you if you have ever had a sunburn. As you have realized, the sun's rays do burn.

How does heat reach us from the sun? By conduction? Hardly! As you have learned, there are 93,000,000 miles between the sun and the earth, and a good deal of it is empty space. There are very few molecules in space. Since molecules are necessary for conduction of heat, you can see that heat could not be transferred from the sun to the earth by this method. You can also see that convection currents could not carry heat across 93,000,000 miles of airless space either. Heat from the sun reaches us by a third method called *radiation.*

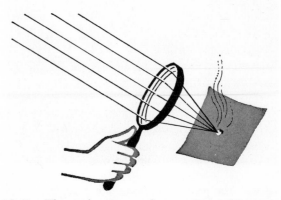

18-7. The sun's rays can be concentrated to produce enough heat to start a fire.

Heat Rays

Have you ever put your hand in front of a hot iron? What reached your hand? Whatever it was, it was (a) invisible and (b) heat-causing. We call these invisible things *heat rays* or *infrared rays*. We can take pictures of hot objects in the dark by means of film sensitive to these " invisible " heat rays (Fig. 18-8). Later on, in the section on " Invisible Heat Rays " (page 313), you will learn more about them.

Right now, it is enough to know that most of the heat we receive from the sun is a result of its radiation of infrared rays.

These rays travel at the speed of 186,000 miles per second — as do all light rays. When they hit an object, they set the molecules in the object moving — molecules in paper, in the steel of an automobile, in the cement of a sidewalk, or in the skin of your face. Whatever they strike, they make its molecules move faster, and the result is heat. For, as you remember, the movement of molecules *is* heat, and the faster their movement, the higher the temperature of the object in which they move.

That is why heat rays from the sun, focused on

Eastman Kodak Co.

18-8. This picture was taken in a pitch-dark room. How? Special film can be used to take pictures in invisible infrared light.

paper, can make the paper burn. That is why the sun's rays coming through the window of your living room can make the room warmer.

Conduction + Convection + Radiation

Perhaps you are now in your living room. Perhaps the sun's rays are streaming through the window and heating the room (by radiation). As the molecules in the floor are heated, they transfer their heat to other molecules, including the air (by conduction). Then as the air near the window is heated, it expands and rises. As it does so, cooler air comes in below and currents begin to circulate in the room (convection). All three methods of transporting heat work for you in your home.

HEATING YOUR HOME

Sooner or later you will have the problem of heating your home. If you own your own home, you will soon be thinking of fuel bills and boilers. And if you live in an apartment, your rent will include the heat and hot water you use. Heat will continue to play an important part in your life.

How Will You Heat Your Home?

Will you use hot-water heat, a hot-air heating system, steam heat, or radiant heating? Whichever one you choose, it must include all three of the following features:

1. a source of heat energy, such as a furnace or stove to burn fuel. (This changes the chemical energy in the fuel into heat energy.)
2. a way of getting the heat to the rooms where you will need it.
3. a way of spreading the heat around the room.

See how these three features are supplied by each of the common heating systems shown in Fig. 18-9.

Saving Fuel — Saving Heat

Whichever heating system you will choose, you certainly won't want to waste money by letting

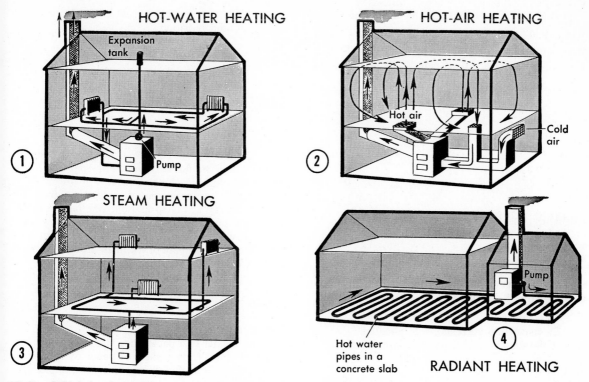

HOT-WATER HEATING

Expansion tank

Pump

①

HOT-AIR HEATING

Hot air

Cold air

②

STEAM HEATING

③

Hot water pipes in a concrete slab

Pump

④

RADIANT HEATING

18-9. Which heating system would you choose for your home? Why?

the heat leak out of your home. Look at Fig. 18-10. Which home is saving fuel? You are right if you think it's the one with the snow unmelted on the roof.

What would make the snow melt on the roof on the house in Fig. 18-10? Heat, of course. Where would the heat come from in the midst of winter? Yes, from inside the house. That would mean the roof is poorly insulated. But look at the roof on the right (Fig. 18-10). The snow is unmelted. The roof is well insulated, and heat is kept inside the house. Fuel is being saved and so is money.

A Warm Climate — Inside

If you use the information you have learned in this chapter, you will know how to keep your home warm when it is cold outside. But sometimes you don't want heat. You want to be cool indoors. For some uses you may even want temperatures below 0° C.

In short you want to have a capsule of perfect weather in your home — warm during winter,

Johns-Manville Co.

18-10. Which one of these roofs is better insulated?

cool during summer, cold in the refrigerator, and freezing in the freezer. In the next chapter we continue our story of indoor weather with a description of how to get rid of heat — of how to keep cool.

Looking Back . . . .

VOCABULARY
Each of the following terms represents a key word useful in understanding the chapter you have just studied. Give a definition of each one.

1. conduction
2. convection currents
3. insulator
4. radiation
5. vacuum
6. infrared rays

EXPLAIN WHY:
- Heat is conducted along the metal handle of a cooking utensil.
- Rock wool and glass wool are placed inside the walls of buildings.
- Poor conductors are good insulators.
- Air is a good insulator.
- A thermos bottle keeps cold fluids cold for several hours.
- When air is warmed, it expands.
- Wind is a convection current in the atmosphere.
- Heat from the sun reaches the earth by radiation.

- The air in your home is heated by conduction, convection, and radiation.

Going Further . . . .

APPLYING PRINCIPLES
1. If radiators in a home were suspended from the ceiling, there would be more floor space. What is wrong with this plan for radiators?
2. Study the ventilation of a room such as the kitchen. Devise a way to find out whether the warm air leaves the room through the upper open window or the lower open window. Draw a diagram with arrows to show the path of warm air from a hot stove to the window.
3. Explain the advantages and the disadvantages of these heating systems: hot-air, hot-water, steam, radiant.

THINGS TO DO
1. Boil water in a paper cup. Make a boxlike container of water from a sheet of paper by folding up the edges and fastening them with tape or clips. Place the container on a ringstand and pour in some water. Gently heat the bottom with a Bunsen burner until the water boils.
2. Trace the heating system in your home. Start with the furnace and explain how a room is heated.

READING FURTHER
Home Heating, Household Finance Corporation. This pamphlet gives you the costs and details of construction and operation of nine types of indoor heating equipment.

19

Keeping Cool

Today we know how to keep comfortably warm in winter. With our knowledge of science we have gone even further. We have learned how to keep comfortably cool in summer, too. The " cooled " movie and the air-conditioned room are becoming a part of daily life. Since food spoils unless it is kept cool, the icebox, refrigerator, and freezer are an important part of daily life, too. In the modern world cooling has become almost as important as heating.

A COOL BODY

Obviously one good way of keeping cool on a hot day is to keep uncomfortable heat from reaching your body. The man in the white asbestos suit is preventing the heat of the flames from reaching his body by surrounding himself with asbestos, a good insulator (Fig. 19-1). Thus heat cannot reach him by either conduction or convection or by radiation.

Absorption and Reflection

While your problem of keeping cool on a hot day is not apt to be so serious as his, still you will be more comfortable if you remember the following principle. All other things being equal, *heat rays warm a dark-colored object more than they warm a white object.*

Minnesota Mining & Manufacturing Co.

19-1. The wearer of this asbestos suit is quite comfortable in this oven heated to 1700 degrees Fahrenheit. The suits are useful in fire-fighting and in industries where repairs have to be made to ovens or boilers.

To illustrate this principle, set up the apparatus shown in Fig. 19-2. Be sure that one bulb or can is painted black, the other with a white paint. Attach a glass tube to each bulb and lower into a jar of water. Put the apparatus in the sun or in the bright light of a lamp for a few minutes as in Fig. 19-2. Now look at the tubes. Why is the level of water lower in the tube leading from the black bulb?

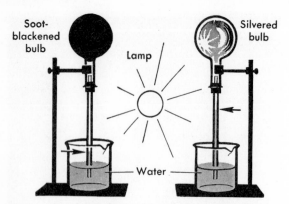

19-2. The blackened bulb absorbs more heat than the silvery bulb. Hence, it forces the water down the tube. Why is the water level higher at the right?

It must have happened because the air in the black bulb has expanded. This can happen only if the air molecules themselves have moved farther apart. This in turn can happen only if the air molecules have gained heat energy. In this case it is from the heat rays (infrared rays) poured out by the sun (or lamp). Since the air in the black bulb expanded, the black bulb must have *absorbed* more radiant heat than did the white bulb. Hence the white bulb must have *reflected away* more radiant heat than the black bulb.

You wear light-colored clothes in summer because they reflect radiant heat. Thus the molecules of the gases of air near you and in your skin are not heated up and their speed does not increase. You wear dark clothing in winter in order to absorb radiant heat.

You've probably seen this principle of absorption and reflection at work in other situations, too, such as these:

1. Have you ever touched a fender of a car (painted black) on a hot day? Next time you have this opportunity touch the chromium as well. You will find the fender much hotter than the chromium. Why?
2. Look at Fig. 19-3. Explain why the tanks containing flammable gasoline are painted a silvery white.

This principle works the other way around, too.

Fill a black container and a white or shiny container with hot water of the same temperature. Be sure the containers are about the same size. Let them stand. Every ten minutes take the temperature of the water in each container. Which container loses heat more quickly?

You will find that the black container loses heat faster. Dark objects radiate heat away faster than light-colored objects do.

1. Why were old coal stoves " blacked "?
2. The inner container of a thermos bottle is silvered on the inside and outside. Why?

In this section we have illustrated the facts that dark-colored objects absorb heat rays and also radiate them more readily than light-colored or shiny objects do. You have also seen how this idea can help you to control the flow of heat.

Molecules That Carry Away Heat Energy

Besides wearing light-colored clothing on a hot day, there is another way you can keep cool.

Suppose the day is hot and " muggy." That is, there is a good deal of moisture in the air and no breeze. You perspire uncomfortably. You turn

19-3. These men are spraying aluminum paint on oil tanks. Most of the sun's heat rays will be reflected by the metal and the temperature kept down. Why is this precaution necessary?

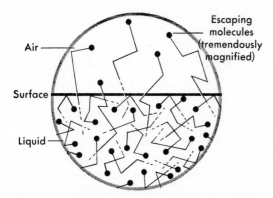

19-4. A molecule of a liquid evaporates only when it has gained enough heat energy from its neighbors to overcome the cohesive force of the molecules in the liquid.

on a fan and you are cooler at once. Why does the fan cool you?

The fan creates a current of air that carries off moist air near your perspiring skin. Thus the perspiration remaining on your skin can evaporate more easily.

Of the billions of molecules in a liquid, which are likely to evaporate, that is, escape into the air? Certainly, those at or near the surface. But not just any of these. Some of the molecules at the surface are moving downward. Furthermore, not all molecules have enough energy to escape (Fig. 19-4). Where, then, will an escaping molecule get the extra energy? It gets this extra energy from nearby molecules bumping it in their eternal zigzag motion. Since the molecules left behind will then have lost some energy, the liquid will become cooler.

You probably can see now that heat is absorbed by the air when a liquid evaporates. This is why the fan cools your skin on a hot day.

Try this on a fairly dry day. Wipe the back of one hand with a piece of moist cotton. Let the water evaporate. What happens? The molecules of water evaporating from your hand remove some of the heat energy from your skin. Your skin becomes cooler.

Try the same experiment using alcohol. You will find that your hand will become cool much faster than when you used water. Why? Alcohol

molecules evaporate faster than water. Thus they carry off heat much faster. An alcohol rub is cooling for this reason.

To evaporate molecules, you see, you need to supply them with extra heat energy. Hence *when molecules evaporate, they cool the surface from which they escape.* This is the principle on which your refrigerator works.

YOUR REFRIGERATOR

Wrap some cloth around the bulb of a thermometer and dip the cloth in some alcohol or some ether. From what you have just learned, can you predict what will happen?

The temperature of the thermometer will drop as the evaporating molecules carry off heat energy. You are observing the principle on which your refrigerator works.

An Ether Refrigerator

Let's design a *make-believe* refrigerator that runs on ether.

A very simple design is shown in Fig. 19-5. It has two containers, one inside the other. In the inner one you put your food. Surrounding it in the outer one is ether. (CAUTION: Ether is flammable. Don't use it near any flames.) With no air molecules to get in their way, the ether molecules can evaporate rapidly. Soon the evaporating molecules of ether cool the inner container and the food inside it.

19-5. Rapidly evaporating ether can lower the temperature of food below freezing point. Why?

Of course this is a very inconvenient and dangerous arrangement. Let us see how evaporation and condensation work in a real refrigerator.

The Refrigerator in Your Home

Examine Fig. 19-6 which is a simple diagram of your refrigerator. There are five important parts.

1. The liquid refrigerant is usually found in a small tank (not marked in this illustration). Ether is never used in real refrigerators. Liquids called *Freon* are generally used. They are nonexplosive, not poisonous, and liquefy easily.

2. A *pump* (P) causes a low pressure in the coils at C, allowing the liquid at R to evaporate. Hence, like the ether in your experiment, it becomes very cold. The cold gas moves around the coils which surround the ice trays, cooling them and forming ice.

3. As the pump sends the molecules of refrigerant into the coils at L, the gas is no longer cool. The molecules have taken heat from the box at C (thus cooling the box) and are now in the state of a warm gas.

4. The coils at L must be cooled. This is done by a fan so that the gas in these coils cools once more and becomes a liquid. The coils make up a small *radiator*. This radiator, usually on the back of your refrigerator against the wall, sends its heat out into the room. Look for it next time you go to your refrigerator.

5. The same pump which causes evaporation also helps condensation. For as a pump pulls at one end of the pipe (helping evaporation at R), it must push at the other end (helping condensation at L). The condensation is helped along by cooling at the radiator coils.

There is still one more device necessary — a device to help make a boundary between the low and high pressure areas created by the pump.

You can see that unless there were a boundary at J (Fig. 19-6), the liquid would be pumped around without ever evaporating, that is, it would never become a gas. In most refrigerators the tube is narrowed at J in such a way that the liquid must come out through a pinhole. This allows the liquid to spray out into the low-pressure side of the tube. Thus the low pressure plus the fact that the liquid is sprayed out in a fine mist helps the refrigerant to evaporate.

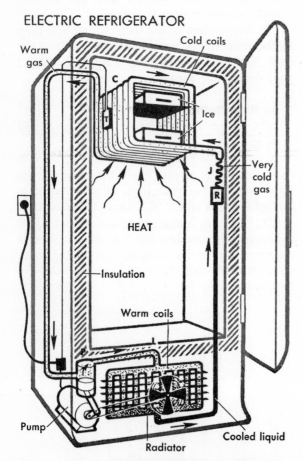

ELECTRIC REFRIGERATOR

Warm gas

Cold coils

C

T

Ice

J

R

Very cold gas

HEAT

Insulation

Warm coils

L

Pump

Radiator

Cooled liquid

19-6. How does the refrigerator use evaporation to cause cooling? Start with the warm gas at the upper left and follow its course. How does it become a very cold gas? The thermostat, T, controls the pump.

The " Gas " Refrigerator

Some refrigerators use a gas flame instead of a pump to circulate the refrigerant.

The heat of the gas flame can be made to produce the high pressure needed to make the gas turn into a liquid after it has evaporated. The " gas " refrigerator needs no motor. Hence it has no moving parts, and makes no noise.

One Hundred Years Ago
Whatever did people do before refrigerators were invented? They used ice — and some still do. It was more expensive (in the long run), inconvenient, and sometimes hard to get.

When our forefathers couldn't get ice, they used cool streams running next to their homes to cool milk and other food. Or they preserved foods by drying (dry or " jerked " venison); or salting (salt pork) or canning (preserves).

Now the modern refrigerator keeps food fresh for long periods of time. For it keeps food at such a low temperature that decay bacteria do not grow. Thus it protects our health.

A COOL HOUSE

In winter you want your house warm. In summer you want it cool. Few of us live in a climate where the temperature is always comfortable. Almost everywhere, particularly in the tropics, keeping cool in the summer is much to be desired.

The Warm House Is the Cool House
Strangely enough, once you have insulated your house to keep it warm inside in winter, you have taken the first step to keep it cool in summer. For if the walls keep heat in, they also keep it out.

During the summer some heat comes through the window glass by both conduction and radiation. If you live in a house built in the past few years, you may already have double windows sealed with a layer of air between them (Fig. 19-7). Since sealed-in air is a good insulator, less heat will be conducted through the window panes from the hot outdoors. Heat rays, of course, can still enter unless you cover the windows with shutters or shade them with trees or an overhanging roof.

Some modern houses are built with an over-

hang. In the summer the sun's direct rays hit the overhang. In the winter, however, the sun's slanting rays pass under the overhang and enter the windows, thus helping to heat the house. Many farmhouses are built to take advantage of this changing angle of the sun's rays.

The " Refrigerated " House
No doubt you have been in a " cooled " movie theater, or in an air-conditioned room. The room has been made into a kind of refrigerator. First, all the windows and doors have been closed. Second, the only air that comes in enters through the air-conditioning unit (Fig. 19-8).

Notice that the air-conditioning unit contains a refrigerator. The air which enters the house must pass the cold pipes of the refrigerator, or pipes of

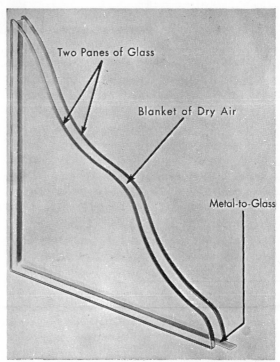

Libby-Owens-Ford Glass Co.

19-7. The sealed layer of air between the glass in double layer windows helps prevent heat from penetrating the room in the summer and from escaping in the winter.

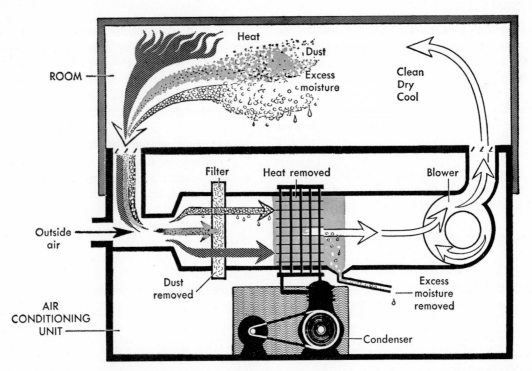

19-8. Diagram of an air-conditioning system. Follow the arrows to see how dust and excess moisture are removed from the air that circulates through the room. Excess moisture is caught in a pan and drained away.

brine (salt solution) which have been cooled by the refrigerant.

As the air goes through the air-conditioning unit, it is also cleaned either by passing through a moist glass wool filter or between electrified plates which attract dust particles. Also moisture is added or removed from the air to give the air you breathe the most healthful humidity.

Thus an air-conditioning unit can provide a room with clean air of just the right temperature and humidity all summer long and all winter.

The Future

Sooner or later, just as the heating systems you have studied in Chapter 18 have become common, so will cooling systems. Even now many home builders are installing systems which both heat the house in winter and cool it in summer. Your home can be made a capsule of perfect weather all year round wherever you may live.

Looking Back . . . .

VOCABULARY

Use these key words in complete sentences to show that you understand their meaning.

1. condensation
2. evaporation
3. refrigerant
4. refrigerator
5. Freon
6. absorption
7. reflection

REVIEW QUESTIONS

1. Why is it better to wear light-colored clothes rather than dark-colored ones in summer?
2. Explain why an alcohol rub leaves you much cooler.
3. Why are the chemicals called Freon used in refrigerators?
4. Alcohol-soaked cloth is wrapped around a thermometer. Another thermometer is left dry. In which thermometer does the temperature fall Why?

5. In condensation, water vapor is changed into liquid water. Is heat taken up in the process, or is heat given off? Explain.

Going Further . . . .

APPLYING PRINCIPLES

1. Make a diagram of a refrigerator and label the main parts. Under your diagram explain where the chemicals (Freons) are condensed and where they are evaporated. Why does a refrigerator need to be defrosted?

2. How may homes be cooled in summer? How may the cooled air be made to circulate to all rooms of the house?

3. A porous clay flower vase was filled with water. Although the room temperature was in the high 80's, the water in the vase was cool to drink. Explain.

4. If possible, examine the way a greenhouse is built. Two layers of glass are used, painted white, with a space between the layers. Explain how the air in the greenhouse is kept warm in the wintertime. What prevents excess heat in the summertime?

TRY THIS

Freeze water by evaporation. In a well-ventilated room, wet the outside of an aluminum cup and place it on a piece of cardboard. Pour some ether into the cup, and let it evaporate. *Caution:* Be sure there is no flame nearby. Also, be careful not to breathe in the ether.

The cooling caused by the evaporation of the ether freezes the water, and the cup sticks to the cardboard. Fanning the surface of the cup will speed up the evaporation. A metal bottle cap may be used instead of a cup.

CHAPTER

20

Our Outdoor Weather

In the preceding chapters you have seen how conduction, convection, and radiation are important in keeping you comfortable indoors. In this chapter we shall see that they have a great deal to do with the weather outdoors, too. Is it too hot out? You can be sure that conduction, convection, or radiation will presently bring you cooler weather. Is it too cold out? You have seen that the only way warmth can ever reach you is in one of those three ways.

WARMING THE EARTH'S ATMOSPHERE

From your study of Unit I you know that the earth is a great ball coasting through airless empty space. Clinging tightly to the earth's surface is a film of air only a few miles thick — our atmosphere. At the bottom of the atmosphere you are warm enough due to the fact that the atmosphere acts like a blanket. What keeps our atmosphere from cooling off and freezing us to death?

The answer is *radiation* from the sun.

The atmosphere does not catch much of the sun's radiation. Most sunlight goes right through the atmosphere to the earth's surface, where it heats the ground. Then the warmed ground heats the air close to it by *conduction*.

You already know that when air is warmed, it expands and rises, forming *convection currents*. Local winds are caused by convection currents in the atmosphere. Local winds stir up the atmosphere, mixing the warmed air with colder air.

Thus radiation, conduction, and convection are all at work carrying heat from the sun to the air around you.

Sea Breezes and Radiation

The seashore is one of the coolest places to be in summer, as you no doubt know. The reason for this is that water is not warmed by the sun's rays as quickly as the land is. Thus, the rising convection currents will be stronger over the land than over the sea. As this heated air rises from the ground, cooler air flows in from the sea to take its place (Fig. 20-1). This is the *sea breeze*. Why are sea breezes usually strongest in the afternoon?

If the air is clear, as night comes, the land radiates its heat away faster than water does. Thus as the land cools off during the night, a gentle *land breeze* may blow from the land out to sea (Fig. 20-2).

HUMIDITY

When we talk about the *humidity,* we refer to the amount of water vapor in the air. The water in air is called *water vapor,* since it is in the form of a gas. And if the air has in it all the dissolved water vapor it can hold, we say that the air is *saturated.* The following experiment will help you to understand this.

When Air Gets Wringing Wet

Dissolve as much salt as you can in half a test tube of water. You can be sure you have dissolved as much as possible when there is a layer of undissolved salt in the bottom of the tube. When a solution has dissolved all the salt it can hold, it is *saturated.*

Warm the tube gently and you will find that more salt will dissolve. You can see the salt is much more *soluble* in hot water than in cold.

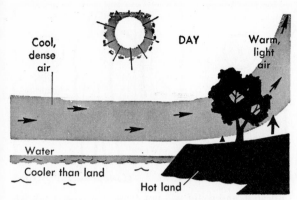

Cool, dense air

DAY

Warm, light air

Water

Cooler than land

Hot land

20-1. What causes a sea breeze? Compare with Fig. 20-2.

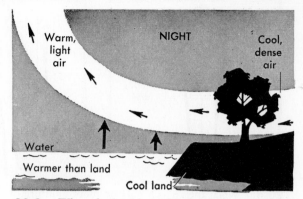

Warm, light air

NIGHT

Cool, dense air

Water

Warmer than land

Cool land

20-2. When the land is cooler than the water, land breezes result.

When you have a saturated solution of hot water, set the test tube aside to cool, and watch it closely. Do you suppose that the water can go on holding all that salt in solution as it continues to cool off?

You will soon see the answer to this question. Tiny crystals of salt appear in the water and eventually settle to the bottom in a miniature snow storm (Fig. 20-3). The salt that the cooling water is unable to dissolve is coming out of the solution. At room temperature once more the water contains the same amount of dissolved salt that it had when you started.

In just the same way, water can " dissolve " in air. Like your hot water dissolving more and more salt, warm air can hold more water vapor than cold air can. In fact, saturated air on a summer day may hold ten times as much water vapor as saturated air at freezing temperature.

What do you think will happen as warm saturated air cools off? As the air cools off, some water vapor will condense to water. You have seen this happen many times. Fog, dew, clouds, and rain are all examples of water formed when air, saturated with water, cools. When temperatures drop below freezing, snow, hail, and frost form.

Relative Humidity

The air surrounding you right now has water vapor in it, but it is probably not saturated. If it contains only 60% of all the water vapor it *could*

hold, the weatherman says, " The relative humidity is 60%." If the air were saturated, he would say, " The relative humidity is 100%."

Relative humidity is the amount of water vapor in the air at a certain temperature compared to the amount the air can hold at that temperature.

A relative humidity of 100% in your classroom would make you very uncomfortable. Even though the thermometer read 68° F., you would probably complain of the heat. Here is the reason. You have seen (page 219) that the evaporation of your perspiration helps to keep you cool. But in a room full of saturated air *none* of your perspiration can evaporate. Thus you are uncomfortably warm even at 68° F.

The *lower* the relative humidity the faster your

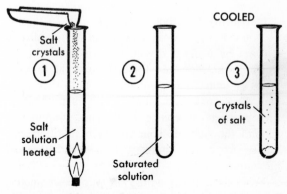

Salt crystals

① Salt solution heated

② Saturated solution

COOLED

③ Crystals of salt

20-3. A cooled liquid can hold less dissolved matter than a warm one.

 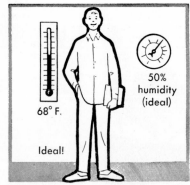 

20-4. When the air can hold no more moisture, it is saturated, and water will not evaporate from your skin to cool you.

perspiration can evaporate and cool your skin. Thus in a classroom at 0% relative humidity you would feel chilly even though the thermometer still read 68° F.

For you to be comfortable, the air around you should be about 68° F. and the relative humidity about 50% (Fig. 20-4).

In winter the air outdoors usually contains very little water vapor. When this air is heated up indoors, its ability to hold water vapor is increased. Hence its relative humidity will fall even lower. It may become so low that your perspiration evaporates very rapidly. You would have to turn the thermostat up to 75° F. in order to feel comfortably warm. Moreover such dry air is unhealthy since moisture evaporates rapidly from your nose and throat, leaving them unprotected and more open to attack by germs.

Measuring Relative Humidity

You can measure the percentage of humidity in a room by using a dry-bulb thermometer and a wet-bulb thermometer. First measure the temperature of your room with the dry-bulb thermometer. Then, make a wet-bulb thermometer by wetting a piece of coarse cloth and wrapping it around the bulb of your dry-bulb thermometer. Fan it for a few minutes, then read the thermometer again.

From these two readings of your thermometer, you can quickly find the relative humidity by using Table 20-1.

How does this method work?

If the air around you is very dry (relative humidity very low), water will evaporate from the wet-bulb thermometer, and thereby cool it. The drier the air, the more rapidly water will evaporate and the more the wet bulb will be chilled.

On the other hand, if the air is saturated (relative humidity = 100%), the wet-bulb thermometer will not cool at all; it will have the same temperature as the dry-bulb thermometer.

Thus by reading a dry-bulb thermometer and a wet-bulb thermometer, you can easily find whether the air is moist or dry. Your humidity-measuring apparatus is called a *hygrometer* (hy-GROM-uh-ter). Two common kinds of hygrometers are shown in Fig. 20-5.

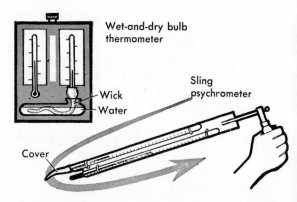

20-5. When you use these hygrometers to determine the humidity, you will want to use the humidity table on page 227.

TABLE 20-1 RELATIVE HUMIDITY

TEMPERATURE OF DRY BULB

	61	62	63	64	65	66	67	68	69	70	71	72	73	74	75	76	77	78	79	80	
41	7	4	2																		41
42	10	8	6	4	2																42
43	14	12	10	7	5	3	2														43
44	18	16	13	11	9	7	5	3	1												44
45	22	20	17	15	12	10	8	6	5	3	1										45
46	27	24	21	18	16	14	12	10	8	6	4	3	1								46
47	31	28	25	22	20	17	15	13	11	9	7	6	4	3	1						47
48	35	32	29	26	24	21	19	16	14	12	10	9	7	5	4	3	1				48
49	40	36	33	30	27	25	22	20	18	15	13	12	10	8	7	5	4	3	1		49
50	44	41	37	34	31	29	26	23	21	19	17	15	13	11	9	8	6	5	4	3	50
51	49	45	42	38	35	32	30	25	24	22	20	18	16	14	12	11	9	8	6	5	51
52	54	50	46	43	39	36	33	31	28	25	23	21	19	17	15	13	12	10	9	7	52
53	58	54	50	47	44	40	37	34	32	29	27	24	22	20	18	16	14	13	11	10	53
54	63	59	55	51	48	44	41	38	35	33	30	28	25	23	21	19	17	16	14	12	54
55	68	64	60	56	52	48	45	42	39	36	33	31	29	26	24	22	20	18	17	15	55
56	73	69	64	60	56	53	49	46	43	40	37	34	32	29	27	25	23	21	19	18	56
57	78	74	69	65	61	57	53	50	47	44	41	38	35	33	30	28	26	24	22	20	57
58	84	79	74	70	66	61	58	54	51	48	45	42	39	36	34	31	29	27	25	23	58
59	89	84	79	74	70	66	62	58	55	51	48	45	42	39	37	34	32	30	28	26	59
60	94	89	84	79	75	71	66	62	59	55	52	49	46	43	40	38	35	33	31	29	60
61	100	94	89	84	80	75	71	67	63	59	56	53	50	47	44	41	39	36	34	32	61
62		100	95	90	85	80	75	71	67	64	60	57	53	50	47	44	42	39	37	35	62
63			100	95	90	85	80	76	72	68	64	(61)	57	54	51	48	45	43	40	38	63
64				100	95	90	85	80	76	72	68	65	61	58	54	51	48	46	43	41	64
65					100	95	90	85	81	77	72	69	65	61	58	55	52	49	46	44	65
66						100	95	90	85	81	77	73	69	65	62	59	56	53	50	47	66
67							100	95	90	86	81	77	73	69	66	62	59	56	53	50	67
68								100	95	90	86	82	78	74	70	66	63	60	57	54	68
69									100	95	90	86	82	78	74	70	67	63	60	57	69
70										100	95	91	86	82	78	74	71	67	64	61	70
71											100	95	91	86	82	78	74	71	68	64	71
72												100	95	91	86	82	79	75	71	68	72
73													100	95	91	87	83	79	75	72	73
74														100	96	91	87	83	79	75	74
75															100	96	91	87	83	79	75
76																100	96	91	87	83	76
77																	100	96	91	87	77
78																		100	96	91	78
79																			100	96	79
80																				100	80
	61	62	63	64	65	66	67	68	69	70	71	72	73	74	75	76	77	78	79	80	

TEMPERATURE OF WET BULB

Suppose the dry-bulb thermometer reads 72° F. and the wet-bulb thermometer 63° F. Look down the column in the table giving the dry-bulb temperature. Then look across the line giving the temperature of the wet-bulb thermometer. The number in the box where the column and the line meet is the percentage of relative humidity, 61% in this example.

HYGROMETERS

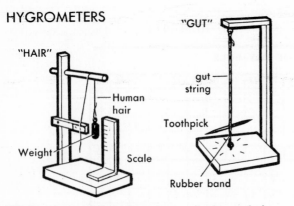

20-6. A simple hair hygrometer can be made in a few minutes by using one long hair (preferably free of oil). You may also make the simple hygrometer shown from a gut string that twists and untwists as the humidity changes.

Both hygrometers shown in Fig. 20-5 require the use of Table 20-1 to find the humidity. An even simpler form of hygrometer containing a long human hair (Fig. 20-6) can be made to show the relative humidity directly on a dial. This hygrometer works because human hair contracts in dry weather and stretches in damp weather. You will find it an interesting and easy project to make such a hygrometer.

Wringing Water Out of the Air

You have just seen that when air is warmed, its relative humidity decreases. On the other hand, you know that if air is cooled, its ability to hold water vapor is reduced and hence its relative humidity is increased. If you cool air far enough, its relative humidity will soar to 100% and dew, fog, clouds, rain, or snow will begin to form. The temperature at which condensation of water vapor takes place is called the *dew point*.

Surely you have seen moisture-laden air being cooled below its dew point. For example:

On a warm summer day dew forms on the outside of a glass of ice water as the humid summer air is chilled and can no longer hold all its water vapor.

On a winter day moisture forms on the mirror or the inside of the bathroom window as warm humid air in the bathroom is chilled below its dew point.

Perhaps you have been able to "see your breath" outdoors on a cold winter day as your humid breath is chilled below its dew point.

Every time you defrost a refrigerator you are removing water vapor that froze on the ice trays as warm air from the kitchen or from warm food put into the refrigerator was chilled below its dew point.

Certainly you have looked up in the sky and seen fleecy white clouds. Here too is a body of air that has been chilled below its dew point. And every time it rains moist air has been chilled below its dew point.

WHAT MAKES IT RAIN?

Anything that cools the air below its dew point tends to form clouds and very possibly rain or snow.

There are several common ways by which air is cooled in large quantities to make clouds, rain, snow, dew, or fog.

One way that often occurs in nature is shown in Fig. 20-7. Here you see winds blowing against a mountainside and being pushed upward. As the air rises toward the top of the mountain, it will expand. (Remember, air expands as the pressure on it grows less.) As air expands, it cools. If the mountain is high enough, the air will be cooled below its dew point before it reaches the top. A cloud will form, and rain may fall presently.

This is precisely what occurs along the west coast of the United States as winds off the Pacific Ocean are pushed up the slopes of the Sierra Nevadas. No wonder there is excellent farming land along the West Coast; the soil has sufficient water from the heavy rainfall.

The farmer just to the east of the Sierra Nevadas has a much harder time though. The winds that reach him over the crest of the mountains have lost much of their moisture. Moreover, as they descend the eastern slopes the air is compressed and hence grows warmer. At once its rela-

WEST   Cooling causes rain, snow   EAST

Rising air cools

Descending air is heated

Picks up moisture

Desert

20-7. Clouds moving over mountains cool as they are lifted up, causing condensation of rain or snow.

tive humidity decreases. Do you see how the dry air, cloudless sky, and dry lands of Nevada and Utah are caused?

Warm and Cold Air Masses

But you do not have to have a mountain range to push moist air uphill. Most bad weather occurs along the boundary between a *warm air mass* and a *cooler air mass*. This boundary is called a *front*. When a large mass of moving warm air (that may have come up from the Gulf of Mexico) collides with a large mass of cool air, there is almost sure to be rain along this warm front. The warm air, being lighter than the cool air, slides uphill over the cool air exactly like the moist ocean air being forced upward by the Sierra Nevadas or

Rocky Mountains (Fig. 20-8). This leads to clouds and rain or snow for the same reason as previously explained.

If moving cool air runs into a mass of warm air, the same result will occur at this cold front. The cool air slides underneath the warm air and wedges it sharply upward (Fig. 20-9). You may have observed that cool water flows beneath the warm water in a bathtub in a similar way.

Daily Weather

All over the United States cool masses of air from the north and west are meeting and mixing with warmer air masses from the south and southwest. These masses of air, each covering many states, and sometimes the entire country, slowly

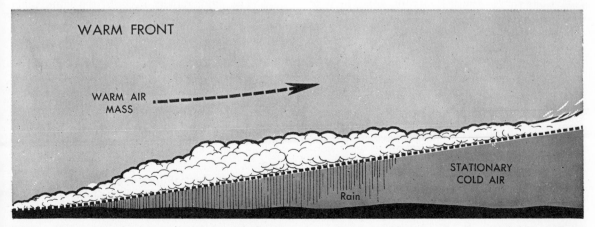

WARM FRONT

WARM AIR MASS

STATIONARY COLD AIR

Rain

20-8. When a warm air mass meets a cold air mass, the moisture in the warm air mass condenses to form clouds. Then it may rain.

20-9. The heavy cold air pushes under light warm air. The rising warm air cools, condenses, and forms storm clouds. Then there may be a thunderstorm.

drift eastward as they twist and turn and mix. Fig. 20-10 (left) is a partial reproduction of a daily weather map in which you can see the weather map boundaries between air masses, called *fronts,* marked in heavy lines. Look at the weather map in Fig. 20-10 (right) showing the fronts the next day. You will see that the pattern of fronts has drifted eastward, changing shape, perhaps spilling rain or snow as the fronts move forward.

Weathermen study the movement of air masses and fronts as well as many other conditions such as temperature, humidity, and wind velocity in order to predict the kind of weather likely to occur. Long-range forecasts are of great help to aviation, industry, and agriculture.

Thunderstorms

We have seen that air can be pushed upward by running into mountainsides or by a warm and a cool air mass bumping into one another. However, there is a third way by which air is caused to rise and cool and form clouds and rain. A thunderstorm is a good illustration of what happens (Fig. 20-11).

Thunderstorms usually occur when the air is very warm and contains a great deal of moisture. Under these conditions a chain reaction of great violence can occur. It acts like this:

1. Warm humid air rises, perhaps as a convec-

tion current on a sunny summer afternoon.
2. As the air rises, it cools. It is cooled below its dew point, and water vapor condenses to form a cloud. Rain falls.
3. As water vapor *condenses,* heat is *released.* (This is the opposite of *evaporation* when heat is *absorbed.*)
4. The heat released by condensation of water vapor warms the air and causes it to expand.
5. As the air expands it becomes less dense, more buoyant, and hence rises faster.
6. The faster it rises the more rapidly it cools.
7. The more rapidly it cools, the more water vapor condenses.
8. The more rapidly water vapor condenses, the more heat is released.
9. The more rapidly heat is released, . . . And the cycle starts over again.

Over and over again, faster and faster, these steps are repeated. The harder it rains the more violently the warm moist air rushes upward. Its vertical speed can reach more than 200 miles an hour.

The power of a thunderstorm results from the release of heat by the condensing water vapor within it. Fueled by this source alone, a big thunderstorm releases more energy as it runs its course than several atomic bombs.

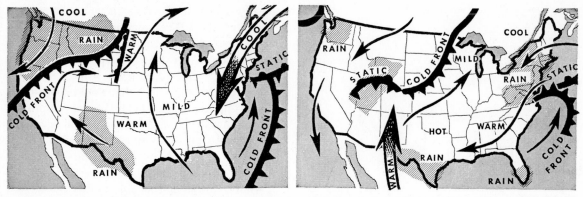

20-10. Compare these two weather maps — mapped on successive days. How has the position of the fronts changed? What has caused the change? Can you explain the fronts marked " warm " and " static "?

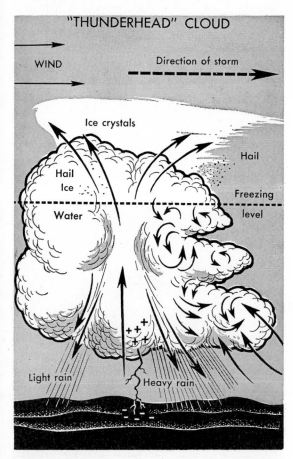

20-11. Study this diagram of a typical thunderhead. Notice its size and the violent air currents inside the cloud. Why is it dangerous to fly through this cloud?

Lightning

In its violence the rising air splits big droplets of rain into little ones. This process gives each little droplet a tiny electric charge much as when you rub a glass rod with silk. Presently, when the electric charges between different parts of a thundercloud or between the cloud and the ground become great enough, they will flow together once more in a flash of lightning. *Lightning* is an enormous electric current flowing through the air for a fraction of a second. The heat of a lightning flash expands the air with explosive force — not to mention anything the lightning hits! — and the resulting sound is *thunder*.

Notice how the energy of thunder and lightning comes from the energy of the thunderstorm wind — which in turn comes from the heat energy of condensing water vapor.

If you live on a farm or on a house on a hilltop, you may have lightning rods on your roof (Fig. 20-12). A *lightning rod* is a pointed rod on the top of a building. It is connected by a heavy wire to a metal plate or a pipe buried in the ground. A lightning rod protects your house because it prevents the collection of an electric charge large enough to cause lightning. As a charge-laden thunderstorm drifts over your house, electric charge flows from the earth up the lightning rod and off its sharp point into the air, tending to neutralize the opposite charge on the cloud.

20-12. The lightning rods on the barn conduct the electric current harmlessly to the ground. (The negative charge in the cloud repels electrons in the ground, thus giving the ground an opposite, or positive, charge. Hint: why is lightning attracted to the ground?)

Moreover, if lightning does strike your house anyway, the heavy wire from the lightning rod provides an easy highway for the lightning to travel harmlessly down to the ground. Buildings protected with lightning rods can be struck again and again without any damage. The Empire State Building in New York City has been struck by lightning as often as once a minute during thunderstorms without any harm to the building or to the people in it.

Man-made Weather

Man has found a way of his own to make it rain! The day is still a long way off when a farmer can control the rainfall on his crops, but man's first steps in controlling the weather have already been taken. In 1947 Dr. Vincent Schaefer found he could make it snow by sprinkling pellets of dry ice into clouds under just the right conditions (Fig. 20-13).

It takes an experienced scientist to know when a cloud or moist air can be successfully " seeded " with dry ice. Also unfortunately, the right kind of conditions for successful seeding do not seem to occur very often.

If you are looking for clouds or for moist air to " seed," you must find some which are already cooled below the dew point. Moreover, you must be sure that you have air whose humidity is *more* than 100%! Yes, air *can* have a relative humidity over 100%. Under some conditions air can be cooled far below its dew point before water vapor begins to condense. Some clouds, too, contain extra water vapor that would condense at once if only given some help. Dry ice can provide the help needed. It acts as a center on which the extra water vapor can fasten itself briefly and turn into rain or snow. Crystals of silver iodide seem to work well, too.

While you may not be able to find and to seed a cloud in order to make rain yourself, you can easily do an experiment that illustrates the principle. In a very clean flask prepare a hot saturated solution of photographer's " hypo " (sodium thiosulfate). Pour some of the hot saturated solution into another clean flask in order to get rid of any undissolved crystals in the bottom of the flask. As your solution cools, you might expect a gentle rain of " hypo " to form and to settle to the bottom as it did in your experiment with salt early in the chapter. But no such thing happens! Even at room temperature your solution remains clear.

General Electric Co.

20-13. Here Dr. Vincent Schaefer is experimenting with dry ice to make snow.

Your solution now resembles a cloud whose relative humidity is far above 100%, a cloud from which water vapor *would* condense if only it were seeded. Now you should seed your " hypo " solution. You do this by dropping in one tiny crystal of " hypo." At once the extra " hypo " in the solution crystallizes. There is so much of it that the contents of the flask actually becomes solid! Your seeding experiment works in a way similar to Dr. Schaefer's famous cloud-seeding experiment.

It is very likely that man-made rain will be of increasing benefit to the farmer. Today many men are hard at work learning how to cause rainfall. You will probably be hearing about their progress throughout your lifetime.

Looking Back . . . .

VOCABULARY

The following are the key words to the main ideas in this chapter. Give a definition for each term.

1. clouds	8. land breeze
2. dew	9. rain
3. dew point	10. relative humidity
4. fog	11. saturated
5. front	12. sea breeze
6. humidity	13. snow
7. hygrometer	14. wind

REVIEW QUESTIONS

1. What are the causes of land and sea breezes?
2. What conditions make vapor condense?
3. In air having the same amount of moisture, why does warm air have a lower relative humidity than colder air?
4. How can we measure relative humidity?
5. How can you determine the relative humidity with the aid of a hygrometer?
6. Compare the amounts of moisture that may be held by warm air and cold air.
7. What are the factors that affect the amount of rainfall in your locality?
8. Trace the cycle of events in a thunderstorm.

Going Further . . . .

THOUGHT QUESTIONS

1. Why does fanning make you feel cooler?
2. How does a lightning rod protect a building?
3. Which air has more moisture — air with a relative humidity of 40% or a relative humidity of 60% (assuming that the temperature is the same)?
4. Why do you feel warmer when the temperature is 80° F., relative humidity 80%, than in air which is 87° F. with a relative humidity of 50%?
5. Study the weather map in a newspaper for two or three days in succession. Trace the path of one warm front and one cold front. What kind of weather often results when a warm front meets a cold front?
6. Explain how clouds can be " seeded " to cause rain to fall.

THINGS TO DO

1. Show what happens when a warm front meets a cold front. In a kettle with a spout boil some water. Hold up a cold plate of glass near the steam from the spout. What happens at the point of contact when this " warm front " meets the " cold front "? This is condensation of water vapor into water.
2. Make a cloud. Attach a rubber bulb to a flask by means of a tube in a one-hole stopper. Wet the inside of the flask and put the stopper in place. In a short while the air in the flask will become saturated. Now press the bulb, hold it for a few seconds, and then release it suddenly. A cloud should form in the flask. If it does not, try pressing and releasing the bulb again. The cloud forms because the sudden expansion cools the air so that the dew point is reached.

If smoke from a match is put into the flask, the cloud will be more intense, because the dust particles act as centers for the droplets to form.

READING FURTHER

Weather Wise, American Meteorological Society, Boston, Mass., a magazine that includes simple experiments you will find interesting to do.

All About the Weather by Ivan Ray Tannehill, Random House, 1953. This book tells a great deal about the weather without using technical language.

Understanding the Weather by Morris Longstreth, Macmillan, 1953. Written for the general reader, this book tells what tools the amateur needs to predict the weather, and how to use them.

Weathercraft by A. F. Spilhaus, Viking, 1951, tells how to assemble and operate a home weather station with materials that may be found around the house or be bought in a dime store.

Putting Electricity to Work

IF YOU have just been doing hard physical labor for an hour, you will be sorry to learn that a one-tenth horsepower electric motor could have supplied about the same amount of energy for just two-fifths of a cent! Yes, one whole horsepower of electrical energy costs today around four cents an hour. At the touch of a switch you surely have the energy of several horses at your command *right now*. Lighting and heating your house, cooking, traveling in elevators and trains, using radios, telephones, and TV, you command more physical power than the richest Roman of 100 B.C. with his hundreds of slaves — more indeed than many wealthy Americans of the year 1900.

Electricity has given us more than power. It has given us ways of exchanging ideas and news instantly with people half a world away. Radio, TV, and the telephone give us pleasure and knowledge undreamed of a century ago.

Electricity even extends our senses so that with its help we can see invisibly small objects, perform mathematical calculations at lightning speed, detect invisible rays, heal sick bodies faster, peer through fog, darkness, and solid objects, or predict the outcome of elections — to mention only a few of its talents.

In doing so much of man's work, electricity gives us the greatest gift of all. It relieves us of drudgery and gives us time and opportunities for other things — to explore our human powers, to realize our capabilities, to try to understand the world around us.

In this unit we shall take a close look at this extraordinary form of energy — one of the most versatile and powerful servants of man.

◀ *Each minute giant transformers channel electrical energy to homes and factories.*

CHAPTER 21

Sparks and Shocks

In this chapter, you will be looking at electricity as scientists saw it more than 200 years ago — about the time of the American Revolution. You will see the small signs — twitching and swaying, mysterious attractions and repulsions — from which men have brought today's amazing science of electricity, that has done so much to shape the world you live in.

One of the most important discoveries made was the Leyden jar. It is still in use today. And how it was discovered makes an unusual story.

STORING ELECTRICAL CHARGES

The man in the powdered wig and lacy ruffled shirt is about to make a shocking discovery.

The time is 1746. The scene is a science laboratory in Leyden, Holland (Fig. 21-1). The question before the professor and his assistants is: What will happen if electricity is conducted into a flask of water?

One assistant cranks the electrical machine, and the glass globe spins. The professor holds his hands against the whirling globe. The friction of his hands rubbing the glass makes electricity. The electricity is taken off the glass by the chain dangling on it and conducted by the attached chain to the metal rod. From the rod the electricity can get to the water by way of the second chain.

Cuneus, the other assistant, holds up the flask so that the chain touches the water. The machine whirs softly. All eyes are on the flask of water.

Nothing happens.

Cuneus raises a hand to unfix the chain from the rod. Suddenly there is an enormous spark, a crash as the flask smashes on the floor, and Cuneus slumps to the ground, unconscious. A tremendous amount of electricity has been produced, far greater than ever before. That magnificent spark . . . !

Thus was the " Leyden jar " discovered — the " storer-up " of electricity known to us as the *capacitor* (kuh-PASS-ih-tohr) or *condenser*. It is used in every radio and television set today. Its discovery opened up new paths into the strange, unknown world of electricity, new paths for the explorers. It was some time, however, before the professor of Leyden and his scientific colleagues could explain how the Leyden jar worked.

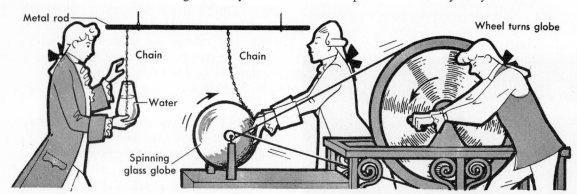

Metal rod — Chain — Water — Chain — Spinning glass globe — Wheel turns globe

21-1. Discoveries in science have often come unexpectedly. This was one — the discovery that electricity could be stored.

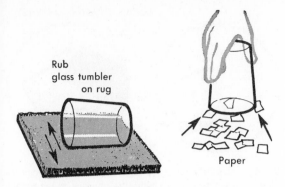

Rub glass tumbler on rug

Paper

21-2. Charged with electricity, the glass attracts uncharged bits of paper.

To see what the explanation was we shall need to do some experiments of our own — safe ones! We shall need to learn what the Leyden professor and other learned scientists knew about electricity at the time of Cuneus' painful accident (from which he recovered).

CHARGE IT

Hold the bottom of a glass tumbler close over some very small bits of light paper. What happens? Nothing.

Now rub the tumbler vigorously, with a cloth or on a carpet, and hold it above the bits of paper (Fig. 21-2). What happens now shows that the paper fragments are *attracted* by the glass. By rubbing, the glass of the tumbler has become *charged with electricity*. It attracts the *uncharged* paper.

Charge It! — Glass

Does this attraction work only on bits of light paper?

Balance a ruler — or even a yardstick — on the rounded back of a book. Charge the tumbler again by friction — rubbing. Bring it close over one end of the ruler. The force of attraction is present.

Balance a metal rod in the same way — or hang it in balance from a thread. Is there attraction between the metal and the charge of elec-

tricity on the glass? You can test other materials as well.

Friction charges glass with electricity.

The charged object attracts uncharged objects.

This accounts for the spinning glass globe of the "electrical machine" used by the professor at Leyden, and what happened when he rubbed his hands against it. Glassy substances in general can be charged with electricity.

As long ago as 600 B.C. a Greek named Thales (THAY-leez) observed that a lump of amber attracted small particles in a similar way when rubbed. In fact, the Greek word for amber is *electron*.

Charge It! — Rubber

Blow up a rubber balloon. Rub it with your hands. Hold it over some tiny bits of paper. The balloon has become charged with electricity and will attract uncharged bits of paper just as the glass tumbler did. In fact, it may even stick to the wall.

This shows that, like glass:

Rubber can be charged with electricity by friction.

The charged object attracts uncharged objects.

Blow up another balloon, and charge it. Hang the two charged balloons with string or thread as shown (Fig. 21-3). They *repel* each other.

Something new has appeared, since the two balloons push away from each other. Charged rubber repels charged rubber.

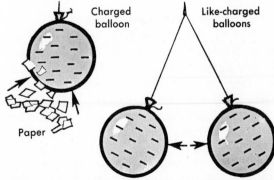

Charged balloon

Like-charged balloons

Paper

21-3. One balloon, charged with electricity, attracts uncharged paper; but two balloons, charged alike, repel each other.

Will charged glass repel charged glass, too? If you charge a glass rod, suspend it, and bring another charged glass rod up to it, you'll see that they do repel each other.

It seems as if charged things do repel charged things. But all of the evidence is not in yet. There is one more trial to make. You have tried glass to glass. You have also tried rubber to rubber. Now try glass to rubber.

Charge It! — Glass and Rubber

What do you think will happen if charged glass is brought close to charged rubber? Attraction? Repulsion? Or nothing at all?

Charge the glass tumbler by rubbing it. Charge the balloon by rubbing it. Bring the tumbler to the balloon. They cling together. There is *attraction* between these two charged bodies.

Charged glass repels charged glass. Charged rubber repels charged rubber. But charged glass *attracts* charged rubber.

After many experiments, scientists then agreed that *there must be two different kinds of electrical charges.* One kind is made by rubbing glass. The other kind is made by rubbing rubber. How these electrical charges behave is summed up in these *electrostatic laws,* as scientists have called them:

– Charges of the *same* kind *repel* each other.
– Charges of *different* kinds *attract* each other.

Try these principles on the demonstrations you have just seen. You will find that they describe what happens every time.

Two Charges: Two Electricities?

There are two different kinds of *charge* at work in our demonstrations. One kind of charge is made by rubbing glass; the other kind by rubbing rubber. Does this mean that there must be two different kinds of *electricity* at work?

Some scientists thought so, at one time. They spoke of "vitreous electricity," made with glassy substances, and "resinous electricity," obtained from rubber-like material. This theory worked well. It explained the electrical attractions and repulsions that were known then.

However, Benjamin Franklin proposed a sim-

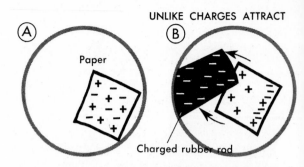

UNLIKE CHARGES ATTRACT

21-4. Negative charges can move about; positive charges are fixed. Here negative charges move away, repelled, but positive charges stay in place and attract paper to the charged rod.

pler theory. And as new things were found out about electricity, his theory turned out to be the best one.

Franklin suggested that there was only one kind of electricity — not two kinds. Everything, he said, has the "electric fire" in it. But if some of the "electric fire" is drawn out of an object, so that it has *less* than its normal amount, it becomes charged one way. If an object somehow acquires *more* "electric fire" than its normal amount, it becomes charged the other way. Thus, Franklin accounted for the two kinds of charges with one kind of electricity.

Suppose, said Franklin, that glass gains a surplus of electricity when it is rubbed. Then we will say that glass is *plus,* or *positively charged.* And let us suppose that rubber loses some of its normal amount of electricity when it is rubbed. We will say that rubber is *minus,* or *negatively charged.*

An object that is *uncharged* simply has equal amounts of positive and negative charges — like the piece of paper shown in Fig. 21-4-A.

This worked out well enough so that today we are still using Franklin's *positive* and *negative* labels for charges. We think of the positive charges in a solid object as being fixed, unable to move, while the negative charges can move about. So, when a charged rubber rod is brought near a bit of uncharged paper and attracts it (Fig. 21-4-B), we can account for this behavior. The rubber rod has a great surplus of negative charges (shown by

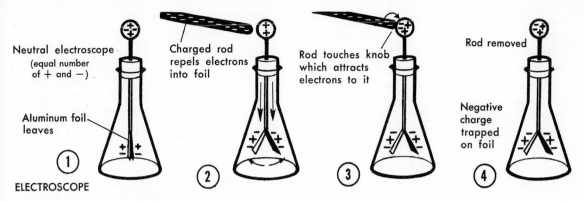

Neutral electroscope
(equal number
of + and −)

Charged rod
repels electrons
into foil

Rod touches knob
which attracts
electrons to it

Rod removed

Aluminum foil
leaves

Negative
charge
trapped
on foil

(1) ELECTROSCOPE   (2)   (3)   (4)

21-5. Here is one way an electroscope can be given a negative charge of electricity. If this charged electroscope is brought near a positive charge, what will the foil leaves do?

minus signs). When it is brought near the bit of paper, the *like* charges in the paper are *repelled;* they move away to the other end of the paper, where their influence is weak. But the fixed positive charges are strongly *attracted* to the *unlike* negative charges on the rod. Thus the *uncharged* paper is attracted to the *charged* rod.

The simple and ingenious little instrument called the *electroscope* was used by scientists and experimenters to tell which kind of charge they were dealing with — positive or negative. You can easily make one, using aluminum foil instead of the precious and fragile gold leaf used in those days (Fig. 21-5).

If you keep in mind that only the negative charges move about, and remember the electrostatic laws of attraction and repulsion, you can easily explain why the leaves of the electroscope behave as shown.

The Jar of Electricity

In Fig. 21-6 you see a jar for storing electricity. It is an improved Leyden jar. You can easily make such a Leyden jar for your science class. Any wide-mouthed glass jar will do. Coat the inside smoothly and tightly with a layer of tin foil or aluminum foil to about an inch from the top. Coat the outside in the same way. (The metal foil is a *conductor,* which means that electricity can flow through it easily.) Why this odd construction? What you have learned about electric charges will

explain it — and explain what happened to Cuneus the experimenter, too.

One layer of foil can hold a *negative* charge. The other layer can hold a *positive* charge. The two charges strongly attract one another through the glass. It is this strong attraction between positive and negative charges that holds each charge onto the foil. They cannot flow together through the glass because glass is *not* a conductor. Materials that do not conduct electricity are called *insulators.* (A third type of material, *semi-conductors,* may or may not conduct electricity depending, among other factors, on their temperature.)

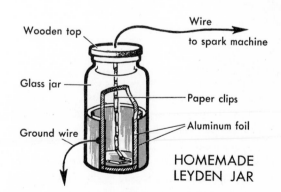

Wooden top

Wire
to spark machine

Glass jar

Paper clips

Ground wire

Aluminum foil

HOMEMADE
LEYDEN JAR

21-6. A positive charge on the metal coating inside the Leyden jar will attract and hold, through the glass, a negative charge of electricity on the metal outside. Today we call this storer of electricity a condenser or capacitor.

To carry a charge onto the inside foil of your Leyden jar, arrange a chain of paper clips (or flexible wire) that is supported through a hole in a wooden lid of the jar. Then connect the chain to one terminal or knob of your school's spark machine or other source of electric charge.

Connect the outside foil to the earth itself through a water pipe, which is a good conductor. Now as you operate the spark machine, electric charge flows onto the inside foil of your Leyden jar. At once, obeying the laws of electrostatics, an opposite charge is formed by repulsion on the outside foil. If you now carefully disconnect the wires leading to your jar, you will have a jar of electricity.

Careful! If your school's spark machine is a big one be sure your teacher helps you use it. The tinfoil on the outside of the jar is charged. When you touch it, your body acts as a conductor and connects it to the ground. Remember Cuneus! It is easy to get a shock from a Leyden jar. One way to get a bad shock is to put one hand on each foil of the jar, for then the positive and negative charges can flow together — through you!

A *shock* is the feeling of electricity flowing through your body. You can also get a shock if any part of your body connects the two wires in an ordinary lamp cord. You should be very careful when you work with electrical equipment and *know what you're doing.* Shocks can be dangerous!

LIGHTNING

The sudden flash of brightness, the ripping apart of a great tree, or the shattering of a church steeple, then the crash of thunder — this destroying force from the heavens seemed to our ancestors to be a tool of the gods. Magic charms, prayers, and sacrifices to the gods seemed to be all ancient man could do about it.

Watching the flash, hearing the crack of a spark jumping from an " electrical machine " or a Leyden jar, some experimenters had an odd idea. " That looks like lightning, too," they said.

Lightning: Big Spark?

Could lightning be *electricity?* Scientists were learning things about electricity, learning how to handle it, control it, finding laws it seemed to obey. If lightning were electricity, then perhaps something could be done to control lightning.

How could one find out if those thunderclouds held electricity? The problem teased many experimenters.

Playing with Fire

Franklin had an idea. " The electric fluid is attracted by points," he wrote. (He had seen how easily sparks from his electrical machine passed between pointed conductors.) Then why not raise

21-7. Benjamin Franklin was lucky to have survived this dangerous experiment. Some scientists were killed while repeating it.

an iron rod 20 or 30 feet long, " pointed very sharp at the end," on some high place? Perhaps it will draw " electric fire " from a thundercloud — if there is any there. Let the rod be mounted so that the " fire " must jump a gap on its way to the ground. Perhaps sparks will be seen — like those from an electrical machine.

A French scientist named d'Alibard (dahl-ih-BAHR) determined to try the idea. An iron rod 40 feet high and properly insulated was put in charge of an old soldier, near Paris. On May 10, 1752, a thunderstorm approached. The soldier held a wire connected to the ground near the insulated rod. A stream of sparks crackled between rod and wire! The thundercloud contained electricity.

Meanwhile Franklin, knowing nothing of this experiment, thought of another way of finding out if thunderclouds were charged and performed his famous kite experiment (Fig. 21-7). He " drew " the " electric fire " down the kite string — a good enough conductor when wet — from the pointed metal rod he had fastened to the kite. To his great joy sparks jumped between the key and his knuckles. *Lightning and electricity were the same.* Thunderclouds somehow collected big electric charges. Lightning was the big spark as the charge flowed away to the ground or to another charged cloud. (See Chapter 20 under Lightning.)

Using the knowledge that he had obtained from his experiments, Franklin invented the *lightning rod.* You will find this discussed on page 231 and shown in Fig. 20-12.

Research today has shown that a flash of lightning is much more complex than it was imagined to be then. While electric charge does leak from the pointed end of the lightning rod during a thunderstorm, it seems unlikely that it has much effect on the tremendous charge in a thundercloud. There is no doubt, however, that the rod furnishes an easy path for the lightning to flow to the ground harmlessly.

More Research — and Not Enough Electricity

Research, experiments, exchange of ideas among scientists about the nature of electricity

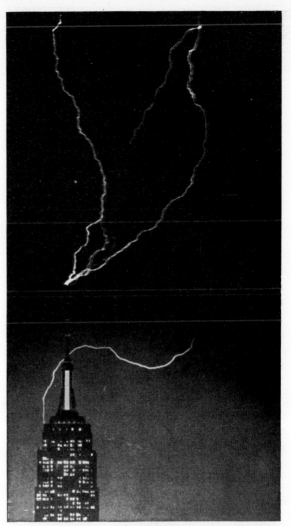

Herald-Tribune Photo by Hal Bergson

21-8. The metal lightning rod on top of the Empire State Building, the tallest building in the world, safeguards the building against lightning.

went quietly on. New knowledge and instruments and new ways of doing things were being found. Electrical machines were improved. Some had glass disks six feet in diameter and worked up a crashing spark several inches long. The Leyden jar condenser idea was improved. Bigger charges could be stored.

There was one big problem, however. The electricity made by electrical machines came in brief sparks, and not in a steady stream. No way of making an even, steady flow of the "electric fluid" was known. It ought to be possible, somehow, the experimenters felt.

MAGNETISM

Meanwhile there was another big puzzle, and not a clue in sight. Electrified things showed attraction and repulsion for each other. *Magnets* also showed attraction and repulsion for each other. And the laws of magnetic attraction and repulsion sounded curiously like the laws of electrostatics.

In spite of this remarkable resemblance, no connection could be found between magnetism and electric charge. Magnetism did not repel or attract an electric charge. An electric charge had no apparent effect on magnetism.

Was the strange resemblance just a coincidence? No, some experimenters felt, there must be some connection between magnetism and electricity.

Magnets and Magnetism

By Benjamin Franklin's time, scientists were sure of these facts about magnets and magnetism.

1. That a magnet attracted iron and steel.
2. That the magnetic force was concentrated at places called *poles.*
3. That one pole of a magnet would point northward, if it were free to do so, and the other would point southward; hence the names, *north* (pointing) *pole* and *south* (pointing) *pole,* given to the ends of a magnet.
4. That the magnetic force could go through some materials, such as wood, paper, or glass.
5. That a natural magnet could be used to make other magnets.
6. That like magnetic poles repelled each other, unlike poles attracted each other.

Here was that strange resemblance:

Like poles repel, unlike poles attract: law of magnetism.

Like charges repel, unlike charges attract: law of electricity.

Moreover, a scientist named Coulomb (koo-LOHM) had *measured* the forces of electric charges attracting or repelling each other, and also the forces of magnetic poles pushing or pulling each other. He found that they were alike mathematically.

Sperry Gyroscope

Abercrombie Fitch

21-9. On the left is a 17th-century compass. On the right is a modern compass weighing two pounds designed for use in small boats.

Yet no matter how experimenters tried it, a magnet showed no effect on an electric charge. A charge had no effect on magnetism. Perhaps the resemblance was an accident after all. Perhaps there was no link.

It was a tantalizing puzzle — as much of a puzzle as the problem of making electricity in a steady stream or current, instead of just in spurts.

Oddly enough, the two puzzles were linked together. Solving the second one — getting a steady current of electricity — was to lead to solving the first. This led to discoveries and inventions in electricity beyond the wildest imaginings of anyone who ever rubbed a glass rod with a silk handkerchief, or cranked an electrical machine, or sent a kite into a thundercloud.

The clue that led scientists to a steady current of electricity was a strange one, as you will see by reading the next chapter.

Looking Back . . . .

VOCABULARY

Each of the following expressions represents a key idea in this chapter on electricity. What is the meaning of each of these expressions?

1. charge	7. lightning
2. electroscope	8. insulator
3. Leyden jar	9. conductor
4. lightning rod	10. shock
5. pole	11. electrostatic laws
6. condenser	

EXPLAIN WHY:

- When two objects are rubbed together to produce an electric charge, one object always becomes positively charged, the other always becomes negatively charged.
- Only one kind of electricity is needed to explain positive and negative charges.
- Franklin's experiment showed that lightning was a big electric spark.
- A metal rod held in your hand could not be charged by rubbing it on other objects.

Going Further . . . .

APPLYING PRINCIPLES

1. With the help of a diagram explain how an electroscope is used to tell what kind of a charge is present on an object.
2. Show how you would protect a barn from being destroyed by lightning. Explain why your method works.
3. Why don't modern steel office buildings need lightning rods?
4. In what ways are electrically charged objects similar to magnets?
5. In what ways do electrically charged objects differ from magnets?
6. Explain why it would be dangerous to grab a freely hanging rope from a dirigible if you were standing on the ground.
7. What is the purpose of the flexible wires sticking up from the roadway just in front of highway toll booths?
8. Why do sheets of paper sometimes stick together unmanageably as they come out of a mimeograph machine?

TRY THESE

1. A charged rod is brought near a positively charged electroscope. The leaves fly further apart. Is the rod charged positively or negatively? How do you know?

2. Rub a hard rubber comb on fur or wool and bring it near a thin stream of water from a faucet. The attraction of the charged comb for water will cause the stream to swerve sharply.

3. Blow up several balloons, rub them on your sleeve, and bring them near the wall or ceiling. If it is a dry day, the balloons will remain on the walls or ceiling by electrical attraction for quite a while. Try bringing the two balloons together and note the repulsion.

READING FURTHER

Exploring Electricity by Hugh K. Skilling, Ronald Press, 1948. This book tells the story of electricity and the scientists who contributed to its development.

The Bright Design by Katherine Shippen, Viking, 1949. The lives of people who played important parts in the progress of electricity.

CHAPTER

22

Harnessing Electric Currents

The professor of anatomy was puzzled — and fascinated. He had dissected some frogs' legs, and had hung them outside to dry. Every few moments one of the legs twitched as if it were alive. Most unusual!

About 1780, this same Professor Galvani had seen a frog's leg twitch that way when a charge of electricity from an electrical machine was sent through a dissected frog's leg, even though it was no longer part of a live frog. He himself had tried that experiment many times.

What puzzled and fascinated him now was that there was no electrical machine at work. Yet from time to time a leg would twitch, *just as if it were receiving an electric shock.*

ELECTRICITY FROM CHEMICALS

Again and again Galvani examined the row of frogs' legs. Each leg hung from a copper hook, each hook dangled from the iron railing. There was no clue at all to this strange business — until he happened to press a frog's foot against the iron railing — and the leg twitched. He pressed foot to

railing again. The frog's leg jerked again. Certainly it looked like electricity at work . . .

Like the good scientist he was, Luigi Galvani then tried many experiments to investigate this new phenomenon. He found that the frog's leg twitched only when two different metals were used. He observed that the strength of the twitch varied with different metals.

He decided, after many experiments, that it *was* electricity that caused the frog's leg to jerk, and the electricity came out of the leg itself. It was " animal electricity."

As a scientist should, Galvani wrote out an account of his experiments and his theory explaining the results — the theory of " animal electricity."

Professor Volta Disagrees

A copy of Professor Galvani's article on this new kind of electricity traveled a hundred miles away. There another professor read it. He was Alessandro Volta, a professor of physics. At first Volta agreed with Professor Galvani's theory that this electricity came from the animal itself. However, as he did experiments of his own, Volta began to doubt Galvani's theory and to suspect that the electricity came from something else.

Professor Volta had an advantage, too. He had invented an unusually sensitive *electroscope.* With it he could find (and identify) tiny traces of electricity, where ordinary electroscopes failed to show electricity at all.

He showed that electricity could be made without using frogs' legs at all. It was just a matter of arranging *two different metals* so that they were *separated by a conducting liquid.* Salt water would do for the liquid, and for the two different metals a piece of zinc and a piece of copper worked well. Standing apart in the liquid, the zinc became positively charged and the copper picked up a negative charge of electricity. He found all this out with his sensitive electroscope. If the two metals were now connected by a conducting material like wire (or even frogs' legs), electricity would flow between them.

The electricity from this *cell,* as we would call it now, was very feeble. It did not compare with the crashing sparks that electrical machines could deliver, but it did prove something extraordinary: *Electrical energy could be made out of chemical energy.*

Volta's "Pile"

Professor Volta did many more experiments. He tried many different metals and liquids, in all sorts of combinations. He found that two different pieces of metal could produce electricity if they were simply separated by a piece of cloth or paper moistened with the liquid (Fig. 22-1).

He found something even more astonishing. If these single cells were stacked on each other in a pile, they somehow combined to make a stronger flow of electricity.

He stacked up 60 or more pieces of zinc and copper, with moistened cardboards between — and called it a "pile" (Fig. 22-1). It behaved like a very weak Leyden jar, he reported, but it did not need to be charged and recharged as an electrical machine — as a Leyden jar did. He had invented the first electric *battery*. Even today a battery consists of a number of cells connected together so as to give a higher voltage than with one cell.

He pointed out that the electricity coming out of his "pile" wasn't a "there-and-gone" spurt like a spark; it was coming out in a *steady stream.*

DuPont

22-2. Today's car batteries look different from Volta's pile of cells — but the principle is the same.

If you try the following simple experiment, you can see for yourself the evidence that this electricity flows in a steady stream.

The Taste of Electricity

Perhaps using a lemon, a penny, and a dime for your experiment does not seem at first like evidence. But notice that you have two different metals in the penny and the dime. Remember that within the lemon is an acid liquid. When you put the coins into slits in the lemon, you have made a simple electric cell (Fig. 22-3).

Now, place your tongue against the coins. Your tongue acts as a conductor. It makes a path for the electricity just as Galvani's frogs' legs did.

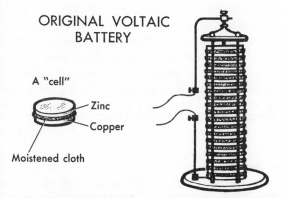

ORIGINAL VOLTAIC BATTERY

A "cell"

Zinc

Copper

Moistened cloth

22-1. With a "pile" of these cells Professor Volta made a steady stream of electricity from chemicals. This was the first electric battery.

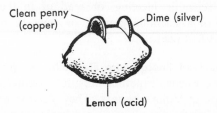

Clean penny (copper)

Dime (silver)

Lemon (acid)

22-3. The principle of Volta's cell — two different metals in an acid liquid. Put your tongue to the coins.

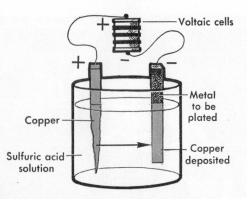

22-4. Electricity can carry a metal, such as copper, atom by atom through a liquid and deposit it on some other metal. This is called electroplating.

Notice the taste sensation. Also notice that the taste sensation *continues* only as long as you keep your tongue against both of the coins.

Over 150 years ago — back in 1800 — Volta touched his tongue to one of his " piles." He observed that taste sensation. He also observed that the sensation lasted while his tongue made a path for the electricity. He concluded that the sensation in his tongue lasted because the electricity was flowing in a steady stream.

Volta was right. What the experimenters with electricity needed had been found. Volta's cell produced a steady flow of electricity.

Paper Work

As scientists do, Professor Volta " wrote up " his experiments. He described them in detail so that other scientists could repeat them. A flood of experiments began to pour forth. The science of electricity seemed to grow almost overnight. No one knew what discovery he would hear of at the next scientific meeting, or read of in the next issue of a scientific journal, or what he himself would find next.

Chemical Energy into Electrical Energy

Two English experimenters, for example, made a copy of Volta's battery. They put the ends of two wires from the battery into water. A stream of tiny bubbles began to climb each wire to the surface of the water!

Using the kind of apparatus shown in Fig. 4-8, they collected the gas in the bubbles. As the water level in each container was forced down by bubbling gas, they saw that about *twice* as much gas was gathering at the negative wire as at the positive one. Water, they knew, was supposed to be made up of hydrogen and oxygen — two hydrogen atoms for every oxygen atom. Was it possible that these gases were hydrogen and oxygen? They kept the experiment going for 13 hours, then tested the gases. The larger volume of gas *was* hydrogen, the smaller *was* oxygen; there was twice as much hydrogen as oxygen. The flow of electricity had, it seemed, broken down the water into its chemical parts, as you may have already seen when you read Chapter 4.

Many more experiments proved that water molecules were *decomposed* by electricity flowing through them. If certain chemicals were added to the water — a little sulfuric acid, for instance — the flow of electricity was improved and the process went on more rapidly. Soon experimenters were passing electricity through chemical compounds whose make-up was unknown, and splitting them into chemical elements that could be identified or — sometimes — into a new chemical element. Scientists found that the electric flow could carry a metal like copper, for example, atom by atom through a liquid, and deposit it in a fine smooth coating on the other pole of the cell (Fig. 22-4). Manufacturers use this same principle for plating objects with silver or gold.

Aside from the many practical applications of these discoveries — such as *electroplating* — they gave some clues to scientists. They gave a clue to the nature of matter, which seemed somehow to be bound up with electricity. They gave a clue to the nature of electricity itself. Later we will follow up these clues, as scientists did.

Better Cells

If you make the simple voltaic cell shown in Fig. 22-5, you will find that it does make electricity. But the flow of electricity soon weakens and halts. Has the cell stopped changing chemical

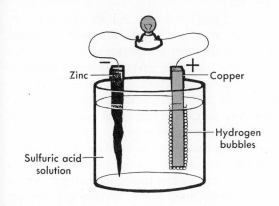

22-5. This simple cell has stopped producing electricity. Do you see why?

energy into electrical energy because the chemical energy is used up? No, it stops because something is blocking the energy-releasing process.

Here is what happens. As this simple cell makes electricity out of chemicals, hydrogen bubbles form at the positive (copper) pole. Instead of rising to the surface, the bubbles cling to the positive pole. They form a layer of hydrogen gas that blocks further chemical action. The flow of electricity stops.

To get around this difficulty, several other types of cells were invented. Among them are the two cells we use today, the "dry" cell and the storage battery (Fig. 22-6). When we "charge" the storage battery we reverse the process of changing chemical energy into electricity.

All these cells work on the same basic principle. When two different conducting substances — like copper and zinc, or carbon and zinc, or lead and lead peroxide — are separated by conducting chemical solutions, they become charged with electricity. One substance becomes positively charged, the other negatively. If the two substances are connected to each other by a conductor, electricity flows. This flow will continue until the flow is blocked or until one of the materials is all used up.

So early experimenters, furnished with reliable cells and batteries of cells, now had the continuous electric flow they wanted. Now they could resume their search for an answer to the old puzzle. Is there a link between electricity and magnetism? For 20 years after Volta invented the cell, the answer to that puzzle stayed hidden. Then at last it popped out unexpectedly on a table in front of a science class in Denmark.

ELECTRICITY FROM MAGNETISM

The story goes that Professor Oersted (ERsted) was lecturing to a science class that day. He had on the table before him a cell, some wire, and a magnetized compass needle.

He connected one end of the wire to one pole of his cell. It happened that the magnetized needle was standing underneath the wire. He connected the other end of the wire to the other pole of the cell. Electricity flowed through the wire. He saw

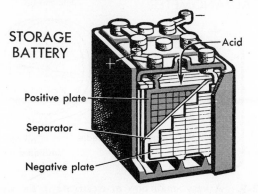

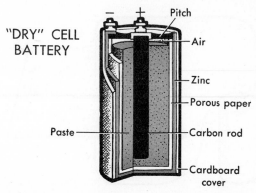

22-6. These successors to Volta's simple cell still work on the same principle: two different conductors separated in a conducting chemical solution produce electricity.

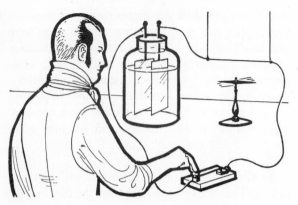

22-7. Professor Oersted unexpectedly discovered the link between electricity and magnetism.

the needle swing around under the wire (Fig. 22-7).

He realized that he had just seen what he and other scientists had long been seeking — the link between electricity and magnetism.

Accidents and Failures

You might call Oersted's discovery of the link between electricity and magnetism an accident. It was unexpected, certainly. But unexpected as it was, *he understood what it meant.* He understood because he had been experimenting with electricity and had been looking for that link.

When Oersted saw the magnetized needle swing under the wire, he realized at once that flowing electricity had magnetism around it.

Oersted published a careful account of his experiments with the magnetic effects of an electric current. When other scientists read his paper, they set up their own cells, wires, and magnetized needles, of course, and checked his results. Then they went on to try experiments of their own, to see what more they could find out about the magnetic effects of flowing electricity.

The experimenters took many wrong turns, went up a lot of " blind alleys," tried many ideas that led nowhere, met failure many times, before the right paths were found. Perhaps it is not fair to call the experiments that did not work " failures." Knowledge of what experiments will *not* work is also part of science.

The Galvanometer

If one wire bearing flowing electricity made a magnetic needle swing feebly, would *two* such wires make the needle swing more strongly? The experiment was tried, and it was found to happen. Then it was found that if a single wire were wound over and under the needle in the form of a *coil,* the magnetic effect of the current was even further strengthened. With this arrangement a very tiny flow of electricity in the coil of wire would make the needle swing (Fig. 22-9).

Thus a very sensitive instrument for detecting the flow of electricity became available. It was christened the *galvanometer* (gal-vuh-NOM-it-er) — in honor of Luigi Galvani. It was simply a

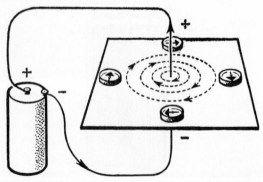

22-8. This experiment shows the direction of magnetic lines of force.

GALVANOMETER

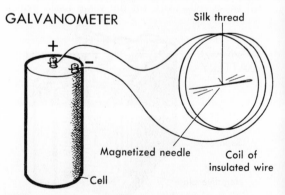

22-9. A very small flow of electricity in the wire coil will make the magnetic needle swing. This is the principle of the sensitive galvanometer.

magnet mounted like a compass needle to move within a coil of wire. When a small spring was fastened to the magnet to hold it against the magnetic force of the electricity, the turning of the magnet was a measure of the strength of the magnetism. The magnetism in turn was a measure of the electric current. The galvanometer took the place of some older ways of estimating how much electricity was flowing — giving oneself an electric shock, for example.

Today's galvanometers and many other kinds of electric meters make use of a moving coil within a fixed magnet. In principle they are just the same as the first galvanometers. The next time you see an electric meter measuring current see if you can find the fixed magnet and the moving coil at the base of the pointer.

Measuring Electricity: Ohm's Law

In the midst of this tangle of electrical experiments and results, a German scientist, Georg Ohm, produced a simple description of how electricity behaves. He produced what scientists call a law. *Ohm's Law* is one of the most important laws used by scientists and engineers today to control electricity.

Ohm had studied some laws describing how heat flows. These heat laws had been developed by a French mathematician, Jean Fourier (foo-RYAY). The idea came to Ohm that perhaps the flow of electricity behaved the same way as the flow of heat.

Let us imagine, said Ohm, that there is some sort of *force* that drives electricity through a wire. Let's call it the *electromotive force*. A cell supplies a certain amount of this electromotive force.

Electromotive force is needed to push the electricity through the wire because there is *resistance* in the wire. This resistance has to be overcome if the electricity is to get through.

One thing more, said Ohm. If the *electromotive force* is strong enough to overcome the *resistance,* electricity will flow. Let us call the flow of electricity the *current.*

Now if *one* cell contains a certain amount of this electromotive force, and drives a certain

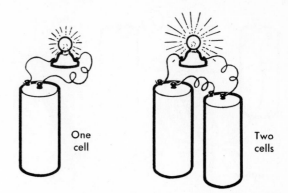

One cell   Two cells

22-10. Two cells, with twice as much electromotive force as one cell, drive twice as much current through the resistance, in this case a lamp.

amount of current through a certain resistance — what will *two* cells do? Will there be twice as much electromotive force? If so, what will happen to the amount of current?

What Ohm found, by many experiments, is shown in Fig. 22-10. *One* cell connected to a resistance produced a certain current of electricity. *Two* cells connected as shown to the same resistance produced *twice* as much current.

Two cells could drive that amount of current produced by one cell through *twice* as much resistance as before. Hence, using two cells seemed to double the electromotive force. Ohm tripled the electromotive force by using three cells, and the current became three times as large as it had been with one cell.

It's easy to sum up the results of Ohm's experiments. The current increases when the electromotive force is increased, or when the resistance is reduced. We can say this even more accurately. *The current varies directly in proportion to the electromotive force.* Thus tripling the force triples the current. On the other hand, *the current varies in inverse proportion with the resistance.* Thus doubling the resistance halves the current; tripling resistance cuts the current to a third of what it was, and so forth.

All this is much easier to say in mathematical shorthand:

$$\text{Current} = \frac{\text{Electromotive force}}{\text{Resistance}}$$

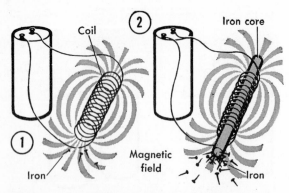

22-11. (1) When electricity is flowing through a coil of wire, the coil behaves like a bar magnet. (2) An iron core strengthens its magnetism.

There was still the matter of deciding in what *units* current, electromotive force, and resistance could be measured. Two international conventions of scientists discussed electrical units and chose units called the *volt* (for measuring electromotive force), the *ampere* (for measuring current), and the *ohm* (for measuring resistance). The unit of resistance called the ohm, for example, is the resistance of a " wire " of mercury 106.3 centimeters long and one millimeter square in cross-section.

So Ohm's law can also be written:

$$\frac{\text{Current}}{\text{in amperes}} = \frac{\text{Electromotive force in volts}}{\text{Resistance in ohms}}$$

Being in the shape of a mathematical formula now, all sorts of convenient mathematical tricks and jugglings can be done with it. You'll find examples at the end of the chapter (in the section " Going Further ") to give you some idea of how useful and powerful Ohm's Law is.

The Powerful Coil of Wire

Scientists read of Oersted's discovery of the magnetic effect of the electric current. They repeated his experiments. Then, of course, they began to think up experiments of their own to show this magnetic effect.

Now came a discovery that looked unimportant at first. But it began to grow, and soon there was no holding it. It came out of the scientist's laboratory and changed the size of the world. It changed the world's power supply, too.

It began very simply. A French scientist named François Arago (ahr-uh-GO) wound a wire into a coil. He sent the electric current from a cell through the coil. *He found that the coil behaved like a bar magnet.* It had north and south poles. It attracted or repelled other magnetic poles, as a magnet would. It drew unmagnetized iron to it. In fact, iron filings sprinkled around it showed the same magnetic pattern as a bar magnet does (Fig. 22-11).

There was a difference, however. When the electric current in the coil was cut off, the magnetism disappeared — at once. *The coil's magnetism could be turned on and off.* As you know, the magnetism in a bar magnet can't be started and stopped in that way at all.

Scientists found that if a bar or rod of soft iron were put into the coil, the magnetism was greatly strengthened. If more turns of wire were used, the magnetism was strengthened still further. If more cells were connected to send more current through the coil, the magnetism became stronger still. (You can see these facts for yourself if you try the experiment shown in Fig. 22-12.)

If the soft iron rod were bent into the shape of a horseshoe and then wound with wire, it became a most powerful magnet when the current was

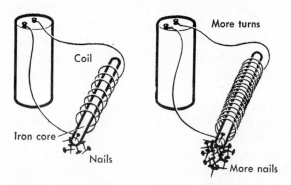

22-12. More turns of wire strengthen the coil's magnetism. More current in the coil will also strengthen its magnetism.

United States Steel

22-13. This electromagnet is used to separate pieces of iron and steel from coal.

sent through the coiled wire. This arrangement of wire wrapped around a soft iron core is called an *electromagnet*. An electromagnet can support a weight greater than its own weight (Fig. 22-13).

Here was electricity turned into an actual *force*. Moreover it was a force that could be switched on or off in an instant. Couldn't this force be put to work somehow?

Putting the Electromagnet to Work

Scientists knew that the more coils of wire one wound around the iron core of an electromagnet, the stronger the magnet would be. But using bare wire as they did, they could wrap only a few turns on a core. The wires could not be allowed to touch each other. The core had to be varnished to *insulate* it from the current, that is, to prevent the current from escaping from the wire to the core.

At last the idea of *insulating the wire* occurred to someone. He wrapped the wire in silk, or other nonconducting material, as wires today are wrapped with rubber or plastic material. With insulated wire, turn upon turn could be wrapped around the iron core. The power of electromag-

nets took an upward bound. Joseph Henry, an American scientist, made an electromagnet that supported a ton of weight (using a surprisingly small current).

Scientists had known for some time that electricity could travel great distances through wires or other conductors. But it always arrived much weakened at the end of the trip. Just the same, the idea that electricity might in some way be used to carry a message had teased many scientists and inventors. They had tried out many strange and interesting electric telegraph schemes — with no practical success.

Here now was the electromagnet. It could attract a piece of metal, cause a needle to swing, make a visible signal. But experiments had already shown that the current needed to operate an electromagnet could travel only a short distance through wire (to the magnet) before it became uselessly weak.

Joseph Henry showed, however, that with the right arrangement of coils on the electromagnet, and the right connections between cells and magnet, the current could travel more than a mile — and then magnetize the electromagnet. Indeed, he had one of his electromagnets ring a little bell when it received the long-distance current over a mile of wire strung around his classroom. The path to the magnetic telegraph was open. You can read in Unit 9 on "Communications" how an American portrait painter named Morse carried this idea to success.

The Electric Motor

In one way the electromagnet is like a bar magnet. It has a north pole and a south pole (Fig. 22-14A) when an electric current flows through its coil. However, there is another interesting fact about the electromagnet. When the direction of the current through the coil changes, the magnetic poles change too (Fig. 22-14B). North becomes south; south becomes north. The polarity of the electromagnet is controlled by the direction of the current. Fig. 22-14C shows you how to tell which is the north and the south pole when you know the direction of the current.

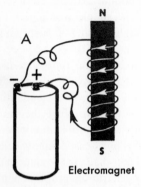
A

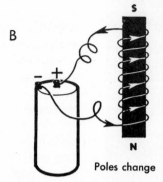
B

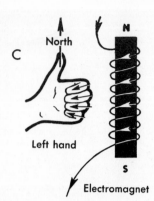
C

Electromagnet

Poles change

North

Left hand

Electromagnet

22-14. If the direction of electric current flow is changed, the poles of the electromagnet change places. Put the fingers of your left hand around the coil in the direction of current flow (from − to +), and your thumb will point to the electromagnet's north pole.

This suggested to inventors that, perhaps, by changing the poles of an electromagnet at just the right instant, a pull could be changed into a push. If this could be done, then perhaps something could be pushed and pulled into a spinning (or rotary) motion. A bar magnet on a pivot simply lines up with a fixed magnet and stays that way (Fig. 22-15 left). But if the poles of the bar magnet could be reversed repeatedly, it ought to spin (Fig. 22-15 right).

The problem was at last worked out as shown in Fig. 22-16. There you see a simple electric motor. The *commutator* performs the important job of reversing the direction of the current at the right instant. Hence it reverses the poles of the rotating electromagnet. Look closely at the north pole of the rotating electromagnet. Being a north pole, it is attracted to the south pole of the fixed magnet. When the two poles are close together,

however, the commutator reverses the direction of current flow in the coil. The north pole becomes a south pole. Hence it is repelled, and continues on its way.

Replacing the permanent magnets by electromagnets was an easy step. A way was soon found to put several electromagnets in action around the rotating shaft to get a smooth succession of pushes and pulls as well as a more powerful motor. Many of the machines in the home, such as the sewing and washing machines, ironer, mixer, and oil burner are run by electric motors.

It is possible to keep the poles of the spinning electromagnet unchanged (by keeping the electromagnet current in one direction), and change in-

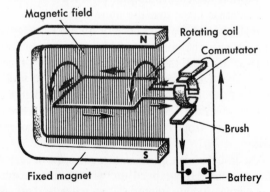

Magnetic field

Rotating coil

Commutator

Brush

Fixed magnet

Battery

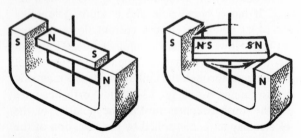

22-15. If you could suddenly change the poles of the pivoted magnet, it would swing away. This is the germ of the electric motor idea.

22-16. Follow the path of the current (from − to +) and see how the commutator does the trick of changing the poles of the coil of wire as it rotates, making a practical electric motor.

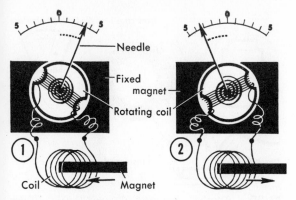

22-17. Faraday's discovery: to produce electricity from magnetism, the magnet must be *moving* in or out of the coil.

stead the polarity of the fixed magnets, at the right moment. This is done in some motors.

ELECTRICITY FROM INDUCTION

Electricity produces magnetism. Is it possible for magnetism to produce electricity?

Michael Faraday, the scientist who had done many of the important experiments in electromagnetism and in electrochemistry, felt that it might be possible. Yet for years he found no clue. Time and again he set a magnet inside a coil of wire and tried to find a trace of current through his galvanometer. He found none. Other experimenters tried, and found nothing.

One day Faraday *thrust* a bar magnet into a coil of wire, and as the magnet moved, the needle of the galvanometer twitched. It merely flickered over to one side, and went back. When he held the magnet in the coil, the needle showed nothing more. Then as he drew the magnet out of the coil, the needle flickered again, the other way. You should try Faraday's famous experiment for yourself (Fig. 22-17).

It was no wonder he hadn't found this before. The magnet had to be moving through the coil to produce electricity. Magnetism had to be moving to make electricity, just as electricity had to be moving (as a current) to produce magnetism.

The Generator

Faraday had found that a moving magnet can create electric current in a wire. He applied this newly found principle to build the first generator to turn mechanical energy into electricity. Outside of the fact that Faraday's generator was cranked by hand, it was no different in principle from the giant generators of today.

Faraday not only made a generator; he explained how it worked. He thought of the magnetism around a magnet as *lines of force*. The lines of force follow the pattern of iron filings sprinkled around a magnet, stretching from one pole to the other. In the case of a horseshoe magnet, for instance, they stretch across from pole to pole.

When any conducting material moves across the lines of force of a magnet, an electromotive force is generated in the conductor, said Faraday (Fig. 22-18).

When the magnet is thrust into the coil, some of the lines of force around the magnet are cut by the wires of the coil. Result: an electromotive force in the coil that causes current to flow as long as the lines of force are being cut.

Faraday observed also that when a conductor cuts across magnetic lines of force one way, the current in the conductor goes in one direction. Then, if the conductor crosses the lines of force

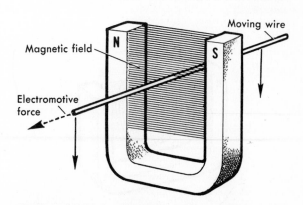

22-18. Making electricity with a magnet. Cut across the lines of force with a conductor, such as a wire. Electromotive force will be generated and — if there is a path for it — current will flow.

in the opposite direction, the current goes the other way through the conductor.

Alternating-Current Generator

Imagine a light bulb attached to a coil of wire, as in Fig. 22-19. Imagine that the coil lies between the poles of a strong horseshoe magnet. The coil (and the bulb attached to it) is made to spin as shown. What will happen?

Since the coil is cutting the lines of force of the magnet, an electromotive force will be set up in the coil. Current will flow. The bulb will light. Here is a simple generator.

But it has an odd feature. The current it makes does not flow in a steady stream in one direction. It flows back and forth in the wire. It *alternates* its direction of flow as the wires of the coil cut the lines of the magnet first in one direction, then in the other.

Alternating current, or A.C., is widely used today because it can be so conveniently sent from place to place. To send a current through wires over a long distance requires a high electromotive force, or voltage. But when the high-voltage current reaches its destination, it must usually be changed to a lower voltage, so as to be safer for use in the home, for example. The voltage of alternating current can be very conveniently changed. A highly efficient and automatic machine called a *transformer* does the job.

22-19. This spinning coil produces an alternating (or back-and-forth) current as it cuts the lines of force. Giant generators work on this simple principle.

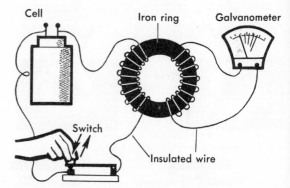

22-20. Another Faraday discovery: the transformer. A growing or shrinking current in the first coil creates — induces — a current in the second coil.

Induced Current and the Transformer

Faraday wound two pieces of insulated wire around an iron ring as shown in Fig. 22-20.

The wires did not touch each other. Nor could the current from the cell, flowing through one wire, get into the other. Yet when the current began in the first wire, the galvanometer showed a brief current in the other, independent coil of wire. As the current in the first wire ceased, the galvanometer showed another brief current in the opposite direction. In some way, the first current *induced* another current in the second wire.

Faraday was able to explain this *induced current*. When the current from the cell starts to flow, it creates magnetic lines of force. As they grow with the growing current, they cut the second wire, and generate a current there. When the current is cut off, the lines of force collapse, and they cut the second wire again, generating current again.

There was something more. If the turns of the second coil of wire were, say, ten times as many as the number of turns on the first coil, the voltage of the second current would be ten times that of the first current. (The amperes of the second current would be one-tenth the first current.)

If the number of turns on the second coil were less than the number of turns on the first, the voltage of the induced current would be correspondingly less than the voltage of the first current.

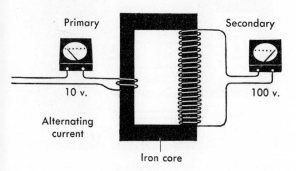

Ⓐ STEP-UP TRANSFORMER

Primary

Secondary

10 v.

100 v.

Alternating current

Iron core

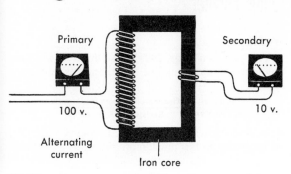

Ⓑ STEP-DOWN TRANSFORMER

Primary

Secondary

100 v.

10 v.

Alternating current

Iron core

22-21. One reason why alternating current is so widely used: the transformer can efficiently change it to convenient voltage.

The transformer shown in Fig. 22-21 works on this principle, efficiently changing voltage (and amperes) of alternating current.

Summing Up

In your town's power station the coils of electric generators spin swiftly and smoothly day and night. Faraday's principle is hard at work! The generators are probably turned either by water power or by steam. From them flow thousands of amperes of alternating current at a rather low voltage.

Less electric power is lost along the way, however, if it is sent out at a *high* voltage. To boost the voltage, big transformers are set up just outside a power station. Look for the transformer

yard the next time you go by a power plant (Fig. 22-22).

Electricity leaves those transformers at voltages as high as 200,000 volts and flows out over the power lines on its way to you. Look at those big insulators, needed to keep such high-voltage electricity from leaping to nearby metal objects in a lightning-like spark. No wonder electric generators cannot possibly generate electricity at that high voltage in the first place.

Over the power lines, toward your home, flows high-voltage alternating current. Near your home another transformer lowers the voltage to a safer level before the power is carried around your town on poles or underground cables. Finally atop a nearby pole or in an underground vault is one more transformer that reduces the electricity in one final step to 110 volts that is now available for your use.

Here at last is the energy from falling water or burning coal, ready at the flick of a switch to perform a thousand jobs for you, silently and cheaply. Surely electricity is one of your most extraordinary servants.

Westinghouse Electric Co.

22-22. In practice, the transformer may look like this giant one in the transformer yard of a power station.

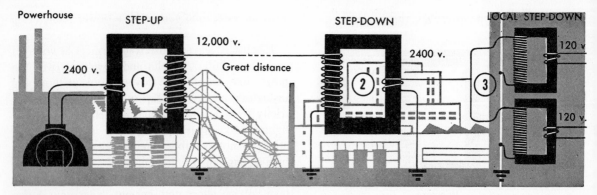

Powerhouse — **STEP-UP** — 12,000 v. — Great distance — **STEP-DOWN** — 2400 v. — **LOCAL STEP-DOWN** — 120 v.

2400 v. — ① — ② — ③ — 120 v.

22-23. Electricity travels more efficiently at high voltage, but is used in our homes at low voltage: more work for transformers! What is the difference between a step-up and a step-down transformer?

Looking Back . . . .

VOCABULARY

What is the meaning of each of the following key words in this chapter?

1. cell
2. galvanometer
3. electromotive force
4. electrical resistance
5. electric current
6. volt
7. ohm
8. ampere
9. electromagnet
10. commutator
11. induce
12. transformer
13. alternating-current generator
14. battery

REVIEW QUESTIONS

1. Explain how Galvani discovered "animal electricity."
2. Describe Volta's first electric cell.
3. How does a battery differ from a cell?
4. Describe an experiment to show that some molecules can be taken apart by electricity.
5. Describe Oersted's discovery.
6. How does a galvanometer work?
7. State Ohm's Law.
8. What happens to the current through a circuit as its resistance is increased?
9. Draw a diagram showing how you would make an electromagnet and connect it to a source of electric current.
10. Why must most electric wires be insulated?
11. With the help of a diagram explain how a simple electric motor works.
12. With the help of a diagram explain how a simple electric generator works.
13. With the help of a diagram explain how a transformer works.

Going Further . . . .

PROBLEMS TO SOLVE

You saw (on page 249) that Ohm's Law shows how current, electromotive force, and resistance are related.

$$\text{Current (I) in amperes} = \frac{\text{Electromotive force (E) in volts}}{\text{Resistance (R) in ohms}}$$

Remembering what the letters I, E, and R stand for, we can write all this much more simply as a formula:

$$I = \frac{E}{R}$$

Let us look at an easy example in order to see how this formula is used.

How much current will a one-volt cell push through a resistance of one ohm? Here $E = 1$ and $R = 1$ so our formula says

$$I = \frac{E}{R}$$
$$= \frac{1}{1}$$
$$= 1 \text{ ampere}$$

Again, your home lighting circuit probably has an electromotive force of 110 volts. How much current will flow through your electric heater, whose resistance is 10 ohms? The answer?

$$I = \frac{E}{R}$$
$$= \frac{110}{10}$$
$$= 11 \text{ amperes}$$

See now if you can find how much current the 55-ohm bulb in your reading lamp draws from your

110-volt line. Work it out yourself before looking at the answer (1) at the bottom of this page.

Of course Ohm's Law can be used to find resistance or voltage, too. If you measure the current flowing through a 5000-ohms resistance and find that it is 0.1 amperes then you can be sure that the electromotive force, E, pushing current through the wire is

$$0.1 = \frac{E}{5000}$$
$$E = 0.1 \times 5000$$
$$E = 500 \text{ volts}$$

See if you can find the resistance of a wire through which 6 volts forces 24 amperes. Again the answer (2) is at the bottom of this page.

If you go on with your study of electricity or explore some of the experiment books listed on this page, you will find yourself using Ohm's Law constantly.

ADDITIONAL PROBLEMS

1. Fill in the blanks in the following table:

	Amperes	Volts	Ohms
(a)	40	2	—
(b)	—	75	15
(c)	½	110	—
(d)	14	—	3

2. If half an ampere flows through the filament of your desk lamp when it is connected to a 110-volt line. what is the resistance of the filament?

3. How much current flows through an electric doorbell whose resistance is 3 ohms if it is connected to a 6-volt battery?

4. What is the resistance of an electrical appliance that draws 6 amperes from a 120-volt electric line?

THINGS TO DO

1. Make a battery, using zinc, copper, and a desk blotter. Cut the metal and blotting paper into 2-inch squares (about 20 of each). Then pile them one on the other in this order: copper, blotting paper, zinc, copper, blotting paper, zinc, etc. End with a sheet of zinc. Fasten the pile together with thread (do not use metal for fastening). Attach a wire to the zinc plate at one end and another to the copper plate at the other end. Soak the entire pile in a solution of bicarbonate of soda. When the blotting paper is wet

with solution, remove the pile from the solution. Your battery is ready. Touch the ends with moist fingers and see if you get a slight shock. Test the voltage with a voltmeter. This arrangement was the first battery made by Volta and is known as a "voltaic pile."

2. Make a lead storage cell. Insert two pieces of lead into a dilute solution of sulfuric acid, and connect them to opposite terminals of a source of current of about 3–8 volts (such as an automobile storage battery or car generator). After a short while, disconnect the wires from the source and try to ring a bell or light a flashlight bulb with your charged cell. Observe that a brownish coating of lead peroxide has formed on one of the lead strips.

3. Make an electric motor. The field magnet (in Fig. 22-24) is made from a thick strip of iron bent into a U shape and nailed down to a base of wood. Wind several hundred turns of magnet wire around the iron as shown. Be sure the windings are in opposite directions on each arm of the U. The armature is made by winding about 50 turns of magnet wire on an iron rod (cut from a nail) inserted half way into a piece of dowel stick. A metal strip serves as the commutator. Mount the dowel stick so that it will rotate freely. Connect as shown, and the motor should operate.

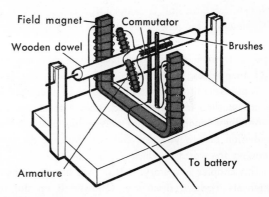

22-24. Try making this electric motor.

READING FURTHER

Electrical Things Boys Like to Make by Sherman R. Cook, Bruce Publishing Co. An excellent illustrated collection of projects and experiments including practical shop notes and home wiring instructions.

Experiments with Electricity by N. F. Beeler and F. M. Branley, Crowell, 1949. Many simple home lab experiments and tricks illustrating basic principles of electricity.

(1) 2 amperes. (2) 0.25 ohms.

CHAPTER

23

Taming the Electron

When you look at television, you are watching pictures drawn with electricity — drawn on one side of an odd-shaped tube called a picture tube.

You may think of the picture tube as a recent invention. Yet if Michael Faraday, Wilhelm Roentgen (RENT-g'n), and other scientists who worked with electricity more than half a century ago could look at a TV picture tube now, they would not find it completely strange. They would recognize it as the offspring of some odd-shaped tubes they had worked with themselves.

These scientists, with their tubes and their active minds, pushed into unexplored regions of electricity. What they found there not only made possible the television picture you see, but had much to do with shaping the world in which you are living.

This chapter is a story. It is a case history of how scientists made a discovery, followed it up out of pure curiosity, and ended by learning about an important building material of the world we live in — the electron. It is the story too of how such new knowledge was then put to practical use for the benefit of all of us.

ELECTRICITY THROUGH EMPTY SPACE

The room is almost dark. There is the rhythmic pounding of an air pump at work, and the buzz of a high-voltage machine. A man watches a long glass tube, waiting.

First, pink streamers of electricity appear at one end of the tube. They grow until they fill the whole length of the glass tube. As the pump pounds on, the streamers turn to a rosy pink glow of light that fills the tube. Then the glow separates into shimmering bands of light that slowly disappear. The tube grows dark. The pump sounds as if it could work no harder. The high-voltage machine buzzes on. No further change can be seen in the tube now.

The man is William Crookes. The time is 1880. He is watching the strange behavior of an electric current sent through a long glass tube, *as the air is gradually pumped out of it.*

Crookes' Tube

Crookes' long glass tube has a metal contact sealed through each end, and a small opening on one side (Fig. 23-1). A *vacuum pump* is attached to the opening by a stout hose. As the pump works, it takes air from inside the glass tube, gradually producing a vacuum.

The metal contacts in the ends of the tube are connected by wires to a source of high-voltage current. The metal contact connected to the positive terminal of the high-voltage current is called the *anode;* the contact wired to the negative terminal is called the *cathode.*

At the beginning of the experiment, there is

CROOKES' TUBE

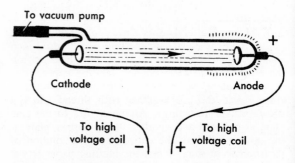

23-1. Sir William Crookes watched the strange behavior of electricity as air was pumped out of this sausage-shaped glass tube.

air at ordinary atmospheric pressure in the tube. When the high-voltage coil is turned on, nothing happens within the tube. The gap between the metal contacts — anode and cathode — is too big for the current to leap. In other words, the electrical resistance of the air between the two contacts is greater than can be overcome by the voltage driving the current.

But as the vacuum pump begins to take air out of the tube, the air remaining in the tube grows thinner and thinner, and its electrical resistance begins to fall. Electric current begins to flow, and the effects that have been described are seen in the tube.

When almost all of the air has been pumped from the tube, no light at all comes from within it. The current continues to flow through it, from metal contact to contact, invisibly. Only the glass at the opposite end of the tube from the cathode glows with pale fluorescent light.

Years before this, Michael Faraday had already seen the odd light of electricity flowing through a partial vacuum in a tube, but his pumps had not allowed him to get a very good vacuum. Heinrich Geissler had managed to try various gases in the tube, instead of air, and found that they gave off different colors. Neon gas, for instance, glowed red.

What did it tell about the nature of electricity?

A Cross, a Paddle Wheel, and Red-hot Metal

Crookes had several more curious tubes. They were all like the one we have just described. They each had an anode, a cathode, and so little air inside that the electric current was invisible and gave no glowing signals of its passing.

But one tube had a metal cross standing within (Fig. 23-2A). Connected to high voltage in such a way that the contact opposite the cross was the cathode, the cross cast a shadow on the end of the tube. The glass glowed with fluorescent light everywhere except directly in back of the cross. It looked as if something were being sprayed from the cathode. Whatever it was made the glass fluoresce, but didn't pass through the metal of the cross.

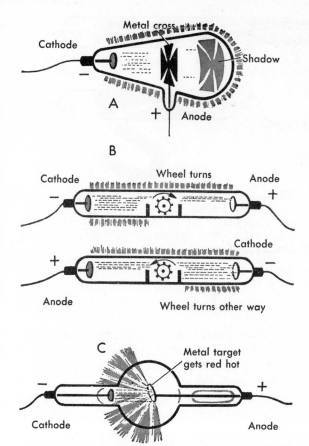

23-2. More of Crookes' odd glass tubes. What did the shadow (A), the turning paddle wheel (B), and the red-hot target disk (C) suggest to Crookes about the nature of electricity?

Another of Crookes' tubes had a paddle wheel inside, cleverly mounted so that it could turn in either direction along the tube (Fig. 23-2B). When current flowed through this tube the wheel always turned away from the cathode, the negative terminal. Something seemed to be coming from the cathode again.

Still another tube had a fragment of platinum fixed inside it above the cathode. The cathode was shaped so as to focus on the platinum (Fig. 23-2C). When the current flowed, the platinum became red hot. " There are *rays* coming out of the cathode," said scientists. They were christened *cathode rays*, accordingly. Crookes suggested that it was an odd sort of ray that could move

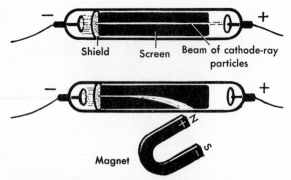

Shield Screen Beam of cathode-ray particles

Magnet

23-3. No particle can be smaller than an atom, said some scientists. But this experiment by Thomson (and a later one by Millikan) showed that they were wrong. The cathode-ray particles were much smaller than atoms.

a wheel and also heat a fragment of metal to redness. It was rather like a stream of tiny particles, he suggested, each one of them carrying a negative charge.

Some scientists could not accept Crookes' suggestion that the cathode rays were a procession of particles. They had a good objection. One experimenter, named Hertz, had put a very thin sheet of metal inside a cathode-ray tube. He reported that if the metal were thin enough, the cathode rays went right through it. Now, said scientists, to go through a sheet of metal, which is a sheet of atoms, a particle would have to be much smaller than an atom. But atoms are the smallest particles of matter. Nothing can be smaller. Therefore, said some scientists, cathode rays cannot possibly be made of particles.

There the matter stood, hotly argued by scientists, for some years.

A Famous Experiment

Then in 1897 an English scientist, J. J. Thomson, did a history-making experiment in a laboratory in England.

When a motorcycle policeman waves a speeding car over to the side of the road, how soon can the speeding car stop? It depends on how fast it is going, doesn't it? It depends too on how heavy the car is — what its mass is, as the scientist would say. In fact, you could tell something about the masses of different cars by watching how

quickly each one pulled over to the curb, other things like speed being equal.

Thomson's experiment was similar to this. Thomson made a cathode ray pass between the poles of a strong magnet. The magnet's field bent the ray from its straight path (Fig. 23-3). The amount of bending depended on the particle's speed, its electrical charge, and its mass.

Knowing the speed of his cathode-ray particles (from other experiments), and watching how sharply they swerved, Thomson was able to find the amount of electric charge on each gram of his cathode-ray particles. He found it was a very large number.

How large? Imagine a town of 1000 houses, all using their electrical equipment full force. One gram of electric charge flowing through the power lines of the town will keep all 1000 houses supplied for over one hour.

An Important Conclusion

What was the use of J. J. Thomson's experiment? Shortly after he measured the charge on a gram of cathode-ray particles, other scientists measured out a gram of charge flowing:

1. through a wire carrying an electric current
2. through an electroplating solution
3. off a heated wire in a vacuum tube
4. off a charged Leyden jar
5. out of a photoelectric cell (like a photographer's exposure meter) when light shone on it
6. from atoms of gas that had electric charges knocked off them.

In every one of these cases one gram of particles carried the very same negative charge. The conclusion was that all these forms of electricity are also streams of tiny negatively charged particles identical with Thomson's cathode-ray particles. Thomson named these particles of electricity *electrons*.

The Electron

Thus J. J. Thomson discovered the electron, and electricity was shown to be a flow of such electrons.

Evidence continued to pile up. In 1917 an American experimenter, Robert A. Millikan, succeeded in measuring the charge on a single electron. From this and from Thomson's measurement it became possible to find the mass of a single electron.

No wonder electrons could pass between the atoms in thin sheets of metal. One hundred thousand of them side by side would barely stretch across the width of one hydrogen atom.

Imagine a bowl of water the size of a basketball. Magnify this bowl until it is the size of our entire earth. On this scale the water molecules are now the size of grains of coarse sand. But electrons are still invisible! In fact they could barely be seen under an excellent microscope. Can't you imagine how easily such tiny electrons could trickle through the sand-sized atoms?

These tiny negative particles of electricity are part of our lives in all sorts of important ways. For one thing, they are a part of the atoms of your body and of everything you see around you. You will remember from Chapter 5 that each atom is made of a positively charged center with one to a hundred electrons whizzing around it like angry flies. Thus the tiniest piece of your skin that you can see is composed of billions of billions of atoms, which in turn contain billions of billions of electrons. If you could remove by magic all electrons from your body, all that would remain of you would be a monstrously large positive charge that would quickly vanish in an atom-bomb-like flash.

Every day we see the effects of electrons on the loose.

– All electric currents are a flow of electrons. (Can you name 20 devices in everyday use that depend on the flow of electrons in wires?)
– Electrons are boiling off the red-hot filaments inside your radio tubes.
– They pour out of the metal surface of a photoelectric cell when it is struck by light.
– When they strike some chemicals, such as the coating of your TV picture tube or a fluorescent lamp, they make the coating give off light.

– When enough of them go through a wire at once, they make it hot enough to give off light — as in any toaster or light bulb.
– When they whiz through gases, they make the gas give off light — as in a neon sign or in the Northern Lights or in lightning or in ordinary sparks.
– When they hit other atoms hard enough, they cause metal to give out X rays, used by your doctor and dentist to see your bones.
– As they move, they produce magnetic lines of force, as Oersted found.
– When they surge back and forth in a wire at high speed as an alternating current, they give off radio waves of various kinds that we shall learn more about in Chapter 31.

These are only a few of the many effects of electrons at work. You have already seen some of the ways these chips of atoms are put to work to serve you in your daily life. In the rest of this chapter we shall take a look at a few more important uses for these versatile particles.

USING THE INVISIBLE TO SEE THE INVISIBLE

Electrons themselves are far tinier than you can ever imagine. Yet they have proved to be just the thing for seeing hidden objects like the bones of your body or flaws deep inside steel girders. Also they turn out to be fine things to use instead of light for looking at objects too tiny to be seen under ordinary microscopes. Yes, invisible electrons are used all over the world today to peer at invisible objects!

Light in the Darkness

Imagine another darkened room. Wilhelm Roentgen, a bearded middle-aged professor of physics in a German university, is experimenting with a cathode-ray tube. He has covered the tube completely with cardboard. He turns on the current from a high-voltage source.

In the darkness, something catches his eye. There is a glowing patch of light several feet from

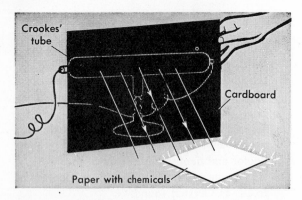

Crookes' tube

Cardboard

Paper with chemicals

23-4. The discovery of X rays: A Crookes' tube covered with cardboard, a piece of paper coated with chemicals that unexpectedly glowed in the dark.

his tube. It is a piece of paper coated with fluorescent chemicals.

But what rays can be striking the chemicals now? Certainly not cathode rays. They cannot travel such a distance. Besides, the tube is wrapped in cardboard. If these rays are coming from the tube, *they are coming right out through the cardboard* (Fig. 23-4).

Wilhelm Roentgen starts the first of many experiments to find out why his coated paper fluoresces. He finds that rays do indeed come from the cathode-ray tube, not from some other part of his apparatus. They come from the positive terminal at the end of the tube that is being struck by the cathode rays. Crookes and other experimenters must have produced these rays many times, without knowing it. He finds that the higher the voltage of the electric current, the more intense are the rays.

Moreover the rays go right through solid objects! A book of a thousand pages, held between the chemical-coated paper screen and the tube, does not hinder the chemicals from lighting at all. Two packs of playing cards, sheets of rubber, blocks of wood — none of these prevent the rays from reaching the screen and making it glow. But thicker blocks of wood cast a faint shadow. And sheets of metal made thick enough seem to stop the rays. Lead, for example, can halt the rays very effectively.

" X " for Unknown

" If the hand is held between the discharge tube and the screen, the dark shadow of the bones is visible within the slightly dark shadow of the hand. Since the rays affect photographic film, such shadow-pictures can be recorded." So wrote Roentgen, in December 1895, in his scientific report. Within a few months, doctors and surgeons were applying the rays to medicine (Fig. 23-5).

" To distinguish these from other rays I will call them X rays," Roentgen wrote. " X " stood for the unknown. His report caused a sensation in the scientific world and set off a growing wave of experiments. It stirred the minds of the public at large, too. X rays became the topic of the day, and all sorts of possible uses were thought of. In New Jersey a law was even proposed forbidding the use of X rays in opera glasses!

The Modern X-ray Tube

Although the X-ray tube used by your dentist is more complex than the model that Roentgen and his fellow-experimenters used, its principle is exactly the same (Fig. 23-6). Its main parts are the *cathode, target,* and *anode*. The coil of wire,

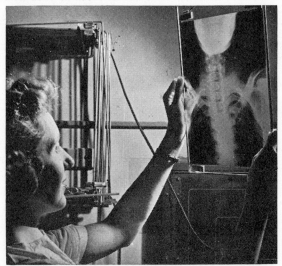

23-5. This medical technician is looking at an X-ray photograph for a doctor. Can you see part of the head, shoulders, and spine?

called a *filament,* is strongly heated by an electric current. When the filament glows brightly, it is hot enough to boil off electrons.

A strong electric force is now applied to pull the electrons down the tube toward the block of metal called the *target.* If the electric force is strong enough, the electrons will smash into the target at a very high speed. As a hammer makes sparks of visible light when it strikes a rock, the electrons' energy is splashed out as very short wave-length X rays.

The greater the electric force pulling the electrons through the tube, the more energy they will have when they hit the target. Also, the more penetrating will be the X rays driven out of the target. Sheets of lead around the tube prevent the radiation from going where it is not wanted, an important precaution, since an overdose of X-ray radiation is harmful. Some of the early experimenters suffered serious " burns " before this was realized.

Your dentist's X-ray equipment also provides the required high-voltage current for the tube, and contains timing devices to regulate the length of the X-ray exposure.

X rays were by no means limited to medicine. The discovery of X rays made scientists alert to the possibility of still other invisible rays. So when a French scientist named Antoine Becquerel (beh-KREL) found an exposed photographic plate under some uranium compound he had put in a drawer, he did not throw the plate away; the idea of invisible radiation at work crossed his mind. This led to the discovery of radioactivity, and a chain of experiments and theories that shook the world, as you have read about in Unit 2 and Unit 4.

X-raying Atoms

In the hands of the physicist, X rays are a powerful instrument for probing into the structure of matter itself. Just as light can be beamed into a dark place, X rays can be beamed into crystals, for example, and the pattern of rays that comes out again tells something of the structure of matter. In fact it was by firing X rays at each of the

X-RAY TUBE

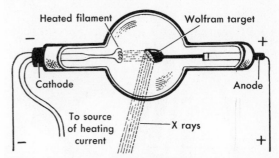

23-6. Electrons (cathode-ray particles) that boil off the hot filament smash into the metal target and give off energy in the form of X rays.

chemical elements that scientists learned how electrons are arranged in the outer layers of atoms.

This is another way electrons have given us eyes to see the invisible.

The Electron Microscope

Have you ever looked at tiny objects through a microscope?

If you have ever looked through one, you probably know that a microscope contains several glass lenses for bending light rays. The very best microscopes can bend and twist light rays until the tiny object you are examining is enlarged 2000 times. That's enough to make the period at the end of this sentence look as big as a manhole cover (about 30 inches across).

The woman in Fig. 23-7 is looking at a virus magnified 100,000 times! Of course she is not using an ordinary microscope. Her microscope needs no glass lenses. In fact it doesn't even need any light! Instead of light, her microscope uses a beam of electrons to " look " at tiny objects. Instead of lenses her microscope uses magnets to bend and twist the beam of electrons. It sounds a little bit like J. J. Thomson's cathode-ray tube, doesn't it?

In such an *electron microscope,* beams of electrons show us details of tiny objects 50 times smaller than do the most powerful light-using microscopes. Under an electron microscope the period at the end of this sentence would be magnified

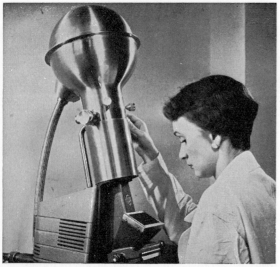

Radio Corp. of America

23-7. The electron microscope (left) uses a beam of electrons instead of light to magnify objects. The virus above is invisible to the most powerful light microscope, but visible by means of electrons.

to half the length of a football field (150 feet). Thus an electron microscope can actually let us examine a single molecule (Fig. 23-8). It can show us disease germs far too small for study with ordinary microscopes. Surely you can see that this

wonderful instrument is enabling us to enlarge enormously our knowledge of chemistry and medicine. There is no way of knowing what new discoveries and new understandings we may soon get by means of it. Watch the science columns in your newspapers.

Science at Work

If you look back over this chapter you will find that you have good examples of how scientists work.

Notice how these early workers had no practical purposes in mind as they worked away in their laboratories. Crookes, Roentgen, J. J. Thomson, and Millikan worked hard in their laboratories because they were curious, and discovery was exciting. They wanted to learn about the world around them.

When they found and identified the electron and proved that electrons were what electricity was made of, they had learned a big new important fact about the world around them. To them this discovery made all the hard work, false starts, and endless difficulties well worthwhile. They had added to knowledge.

Today we call work similar to the kind these scientists did in their laboratory studies *basic research* or *pure research*.

Standard Oil Co. (N.J.)

23-8. The invisible becomes visible: under the electron microscope, with a magnification of 27,000, these tiny particles of cuprene make a weird picture. Cuprene, a solid substance, is a polymer made from gaseous acetylene.

"Pure" scientist at work

IDEA

Applied scientist at work

USEFUL INVENTION

You, the consumer

23-9. Basic or " pure " research is done just for the sake of knowledge itself. Often, however, a scientist doing applied research will use such knowledge to produce important practical results. Thus applied research is dependent upon the results of pure research.

For many scientists pure research gives satisfaction enough for a lifetime of hard work. Other scientists find more fun — yes, for scientists, science is *fun* — in turning such discoveries into useful inventions like X-ray machines or electron microscopes or television tubes.

But research in pure science is one of the important careers in our modern chemical and physical world (Fig. 23-9).

Looking Back . . . .

VOCABULARY
The following terms represent the key words in this chapter. What is the meaning of each of these expressions?

1. vacuum pump
2. anode
3. cathode
4. cathode rays
5. electron
6. X ray
7. electron microscope
8. pure or basic research

REVIEW QUESTIONS
1. Explain how Crookes' tube produced cathode rays.
2. Describe some of the effects of cathode rays.
3. What conclusion did Crookes draw from the effects in his tubes?
4. How did Thomson measure the amount of charge on a gram of cathode rays?
5. What was the use of J. J. Thomson's experiment?
6. Describe how an X-ray tube works.

Going Further . . . .

EXPLAIN WHY:
- Roentgen knew his rays couldn't be cathode rays.
- Crookes thought his cathode rays were negatively charged and were particles.
- Scientists believe electricity is a stream of moving electrons.
- A beam of electrons can fly through thin sheets of solid metal.

APPLYING PRINCIPLES
1. Explain why the electron microscope is such a very useful instrument.
2. Name ten different kinds of places you commonly see electrons at work.
3. Name three important uses for X rays.

THINGS TO DO
Make a wire glow. If you have a dry cell to spare, attach an inch or two of thin iron wire to copper wires and then to the terminals. The wire may get red-hot and break. Even if it does not get red-hot, do not touch it until you have disconnected the ends.

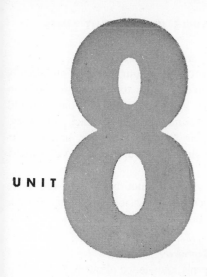

Lighting in Your World

You MAY be surprised to learn that there is a lot of light in the room around you right now that your eyes *cannot see!* Invisible rays are flooding over you from all directions.

Dangerous? No, not at all. Many are useful. There are rays that make your radio work and rays that can be used to cook your dinner. There are mysterious rays from outer space and even invisible rays being given off by your own body!

In this unit you will find out more about these invisible rays. You will read about their more dangerous cousins, too — " black light " that kills germs, X rays that can shine through solid metal, and the powerful rays given out by exploding atoms.

The light your eyes *can* see has many uses, too. Eyeglasses, cameras, telescopes, movie projectors, and microscopes all bend and twist rays of visible light to help you see better the world you live in. Do you ever wonder how they *really work?* In this unit we shall do a number of experiments to see for ourselves how all these tools work and how they are used to make our lives more comfortable.

What *is* light, anyway?

Surely we should look more closely at this strange stuff called " light." We shall find that there is still a mystery about it. There is even some mystery about how your eyes see light and color, too. In fact you will find that the more science tells us about light and its many uses, the more questions it raises for us to explore — new and mysterious questions.

This unit on light will answer many questions for you, but it will also challenge you to ask many new ones.

◀ *Scientists, by applying physical laws, use light to perform useful services.*

How Light Helps You To See

You have five senses: touch, taste, sight, sound, and smell. Which of them tells you the most about the world around you?

If you keep your eyes tightly shut for as little as five or ten minutes, you will agree that your eyesight perhaps tells you more than any of your other senses.

But you need more than good eyesight in order to see well. In a dark closet, you cannot see anything even if your eyes are working perfectly. In addition, you need enough light.

Let's see what a few experiments can show us about light.

LIGHT TRAVELS IN STRAIGHT LINES

Can you see around a corner?

Put your feet under your chair. You already know you won't be able to see them, for you know that the light coming from them would have to bend around a corner to reach your eyes.

Now tap your foot on the floor under your chair. Do you find that sound can travel around corners?

Light and sound do not behave in the same way. Light does not, at least to any large extent, seem to go around corners. Sound does.

A Simple Camera

We can use this knowledge about light to make a simple viewer as shown in Fig. 24-1. Point the pinhole at some brightly lit object, and you will see a small image of it on the wax-paper screen. The image is *upside down.*

The reason it is upside down is easy to see. Follow the path of light from the top of the candle through the pinhole. Since *light does not bend around corners,* where must it hit the screen? Likewise trace the light from the bottom of the candle, and you find your candle upside down on the screen!

If you put a camera film in place of the wax-paper screen as in Fig 24-1, you will have a simple camera. Your *pinhole camera* will work better if the inside is black and if no light is allowed to leak in except through the pinhole. Of

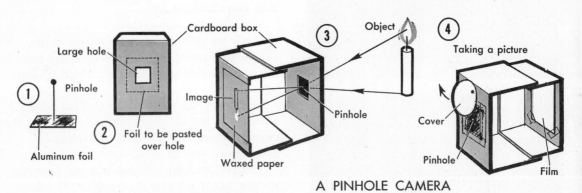

A PINHOLE CAMERA

24-1. A pinhole camera shows an image upside down.

course, you have to go into an absolutely dark closet to put in and remove the piece of film.

You can take very good photographs with a pinhole camera. You get the best pictures when your pinhole is very tiny. However, when the pinhole is tiny, so little light falls on your film that you must expose your film for several minutes. This length of time is a serious drawback, but it will not prevent your making a collection of pictures of motionless objects such as trees, flowers, or buildings.

You will learn how " faster " cameras work in Chapter 26.

Shadows

Have you ever tried to make shadows of weird animals and funny faces on the wall of a darkened room? If you have, you have been using the fact that light travels in straight lines instead of in curves. For the rays of light travel from the lamp toward your fingers and on past them *in straight lines* to the wall. Would there be a shadow on the wall if light went around corners the way sound does?

You may have noticed that if the light source is small, your shadows are quite sharp. But if your light source is a broad one, your shadows have blurry edges. The lamp you are using as you read this book is probably a good example of a broad light source. See if your fingers don't cast blurry-edged shadows on the pages.

Why blurry? From Fig. 24-2 you will see that a broad source of light really *acts* like a lot of tiny light sources, each one separated from its neighbor, each one casting its own shadow. In some places *all* of the shadows overlap and there the shadow is darkest. But at points near the edges of the shadow only a *few* of the light sources cast a shadow, while other light sources a little to one side of them do not. Around the edges then we have only a pale shadow. If you want to light a room with the fewest possible shadows, why would you use several weak lamps scattered around the room instead of one strong lamp?

Your eyes are strained by trying to see into sharp black shadows in a brightly lit room. Therefore the shadows in rooms are usually softened by using broad sources of light and by using a number of them in the same room. Indirect lighting and fluorescent tubes are still other means of using this same idea to reduce shadows and thus avoid eyestrain (Fig. 24-4).

Eclipses

Another rather broad source of light is our sun. You may have a hard time seeing blurry edges around the shadows of your fingers in sunlight because the blur is so narrow. But when a huge object like the moon comes between us and the sun, we find the dark shadow can be over 100 miles wide. The blurry edges of the moon's shadow are so big that they may cover half of the United States.

This monster shadow falling on the earth is

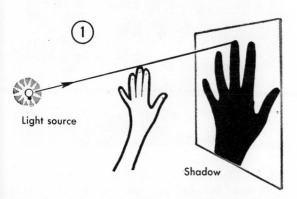

Light source

Shadow

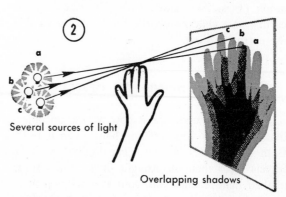

Several sources of light

Overlapping shadows

24-2. A small point of light produces a sharp shadow. However, if the source of light is broad, the overlapping shadows reduce the dark part and increase the partial shadow part.

24-3. Glare from the light reflected from the page will make reading difficult. How would you improve the lighting shown here?

called, as you may know, an *eclipse of the sun* (Fig. 32-7). In the parts of the country where the sun is completely cut off by the moon's disk we say that the sun is in *total eclipse*. But in the blurry edges of the shadow where light from part of the broad sun slips past the moon, we say that there is a *partial eclipse*.

Sometimes the earth passes between the sun and the moon. As this happens, you can watch the shadow of the earth slowly slide across the face of the moon. This is called an *eclipse of the moon* (Figs. 24-5 and 24-6). The shape of the earth's vast shadow on the moon shows us that the earth is round.

WHEN LIGHT SHINES ON OBJECTS

It is easy to understand how we see an object like the sun or your reading light when it is lit. Both are sources of light. The light they make travels from them in straight lines. When some of their light reaches you, your eyes tell you there is a light on, and you need only look back along the rays of light in order to see them.

But your *foot* or your *hand* is not a source of light. You cannot see them in a dark room, for they give off no light of their own. You need a lamp to help you to see them.

How Does Light Help Us to See an Object?

When there is a lamp in your room, light pours away from it in all directions, strikes all the ob-

24-4. Fluorescent lighting gives more light than a " hot wire " bulb for each watt of electricity. Because fluorescent lights are long, they cast fuzzy shadows which are easier on the eyes.

jects in the room that are not in deep shadow, and *bounces* off them in all directions. The bouncing of light is called *reflection*. Thus nearly everything in your room that is struck by light is *reflecting* light. Some of the reflected light reaches your eyes. You need only look back along the reflected rays of light in order to see what it is being reflected from. As you look along the path of the light, your eyes do not see the original lamp. Your eyes see the objects off which the light has just bounced.

Most of the objects you see around you have rough surfaces which reflect light every which way (Fig. 24-7A). As examples of rough surfaces think of dirty glass, tarnished metal, moving water, blotting paper, or scuffed shoes. When a lamp pours light onto objects like these, each place on their rough surfaces reflects light in *all* directions. Each place on the rough surface reflects at least a little light in the direction of your eyes. Hence to your eyes the entire surface seems to be fairly evenly lighted. Light is reflected from these rough surfaces in very much the same way that balls would bounce off a big pile of loose bricks.

But some objects are very shiny. When an object is shiny, it no longer reflects light every which way (Fig. 24-7B). Why do shiny objects reflect light so well? To find out, suppose you polish the dirty glass and the tarnished metal, allow the water to become smooth, put gloss on the paper, and shine the scuffed shoes. In each case you have made the surface *smooth*.

24-5. Phases of a partial eclipse of the moon photographed at five-minute intervals starting with the first appearance of the moon from total eclipse.

To see how light is reflected from smooth, shiny objects, imagine that the pile of loose bricks has been put together neatly to make a smooth wall. Then try once more to bounce balls against it. Do the balls bounce every which way? Or do the balls always bounce off the wall at the same angle they struck the wall?

When a shiny surface is reflecting a spot of light to your eye, all the light that reaches your eye is reflected from the same spot on the shiny surface. Notice how the light bounces off the shiny surface at the same angle it struck it. Do you see how

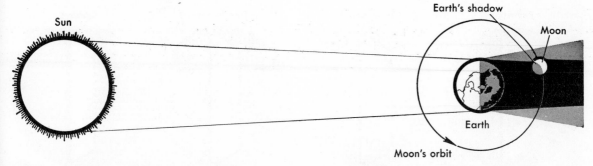

24-6. An eclipse of the moon is caused when the moon moves into the earth's shadow. Whenever the moon moves between the earth and the sun so that its shadow falls on the earth, the sun is eclipsed.

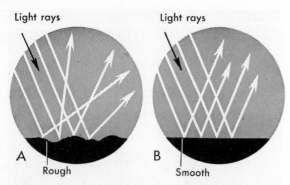

Light rays   Light rays

A Rough

B Smooth

24-7. A rough surface reflects some light in many directions. A smooth shiny surface, like a mirror, reflects most of the light in one direction.

none of the other spots on the shiny surface can reflect the light to your eye since no other light is reflected in the direction of your eye?

If the surface is very smooth, all of the light it reflects goes to your eye, none of it anywhere else. Thus you will see your reflecting spot shine brightly.

Who has not seen the glaring reflection of the sun on a smooth patch of water or off the surface of a well-polished car, or the blinding glare of lights reflected off a rainy road at night?

Have you ever held a book with glossy pages in such a position that it reflected a glare from your reading light into your eyes? Was it easy to read the printed page or see the pictures? Can you use your knowledge of reflection: (a) to choose the best place for your reading light? (b) to say whether schoolbooks should be printed on rough or glossy paper? (c) to decide whether

to paint the walls of a room with flat paint (rough surface) or with glossy surface paint?

Light Does Not Always Bounce

We have just seen that when light shines on an object some of the light is reflected. Thus when some of the reflected light reaches our eyes, we *see* the object. For us to see an object, it has to reflect some light to our eyes.

But you know of many materials that don't reflect *all* of the light that falls on them — water and glass, for example. Much of the light falling on water and on glass goes right on through without being reflected. When light goes right through a material, we say the material is *transparent* (Fig. 24-8). Water and glass are examples then of transparent materials. How many more common transparent materials can you name? Transparent materials *can* reflect light too, but they don't do it very well.

Many objects are not transparent, of course. Objects that do not let light go through them are called *opaque*. When light falls on a smooth opaque surface, it is not all reflected. You see this when you look at a china plate or at something made of opaque plastic. Yet it doesn't go through either! It seems to vanish in the material. The light is said to be *absorbed*.

Thus when light strikes an object, any of three things can happen. The light may be reflected. Or if the object is transparent, the light may go right on through. Or if the object is opaque, the light may be absorbed. Often two or even all three of

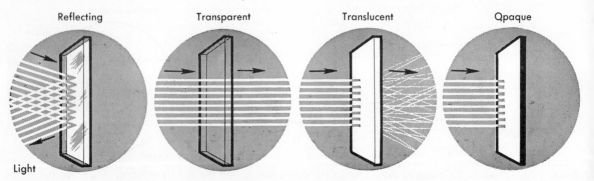

Reflecting   Transparent   Translucent   Qpaque

Light

24-8. What happens when light strikes these various materials?

these can happen at once, as with *translucent* objects. Which of these happens to the light that falls (a) on an amber glass bottle, (b) on your shoes, (c) on this page, (d) on the air of your room? Why can't you see air? See page 274 for the answers.

Mirrors

If you were going to make a mirror, would you choose a material that was: (a) rough, (b) opaque, (c) smooth, (d) transparent, (e) highly reflecting, (f) highly absorbing?

If you chose a, d, or f as your answers, your mirror would not be much of a success. Mirrors, as you can easily see, must be very smooth so that they can reflect lighted objects clearly. They must also reflect as much as possible of the light falling on them. You may have once used smooth water or window glass as a mirror. Why weren't they very good ones?

One of the best ways of making a mirror is to put a thin film of silver (which reflects very well) on a sheet of plate glass (which is very smooth). The silvered side against the glass is protected from tarnishing. In a mirror you look through the glass at this protected reflecting surface.

When you look at yourself in the mirror, the reflection of yourself appears to be back of the mirror. Your image seems to be the same distance behind the mirror as the object — you — is in front of it. But the image is reversed; that is, the right side appears where the left side is, and the other way around.

Some Mirrors Can Fool You

Have you ever seen an " invisible window "?

Of course if it's *really* invisible you can't see it. Surely you have walked along a street, looking in store windows and maybe noticing your reflection occasionally in the big panes of plate glass. Then perhaps you have come to an invisible window. How would you notice it? That's right — no reflections.

From what you know about how glass reflects light, this may seem amazing. The window *does* reflect light from the street, but the window is curved in such a way that none of these reflections is where your eye can see them. In Fig. 24-9, you will notice how rays of light are reflected off the mirror at the same angle as they strike it, just as they are off all mirrors. And you will notice how the tilt of the mirror sends these rays downward away from your eyes, instead of back to your eyes the way most windows do.

Another tricky mirror is used in your automobile headlights. Your headlamp bulb sends out light in almost all directions, just as any light bulb does. But in your automobile headlight you want to make all this light travel in one direction — straight forward. Mirrors make this easy to do. If the mirror were a flat one, light would be reflected in several different directions. But if the

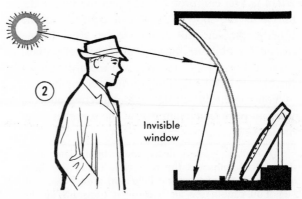

Glare of sunlight

Window

Invisible window

24-9. Flat windows reflect sky light back into your face. Curved windows reflect sky light down where you cannot see it — and the window is " invisible."

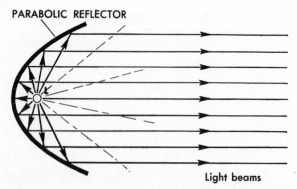

PARABOLIC REFLECTOR

Light beams

24-10. Mirrors of special shapes can reflect light out in a narrow beam. If the direction of the rays were reversed, parallel rays coming in would then be reflected to the point L.

mirror is curved in just the right way, all the reflections can be aimed in just one direction as you can see in Fig. 24-10. This special curved shape is called a *paraboloid* (puh-RAB-uh-loyd).

Parabolic mirrors are used in this same way as reflectors in flashlights and in big searchlights.

Parabolic mirrors have still another interesting use. If a beam of parallel light rays falls on a parabolic mirror, all the rays of light are reflected back to a single small spot (Fig. 24-10). Thus you can use such a mirror to collect a lot of light from some distant light source and concentrate it into a single spot such as your eye.

Astronomers use parabolic mirrors to collect a lot of light from a faint star and concentrate it at their eyes or on a photographic film (Fig. 24-11). You can probably see that the bigger the mirror is the more light it can collect and the brighter the star will appear to be. Here is one reason for building bigger and bigger telescopes. Look at Fig. 24-12, and you will see a picture of the biggest light-collecting mirror ever made.

You can easily see this light-collecting effect if you can get a shaving mirror of the sort that mag-

nifies your face. On a clear day point it at the sun and hold a piece of paper at the point where the reflected spot of light is brightest and smallest. So much sunlight has been concentrated at this point that the paper will probably catch fire. Be careful not to get your eyes or your hand near this spot.

One-way Mirrors

From our experiences with glass we know that even though it lets through most of the light, some is reflected back. A one-way mirror has on it a thin coating of metal, only a few atoms thick, which reflects most of the light, but still lets through a little bit.

If we are in a brightly lighted room and look into such a mirror, it appears like any other

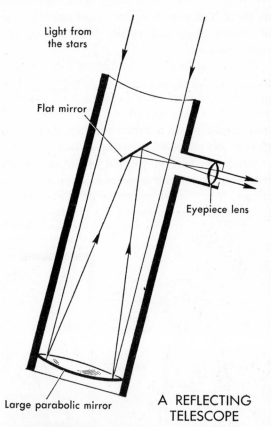

Light from the stars

Flat mirror

Eyepiece lens

Large parabolic mirror

A REFLECTING TELESCOPE

24-11. Many telescopes have parabolic mirrors to collect a great deal of light, thus giving a bright image.

(a) Amber glass reflects some light, lets some through and absorbs the rest. (b), (c) Your shoes and this page reflect some light and absorb the rest. (d) You cannot see air because it transmits all the light that falls on it and reflects none to your eyes.

mirror. But an observer in a dark room on the other side can see us by means of the faint light that still comes through. The observing room is always dark, often with black walls so the observer can easily see by the faint light coming through. If the observing room were brightly lighted and the other room made dark, the mirror would work equally well with the observer now being observed. Such mirrors have become possible only as methods have been invented for coating very thin layers of metal on glass.

BENDING LIGHT RAYS

You can use your new knowledge about light rays in many interesting ways, such as in building cameras and telescopes and eyeglasses and in learning how your eyes work and how mirages are formed.

To begin with let's try a trick with water.

Draw a straight line on a sheet of paper. Over half of the line lay a glass or clear plastic flat-bottomed dish or small aquarium tank with about an inch of water in it. Look at this line from directly above and then from more and more to one side. As you move your head, the part of the line you see through the water seems to move away from you (Fig. 24-13).

When you look straight down through the water at the line, is the line shifted? How must you place your eye in order to make the line shift the most?

Mt. Palomar Observatory

24-12. This giant 200-inch mirror, more than 17 feet wide, is located in the observatory on Mt. Palomar in California. It is the world's largest collector of light for the camera used in photographing faint bodies in the sky.

From Fig. 24-13 you will see that the rays of light coming up through the water are bent most of all where they strike the water at the smallest angle. They are not bent at all if they come out at right angles to the surface of the water. Does this agree with what you have just seen?

Try pouring some more water into the dish. Notice how the depth of the water changes what you see! It seems as though *the light is bent as it*

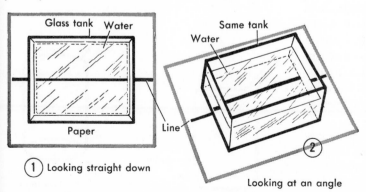

① Looking straight down

② Looking at an angle

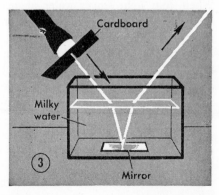

24-13. When viewed at an angle, a straight line below a piece of glass or tank of water appears to be "broken." The greater the angle at which you view it, the greater is the "break." A beam of light shone into a tank of water at an angle is bent, or refracted, when it goes from air into water, or water into air.

goes from water into air. This bending is called *refraction.*

By doing the following simple experiment, you can actually see the ray of light bent (refracted) as it goes from one transparent material to another. The only other equipment you need is a flashlight, a card with a hole punched in it by a pencil, and a few drops of milk or some chalk dust. Stir a few drops of the milk or the chalk dust into the water in your dish. Then, in a dimly lit room shine the flashlight downward at the surface of your dish. To make the beam of light small, hold the card with the pencil hole a few inches in front of the flashlight and a little to one side of the center of the beam (Fig. 24-13). The path of light should be clearly visible as it penetrates the slightly milky water. You can make it visible in the air, too, by tapping a blackboard eraser or a powder puff in front of the flashlight.

Try aiming the beam at the water at various angles. Then try drawing a diagram to show how your various rays are refracted. It should look like Fig. 24-13.

Next shine your flashlight up from beneath the bowl. If the water is not too deep, you will see the ray coming out through the top into the air. This time you can see how it is refracted as it leaves the water.

Careful observation should show that when your light *enters* water at an angle, it is always bent more sharply *away* from the water surface. When your light *leaves* water at an angle, it is always bent a little bit *toward* the surface. Light rays hitting the surface squarely at right angles are not bent either way. All this you can see in Fig. 24-13. Notice carefully that the bending occurs only as the light enters and leaves. Once inside the water, the light goes in straight lines as usual.

If you do similar experiments with other transparent materials, such as glass plates or ice, you will find the light is bent in a similar way.

You can use this knowledge of refraction of light to explain why a beam of light going diagonally through a pane of plate glass is shifted sideways a bit without its direction changing.

Bent Light Rays Can Fool You

This bending of light as it passes from one transparent material to another also explains the following familiar illusion. Put your pencil into the water of a tumbler. If your pencil is tilted, it will seem to be broken where it enters the water (Fig. 24-14). Furthermore, as you look at the end of your pencil in the bottom of the tumbler, you will probably agree that this bending of light makes the water seem shallower than it really is. If you have ever tried to spear fish, you know you must aim below where the fish appear to be.

If you understand refraction, you should now have no trouble explaining the "floating penny trick." Empty your tumbler and put a penny in the bottom of it. Hold a book up against one side so that you cannot quite see the penny over the edge of the book. Now have a friend gradually fill the tumbler with water. Soon the penny will appear, as the tumbler is filled, to float in the water. Can you suggest a reason why the penny appears to float?

Water Can Act Like a Mirror

As you look at Fig. 24-15, you will notice that the ray marked " A " comes out almost parallel to the water surface. You might wonder what would happen to the ray marked " B " which strikes the surface to the left of " A." Why not try an experiment to see?

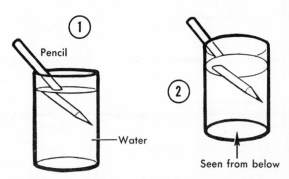

24-14. A pencil in a glass of water seems to be bent at the surface of the water. From above, the pencil seems to be higher than it really is.

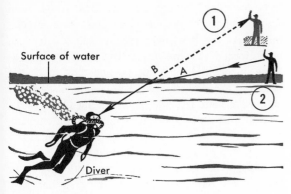

Surface of water

Diver

24-15. Explain why a diver under water, like a fish, sees objects on shore more nearly overhead than they really are.

Hold your pencil once more straight downward into your tumbler full of water. This time look upward through the *side* of the tumbler at the *under* surface of the water. From this position perhaps you can see what has happened to those rays of light nearly parallel to the water's surface that tried to escape up through it. Did they succeed?

Rays that try to escape by striking the water surface at too small an angle will be *reflected* (notice, *not* refracted) back in again. Thus a fish or a diver trying to look up through the surface of the sea will be able to see out directly overhead, or even as much as 48 degrees to the side (Fig. 24-15).

This effect makes it possible to pipe light from place to place. Perhaps you have seen a "light pipe" made out of transparent plastic, and used by doctors and dentists to illuminate parts of the body. Light traveling along the tube cannot escape through the side walls since it always strikes them at too small an angle and is reflected back in again. Would any light escape if the light pipe were bent very sharply into a right angle (Fig. 24-16)?

A Number That Measures Refraction

When you shine light on other transparent materials, you will find that the light behaves very nearly the same way it does with water. But one

Westinghouse Electric Co.

24-16. A "tubeful" of light. In the plastic tube, light is trapped and bent around a turn. It comes out at the flat end and shines on the man's face. Does any light leak out along the tube?

important difference between water and glass and other transparent materials is the *amount* by which they each bend a ray of light entering them from the air. In Fig. 24-17 you will see that a diamond bends light more sharply than either glass or water. Therefore, we say that a diamond *refracts* light more than glass or water.

We use a number called the *index of refraction* to describe refracting ability. Materials with a large index of refraction, like diamonds, bend

REFRACTION

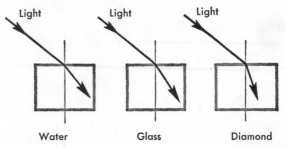

24-17. Water, glass, and diamonds, like other transparent materials, refract light by different amounts.

very sharply a ray of light entering from the air. The smallest index a material can have is 1.000. You will find the index of refraction of several transparent materials in Table 24-1.

TABLE 24-1 INDEX OF REFRACTION

vacuum	1.000
air at 0° C	1.00029
air at 30° C	1.00026
water at room temp.	1.33
ice	1.31
carbon tetrachloride	1.46
glass (crown)	1.51
glass (flint)	1.71
glycerine	1.47
diamond	2.47

Why Is Light Bent?

But *why* is light bent as it strikes the surface of a transparent material at an angle? What is going on inside the ray of light?

You can't see what really goes on inside the ray of light. But if you would like a big demonstration that you *can* see, get together several of your hiking friends. Find a patch of soft or very bumpy ground beside the road, and try a simple experiment illustrated in Fig. 24-18.

In this experiment the line of hikers traveling together across the road represents the beam of

24-18. Notice that when this line of hikers approaches rough ground at an angle, the leaders are slowed down and the line tends to swerve toward the right. How does this resemble the behavior of light waves?

light traveling through the air. The rough field represents the water in your glass dish experiments. As the first hiker reaches the rough field, he is forced to slow down. But his f.iends continue unchecked until one by one they reach the field and are slowed down, too. As the last person enters the field, the line of hikers has changed direction, just as your beam of light did on entering the water in your tumbler (Fig. 24-14). And the change in direction is for a similar reason.

Across the field a hiker does not travel as fast as on the smooth road. In a similar way through glass a beam of light does not travel as fast as in air or in a vacuum. Thus, *the beam is bent as a result of its change in speed* if the light enters at an angle. Actual measurements show that light travels fastest of all in a vacuum and more slowly in materials with a higher index of refraction.

Illusions with Hot and Cold Air

Look back at Table 24-1. You will notice that cold air (0° C.) has a higher index of refraction than hot air (30° C.). Thus light goes faster through hot air than it does through cold air.

Does this seem like a useless piece of information? Lots of information in science seems to be useless until suddenly you find that it explains some important or familiar everyday experience. These measurements of the speed of light in hot air and in cold air explain some experiences familiar to all of us.

For example, it explains why we see what appear to be pools of water in the road ahead of us on a hot sunny day, only to find them vanish as we come closer. Because light travels faster through the hotter air down close to the road's hot surface, light coming toward us low over the road is bent upward to our eye (Fig. 24-19A). It appears to be reflected in the same way it would be if there were a real pool of water on the road.

This same fact about light going at different speeds through hot and cold air explains the quivering of distant objects seen low over the surface of a hot radiator or a bonfire. As air swirls upward over these hot objects some of the

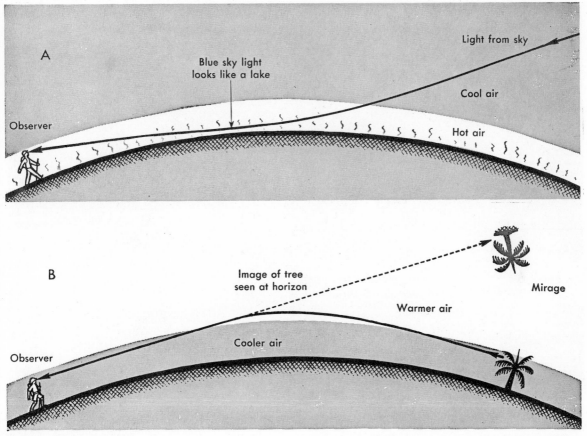

24-19. The bending of light when it travels through layers of air of different temperatures is the cause of mirages. Explain why.

air is hot, some not so hot. Light coming to you through such unevenly heated air is bent first one way then another, until it is badly twisted off course. By the time it reaches you, you see a badly twisted view of the distant object.

This same effect also makes stars twinkle — to the delight of poets and the sorrow of astronomers. The next clear night try looking at the stars close over the top of someone's chimney. The unevenly heated air swirling up makes the images of stars jiggle and dance. If you can look at the stars with a pair of binoculars, you will find this effect is very much increased.

You can demonstrate this quivering of distant objects right inside your room! You do not have to have unevenly heated air. All you need is a

piece of the very cheapest window glass — the kind that makes the world outside look like Fig. 24-20. Why does the uneven and wavy glass surface bend the light in such an irregular way? Move the glass slowly up and down in front of you. Stars drawn on the blackboard will appear to twinkle and the objects you see through it will appear to wiggle about for exactly the same reason as they do when seen over the hot radiator.

A *mirage* is still another strange effect produced by light traveling faster in hot air than in cooler air. Sometimes over a desert warm air rises up off the hot sand and cooler air flows in to take its place. The result will be a layer of warm air lying on top of a layer of cooler air (Fig. 24-19B). Now the rays of light from a distant object will be

Frank Murray

24-20. Uneven glass bends light in odd patterns. When used in windowpanes this is the result.

curved *downward* as they pass along the boundary between the two air layers. Thus an observer may actually be able to see buildings and trees beyond the horizon. You will see from Fig. 24-19 that this effect can even bend light around the curve of the earth's surface. This kind of a mirage would not fool a thirsty traveler in the desert — the reflection of the palm trees and buildings may be upside down! From what you know about mirrors, can you explain why this is so?

There are other kinds of mirages, too, such as the appearance of standing pools of water on the hot road. Would a desert traveler be more likely to be fooled by this kind of mirage?

All the effects we have read about in this chapter are produced by the bending of light as it travels from one transparent material into another of different index of refraction. Mirages, bent sticks in water, twinkling stars, sparkling diamonds,

crinkly appearing window glass, light pipes — all these you can understand when you know some simple facts about light.

Looking Back . . . .

VOCABULARY

Each one of the following words or expressions represents a key idea in the chapter you have just studied. Give a definition of each term.

1. pinhole camera
2. total eclipse
3. partial eclipse
4. transparent
5. opaque
6. absorb
7. refraction
8. reflection
9. index of refraction
10. mirage
11. parabolic mirror

EXPLAIN HOW:

- An eclipse of the moon supports the idea that the earth is round.
- You can see your reflection in smooth water but not when the surface is rough.
- A mirage can make you see pools of water that do not really exist.
- You can tell that sound goes around corners but light does not.
- A body of water looks shallower than it really is.
- Water can act like a mirror.
- Light is bent as it goes into glass.
- Hot air rising over a fire or a radiator makes distant objects seem to jiggle and dance.
- A mirror makes your left hand look like a right hand.
- Warm air makes stars twinkle.
- Some pavements are shiny on rainy nights.

Going Further . . . .

PROBLEMS TO SOLVE

1. Draw a diagram of a pinhole camera, and explain why the pictures it takes are upside down.
2. Draw diagrams to explain why a faraway or tiny lamp casts sharp shadows, while a nearby tubular fluorescent lamp casts shadows with blurry edges.
3. Draw a diagram of a partial eclipse.
4. Draw lines to show a beam of light shining on a rough surface. Now draw more lines to show how the light is reflected.
5. Show how light is bent as it goes from air into water.
6. Show how light is bent as it goes through a flat pane of window glass.
7. Draw a diagram showing how a parabolic mirror works.

APPLYING PRINCIPLES

1. Explain why it is better to have your reading lamp behind you or to one side when you are reading.
2. Why is a book easier to read when it is printed on a paper with no glare than when it is printed on shiny or glossy paper?
3. Explain how one-way mirrors work.
4. Why is it easier on your eyes to have several small lamps around a room rather than one big bright one?

5. How does " invisible " window glass work?
6. Show how the reflecting mirror of an automobile headlight works.
7. How does a " light pipe " work?
8. Why does a frosted light bulb give less glare than a clear bulb would?
9. Why are venetian blinds better than window shades for controlling the light in a room?

TRY THESE

1. When you walk toward a mirror at two miles an hour, how fast do you approach your image as seen in the mirror?
2. When your watch as seen in a mirror seems to read 8:15, what time is it really?
3. When you try to spear fish in a pool, should you aim directly at the fish? Explain.
4. Light travels 124,000 miles a second in glass and 140,000 miles a second in water. Which has the higher index of refraction — glass or water?
5. Can you arrange two big mirrors so that they show the back and the side of your body at the same time? Try drawing the rays of reflected light.

THINGS TO DO

1. Make a periscope to help you see around corners. All you need are two mirrors arranged as in Fig. 24-21.
2. Here is a good party game. Set up a mirror on edge on the table top. In front of it put a sheet of paper with a square drawn on it. Next set a book on edge in front of the paper so you cannot see the paper except by looking in the mirror. Now take a pencil and try to trace over the square. You will find it surprisingly hard.

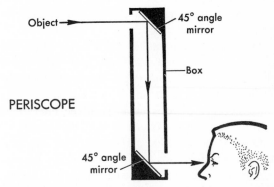

24-21. A periscope changes the direction of light by reflecting it twice, both times through an angle of 90 degrees.

Your Eyes—Two Built-in Lenses

You see your eyes in a mirror every day. How well can you draw a picture of them?

Try drawing an eye, putting in all the details you can remember. Then check your drawing by looking at your eyes again in a mirror. How good an observer have you been all these years?

HOW YOUR EYE SEES

In the center of a white eyeball, have you drawn a colored ring? This colored ring, called the *iris,* is about ½ inch across and gives your eyes their brown or blue coloring.

Did you draw a smaller *black* circle filling the center of the colored iris diaphragm? The black circle, called the *pupil,* is a transparent hole that lets light through to the inside of your eye. It looks black because there is no light in the interior of your eyeball to help you see in from the outside.

Over all the outside surface of your eye is a hard moist protective covering called the *cornea.* It would be difficult for you to draw the cornea because it should be quite transparent. However, you may know of someone whose cornea has become diseased and slowly grown opaque, thus pre-

venting light from entering his eye through the iris. Of course this results in blindness unless the diseased cornea can be removed and replaced by a healthy one. You may have read of people donating their healthy eyes to an *eye bank.* An eye bank is a hospital's collection of eyes being saved for the help of patients with various eye diseases.

What Is Inside Your Eye?

Directly behind the iris of your eye is a *lens.* In the world at this moment there are more lenses in the eyes of people and animals than have *ever* been made out of glass in factories. Lenses existed in nature long before men made them from glass.

Sometimes the lens can lose its transparency, just as the cornea can. We call this disease of the lens a *cataract.* Cataracts can lead to blindness, too. Fortunately sight can be restored by an operation if the cataract is not too far along.

Behind the lens is a transparent, ball-shaped *jelly-like mass* filling the center of the eyeball. And finally, coating the very back of this ball-shaped mass is a thin layer called the *retina* — the screen on which the lens focuses its images.

You will find all these parts drawn in Fig. 25-1. The fibers from the nerve cells of the retina join to form the optic nerve that carries " messages " to your brain. In your brain you really " see " (that is, the brain *interprets*) what the rays of light have brought to your retina. You can see all of these parts of an eye for yourself if you get a large fish eye from your local fish market. You will have no trouble locating the iris, the pupil, and at the back, the white string-like optic nerve. When you cut the eye open, you can also see the lens (a small jelly-like bead) and the dark purple light-sensitive retina.

Your Built-in Movie Screen — the Retina

The light-sensitive surface of each retina is made up of the tips of nearly 50 million nerves, all sensitive to light. When light falls on any one of the special ends of these nerves, it sends a message to your brain and you become aware of light shining in your eye. When the lens of your eye focuses a large object, such as this page, on your

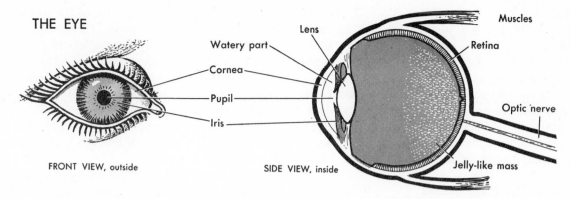

THE EYE

FRONT VIEW, outside

Watery part
Cornea
Pupil
Iris

Lens
Muscles
Retina
Optic nerve
Jelly-like mass

SIDE VIEW, inside

25-1. There are many parts inside your eye. The iris and the lens are especially important in focusing an image. The nerve cells in the retina send messages along the optic nerve to your brain, and you " see."

retina, then thousands of retina nerve cells are all prodded into sending signals to your brain.

An imaginary model of the retina of one of your eyes could be made as follows: On a round bowl-shaped tabletop, 85 feet across, assemble 50 million matches in an enormous bundle with their heads all pointing up. To the bottom end of each match, attach a thread and collect all the threads into one rope running down off the table. You would have a model of the retina of your eye magnified one million times. The rope represents the optic nerve carrying to your brain the signals from each nerve ending (match head). As you read this printed page, millions of these nerve endings in the retina of each eye (Fig. 25-1) flash the impression along the optic nerve to your brain.

You could make your model eye even more accurate if you used two kinds of matches — matches with big heads and matches with little heads. Near the center of your model you would use mostly matches with big heads. These could represent the nerve endings (called *cones*) by which you see color. Away from the center of your model you would use mostly matches with small heads. These are models of the nerve endings (called *rods*) by which you see faint light (Fig. 25-2).

You can do two experiments to test what the rods and cones of your own eyes do.

1. To prove that *the rods around the sides of your retinas are unable to see color*, ask one of

your friends to walk slowly around you from behind. Stare straight ahead of you. When you are *first* aware of your friend moving into view, ask yourself what color his suit or her dress is. You will find you can see him moving " out of the corner of your eye " long before you are aware of color.

2. To prove that *the rods of your eyes are more sensitive to light* even though they cannot see color, go outdoors on the next clear night and see

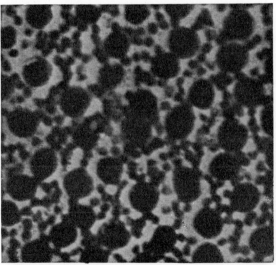

Dever from Black Star

25-2. This is a microscopic view of the retina. The cones (the large round spots) enable you to see during the daytime. The rods (smaller spots) enable you to see in dim light.

how faint a star you can find. You will discover that the faintest star you can see is much *easier* to see if you look a bit to one side of it, allowing its light to fall on the more light-sensitive rods around the sides of your retinas.

Perhaps you already know that the black and white film you use in your camera is much more sensitive to light than color film is. In this respect black and white film is similar to the more sensitive rods around the sides of your retina.

Lenses for Clear Images

Without a lens in your eye the world would look bright but blurry, much as it does when you open your eyes under water. For your retina to receive a sharp clear image the way a movie screen does, your eye *must* have a lens in it. Let us see how a lens bends light so as to form a clear picture on your retina.

Find a glass lens that is thicker in the center than at the edges. Such a lens is called a *convex* lens. Take it outdoors on a sunny day and try using it as a burning glass. Let sunlight pass through it and fall on a sheet of paper, as in Fig. 25-3. As you move your convex lens in and out away from the paper, you will find a position where all the sunlight falling on the lens has been bent together into one spot on the paper. Careful! The paper will catch on fire. The spot is so hot you must be careful not to get your hand near it. You can see why this type of lens is called a burning glass.

You have just made a picture of the scorching hot sun on your sheet of paper. The burning glass did this in the same way that the lens of your eye forms a picture of distant objects on your retina. If you cover up most of the lens when you are doing this experiment, the picture of the sun on your paper will be dimmer and cooler. Perhaps you can see it before your paper catches on fire.

Fig. 25-4 is a picture of how the burning glass bent the rays of sunlight.

From the distant sun, rays of light strike the surface of the burning-glass lens. From your study of the bending of light in Chapter 24, you know that as the light rays enter the sloping surface of the glass they will be bent. And again as they come out through the sloping surface of the glass they will be bent still more. The lens is curved in such a way that the rays of light are all bent together at one point called the *focus*. We call the distance from the lens to the screen the *focal length* (Fig. 25-4).

Now let us take the last step and see how the lens of your eye focuses an image of a distant friend onto your retina. In Fig. 25-5, you see rays of light from your friend's head striking the lens and being focused to a point on your retina, just as the light from the sun was focused on the sheet of paper. You also see more rays from your friend's feet being brought to a focus at a different spot on your retina. In the same way light from all the rest of your friend's body is focused on your retina to form a clear sharp image.

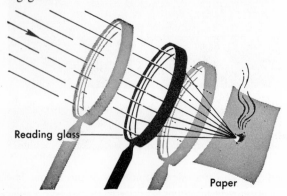

25-3. You can see from this experiment why a convex lens is called a burning glass.

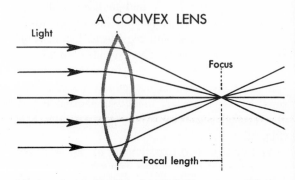

A CONVEX LENS

Light

Focus

Focal length

25-4. A convex lens bends light rays together to a sharp focus.

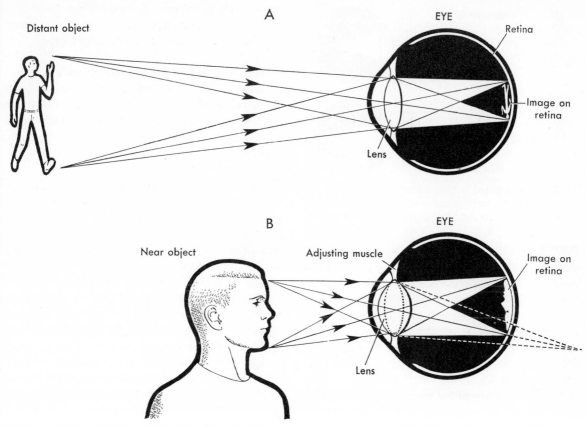

25-5. Muscles in your eyes change the shape of the lens to adjust to different distances. Compare the thickness of the lens in A and B.

Notice that the image is upside down. In this respect your eye is rather like a pinhole camera, isn't it?

The World Turned Upside Down

Notice how the lenses of your eyes focus images upside down on your retina. You may wonder why things don't *look* upside down. Part of the answer is that you really don't see with your eyes anyway. All that your eyes do is to focus light upon the nerve endings of the retinas. The many tiny nerves of your two retinas then send their signals along the two optic nerves to your brain. In your brain, the nerve signals are pieced together and you become conscious of what your eyes are looking at. Your awareness of the things you see, then, does not exist in your eyes — it is

in your brain. Your brain has learned " which end is up " only through long practice and experience.

Oddly, if you were to wear special goggles that turn everything you see upside down, you would find after a few weeks of steady use that your brain had grown used to the change and you saw the world right-side-up once more! This rather uncomfortable experiment has actually been tried. So you see it is not the way rays of light strike the retina that determines how you see things. Rather it is the way your brain interprets the signals sent from the light-sensitive rods and cones in your retinas.

How You Focus Your Eyes

Your friend may be standing across the room from you. As you walk up close to him the rays of

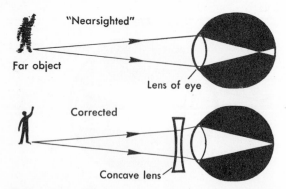

25-6. Nearsighted people have eyeballs which are too long; they cannot focus on distant objects. Concave glasses can balance this defect and allow normal vision.

light from, say, his forehead no longer strike the lens of your eye in quite the same way. As you come very close to him, you get up to where the rays from his forehead are spreading apart as they strike your eye. If your lens goes on bending these rays of light only as much as it did before, the rays from his forehead would be brought to a focus far behind your retina as you can see by the dotted lines in Fig. 25-5.

What must happen for your lens to focus such a nearby object onto your retina? Somehow it must bend the rays of light more sharply than it did before. In other words your lens must shorten its focal length.

The lens of your eye does this in an unusual way. It is made of a rubbery, elastic material. As the muscles holding the lens in place stretch or relax, they make the elastic lens thicker or thinner. The thicker the lens is, the more sharply curved are its surfaces, therefore, the more sharply it bends the light from your friend's forehead.

Hence, as you walk up close to your friend, the lenses of your eyes grow thicker and shorten their focal length enough for him to continue to be focused clearly on your retinas.

When you focus on something close to your eyes, such as this book you are reading, the muscles holding your lenses in focus are being kept strongly contracted. If you continue to read for long periods of time, you may feel these muscles becoming tired. It rests your eyes to look up from

your book from time to time. When your eyes focus on an object more than about 20 feet away, the focusing muscles are completely relaxed.

Why You May Have to Wear Glasses

Many people have eyeballs that are too long. Thus when the focusing muscle is relaxed for looking at distant objects and the lens focuses the image of the distant objects in the usual position, the retina isn't there to receive the image (Fig. 25-6).

People with such extra-long eyeballs can see clearly only when they bring objects nearer to their eyes. Thus they are said to be *nearsighted*.

How do glasses help a nearsighted person to see? They help him to see by making the rays from distant objects spread apart exactly as if the distant object had been held up close to the eyes.

The lenses of the glasses worn by nearsighted people are thinner in the center than at the edges. Such lenses are called *concave* lenses. These help the lenses of the nearsighted eye to focus a clear image on the retina of the extra-long eyeball. They bend the light rays going through the glasses so that the rays strike the lenses in the eyes in such a way that they focus on the retina.

Eyeglasses were invented back around the year 1300. Before that time there had lived millions and millions of nearsighted people who went through their entire lifetimes without ever seeing clouds or stars or distant flying birds clearly!

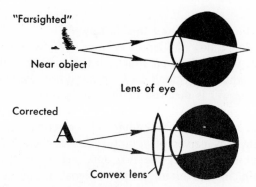

25-7. Farsighted people have eyeballs which are too short. A convex lens helps to focus near objects sharply onto the retina.

25-8. Three views as seen by three different passengers in the back seat: (Top left) To a farsighted person the boy is seen clearly, but the woman is blurred. (Top right) To a nearsighted person the boy is blurred, but the woman is clear. (Bottom) To a person with proper vision, both the boy and woman are clear.

Now many people also wear glasses for another type of eye defect — *farsightedness*. Their eyeballs are too short. Hence the lenses of their eyes have to bend light rays together extra sharply to bring the rays to focus on the retinas. To focus light within so short a distance means that the focusing muscles must keep the lens thick most of the time. This is very tiring and a person can suffer serious eyestrain. Only objects far away can be seen clearly and without strain.

The focusing muscles of farsighted people can be relieved of their tiring extra-hard job by convex lenses which help bend the light rays together. In Fig. 25-7 you see how a *convex* lens placed in front of a farsighted eye helps to focus near objects sharply onto the retina.

There is still a third common eye defect. It is the result of the lenses of the eyes curving more in one direction than in another. This defect is called *astigmatism*. If you have astigmatism an object looks partly clear and partly blurry. You cannot focus your eyes so as to make all of it look

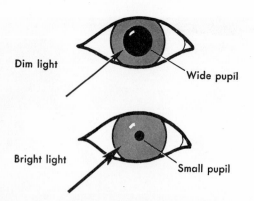

Dim light

Wide pupil

Bright light

Small pupil

25-9. In the dark, the iris in your eye automatically opens slowly to let in more light. In bright light, the iris closes quickly to protect your eye from too much light.

sharp and clear at once. You can correct astigmatism by wearing glasses that curve more in one direction than in another.

Of course if you are nearsighted or farsighted or have astigmatism, you should never borrow the glasses of someone else. There are all *degrees* of these eye defects, and the glasses worn by your friend were carefully matched to his eyes by a skilled oculist. No one else can wear them without risk of serious eyestrain. And if you do wear glasses of your own, they should be checked regularly because your eyes may change with age.

As people grow older, their eye-focusing muscles become weaker, and it becomes harder for them to change the focus of their eyes. Usually they find it easier to focus on distant objects. Thus many elderly people need to wear glasses, because their eye-focusing muscles need help.

Some Special Kinds of Glasses

Some older people find it necessary to help their eye muscles along with two lenses combined into one. The upper part of the lens may help them look at distant objects, and the lower pair may help them when looking down at nearby objects such as a book. Such double-purpose glasses are called *bifocals*.

Still another kind of lens is sometimes used by such people as actors or athletes who would be

handicapped by wearing ordinary glasses. They may wear carefully shaped lenses, called *contact* lenses, that fit directly onto the surface of the cornea and under the eyelid.

Dark Shades for Your Eyes

Have you ever gone into a darkened movie theater and had a hard time seeing your way to a seat? Soon your eyes became adjusted to the darkness and you could see people around you quite easily.

Or have you ever been blinded for a few moments by the glare of a sunlit street as you came out of a movie theater? After a few moments your eyes got used to the bright light and you were able to see easily once more.

How do your eyes get used to changes in the amount of light? You can find out by doing an experiment. Have a friend cover his eyes tightly for a minute or two. Then have him suddenly open them and stare at a bright light. As he does this you should look closely at the black pupils of his eyes. Do they change size? (See Fig. 25-9.)

You can see the same rapid decrease in size in the pupils of your own eyes by standing be-

Swiss National Tourist Office

25-10. Snow reflects much of the sunlight falling on it. Skiers and Arctic explorers shield their eyes from the glare with dark glasses.

25-11. The world's largest reflecting telescope has a mirror 200 inches in diameter. In the tank, seen in the background, the glass mirror is coated with a thin layer of metal to increase its reflecting power.

fore a mirror in a dimly lit room for a minute or two and then turning on a light.

Either one of these experiments should show you that in bright light the pupils of your eyes quickly grow smaller. If you have ever been blinded for a moment by the sudden glare of automobile headlights at night, you know how too much light makes it hard to see. Why do people have to wear dark glasses on a sunlit beach or in a sunny snow-covered countryside? (See Fig. 25-10.)

On the other hand, to see dimly lit objects your pupils must open wide in order to let in as much of the faint light as possible. It may take ten minutes for them to open wide enough for you to see objects in a *very* dimly lit room.

If your pupils could open up wider, you could see even fainter objects. You cannot open your pupils any wider, but you *can* crowd a lot more light into your eyes. A big convex lens can collect all the light that falls on it and focus it into a tiny beam that your eye *can* use. Night glasses are binoculars that do this.

And astronomers can see *very* faint stars by collecting their light with a big mirror like that at the bottom of the large telescope in Fig. 25-11.

The opening and closing of your pupils is managed by the iris — that colored ring you see surrounding the black hole of the pupil. The iris contains a tiny ring-like muscle rather like a small circular rubber band. It surrounds the pupil. When bright light strikes your eye, the tiny iris muscle contracts. It makes the hole of the pupil smaller by drawing the iris tighter around the hole. When the light is too dim, the tiny iris muscle relaxes again and the pupil opens to form a larger hole. The iris muscle does all this without your ever thinking about it.

It is amazing that anything as complicated as your eye could work so smoothly year after year. Yet you will be interested to learn that your eyes are simple compared with the eyes of some animals. For example in Fig. 25-12 you see a close-up picture of the eye of a common housefly. *Each of the tiny spots you see is a separate lens!* Four thousand eyes in all, each one with its own lens, its own iris mechanism, and its own retina — all working together. How strange the world must look to a housefly.

25-12. The eyes of a common housefly. Two large compound eyes are made up of hundreds of separate simple eyes pointing in nearly every direction.

Looking Back . . . .

VOCABULARY

Each of the following expressions represents a key idea in the chapter you have just studied. What is the meaning of each expression?

1. iris
2. pupil
3. cornea
4. cataract
5. lens (of the eye)
6. retina
7. concave lens
8. rods
9. cones
10. focus
11. focal length
12. nearsightedness
13. farsightedness
14. astigmatism
15. bifocals
16. contact lenses
17. eye bank
18. convex lens

REVIEW QUESTIONS

1. How does a lens work?
2. How does your eye control the amount of light falling on your retina?
3. Of what use are the rods of your eyes? What do the cones do?
4. How does the lens in an eye change its focal length?
5. Draw a diagram showing how the eye-lens focuses a clear image of an object far away.
6. Draw a diagram showing how the eye-lens focuses a clear image of an object quite close to it.
7. Draw a diagram showing why a nearsighted person without glasses cannot easily see distant objects.
8. By drawing a diagram, show why a farsighted person without glasses cannot easily see near objects.
9. Draw a diagram showing how glasses help a nearsighted person to see distant objects easily.
10. Show by a diagram how glasses help a farsighted person to see near objects easily.
11. What is astigmatism?

Going Further . . . .

EXPLAIN WHY:

- Your eye-lenses need to change their focal length as you get closer to or farther from an object.
- It is difficult to see an object clearly when it is held much closer than ten inches from one eye.
- It is difficult to see anything in a dimly lighted room when you come into it from a brightly lighted place.
- Elderly people often need to wear glasses.
- It is very dangerous to look directly at the sun without special protection for your eyes.
- The world doesn't look upside down to you.
- Your eyes become tired after you have been reading for a long time.
- You have to wear dark glasses if you spend much time in a sunny snow-covered countryside.
- Astronomers use *big* lenses in their telescopes.

THINGS TO DO

Everyone has a blind spot! The blind spot in each of your eyes is where the nerves from your rods and cones all come together and leave the retina on the way to your brain. You cannot see light that falls on this spot on your retina (Fig. 25-13).

To find your blind spot close your right eye and stare at the X with your left eye. Hold the book at arm's length away from you. Slowly bring the book closer to your eyes, always staring at the X. You will notice that the O suddenly disappears. Still closer the O appears again and the square disappears.

They disappeared because their image fell on the blind spot of your retina at those distances.

READING FURTHER

Eyes, Our Windows to the World, Better Light, Better Sight Bureau, 420 Lexington Ave. New York, N.Y. A simple, well-illustrated free bulletin.

25-13. Close your left eye and look at the O with your right eye. As you bring the page closer, the X disappears; still closer the X appears and the square disappears. Why?

CHAPTER

26

The Camera and Other Uses for Lenses

Lenses serve us in many ways. In our eyes they make it possible for us to see the world around us. In our cameras they make it possible for us to keep a picture record of the past. In motion picture projectors lenses make it possible for hundreds of people to see the same pictures at once. You will also see in this chapter how lenses help us extend our sight into the invisible worlds of the extremely small and the extremely far away.

A camera is built very much like your eye — only more simply.

If you have a camera (with no film in it) open up the back where the film is put in, and see for yourself how it is made. Compare the camera with your eye (Fig. 25-1).

In the camera, just as in your eye, there is a *lens* to bring the light from a distant object to a focus. In the camera, just as in your eye, there is a screen on which the focused light rays form an image. This screen is the photographic *film,* placed at the very back of the camera. In the camera, just as in your eye, there is a kind of iris whose opening can be changed in order to control the amount of light falling on the film. This iris is called the *diaphragm.* Finally, just as your eye has an eyelid to shut out light altogether, the camera has a *shutter* for the same purpose.

Lens, film, diaphragm, and shutter are the important parts of the camera just as the lens, retina, iris, pupil, and eyelid are important parts of your eye.

Changing the Size of the Image

To see how the camera lens makes a clear image on the film let's do some experiments. Get out the convex glass lens you used back on page 284

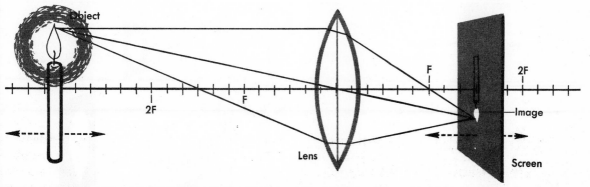

26-1. A convex lens, thicker in the middle, focuses an image of an object. In this drawing, a clear image is shown on the screen when the object is twice the distance of the image from the lens. Which way must you move the screen if you move the object closer to the lens? farther away?

as a burning glass. Provide yourself with a sheet of white cardboard and a candle (or small lamp or flashlight). In a dark or dimly lit room set up all three as you see in Fig. 26-1.

With the candle set up several feet from the lens, move the cardboard in toward the lens until you find on it a clear image of the candle. Notice that the image of the candle is upside down just as images on the retina of your eye are upside down.

Try moving the candle closer to the lens. What must you do to the screen to keep the image on it sharp and clear? You will find that the *closer* you move the candle the *farther* away you must move the screen. Presently, as the candle comes closer and closer to the lens, the screen has to move all the way across the room in order to catch its image clearly.

If the candle is brought *still* closer, you will probably be puzzled to find that its image disappears entirely. The distance between the candle and the lens at the point the image disappears is

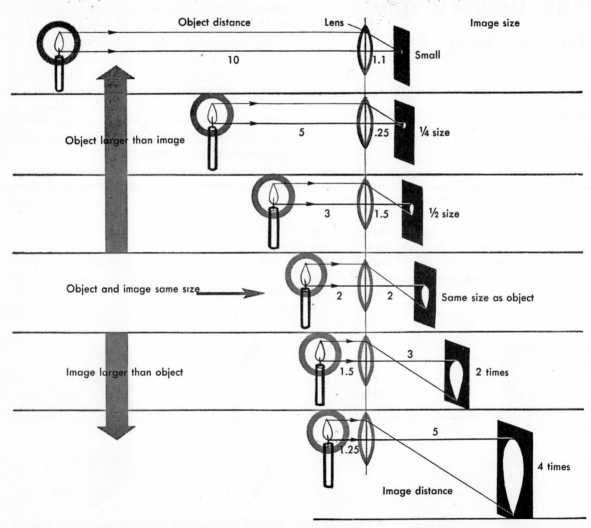

26-2. Notice that the closer the object comes to the lens, the farther the image moves away. When is the image larger than the object? smaller than the object?

the same as *focal length.* If you experimented with this lens as a burning glass (page 284), you will now find the focal length to be the distance you measured from the glass to the focused point of light.

You can probably see from this experiment that the distance of the image from the lens depends on how far away the object is from the lens. *The closer the object comes, the farther the image moves away.* All this you can see in Fig. 26-2.

Set up the candle again as far from the lens as you can, and once more get the image on the cardboard screen. Is the image of the candle bigger or smaller than the real candle? If the candle is *farther away* from the lens than the cardboard is, the real candle is bigger than its image. The candle and its image are the *same size* when they are both the *same distance* from the lens. And finally as you bring the candle still closer to the lens, its image becomes bigger than the object (the real candle) as well as farther away from the lens. When the candle reaches the focal length, the image is very big and far away. When the candle is moved still closer, the image disappears.

You can probably see from this experiment that the size of the image depends on how far it is from the lens. *As the image is formed farther and farther from the lens it gets bigger and bigger.* All this you can see in Fig. 26-2.

In these experiments your lens has worked in just the same way it did as a burning glass. Each point on the candle has sent out light in all directions. When the rays of light from a point on the candle hit the surface of the lens, they were bent (refracted) by the curved surfaces of the lens so that they came together once more at a single point on your screen (Fig. 26-3). But *every* point of the candle flame sent out rays in the same way. And in the same way the rays from every point were focused on your screen. All together they formed a clear image.

Now let's see how a lens works in a camera.

The Lens in Your Camera

Your eye changes its focus by changing the focal length of its lens. For example, you will re-

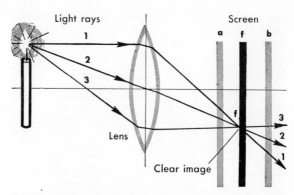

26-3. A clear image is formed where light rays going through different parts of a lens are all focused at the same point on the screen. The screen must be at *f* for clear focusing of the image.

member that the lens of your eye is made thicker in order to bring nearby objects to a focus on the retina. But the focus of the camera is changed by *moving* the lens. From your experiments with a lens just now, you will also remember that an object coming closer to the lens was kept in focus by moving the image screen away from the lens. In a similar way, in the camera this image distance is changed by moving the lens in and out from the film. Try moving the focusing knob on a camera. As you set it on greater and greater distances, you will notice that the lens moves closer to the film.

A box camera has no focusing adjustment. Its lens is focused permanently on objects about 10 feet from the lens and beyond.

The More Important Adjustments

Your eye adjusts itself to various lighting conditions by changing the size of the pupil opening. On most cameras there is an adjustment near the lens which you use to do the same thing — that is, to open and close the diaphragm. Usually the adjustment is marked with a series of numbers; these numbers are called *f* numbers (not to be confused with F for "focal length"). Small *f* numbers tell you that the diaphragm is open wide for letting in the most light possible (Fig. 26-4). Thus the *larger* the *f,* the *smaller* the opening. Usually the size of the opening is reduced by half

26-4. Adjusting the exposure. At the upper left is a scale for the exposure time in fractions of a second (50 means $\frac{1}{50}$ of a second). At the bottom is the scale for the lens opening, or f number. As the f number is increased, the iris over the lens closes and lets in less light. These two settings, exposure time and lens opening, must always be set properly to get the right film exposure.

its area each time you move the adjustment to the next larger f number.

A box camera has no diaphragm adjustment. It is usually set at about $f11$.

Just as your eyelids are closed when your eye is not in use, the shutter of the camera stays closed unless you want light to fall on the film. Of course you use your eyes in a little different way. Your eyes are open most of the time and as a result your retinas can record moving objects. But if you leave the camera shutter open for more than a moment, moving objects are recorded on the film as a blur (Fig. 26-5). Have you ever seen a photograph in which a speeding automobile appeared only as a blur? What should the photographer have done in order to show the automobile clearly?

If you say that the shutter shouldn't be left open so long — you are right. If the shutter can open and close before the moving object can move

26-5. A moving object photographed with an exposure of one twenty-fifth of a second will be blurred. What changes would give you a clearer picture?

far enough to cause a blur, you will have a sharp clear picture.

You can see this very quickly by experimenting with your own two built-in cameras — your eyes. When you are watching a busy city street, or people walking about, or some other moving object, close your eyes for a moment. Then open and shut them again very quickly — a kind of blink in reverse. If you do it quickly enough and keep your eyes closed afterwards, you will find, just as a camera does, that the moving objects seem to be motionless. A photographer would say that you had " stopped " the motion. You will also find that the faster the object is moving, the shorter your peek has to be in order to make the object seem to be motionless.

In Fig. 26-6 you see a picture taken by a camera which took an extremely short peek, an exposure of two-millionths of a second. This peek is so brief that even a bullet didn't appear to move. Many cameras can take exposures as short as $\frac{1}{300}$ of a second, which is quick enough to make most common moving objects appear to stand still. A box camera has only one shutter speed, usually about $\frac{1}{30}$ of a second.

How Diaphragm and Exposure Time Work Together

If you have ever taken any photographs, you probably know that when you make your exposure time too short, not enough light can enter your camera. Therefore, your film will be *underexposed* (Fig. 26-7). Yet if you are trying to take a picture of a rapidly moving object, you *must* make the exposure time very short or else your picture will be blurred. How do you keep the exposure time short enough to "stop" the moving object and at the same time get enough light into the camera to expose the film properly?

You solve this problem by opening the diaphragm wider — by setting the adjustment to a smaller *f* number. Cameras whose diaphragms can be opened up to *f*1.5 or *f*2 are said to be *fast* cameras. With the diaphragm opened up to *f*1.5, you can take pictures of moving objects in rather dim light.

For taking pictures of objects in very bright light the diaphragm is closed down. If the object is not moving very rapidly, you may be able to close the diaphragm down to *f*22 and still get enough light to expose the film properly. Finally, if the object is brightly lit and is not moving at all, you will be able to take its picture with a pinhole camera (see page 268). Most pictures made with pinhole cameras have to be *time exposures,* which means the film has to be exposed for several seconds or longer. Hence the object you are photographing with a pinhole camera has to be motionless.

What Is a "Good" Camera?

Inexpensive cameras have a single simple lens such as the one you may have experimented with back in Chapter 24. Cameras with a single lens do not always take very clear pictures. There are at least two reasons for this.

One reason why a single lens does not always make clear pictures is that the rays of light through the outer edges of the lens do not come to a focus at quite the same place as the rays passing through the center of the lens. You can see this shown in Fig. 26-8. This very serious defect is

General Electric Co.

26-6. Effect of a bullet "stopped" with an exposure of one two-millionths of a second. Special lights and cameras are needed for such very short exposures.

called *spherical aberration*. In a camera, spherical aberration makes it impossible for the lens to bring all rays of light to a focus at once on the film. Your picture would be blurry.

One remedy for spherical aberration is to cut out the rays of light passing through the outer edges of the lens. This is done, of course, by closing down the diaphragm to a higher *f* number. Although this reduces the amount of light entering the camera, it does make it possible to take clear pictures.

You can observe the same effect with the lenses of your own eyes. Close one eye. Bring this printed page up toward your open eye until the print begins to look blurry. Your eye now has spherical aberration. To remedy it, make a narrow slit between two fingers, and hold this slit close in front of your eye. Do you notice that although less light enters your eye the image becomes clearer?

While a single lens will begin to show spherical aberration if it is opened up much wider than *f*11, it is possible to make a lens that will have practically no spherical aberration. To make it we have

26-7. (Top left) An underexposed photograph. The whole picture is too dark. (Top right) A properly exposed photograph. Light and dark areas are as we see them. (Bottom left) An overexposed photograph. Everything is too light.

to use a combination of several lenses of various shapes.

Even after spherical aberration has been carefully removed from a single lens by closing off the rays going through the outer edges, it still has a second troublesome defect. A single lens does not bring all *colors* of light to a focus at the same place. The image it forms will have rainbow-colored fringes. This defect is called *chromatic aberration*. There is no simple remedy for chromatic aberration in a single lens. But like spheri-

cal aberration, color troubles can be reduced by using a combination of lenses of several different shapes and made of several different kinds of glass.

In Fig. 26-9 you see a combination of lenses which eliminates both kinds of aberration very well. With such a combination of lenses it is possible to take excellent clear pictures with the diaphragm open even to *f*1.5. But such excellent lenses are expensive to make. This is why a " good " camera costs so much.

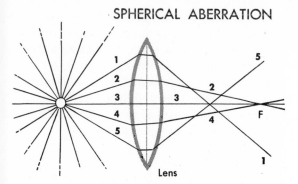

SPHERICAL ABERRATION

26-8. Light rays (1 and 5) passing through the outer parts of a single lens do not focus at the same point as those passing through the central part (2, 3, 4). The image is blurry due to spherical aberration.

Getting the Proper Exposure

How do you know where to set the diaphragm adjustment and the time of exposure when you are about to take a picture?

Perhaps you have seen a printed card of instructions that tells you approximately what settings should be used with various lighting conditions. These written instructions are not at all expensive.

But to find settings for special lighting conditions (very bright or dull days), a good photographer uses an exposure meter. Inside an exposure meter is a *photoelectric cell* which makes a tiny electric current when light falls on it. A sensitive electric meter records the current on an easy-to-read dial which is also marked off to show you light intensity. In Fig. 26-10 you see an exposure meter that measures the brightness of light quickly and accurately.

To find the proper exposure for a picture, you set dials on a scale showing the brightness of light and also on a number that measures how sensitive the film is. You can then read from the dial the *f* number that will give you a properly exposed picture. In other words, if you decide on your exposure time, you can then read from the dial the *f* number that will give you a properly exposed picture. Notice in Fig. 26-4 that if your exposure time is very brief, you will use a small *f* number (wide lens opening). If you decide on a longer ex-

posure, you must use a large *f* number (small lens opening). Film gets the proper amount of light only if you select the *f* number that pairs correctly with the selected time and exposure.

If your object is moving, you must choose one of the brief exposure times — just how brief, you must learn by experience. If you have several choices, you should try to choose the longest exposure time you safely can without risking a blurred picture.

Recently, various semiautomatic exposure devices, built into the camera itself, have become popular. Many of these indicate the proper exposure by the lining up of two pointers in a viewing device. One pointer responds automatically to the amount of light falling upon a built-in photoelectric " eye." The lens diaphragm is then adjusted by the operator until the other pointer, connected to the diaphragm, is brought into line. Due to ingenious connections between the exposure meter and the diaphragm the operator is then assured of the proper exposure.

There are also available, particularly in 8 mm. motion picture cameras, fully automatic exposure models. The photocell's small current directly regulates the diaphragm opening.

General Electric Co.

26-10. A typical photographic exposure meter. Light falling on a photoelectric cell creates an electrical current which turns the pointer. Dials show what exposure will give the best pictures for the film used.

Depth of Field

Here is the reason why you must choose the longest possible blur-free exposure time and hence the largest possible *f* number. You may have focused your camera on an object ten feet away. For a good picture you usually want to have the less important objects in the far background and also those in the near foreground to appear sharply defined. A photographer would say that you want as much *depth of field* as possible. Your picture will have the greatest depth of field when the diaphragm opening is as small as possible. Thus if you use a large *f* number your picture has a greater depth of field than when you use a small *f* number. This is why you should usually use the largest *f* number and longest exposure time you can without risking a blurred picture.

MORE USES FOR LENSES

How would the inside of a camera appear to a fly trapped in it?

Perhaps you can imagine the fly sitting in darkness. Then suddenly the shutter is open to take a picture. If he is facing the camera film, he will see an image flash onto the film. The image will appear upside down. Behind him shines a bright light pouring through the camera lens (Fig. 26-11).

If you have ever sat in a darkened room and watched pictures being projected on a screen by a slide projector, you will already know what the fly saw as he sat inside the camera watching a photograph being taken. The arrangement of screen, audience, lens, and light source is exactly the same in both cases (Fig. 26-12), except that the image you see is right side up.

The Slide Projector

A slide projector works in very nearly the same way as a camera. There are, to be sure, a few differences in the *sizes* of things. For instance, in a camera the object is often several yards from the lens, and its image is only a few inches from it. You will remember from your experiments on page 292 that this will lead to an image on the camera film *smaller* than the object. In a *slide projector,* the object is only a few inches from the lens — and the image (on the screen) is several yards from it.

A minor difference is that the object photographed by a camera *reflects* light into the camera lens, while the image thrown by a slide projector is light *transmitted* through the transparent film. You can see all this for yourself very simply if you will set up once more the experiment with the lens described on page 293. This time use a lantern slide with a light behind it for your object.

In the camera and in the slide projector, just as in your eye, the image is turned upside down.

CAMERA

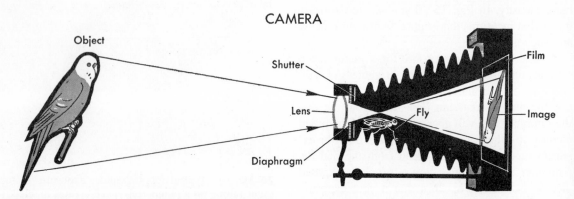

26-11. The shutter springs open for an instant, a focused image appears on the film, and chemical changes record the image. Why is a diaphragm needed? Why is an adjustment for distance needed?

SLIDE PROJECTOR

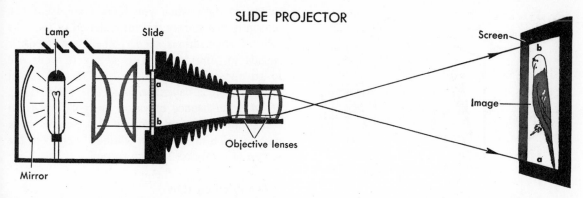

26-12. A mirror behind the lamp and lenses in front form a bright beam on the slide or film. The front, or objective, lenses focus an image of the slide on the screen.

How must you place the slide in the projector so that it will appear properly on the screen? That's right — upside down.

The Enlarger

The enlarger is another device that works in the same way as the projector. If you put a camera film in place of your projection screen, you would expect to make a very big picture from a small negative. This is just what you do in order to make a photo-mural.

If you want to make a print of smaller size, how would you change the slide projector? An ordinary darkroom *enlarger* is rather like a slide projector with a lens of shorter focal length. In Fig. 26-13 you can see how the negative is placed in a frame in the enlarger beneath the light source. Light shines downward through the negative. The lens focuses an image of the negative on a sheet of photographic paper. Just as with a camera, you control the light by adjusting a diaphragm over the lens.

How Does the Movie Projector Work?

The movie projector has the very same arrangement of object, lens, and image that the slide projector and the enlarger have.

But how can it make the movies move? Here is a very simple experiment that will show you.

Make a flip booklet of something in motion,

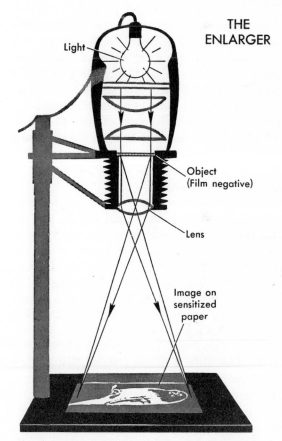

26-13. A photoenlarger works like a projector to form a large image on the sensitive photographic paper.

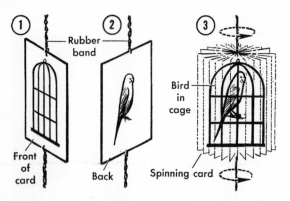

26-14. Make a card like the one shown here. Then spin the card rapidly on a string. You will "see" the bird in the cage. In your eyes the images of the bird and the cage persist so long that you believe you see both at the same time.

like a man running or an airplane landing. First cut about 24 to 40 pieces of blank paper, 1 inch by 2 inches. On each draw a picture of the same object, with each in a slightly more advanced stage of motion. Fasten your set of drawings together on one side. Now let about 10 pages a second flip out from under your thumb. The object moves in jerks, doesn't it? Now let the pages turn faster. By the time you are running through about 24 pages a second, the object will appear to be moving fairly smoothly.

In exactly the same way the movie projector makes a picture move by quickly flashing one picture after another onto the screen, each picture a little different from the one before. If the pictures follow one another as slowly as 10 or 15 each second, you can notice a flickering on the screen. But if they flash by as fast as 24 a second, your eye can no longer see the change from one picture to the next.

The projector also has a shutter which covers up the film while it is being pulled past the lens from one picture to the next. You see each picture on the screen for only about $\frac{1}{30}$ of a second as it pauses in front of the lens and the shutter opens. Then during the next $\frac{1}{120}$ of a second it takes to shift from one picture to the next the screen is dark again. You do not notice such a brief time of darkness any more than you notice

things go dark when you blink your eyes. The reason is that during this tiny interval of time the cells of your retinas keep right on sending their signals to your brain. This ability of your eye to go on seeing for a short time after the light is turned off is called *persistence of vision* (Fig. 26-14). Persistence of vision prevents you from seeing the flicker in between the pictures as a motion picture projector flashes them on the screen at a rate of 24 each second.

The Reading Lens

All of the uses for lenses you have read about so far — the eye, the camera, the slide projector, the enlarger, and the movie projector — use a lens that focuses a bright image *onto a screen upside down.*

But in some useful instruments lenses work in a different way. For example, a very simple use for a lens in which you do *not* focus an image upside down on a screen is the ordinary reading lens.

Get out your lens once more. Hold it so that you see through it a magnified image of the letters on this page. Are the letters upside down? No, not if the lens is close enough to make a magnified image. Can you project your enlarged image on a screen? Try it. You will find that you cannot. Clearly then your lens is not working in the familiar way it did in the eye and the camera and the projector, is it?

See if you can tell what is changed. You might find out once more the focal length of your lens. And how far did you hold your reading lens from the page just now? It was *closer* than the focal length, wasn't it? Here then is a difference between the reading lens and your camera or projector lens.

You have already seen this arrangement before. In your experiments with your lens back on page 292 you brought the object up closer than the focal length, too. And you watched the image on your screen disappear as you did it. Now at last you have found the lost image again. The image appears to be on the *same* side of the lens as the object is.

Thus you see that *when the object comes closer to the lens than its focal length, the image appears magnified and on the same side as the object.*

As you would expect from the experiments described on page 293, this image can never be thrown on a screen. You see an image only because the lens in your eye helps form the image on your retina. Because no real image can be thrown on a screen or film, such an unreal image is called a *virtual image. Virtual images are formed whenever the distance of an object from a lens is less than the focal length of the lens.*

Generally a reading glass has a focal length of about 6 inches, but some are more and some less. How much it magnifies depends upon how close it is to the object. How near your eye is to the lens makes little difference. As you move the lens away from the object, the image gets larger. But when this distance is larger than the focal length, the image you see gets blurry.

You can check on the amount of magnification possible with several reading glasses or hand magnifiers. Hold the center of the lens over the "0"

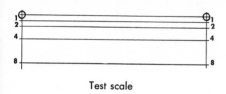

Test scale

How it looks:

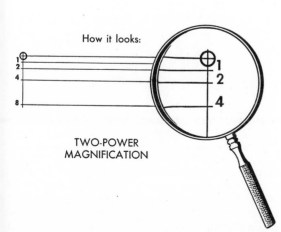

TWO-POWER
MAGNIFICATION

26-15. A test scale for finding magnifying power.

in the right-hand side of Fig. 26-15. Close your left eye and look through the lens with your right eye. Gradually move the lens toward your eye. Keep the lines marked with "0"s together. Notice against the left-hand scale where the line marked "1" shows through the lens. It should be near "2." If so, the magnification is "two times."

Notice that you can magnify only a small area with such a lens. Perhaps you will also notice that the images near the edge of the lens are less sharp than those in the middle; some may even have a fringe of color. These are the same lens troubles we discussed in the section on "good" cameras.

The Microscope

With a microscope you can see things so tiny that they are invisible to your unaided eye. Fig. 26-16 is a picture of some of the tiny bacteria that give you the disease called tuberculosis. You see their portrait as it was photographed through a microscope. Actually they are so tiny that 5,000 to 6,000 of them would make a line an inch long.

Do you see why the microscope is such an important tool in understanding disease and in fighting disease?

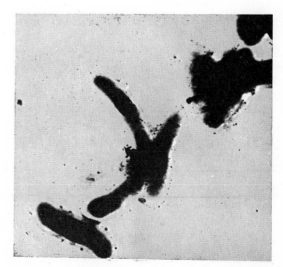

Radio Corp. of America

26-16. Tiny tuberculosis bacteria, normally invisible, can be seen or photographed through a microscope.

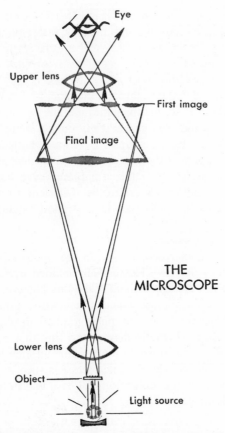

THE MICROSCOPE

26-17. The lower lens of a microscope forms a large image which we look at through another magnifying lens (the upper lens). With various pairs of lenses we can get different degrees of enlargement up to 2,000 or more times the size of the object.

Microscopes are also used by geologists to study rocks. The shape of the tiny particles the rock is made of gives geologists clues to oil and other valuable minerals in the earth.

The biologist uses a microscope to study the tiniest living things in his search for the secrets of life.

The metallurgist studies metals with it, looking for ways to make them stronger or harder.

The detective uses the microscope, looking for invisibly small clues to a crime.

The chemist, the engineer, the jeweler, and manufacturers of all kinds of familiar products use the microscope in one way or another to see

things invisibly small to the unaided eye — to learn more about them or to make them better.

The microscope is a very important tool in the world you live in.

How does it work?

A microscope uses *two* lenses. The lens nearest to the object being magnified works like a camera or a projector lens. The lens closest to your eye works like a reading lens.

When a scientist studies tiny bacteria, he places them on a thin slide of glass just below the end of the black tube. In the very bottom tip of the black tube is the first lens. The bacteria are just outside the focal length of the first lens. Hence the

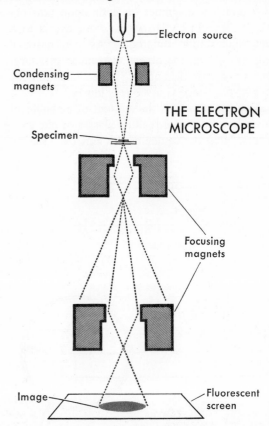

THE ELECTRON MICROSCOPE

26-18. The electron microscope uses "magnetic lenses" to focus an electron stream on a fluorescent screen. A camera can be used to record this image for later study. Such image formation by electrons is possible due to their wavelike properties as discussed on page 310 of the text.

first lens makes a very much magnified image of the bacteria, in the same way that your lens on page 292 made a magnified image of a candle.

The magnified image made by the first lens is formed up inside the black tube. It *could* be thrown on a screen, but it isn't. Instead the second lens up by the eye of the scientist is being used to look at this image.

The image is a tiny bit *closer* than the focal length of the lens at the top of the tube. Hence the scientist is using the top lens like a reading lens. He sees a magnified view of the image formed by the first lens.

Thus the image of the bacteria is magnified *twice,* once by each lens. Working together in this way the lenses of a very powerful microscope can magnify as much as 2,000 times!

In good microscopes various troubles such as spherical aberration and chromatic aberration are avoided by using as many as seven lenses together in place of the first lens. And for the same reasons most microscopes have at least two lenses up by your eye at the top.

Even more powerful microscopes can be built. But they do not use light. They use a focused beam of electrons instead. Such an electron microscope (see Fig. 26-18 and text, pages 263–64) can magnify objects as much as 100,000 times!

Looking Back . . . .

VOCABULARY

Each of the following expressions represents a key idea in this chapter. Show you understand its meaning by defining each one.

1. diaphragm
2. shutter
3. fast lens
4. time exposure
5. underexposed (photograph)
6. spherical aberration
7. chromatic aberration
8. depth of focus
9. enlarger
10. persistence of vision
11. virtual image
12. f numbers
13. exposure meter
14. electron microscope

REVIEW QUESTIONS

1. Describe what happens to the size of an image as you bring an object closer and closer to a lens.
2. Describe what happens to the location of an image as you bring an object closer and closer to a lens.
3. Describe how you would adjust the diaphragm and the time of exposure in order to take a picture of (a) a motionless object in dim light, (b) a moving object in dim light, (c) a very rapidly moving object in bright light, (d) a motionless object in bright light.
4. For which situations in question 3 could you use a pinhole camera?
5. In which situations in question 3 could you get the greatest depth of focus?
6. In what ways is a camera similar to your eye?
7. What lens-using instruments form virtual images?

EXPLAIN WHY:

- Motion pictures do not seem to flicker if the pictures follow one another at about 24 a second.
- You should usually choose the largest possible f number when taking a picture.
- The image a convex lens makes of a distant object is upside down.
- The right-side-up image made by a reading lens can never be thrown on a screen.

Going Further . . . .

APPLYING PRINCIPLES

1. What are the three most important adjustments to make on a camera before you take a picture?
2. What is a " good " camera?
3. If a slide projector throws too small a picture on a screen, how can you make the picture bigger?
4. Draw a diagram to show how a reading lens works.
5. How can you reduce spherical aberration in your camera?
6. Explain how a slide projector works.
7. Explain how an enlarger works.
8. Explain how a movie projector works.
9. Draw a diagram to show how a microscope works.

THINGS TO DO

1. Open up the back of a camera, and tape a piece of waxed paper over the opening. If you keep the shutter open by setting it for a time exposure, you can now see how the focusing and diaphragm adjustments work. Try focusing on nearby and on distant

objects, noticing in each case which way the lens moves in order to make a clear image on your waxed screen. You will see the images better if you cover your head and the back of the camera with a dark cloth to keep out stray light.

2. You can make a real microscope if you will set up two lenses as described on pages 302–03. Your microscope will have severe chromatic and spherical aberration, but it will show you tinier things than you can see with your unaided eyes.

3. You can make a telescope, too. The best ways of doing this are described in the book *Amateur Telescope Making* edited by Albert Ingalls. You can probably make a telescope good enough to show you the rings of Saturn, the moons of Jupiter, and the mountains on our moon.

READING FURTHER

New Guide to Better Photography by Berenice Abbott, Crown, 1953. This book contains up-to-date facts about exposure, developing, printing, lighting, and color photography.

Short Cut to Photography by Godfrey Frankel, Sterling, 1954

Write to Eastman Kodak Co., Rochester, New York, for their pamphlets which give many explanations useful to beginners in this interesting hobby.

27

What Light Is and How It Is Made

Ask your friends if they can think of anything that can travel both through solid objects and through a vacuum. If they are stumped by the question, you might give them a hint: it travels silently and at enormous speed. No doubt, you know the answer. It is *light*. But can *you* answer the question: what *is* light? What is this strange stuff that can pass through water and through solid glass? What is it that can travel through millions of miles of empty space on its way to us from the sun?

WHAT IS LIGHT?

We can say two things right away about light that may help us to answer the question. (1) Light is a kind of energy, and (2) light travels at a definite speed that can be measured.

Light Is a Kind of Energy

You will remember that energy simply means the ability to do work. Surely, then, light is a form of energy.

For it is the energy of light that prods the retinas of our eyes to see.

It is the energy of light that makes the chemical changes on the film in a camera that makes a picture possible (Fig. 27-1).

It is the energy in light that warms the earth and thus causes winds, often of very great destructive power. The energy to do the damage caused by a tornado or a hurricane first came to the earth in the form of sunlight (Fig. 27-2).

It is the energy of light that green plants take up to make all the world's supply of food (Fig. 27-2).

It is the energy of light that pushes the tails of comets always away from the sun.

And it is the energy of light from the sun that warms the whole earth and keeps us from quickly freezing to death.

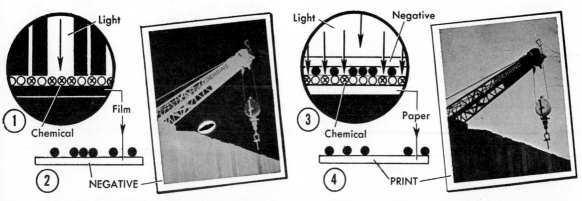

27-1. How a photograph is made. (1) Light falls on the sensitive chemicals of a film. The film grains marked X are changed by the bright light which hits them. (2) After being developed and fixed, the changed, or illuminated, grains show black. This is a " negative " of the original image. (3) When light goes through the negative onto a fresh piece of film or sensitive paper, we have a picture like the original image.

Wide World Photos

Ewing Galloway

27-2. The energy of light can cause destructive hurricanes or help the green plants manufacture the food they furnish us.

Surely light is an *important* kind of energy. In fact, when the sun is overhead, it is pouring light energy onto the earth at the rate of 0.1 horsepower per square foot.

Man has learned to control the various forms of energy which can be turned to light.

The Speed of Light

If you try to measure the speed of light, you will quickly find that it travels faster than anything you know. It is so speedy that it is very hard to measure the tiny fraction of a second it takes to cover any measured distance on the earth. In fact, the speed of light is the fastest possible speed.

But in 1675 the Danish astronomer, Ole Roemer (RER-mer), found a speedway big enough to measure light's tremendous speed. As his speedway he used the distance across the earth's path around the sun. As his light he used the light from one of the moons of the planet Jupiter.

As you have learned, the earth moves around the sun once each year in a path that is roughly 186,000,000 miles across. Farther out from the sun the planet Jupiter travels around in a larger path. Jupiter has several moons that revolve around it (Fig. 27-3).

After watching one of Jupiter's moons for a while a person can easily predict the exact instant when it will disappear and then appear again from behind the big planet. Suppose you wait until the earth is at A, on the side of the sun nearest to Jupiter. Then through your telescope you time the tiny moon as it goes around and around Jupiter. Soon you are able to predict each moment when it will appear again from behind the planet. Since your measurements are accurate, you even make your predictions for six months in advance, when the earth will have swung to B, halfway around the sun.

You wait six months. The earth reaches B, and you get ready to check up on your predictions.

You watch for the moon to appear on schedule — but it is late! Finally it shows itself 1000 seconds later than you predicted (about 17 minutes). This delay is due to the time it took light to travel the *extra* 186,000,000 miles from A to B (Fig. 27-3).

If you will divide the diameter of the earth's orbit by the number of seconds it took light to go across it, you will find how fast light travels. Study Fig. 27-3 again. The answers are there.

The correct answer: 186,000 miles a second!

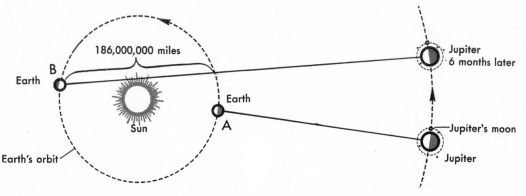

27-3. Study this diagram. What is the speed of light? How did Roemer arrive at this figure?

Since Roemer made his measurement, many other scientists have confirmed this figure by even more accurate methods.

Particles or Waves?

You have seen that light is made of *something* that has energy and travels at enormous speed.

What is this something?

To this riddle scientists have found *two* possible answers.

One answer was suggested over 250 years ago by the great English scientist, Sir Isaac Newton. He was sure that light was a stream of tiny particles. He proposed that any object that gave off light was really firing off streams of these tiny particles in all directions at 186,000 miles a second. When they struck a transparent object like glass, they were able to go right through. Other objects stopped (absorbed) them, and still other objects like metals, bounced them off (reflected them).

Newton explained color by saying that light of different colors was produced by particles of different sizes. Such a stream of particles would naturally have energy of motion in much the same way as a spray of water droplets coming out of a hose.

A second answer was proposed, also about 250 years ago, by the famous Dutch scientist, Christian Huygens (HOY-genz). He thought of light as a kind of wave motion. Energy can be carried by waves, as you must know if you have ever been out in a boat or at the seashore in rough weather. The energy of the waves rocked the boat. Huygens explained different colors by saying that his waves of light, measured from the crest of one wave to the crest of the next, come in different lengths.

Who was right — Newton or Huygens? Let us look at the evidence.

Why Light Seems to Be Made of Waves

Get a piece of rope or clothesline ten or fifteen feet long and tie one end of it to a table leg (Fig. 27-4). Hold the rope by the other end and pull it tight. Now make some waves in the rope by giving it up-and-down jerks. You will notice that the waves travel along the rope at a definite speed. You will notice that measured from crest to crest your waves have a definite length. And you *may* notice, if your table is not very heavy, that your waves carry enough energy to make the table move. In all these ways your waves have properties similar to the light waves described by Huygens (Fig. 27-4).

Now pass the rope through two narrow slotted frames, as shown in Fig. 27-4. What happens to the waves if both frames are vertical? Now have a friend hold one of the frames in the horizontal position shown and try again. Do your waves now reach the table? If they do not can you see that it is because one of the slots now blocks up-and-down motion of the wave in the rope? Remove the rope and *look* through the crossed slots toward

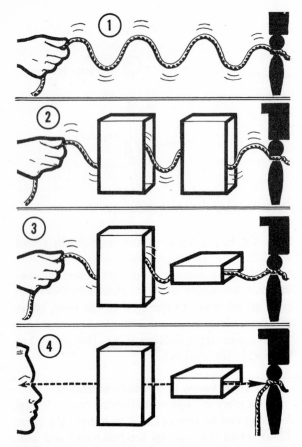

27-4. Imagine a light wave as resembling the wave sent along the rope in this drawing. Polaroid material acts toward light just as the slotted frameworks act toward the wave along the rope.

the table leg. Although waves cannot go through your crossed slots, couldn't a bullet be fired through them to the table?

Particles such as bullets can go through; waves can't. Here is an experiment that turns out differently for waves and for particles.

It happens that scientists know of several kinds of crystals whose atoms act like the slots of your frameworks when light passes through them. When a large number of one of these kinds of crystals is properly spread out on a sheet of transparent film, we have the material called *polaroid.* Its crystals act like a lot of tiny invisible slots. Light goes through the " slots " of polaroid as

easily as your rope waves went through the first framework. But if you hold a second sheet of polaroid in the path of the light and rotate it, you find that it acts just like the second slot did with the rope waves (Fig. 27-5). When its " slots " are turned through 90°, the light can no longer get through it.

Thus when light passes through sheets of polaroid, the light acts as if it were waves. For if light were made of particles, it is hard to see how it could be completely blocked by the rotation of the second polaroid — any more than bullets would be entirely blocked by turning the frameworks at right angles.

Uses of Polaroid

A beam of light from a light source acts as if it were made of a very large number of tiny waves, like those running along your rope. Some of the waves wiggle, or as the scientist would say, *vibrate,* up and down. Some of them vibrate from side to side, and others vibrate in all other directions in between.

When the beam passes through a sheet of polaroid, the only waves that get through are those

Polaroid Corp.

27-5. Crossed polarizers. Each strip of polarizing material alone lets light through. But when the two are crossed, no light gets through.

vibrating in the direction of the "slots" formed by the tiny crystals in the sheet of film. The light that gets through is said to be *polarized*.

But light is polarized in other ways than by the use of polaroid screens.

For instance, the light being reflected into your eyes by the pages of this book *right now* is partly polarized, though your eyes do not see this fact. For polarized light *looks* exactly the same as ordinary unpolarized light. Also light reflected off water or glass is always partly polarized. Light from the sky is polarized. And even starlight is partly polarized.

You have seen that polarized light can be stopped in much the same way as your second framework stopped the wave in your rope.

You can check up on this for yourself if you have a piece of polaroid or a pair of polaroid glasses handy. As you rotate your polaroid, examine through it the light reflected from this page. Do you find a position of your polaroid for which the light grows dimmer? You will find this dimming effect especially great if this page is arranged to reflect a good deal of glare into your eye. For the glaring light is the most strongly polarized.

Look through your rotating polaroid in various directions at the blue sky. You will notice that sky light is polarized more in some directions than in others.

But best of all, try out your polaroid on light glaring off a wet highway at night, or try it on the blinding light reflected on a sunny day from the surface of a lake or the ocean or try it on sunlight glinting off windows. Do you notice how it is able to cut out the glare and allow you to see more clearly? Here then is one of the most important uses of polaroid.

Why Light Seems to Be Made of Particles

You will remember that the Dutch scientist, Huygens, thought that light consisted of waves. And you have just seen how the story of polarized light seems to prove he was right.

But Sir Isaac Newton disagreed with him. Newton thought light really was made up of par-

ticles. Is there any evidence that Newton was right, too? You will be surprised to learn that there *is* evidence that light is made up of particles (photons). Some of this evidence is the "photoelectric effect."

You met the photoelectric effect when you learned about a photographer's exposure meter (page 297). When light shines on some kinds of metal — such as selenium (seh-LEE-nee-um) or cesium (SEE-zee-um) — it drives electricity out of the metal in the form of electrons. It is these electrons flowing through a sensitive electric meter that tell the photographer how much light is falling on his exposure meter. And it is these same electrons driven out of the sensitive metal by the action of light that makes us think light is composed of particles — not waves (Fig. 27-6).

Ever since scientists discovered the photoelectric effect back in 1887 they have been unable to explain how a *wave* could concentrate enough of its energy onto a single tiny electron to pry it loose from the metal.

The problem is rather similar to the problem you would have in explaining why a large post was knocked over on a battlefield. You know that the blast wave of an exploding shell *would* have enough energy to do it if it could all be concentrated on the post instead of spreading its effects widely over the landscape. But you find it far easier to explain the fallen post by saying that it was knocked over by a flying shell fragment.

In the same way, the energy of a *wave* of light

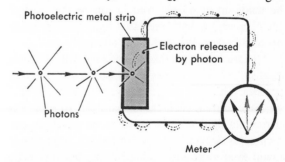

27-6. Light falling on certain metals creates an electric current. This is the photoelectric effect. Because the electric current increases when the light brightens, this effect can be used by photographers to measure the brightness of the light.

is spread over an area of several whole atoms. It could scarcely funnel all of its power onto the much tinier electron — as it would have to do in order to blast it loose. Only when we think of the energy of light as being in the form of a spray of tiny particles is it easy to see how one such particle could concentrate all its energy onto one electron and knock it loose from the metal.

Uses of Photoelectric Cells

Photoelectric cells do many useful jobs. They can be made to turn on or turn off an electric current whenever a light is flashed onto them, or when a light already shining on them is cut off.

For instance, you have seen photoelectric cells used to set off a door-opening device when you cut off a beam of light by walking in front of it. Photoelectric cells are used in factories, too, for counting parts moving along a conveyor belt in front of them. You can arrange a photoelectric cell to cause a motor to open your garage door at night when the car headlights shine upon it. Or one can be made to turn on the light of a lighthouse when night falls, thus doing the work of a lighthouse keeper.

All these and many other uses of photoelectric cells are daily proof that a light beam consists of a stream of tiny particles.

Waves or Particles?

By now you should be quite puzzled! In the first part of this chapter you have seen that light must be made up of waves. And in this second part of the chapter you have seen that light must be made up of particles. What *is* light, anyway?

The truth is that this so-called " wave-particle dualism " is one of the great puzzles of modern physics. The best one can say, at present, is that we have to treat each case separately. In some experiments light acts as particles, in other experiments, as waves. The wave-particle dualism is made even more interesting by the fact that electrons and other atomic particles have, in turn, been shown to act as waves. This fact, strange as it may seem, is the basis for many important practical developments such as the electron microscope. In this device, streams of electrons can be focused by magnets, just as light is focused by lenses. Since the wave length of electrons is much shorter than that of light, details not visible by ordinary microscopes become visible. So, the wave nature of electrons discovered by physicists aids biologists.

HOW LIGHT IS MADE AND MEASURED

How would you like to study your lessons at night by candlelight or by the flickering light of a wood fire? Too feeble, you say? Yes, such weak light *is* very hard on your eyes. But for over 200 years after the arrival of the Pilgrims in 1620, *all* Americans studied their lessons by such lights as these.

Now that brighter light sources have been invented, perhaps you would prefer lots and *lots* of light to read by. How would you like to study your lessons at night by the light of a searchlight as great as in Fig. 27-7? Too much light? Yes, such a brilliant light source would be even harder on your eyes.

Then, how about using a kerosene lantern? Or a fluorescent lamp? Or a neon sign? Or perhaps a street light? Which of these would you choose? Why didn't you choose the others?

The brightness and color of your reading light *do* make a difference, don't they?

A Measuring Stick for Brightness

Before we can talk about how various kinds of lights work and before we can choose the proper light for a particular purpose, we should learn how the brightness of a source is measured. We need a standard measuring stick for brightness — what the scientist calls a " unit " of brightness.

Just as length may be measured in a unit called a " foot " and money may be measured in a unit called a " dollar," the brightness of a light source is measured in a unit called a *candlepower.*

As you can easily guess, a candlepower is the brightness of a candle which has been carefully made in a certain way.

Compared with the light of the standard candle,

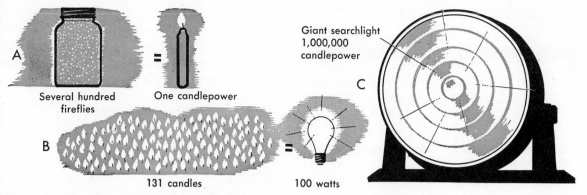

A — Several hundred fireflies

= One candlepower

B — 131 candles

= 100 watts

Giant searchlight 1,000,000 candlepower — C

27-7. The brightness of a light is compared to that of a special standard candle.

a firefly has a brightness of a few hundredths of a candlepower, an ordinary 100-watt light bulb has a brightness of 131 candlepower, and the great searchlight in Fig. 27-7 has a brightness of 1,000,000 candlepower.

Many Light Sources Also Produce Heat

Until about 1940 nearly all the sources of artificial light used by man depended upon *heat* to make them work. The woodfire, the candle, the kerosene lantern, illuminating gas, and yes, even the ordinary light bulb — all of these give off light only when something is strongly *heated*. A burning fuel gives off light because the gases given off are made very hot by the chemical reactions of burning. An ordinary light bulb gives off light because a fine wire inside it is made very *hot* by the electric current passing through it.

How Does an Ordinary Light Bulb Work?

George Washington's birthday ball in 1799 was lighted by 1000 candles at a cost of $500. Today we produce the same amount of light in the same time with nine ordinary 100-watt lamps that use 27 cents worth of electricity. Electric light is cheaper than candlelight.

Let us look inside this most common hot light source of all — the ordinary lamp bulb (Fig. 27-8).

If you can find a burned-out light bulb, break it open. First wrap it carefully in newspapers. Then after you have broken it be careful of the broken glass. Inside you should find something that looks like Fig. 27-8. The very fine wire, called the *filament,* is probably broken, which is why the bulb no longer worked. If you examine the filament closely with a magnifying lens, you will see that it is really a tight *coil* of very fine wire.

When the light is turned on, electric current flows through the filament. The current flows through the metal tip in the center of the screw base, up through one of the metal filament supports, through the filament, and thence out through the metal screw of the base.

You will remember from your reading that heat

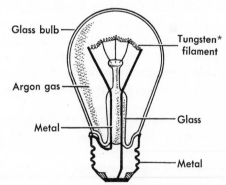

Glass bulb

Tungsten* filament

Argon gas

Metal

Glass

Metal

* An element also known as Wolfram

27-8. A common, machine-made light bulb is complex. The wires carrying the current are insulated in a glass column, and the metal is insulated from the metal thread. They meet the tightly coiled filament of tungsten, which does not melt when it gets very hot and bright. The bulb is filled with an inactive gas, argon, to prevent the filament from evaporating.

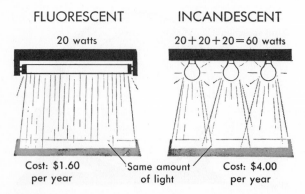

FLUORESCENT	INCANDESCENT
20 watts	20 + 20 + 20 = 60 watts
Cost: $1.60 per year	Cost: $4.00 per year

Same amount of light

27-9. Fluorescent lamps are more than three times as efficient as incandescent (hot wire) lamps. For the same brightness or candlepower, fluorescent lamps are cheaper to operate.

is produced when an electric current flows through a resistance such as a wire. The filament wire has a high resistance, and thus the current flowing through it creates a high temperature — 3000° C. At this extremely high temperature all materials glow brightly. The filament glows with an intense white light. Thus the light of an ordinary lamp bulb comes from a wire raised to white heat by an electric current. The energy of electricity is being turned into energy of heat and light.

The 3000° C. temperature would melt the filament if it were not made of the element *tungsten.* And even a tungsten filament would simply evaporate if the bulb did not contain some gas, whose atoms slow down the evaporation of the tungsten atoms. The inert gas, *argon,* is often used for this purpose.

Notice how most lamp bulbs are frosted on the inside. What is the reason for this? (See page 272.)

The electrical energy you use in a lamp costs money, of course, and you might reasonably ask how much light a lamp produces for each watt of electric power it uses up. A 100-watt filament lamp bulb, such as we have just described, produces 131 candlepower. This is slightly better than 1 candlepower per watt, which we may call the *efficiency* of the lamp.

If one kind of lamp has an efficiency of 1 can-

dlepower per watt and a second kind of lamp has an efficiency of 3 candlepower per watt, which do you think would be the cheaper to use? For the answer to this question read the next section on the *fluorescent lamp.*

Why Use Fluorescent Lamps?

Surely you have seen the long bluish-white tubes of fluorescent lamps often used for indoor lighting. What is their advantage over filament lights?

If you have a fluorescent lamp near at hand, you can quickly find one of its important advantages. Put your hand on the tube while the light is on. Then put your hand on a lighted filament lamp bulb. Do you find that the fluorescent tube is much cooler? Its temperature is less than 50° C. Compare this low temperature with that of a filament lamp.

In which type of lamp is more electrical energy being wasted to produce heat? Which type of lamp would you expect to give more candlepower per watt? Here are the figures:

Lamp	Efficiency
100-watt filament lamp	1.31 candlepower per watt
100-watt fluorescent lamp	3.20 candlepower per watt

As you see, the fluorescent lamp turns almost three times more electrical energy into light than the filament lamp does. Thus you may get about the same amount of light from a 20-watt fluorescent lamp than you now get from a 60-watt filament bulb. The 1,000 candles at George Washington's birthday ball would be outshone by just four of these fluorescent lamps. Clearly, the fluorescent lamp gives more light for less money (Fig. 27-9).

A New Kind of Lighting

Fluorescent lamps have been in use since about 1940. They are the first lights in all of man's long history that do not produce their light by becoming hot. They make their cool light in an entirely different way.

In Fig. 27-10 you see the important parts of a fluorescent lamp tube. At each end is a filament similar to the one in an ordinary filament bulb. To start the lamp an electric current heats the two filaments until they glow. The force of electricity throws electrons off the heated filaments and hurls them down the airless tube. Traveling as fast as 1000 miles a second the electrons crash into atoms of mercury vapor with which the tube is partly filled.

The violent collision between electrons and mercury vapor is accompanied by a tiny flicker of ultraviolet light — light that your eye cannot see, light sometimes called " black light." The invisible ultraviolet light given out by the jolted mercury atoms shines on the walls of the tube. The walls of the tube are coated with a chemical which glows brightly when the ultraviolet light strikes it. Such a chemical is called a *phosphor*. The glow of a phosphor is called *fluorescence*. Once the fluorescence is started, the heating filaments are no longer necessary, and are disconnected.

There are many kinds of phosphors. The phosphor called zinc sulfide glows with a green light, magnesium tungstenite glows with a bluish-white light, cadmium borate glows with a pinkish light.

The most important thing for you to notice about this kind of lighting is that it is cool, and hence more efficient than older types of lamps. The light is made by passing electricity through a cool gas and jolting the gas atoms to give off just light — *not heat*. Compare this with the filament light bulb that must waste electrical energy heating its filament before it can give off any useful light at all.

Other Efficient Gas-filled Lamps

Electrically charged particles sent whizzing down hollow tubes can jolt many other kinds of gas atoms to give off light.

A second familiar example of a lamp that gives off light by this efficient method is the bright yellow lamp often used for lighting highways at night.

Like the fluorescent lamp the yellow highway lamps may be made up of a tube with a heating filament in each end. Just as in the fluorescent lamp, electrical forces pluck electrons off the heated filaments and hurl them down the airless tube. In their wild dash down the tube, they strike atoms of sodium metal. Each collision with a sodium atom causes it to give off a tiny flicker of yellow light. Billions of such collisions every second produce enough light to illuminate a highway brilliantly (Fig. 27-11).

Again the great advantage of such a lamp is that it does not produce light by the wasteful process of heating something. Even more efficient than fluorescent lamps, a sodium lamp produces *five* candlepower for each watt of electricity.

Still a third efficient lamp is the familiar neon sign. Here again an electric current is passed through a tube (not a bulb) from which the air has been removed and which has in it a little neon gas. Struck by speeding electrons neon atoms give off their familiar red glow. Similarly mercury gas gives off a blue light, and helium gives off a pinkish light. In no case do these efficient lighting tubes get much hotter than 150° C.

But why wouldn't you choose one of these efficient sodium or neon lamps for your living room? Would the color be pleasant to live with for long periods of time?

Some Unfinished Business

Do you think that fluorescent lamps or sodium lamps are the most efficient lamps there are?

FLUORESCENT LAMP

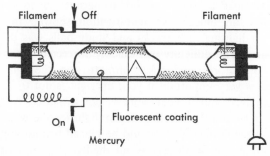

27-10. How does the fluorescent lamp operate?

27-11. Sodium lights provide intense yellowish illumination for a busy street.

Good as they are, you may be surprised to learn that fluorescent lamps turn only 16.5% of their electricity into useful light! This means that if they turned *all* of their electricity into useful light they would be over six times as bright, without using up any more current than they do now.

The Importance of Good Lighting

Between 1939 and 1943 students admitted to West Point had normal eyesight. Yet by the time they graduated the eyesight of one out of every seven had become too poor to permit him to become an officer. An investigation showed that poor lighting in barracks and study halls was the cause. The difficulty was quickly corrected.

In factories and in schoolrooms, too, the lighting is very important if your eyesight is not to be damaged and if your work is not to suffer. Not only should there be a sufficient light for the work you are doing, but it should be placed behind you so that your work area is not shaded or glare cast into your eyes (Fig. 27-12).

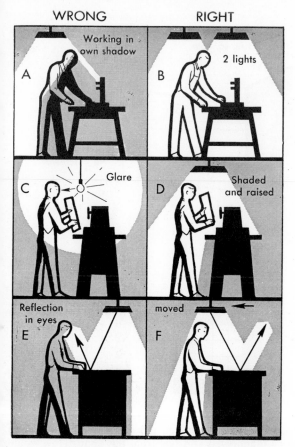

WRONG   **RIGHT**

A — Working in own shadow

B — 2 lights

C — Glare

D — Shaded and raised

E — Reflection in eyes

F — moved

27-12. When you have enough light, properly placed, your work is easier and your eyes are less tired.

How Does Lighting Depend on Distance?

Have you ever walked over to a street lamp at night in order to see better or have you ever been blinded by the headlights of an automobile as it came nearer to you? Then you know that the amount of illumination you get from a lamp depends on its *distance* from you as well as on its candlepower. The farther away a lamp is, the less light reaches you.

You can check up on this fact by moving your book farther and farther from your reading lamp. With no other lights on in the room, hold this book one foot from your reading lamp, then two feet, then three feet from it. What happens to the illumination on this page? Is it half as bright at

two feet? one third as bright at three feet? one fourth as bright at four feet?

You may be surprised to learn that the answer to each of these questions is " no." At two feet the illumination is *not* ½ — it is ¼ of that at one foot. At three feet it is *not* ⅓ — it is ⅑ of that at one foot. And at four feet it is *not* ¼ — it is ¹⁄₁₆ of that at one foot.

Can you see from this how the illumination at seven feet will compare with the illumination at one foot? If your answer is $\frac{1}{7 \times 7}$ or $\frac{1}{49}$ you will be correct. Illumination then does not decrease with the inverse of the distance, as you might think. Illumination on your book falls off with the inverse square of its distance from the light source. An *inverse square* of a number is 1 divided by the square of that number.

You can quickly see why this is so if you will provide yourself with a flashlight, a ruler, and two sheets of cardboard or heavy paper. Near the center of one card cut a hole one inch square. Unscrew the glass and reflector from the flashlight and stand it on end in a darkened room. The tiny bulb of the flashlight acts as a point source of light and will therefore cast sharp-edged shadows. Hold the card with a hole in it one foot from the flashlight (Fig. 27-13). One foot beyond the first card hold up the second as a screen so that the light through the one-inch hole shines on it.

You will notice that the square patch of light on the screen measures two inches on each side. Thus it will have an area of 2 x 2, or 4 square inches. All the light coming through your 1 square inch hole has been spread out into a square with four times as much area. Hence each square inch will be only ¼ as brightly lit as on the card 1 foot from the light.

Likewise at three feet from the flashlight your screen will have a square of light three inches on a side, which is 3 x 3, or 9 square inches in area. Thus the illumination on each square inch will be only ⅑ as great as on the card one foot from the light.

At four feet from the flashlight your square will be 4 x 4, or 16 square inches. Therefore, its

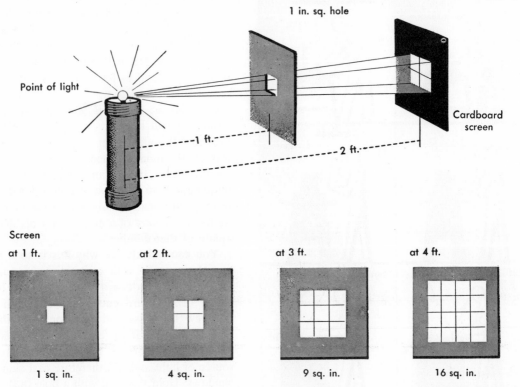

Point of light

1 in. sq. hole

Cardboard screen

Screen

at 1 ft.	at 2 ft.	at 3 ft.	at 4 ft.
1 sq. in.	4 sq. in.	9 sq. in.	16 sq. in.

27-13. The amount of light on each square inch of screen decreases as you move the screen away from the lamp. Can you tell how many square inches would be illuminated at 5 feet from this lamp? How would the illumination on each square inch at 5 feet compare to that on each square inch at 1 foot from the lamp?

surface will have only $\frac{1}{16}$ the illumination it would have at one foot.

In this way you can convince yourself that illumination of an object falls off with the inverse square of its distance from the light source. That is, when you move twice as far from a lamp the brightness of the light you get from it is only $\frac{1}{4}$ as great. Seven times as far away you get only $\frac{1}{49}$ as much light.

Several other kinds of energy behave in a similar way. For example the force of gravity falls off with the inverse square of your distance from the center of the earth. Thus someday when a rocket ship carries a 200-pound man up 4000 miles how much will he weigh at that distance from the earth? The distance from the surface of the earth to its center is roughly 4000 miles. At 4000 miles

above the earth he will be twice as far away as he was when he was on the ground. He will then weigh only $\frac{1}{4}$ as much — that is, only 50 pounds.

A similar law applies to sound, too. Using inverse squares you find that when you move twice the distance from a noise, say of an automobile horn, its sound is only $\frac{1}{4}$ as loud. When you are three times a given distance from a cheerleader, you can only hear him $\frac{1}{9}$ as well.

You see that the idea of inverse squares can be used in a number of different ways. It is very common to find that an idea that you learn in one part of your science course will be useful in some other branch of science. Thus you can use the idea of inverse squares in studying light, the earth's gravity, and sound.

Looking Back . . . .

VOCABULARY

The following are the key words to the main ideas in this chapter. Give a definition to show that you know the meaning of each.

1. polarized
2. wave (of light)
3. candlepower
4. filament
5. efficiency (of a lamp)
6. phosphor
7. fluorescence
8. inverse square
9. tungsten
10. argon

REVIEW QUESTIONS

1. How fast does light travel?
2. What did Isaac Newton think that light was made of?
3. What did Christian Huygens think light was made of?
4. Name some uses of polaroid.
5. What common device acts as though light consists of tiny particles?
6. What is meant by one candlepower?
7. How does a filament light bulb work?
8. How does a fluorescent tube lamp work?
9. What is meant by the " efficiency " of a lamp? Explain.
10. Name some uses of (a) sodium lamps, (b) neon lamps.
11. Do fluorescent lamps turn into light all of the electrical energy they use?
12. What facts tend to show that light is a form of energy?
13. If the sun should suddenly go out, how long would it take for us to know it? The sun is 93,000,000 miles away.

EXPLAIN WHY:

- Light seems to be made of particles.
- Light seems to be made of waves.
- The rotation of Jupiter's moons sometimes seems to get behind schedule by as much as 1000 seconds.
- Light can usually go through one polaroid but can always be stopped by two polaroids if they are turned at 90° to one another.
- Before 1940 nearly all common sources of light depended upon heat to make them work.
- It pays to light a store by fluorescent lamps rather than by filament lamps.
- It would not pay to light cellar stairs or a closet with a fluorescent lamp that was only needed occasionally.

Going Further . . . .

PROBLEMS TO SOLVE

You have seen now how the light falling on your book depends on two things:
1. the candlepower of the light source, c
2. the inverse square of the distance, d, from the lamp.

We can express these two facts much more neatly in a formula than we can in words.

$$\text{Illumination} = \frac{\text{candlepower}}{(\text{distance})^2}$$

or even more neatly

$$I = \frac{c}{d^2}$$

If we hold our book one foot away from the light of one candle, then distance d = 1 foot, and candlepower c = 1 candlepower. Our formula then tells us that

$$I = \frac{c}{d^2} = \frac{1}{(1)^2} = 1$$

One what? The illumination on our book is what is called one foot candle. A *foot candle* is the unit used to measure illumination, and it is the amount of lighting on a surface one foot away from one candle.

Sample Problem. How much illumination falls on a book held 3 feet from a 60 candlepower lamp? Here d = 3 and c = 60.

$$I = \frac{c}{d^2} = \frac{60}{(3)^2} = \frac{60}{9} = 6.67 \text{ foot candles}$$

Now let us see how you can use your knowledge of illumination in a practical way.

Can you figure out how much light falls onto your book from a 100-watt filament bulb 8 feet away in the ceiling of your room?

This problem is harder because you must first find the candlepower of the light source. However, you have already learned the candlepower of a 100-watt bulb. How much was it? It was 131 candlepower. So it isn't so hard after all! Your light source gives off 131 candlepower.

Eight feet away the illumination from such a lamp is

$$I = \frac{c}{d^2} = \frac{131}{(8)^2} = \frac{131}{64} = 2.04 \text{ foot candles}$$

Now this is the lowest possible figure. Actually, as you can see, a good deal of light is also *reflected* to your book from the ceiling and walls.

Suppose you are using a fluorescent desk lamp 1½

feet from your book. (You can estimate the wattage of fluorescent tubes fairly accurately if you assume the tube consumes 10 watts for each foot of length.) If your lamp has three feet of fluorescent tube it draws $3 \times 10 = 30$ watts. A fluorescent lamp has an efficiency of 3.2 candlepower per watt. Thus it gives off

$$30 \times 3.2 = 96 \text{ candlepower}$$

The illumination on your book is then at least

$$I = \frac{96}{(1.5)^2} = \frac{96}{2.25} = 43 \text{ foot candles}$$

Even here the light will actually be brighter than 43 foot candles because of the reflector on the lamp. Thus 43 is the lowest possible figure.

In the following table you will find the dimmest illumination that is satisfactory for various kinds of work.

hospital operating room	75	foot candles
night baseball	30	" "
sewing and close inspection work	30	" "
reading and writing	15	" "
corridors and stairways	5	" "
street lighting	$\frac{1}{20}$	" "
noonday sunlight	10,000	foot candles
bright moonlight	$\frac{1}{40}$	" "

From this table you should be able to say that:
1. Your fluorescent desk lamp that gives at least 43 candlepower is bright enough for reading and writing.
2. Your 100-watt ceiling lamp that gives 2.04 foot candles is not a good reading light unless additional light reflected from the ceiling and walls is about four times as bright as the direct light.
3. To get the proper amount of light to read by a single candle, you would have to hold your page a good deal closer than one foot from it.

TRY THESE PROBLEMS
1. How much light falls on this book when you hold it 5 ft. away from a 50-candlepower lamp? 3 ft. from a 100-candlepower lamp?
2. You wish to replace a 50-candlepower lamp 5 ft. away with a ceiling lamp 10 ft. away which will give you the same amount of light. How many candlepower should the ceiling lamp have?
3. If the lamps in Problem One are filament lamps, roughly what is the wattage of each?
4. On a clear night with a bright moon, could a

town ever safely turn off its street lights and still have enough illumination?
5. You are planning to buy a fluorescent desk lamp that is to stand on a shelf 2 feet above your desk. Must you buy one with two 1½-foot-long tubes? or is a less-expensive lamp with only one 1½-foot tube sufficient for good lighting?
6. You are doing some close inspection work. Four feet above your work table is a 100-candle-power lamp. Is its light sufficient? If it is not, how many candlepower must it be? What would be the effect of the reflector upon the illumination on your table?
7. What must be the wattage of a filament bulb if it is to produce 200 candlepower?
8. What must be the wattage of a fluorescent tube if it is to produce 200 candlepower?
9. How far apart should 200-watt street light bulbs be spaced to give sufficient illumination?

THINGS TO DO
1. You can quickly check on the number of foot candles available for various activities if you obtain a photographer's photoelectric exposure meter. Follow the directions which come with the meter. Most exposure meters contain a photoelectric cell. Light falling on the cell creates an electric current that is measured by a sensitive meter. The meter of most such exposure meters reads directly in foot candles. With such a meter and the knowledge you have gained from this chapter you can quickly measure the lighting at home or in school or in an office and see if the lighting is sufficient.
2. Use a photographer's exposure meter to check up on the inverse square law. To do this you have to be sure that the exposure meter is measuring the light from only one lamp and that there are no reflections from nearby objects. A candle in the middle of a large room or an isolated street lamp outdoors at night are good sources of light for you to measure. Be sure to measure their brightness at several distances.

READING FURTHER
Recommended Practice for Residence Lighting, Illuminating Engineering Society, 1860 Broadway, New York, 1953. Many charts and tables are contained in this book to show what kind of lighting should be found in the home.

Perhaps you would like to find out more about the calculation of illumination, focal distance, etc. You might find high school physics textbooks, such as these, helpful: *Exploring Physics* by Ruchlis and Lemon, Harcourt, 1953; and *Modern Physics* by Dull, Metcalfe and Brooks, Holt, 1955.

CHAPTER 28

Waves of Light— Seen and Unseen

Have you ever noticed the beautiful colors that sunlight sometimes makes as it goes through the corners of a fishbowl or through pieces of broken glass?

Perhaps you noticed too that the glass was not colored. Nor was the sunlight colored either before it struck the glass. Then *where* do you think the mysterious rainbow colors came from? To find out, you might experiment with some rainbow colors of your own.

THE SPECTRUM

The following experiment will show you how you can separate sunlight into its colors. All you need will be a triangular block of glass, called a *prism,* and a sunny room with window shades. When a beam of sunlight is coming through the window, pull down the shades until only a narrow crack is left to let in the sunlight.

In this narrow beam of sunlight hold the prism in the position shown in Fig. 28-1. Look on the opposite wall of your darkened room and you will see a beautiful band of bright colors. This band of rainbow colors is called a *spectrum.* Notice how the colors are arranged in the order: red, orange, yellow, green, blue, indigo, violet. Whenever you see a spectrum, you will find the same colors arranged in this same order.

Your little homemade rainbow made history when it was first produced by Sir Isaac Newton in 1666. Newton did two simple experiments with his spectrum. First he tried to break up the colors even further by letting them fall on a second prism. But the second prism was unable to spread the spectrum out into any more new colors.

On the other hand he found by another experiment that if he arranged the second prism as you see in Fig. 28-2, he could put all the colors back together again into a beam of white light just like the original beam of sunlight!

From these two simple experiments Newton

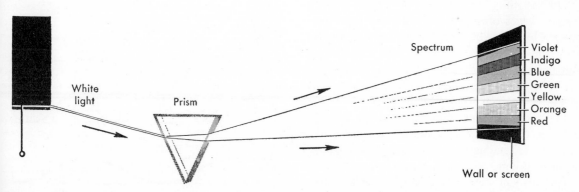

28-1. When a narrow beam of sunlight goes through a glass prism, the whole range of colors from red to violet appears.

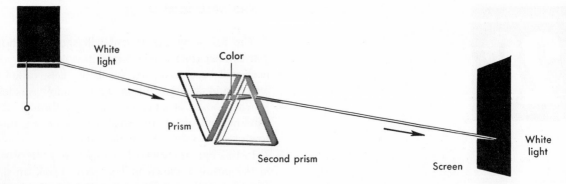

28-2. One prism spreads light out into the colors of the spectrum. A second similar prism turned the opposite way puts the white light back together again.

decided that *ordinary white light is really a mixture of the colors red, orange, yellow, green, blue, indigo, and violet.* Since Newton's time scientists have done many experiments with these little man-made rainbows and have shown beyond any doubt that white light really is a mixture of these seven colors.

What Is Color?

Your little spectrum has helped scientists discover what color really is.

You will remember from your experiments with polarized light that light acts as if it were made of waves. Scientists have found out that colors are due to differences in the lengths of these waves. The waves of red light measure $\frac{1}{30,000}$ of an inch from the crest of one wave to the crest of the next (Fig. 28-3).

Do you think this is tiny? Yet these are the *longest* waves of any of the colors in your spectrum. The waves of orange light are shorter than this, and the waves of yellow light still shorter. But the shortest waves of all are the waves that make violet light. These waves measure only $\frac{1}{65,000}$ of an inch from crest to crest.

Look around your room. Do you see a bright red object anywhere? It is red *because* the waves of light it is sending to your eyes are about $\frac{1}{30,000}$ of an inch long.

Perhaps you see a blue object somewhere, too. Its blueness is produced by waves only about $\frac{1}{50,000}$ of an inch long (Fig. 28-3).

The white light reflected from this page is white because it contains all wave lengths of light between $\frac{1}{30,000}$ and $\frac{1}{65,000}$ of an inch long.

How Does a Prism Make a Spectrum?

In your study of how lenses work, you saw that as a beam of light enters glass or water at an angle, the beam is always bent. This happens because the part of the light beam that strikes the glass or the water first is slowed down, causing the entire beam to swerve. The more sharply the light swerves, the more it is slowed down.

As you look at your colored spectrum you can see that the violet light *swerves more sharply* than the light of any other color. Thus violet light *travels more slowly* through glass than does any other color.

The longer wave lengths of red light are bent

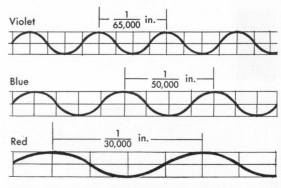

28-3. The color of an object depends on the length of the light waves by which you see it.

the least. Thus light of long wave lengths is slowed down less than any other as it enters glass.

The speed at which various colors of light travel through glass and water can be measured very accurately. Scientists have found that the shorter wave lengths really do travel more slowly through most transparent materials.

Colors from White Light

If you have some pieces of colored glass handy, you can make your spectrum show you still more of the secrets of color.

Hold your colored glass between your prism and its spectrum. If your glass is green, you will notice that it has removed most of the color from your spectrum — except for the green. Likewise a piece of red glass removes from your little rainbow all of the colors except red. And blue glass, you will find, lets only the blue wave lengths through.

Some glass lets through several colors at once. For instance, you can quickly find by experiment that the familiar amber glass, often used for bottles, lets through red, orange, yellow, and green, but no blue or violet light. Thus we conclude that amber light is really a mixture of several colors. A piece of purple glass lets through red and violet but none of the colors in between. Thus we conclude that purple is a mixture of red and violet.

Evidently *the color of a transparent object is due to the color of the light it lets through.* Thus,

while a piece of amber glass may *look* quite transparent, experiments like these can quickly show you that it really lets through almost no light at all except the colors that make amber.

Now you are able to see why a photographer sometimes uses a *filter* to improve his black and white pictures. A filter is a piece of colored glass put in front of the lens in order to cut down on the amount of light of a particular color reaching the film. For example, if you hold an amber filter over your camera lens, what color would it stop? You have just seen that an amber filter cuts out blue light. What effect would this filter have upon the appearance of blue sky in your picture? You will find out by looking at Fig. 28-4.

In the same way, a green filter in front of the lens lets through mostly green light and thus makes foliage appear lighter compared with its surroundings.

Your black and white pictures can be greatly improved if you choose filters carefully. Of course since the filter cuts out some of the light reaching your film, you must usually increase your exposure.

Why Are Colored Objects Colored?

Take a sheet of colored paper and hold it up so that your spectrum falls on it. Are *all* the colors of your spectrum as bright as they were before?

If your paper is green, you probably notice that the red, orange, yellow, blue, indigo, and vio-

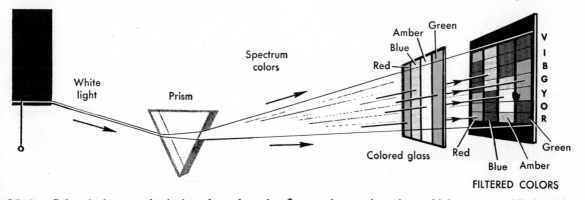

28-4. Colored glass or plastic lets through and reflects only certain colors which you see. All the other colors are absorbed by the glass. Green glass, for example, lets through the green wave length plus a little blue and yellow, but stops other wave lengths.

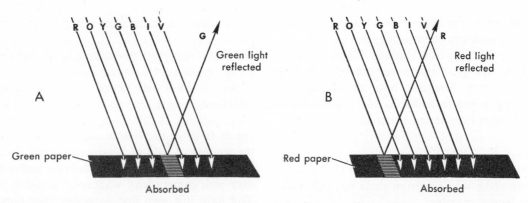

28-5. The color of any opaque object is the color of the light it reflects. What colors are *absorbed* by a green leaf?

let parts of your spectrum look much darker than the green part.

In a similar way you will find that red paper reflects red light better than it reflects any of the other colors of the spectrum.

Thus *the color of an opaque object is caused by the colors it is able to reflect.* Oranges are orange because the only color they reflect well is orange. Green leaves reflect mostly green wave lengths. The white paper of this page is white because it reflects *all* wave lengths.

Why do you put bluing in clothes that have begun to turn yellow from repeated washing? The clothes look yellow because they reflect more light from the yellow end of the spectrum than they do from the blue end of the spectrum. To help them reflect all colors of the spectrum more evenly and

thus appear white, you make up their missing color by adding a blue dye to the wash water.

For the same reason sugar refineries sometimes add small amounts of a harmless dye called *methylene blue* in order to whiten the yellowish color of refined sugar.

When you remember that the color of an object is caused by the colors it is able to reflect, you will be able to understand how a painter is able to mix two colors together to make a third entirely new color. If you can find some yellow and blue chalk or crayon or paint you will be interested to see what happens when you put one of these colors on top of the other. The result is green (Fig. 28-6).

The reason for such an unexpected result is this. The yellow paint really reflects orange, yel-

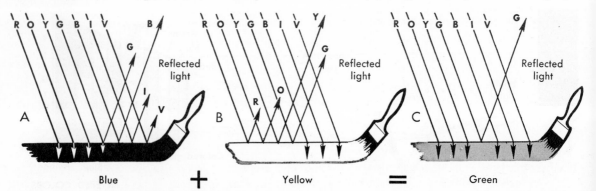

28-6. If you thoroughly mix two paints like blue and yellow, the result you brush on will be greenish. This is the only color reflected by both paints. If only a little yellow is added, only a little green is reflected, and the paint will be dark and " muddy."

low, and *green* light. The blue paint really reflects *green,* blue, and violet light. When they are mixed, the only color that the mixture can reflect is the one color they have in common — *green.*

The color of most paints and crayons is really such a mixture of several colors. Therefore, when two colors are mixed, the mixture will reflect the colors that both had in common. It is usually hard to tell *exactly* what the resulting color will be except by experiment. If you watch a painter trying to match two colors, you may see how hard this sometimes is.

The people who print books and magazines make colored pictures by mixing together colored printing inks. But they often do it in a rather surprising way. If you can get a magnifying lens, examine closely the color of a picture in a magazine or book (or the inside back cover of this book). You will probably see that the color is really made of a large number of tiny dots of several different colors.

If half the tiny dots are blue and half the dots are yellow, the resulting color will appear to be green just as in the case of your crayon-mixing experiment. Similarly a large number of colors can be made by properly mixing dots of only a few colors of printing ink. The dots are so tiny that your eye does not see the individual dots; it sees only the combined effect of all of them taken together.

Colored Objects Also Absorb
Some Wave Lengths

What do you suppose happens to all the other colors that are not reflected? The answer is that they are ab orbed, and their energy is turned into heat. Thus when you cast your spectrum on the red paper, the part of the red paper on which the other colors fell actually became a tiny bit warmer.

When light falls on a ripe lemon, the red, orange, green, blue, violet, and indigo lights are mostly absorbed and make the lemon slightly warmer.

When light falls on a black object, no colors at all are reflected. They are all absorbed instead

and turned into heat. For this reason you are likely to feel uncomfortably hot wearing black clothes in summer.

When light falls on white clothes, all of the colors of the light falling in them are reflected. Since none are absorbed, you are cooler. White, as you remember, is really all the colors of the spectrum taken together (Fig. 28-2).

Thus a light-colored object reflects a good deal of the light that falls on it and absorbs very little. And a dark-colored object reflects very little light. Instead it absorbs light and turns it into heat.

Colored Lights Can Fool You

Perhaps you have a colored light bulb (a red one) somewhere or some red-colored cellophane to put over the end of a flashlight. If you have any such way of making a red-colored light, you can fool your friends with some pretty illusions, and you can learn still more about color.

In a darkened room turn on the red-colored light. Hold in front of it a number of brightly colored objects, and have your friends try to guess the colors. Then take the objects outside in ordinary light and show your friends how they were fooled.

In red light that light blue necktie you were wearing looked black, didn't it? And your friend's white shirt looked red, and his green socks looked black.

Of course you will have no trouble explaining these strange effects to him. For you know that in red light, red is the only color that there *is* to be reflected. If an object *cannot* reflect red, then it reflects no color at all — which makes it look black. And if an object *can* reflect red, then it looks red. That is so even if it ordinarily reflects other colors too. Thus a white shirt looks red, and an amber object looks red and even a purple object looks red.

In *red* light the only color unchanged is *red.*

Perhaps you can try this experiment using light of several other colors, too. The cold blue light of the mercury lamp you sometimes find in photographers' studios is excellent for this experiment. If you make its spectrum with your prism, you will find that it contains yellow, green, and blue, but it has no red color in it at all. Thus red objects seen by this light appear to be black. Look at someone's lips and complexion in the light of a mercury lamp. They appear black and bluish green!

Imagine a dinner party by the light of such mercury lamps. The spinach and beets would appear black and the mashed potatoes bluish green. The meat would look bluish green, too!

How Does Your Eye See Colors?

Although you are aware of colors almost every moment that your eyes are open, scientists are not completely sure how to explain this familiar sensation. They are, however, now aware that several processes are at work which seem to depend upon the type of image that the eye is receiving.

For the simplest kind of image, produced not by a complicated picture but by various colored spots of light, the following explanation has been tried. First, recall from Chapter 25 that the retinas of your eyes contain a large number of specialized nerve endings called *cones*. These cones are sensitive to light and are concentrated near the center of your retinas.

Careful study seems to show that there are three different kinds of cones. Each kind detects a different group of colors. For instance, one kind of cone is sensitive only to red, to orange, and slightly to yellow. The second kind of cone is able to see only a little yellow, but mostly green and some blue. And the third kind of cone can detect only a little green, but a lot of blue and some violet. Fig. 28-7 will help you to keep these facts straight. Let us call these three types of cones the red cones, the green cones, and the blue cones after the name of the color each one of them sees best.

When the green light strikes your retinas, only the green cones scattered about in your retinas react and signal a green image to your brain.

When yellow light strikes your retinas, the green and the red cones both react a little bit. Acting together these two types of cones signal a yellow image to your brain.

This explanation works as far as images formed

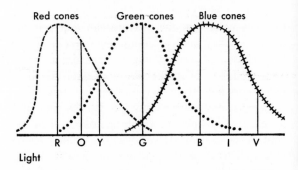

SENSITIVITY TO LIGHT

28-7. Our eyes, like a color film, seem to have three types of color-sensitive cones: some for red, some for green, and some for blue.

by colored spots of light is concerned. It will not, however, serve for the majority of cases found in normal color vision in which the image is not formed simply from spots of colored light.

For normal color vision, recent experiments have shown that the eye does not depend upon picking up a whole range of primary colors from the object. Instead, it was found that a full range of color vision is produced even if the eye picks up light all of the same color! This will happen so long as there is *some* mixture of wave lengths received, say differing tints of yellow. (See the inside of the back cover.)

Apparently what is necessary for normal color vision is not that the eye receive *particular* wave lengths but only that it receive *different* wave lengths. And these different wave lengths can all fall into the same general color range. Thus, even after many years of investigating color vision, there is much to be learned about the mechanisms in the eye and brain which make it possible.

What Is Color Blindness?

One man in every 25 and one woman in every 200 in America is color blind. A color-blind person does not see the same colors that a normal person sees. The reason is that some of the cones in their retinas do not react to colors the way they should.

For example, in one common form of color blindness the red cones of the eye do not work properly. If you have red color blindness, you can never know what red looks like to normal people. To you a red traffic light has a color that is not very different from faint green. Thus color blindness can be a serious matter if you drive a car or a railroad locomotive where you have to obey red and green signal lights.

In other types of color blindness the green cones or the blue cones do not work properly. Then the person is unable to see these colors at all except as shades of gray.

There is even a rather rare form of color blindness in which *all three* types of cones fail to work. If you have this trouble with your eyesight, you cannot see any colors at all. The world appears in shades of black and white, just as in a black and white movie.

Color blindness is inherited, and there is no cure for it.

TELL—TALE COLORS FROM ATOMS

Look at the loops and twists of the tiny ridges of skin on the tips of your fingers. Did you know that no one else in the whole world has exactly the same pattern of loops and twisting ridges that you have? These are your fingerprints. Whenever you touch an object, you leave on it a faint oily trace of your own fingerprint pattern. Even days later a detective can make your fingerprint pattern visible by various means and thus prove that *you* touched the object.

The Fingerprints of Atoms

Atoms have a kind of fingerprint, too.

Every atom in the world can be prodded to give out tiny flickers of colored light. Each kind of atom gives out its own special combination of colors. Like a fingerprint, one of these color combinations is a private mark belonging to just one kind of atom. Hence by looking at colors given off by an atom, a scientist, like a detective, can find out the kind of atom that made them.

Look at the atomic fingerprints in the end papers on the inside front cover. Here you see in the

third row the combination of colors given out by neon atoms in a familiar bright red neon sign. When the light from neon atoms is sorted out into its colors as you see here, this tell-tale band of colors is called the *spectrum* of neon. A spectrum is the row of colors made by sorting out the light of a brightly glowing object.

The second row shows the simple spectrum of sodium. A spectrum does not always have in it *all* of the familiar rainbow colors. The world around you is made of almost one hundred more kinds of atoms besides neon, and each kind of atom has its own special spectrum. Still another sample of an atomic fingerprint is shown in the end papers to show you how very different each one is from the others.

Let's see now how a scientist makes a spectrum and how he uses it to unlock the secrets of nature.

Making a Spectrum

How does a scientist prod atoms to give out their tell-tale colors?

One of the most common ways is to make the atoms extremely hot.

Sprinkle a pinch of table salt into the pale blue flame of a gas stove or a Bunsen burner. Did you see that yellow flicker? It was the tell-tale light of atoms of sodium. You see the same color in the spectrum in the end papers. Almost any material can be prodded to give off its colored light when a small piece of it is put into the 6000° F. heat of an electric arc.

Another trick is to get the atoms to form a gas and let some of the gas into a glass tube from which all the air has been removed. When electricity is passed through the gas, the atoms are prodded into giving off their tell-tale colors. This is exactly what the atoms of neon are doing in the familiar neon sign. The sodium lamps and mercury lamps described in Chapter 27 are also such tubes arranged to pry the special colors of light out of sodium and mercury atoms.

The light these tubes give out — indeed, the light that any prodded atom gives out — contains the atom's special colors all mixed in together.

How does the scientist split up the light into its separate tell-tale colors?

If you remember how a prism works, you can surely answer this question yourself. Light can be split up into its various colors by means of a prism, just as you have seen back on page 319.

When a scientist wants to take some light apart into its various colors, he lets some of it pass through a narrow slit, much as you and Sir Isaac Newton let the sunlight into a darkened room through a crack in the window shade.

The thin sliver of light is then collected by a lens and aimed into the prism. Exactly as with your little homemade rainbow, the prism bends the violet wave lengths of light the most and the red wave lengths the least (Fig. 28-8). It spreads all the tell-tale colors out in a row of colored lines, much as a card player might spread out in a long row all the playing cards he had been holding in a single bunch in his hand.

Finally a small telescope is used to gather the light of each color into a neat sharply focused line whose position can be measured. It is much as if the card player now stood up all his cards on edge.

Now at last the colors are sorted out into their various wave lengths, ready for the scientist to look at them or to take their photograph.

The instrument we have just described is called a *spectroscope*.

Atoms have to be in the form of a gas before they will show their tell-tale spectrum. If they are in the form of solids or liquids when they are heated glowing hot, they give off *all* colors at once.

Thus the light from glowing-hot solids and liquids gives a spectrum that is a continuous band of colors of the sort you made from sunlight or from a hot light bulb filament.

The spectroscope is amazingly sensitive. Its keen eye can spot the wave lengths given out by a tiny pinch of salt hiding in a whole bathtub full of water. It can detect in your blood the few lead atoms you inhaled by sleeping one night in a freshly-painted room. It can spot as little as two parts of aluminum in a million parts of canned condensed milk and thus tell food chemists whether the milk has dissolved any amount of metal from the walls of its can. From the light given out by a pinhead-sized piece of metal it can detect the tell-tale spectrum lines of as many as 70 metals *all at once*.

No wonder the spectroscope is one of the most important tools of modern science. Look at some of the questions it can answer.

Is there too much carbon dioxide in the water of that fish bowl?

Is there any arsenic spray left on that shiny apple?

Where in your body does all the iron go that you get from eating spinach?

What are distant stars made of?

Is there any gold in the sun?

Did that dust cloud really come from the deserts of New Mexico?

Does the iron in that steel girder contain a dangerously weakening amount of sulfur?

Did John Doe die of lead poisoning?

Does that watch spring have any copper in it?

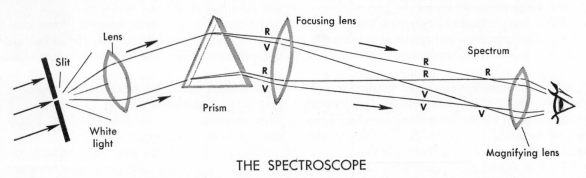

THE SPECTROSCOPE

28-8. The spectroscope is an instrument used to examine spectra and determine their composition.

THE MAGIC OF UNSEEN RAYS

One hundred and fifty years ago the scientist, Sir William Herschel, did some interesting experiments with the spectrum. When he held up a very sensitive thermometer in the various colors of the spectrum, he found that all the colors of light produced heat. Red light produced more heat than any of the other colors. But when he held his thermometer in the dark region just beyond the red end of his spectrum, he made his most amazing discovery. Here, where he could see no light at all, his thermometer soared higher than anywhere else in the spectrum.

Invisible Heat Rays

Invisible rays! This discovery of Herschel's was the first clue scientists had that there could be invisible rays, rays whose wave length was longer than the waves of ordinary red light (Fig. 28-9).

Since Herschel's time these warm invisible rays have been called *infrared* rays. Scientists have studied them so much that nowadays infrared rays are no longer mysterious.

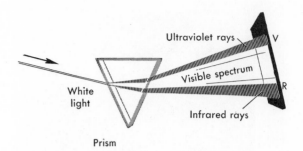

28-9. Sunlight contains waves longer than red and shorter than violet. These "light rays" are invisible to the eye. As a result of many experiments, Herschel found that different colors in the spectrum produced different amounts of heat.

To observe the effect of infrared rays hold your hand up close to a hot light bulb. Does it feel uncomfortable? Then slide a sheet of paper between your hand and the bulb, cutting off the infrared rays. Your hand feels cooler now, doesn't it? If you do not shield your hand, the infrared rays will presently redden your skin.

We know now that *all* warm objects give off

American Museum of Natural History

28-10. (Left) Hazy New York photographed in blue light. No clouds can be seen through the haze. Can you explain why the trees look dark? (Right) The same scene photographed in infrared light. Here clouds can be seen and the rest of the sky is dark. Why do the trees look white?

Raytheon Co.

28-11. Waves similar to radio waves cook food quickly in this new-style broiler.

infrared rays. The sun, electric toasters, light bulb filaments, flames, a tub of warm water, and even your own body all warm up their surroundings by sending out infrared rays in all directions.

We know also that the long wave lengths of infrared rays go through dust and haze much more easily than the shorter waves of ordinary visible light.

In recent years camera film has been invented that is sensitive to infrared light. With such film it is now possible to take some surprising pictures. For example you can photograph hot objects in total darkness simply by the infrared light they give out. And on a hazy day you can photograph distant landscapes invisible to your unaided eye (Fig. 28-10).

An astronomer can even take pictures of invisible stars far out in space, veiled from our eyes

by clouds of dust that lie between them and the earth.

Still Longer Waves of Heat

Have you ever watched a piece of meat cook until it *looked* well done only to find that the inside was still almost uncooked? Perhaps then you wished there were some way of cooking meat from the inside out. Well, there is!

The infrared rays we have just described are not very penetrating. They can only redden the surface of your skin. But rays of longer wave length can plunge deeper into an object, warming it through and through, and even cooking it.

Such heat-generating waves (longer than infrared rays) can cook food inside as well as outside and can do it in a matter of seconds (Fig. 28-11).

If you were to put your hand into a rather weak beam of such waves, they would make your hand extra warm. In fact they create a fever in your hand. A doctor sometimes uses such waves in treating sore muscles. His heating machine is called a *diathermy* (DY-uh-ther-mee) machine.

Sometimes enough of the waves escape to interfere with the neighbor's television set. These heating waves are a tenth to a hundredth of an inch long.

Are There Even Longer Waves?

You may wonder if there can be waves even longer than heat waves. The answer is yes. You may be surprised to learn that you have already had some experience with them. Waves longer than infrared are known as *radio waves*. The shortest radio waves are used in devices such as radar and are anywhere from about half an inch up to a foot long. Waves even longer than these are used to carry TV programs to your antenna from the broadcasting station. Still longer yet are the waves that carry ordinary radio broadcasts to your radio set. The length of some radio waves is several miles from crest to crest!

You will see how these very long waves are put to use when you read Chapter 31.

What Is "Black Light"?

Let's leave the long radio waves and retrace our steps.

From the giant radio waves we return down past the shorter heat waves and infrared waves and come back once more to the tiny waves of light your eyes can see.

Of all the kinds of light your eyes can see you will remember that violet light has the shortest wave length of all. Each wave is only $\frac{1}{65,000}$ of an inch from crest to crest. Do you think these waves are just about the shortest waves there can be?

Far from it! We can stretch our scale of size down to far tinier waves than these.

Just shorter than the waves of violet light are the invisible waves of *ultraviolet* light — the strange waves you have heard called "black light."

Short, invisible ultraviolet waves have several interesting uses.

The ultraviolet waves in sunlight cause your skin to make vitamin D, a chemical important to the proper growth of your bones. It is for this reason that young children need plenty of sunlight.

Ultraviolet waves in sunlight go right through the outer layers of your skin. When they reach the sensitive deeper layers of your skin, these waves give you a suntan. They can even go through thin clouds, which means that you can get a suntan on a cloudy day. But they are stopped altogether by ordinary window glass.

Ultraviolet waves can be dangerous if you are exposed to them for too long, as anyone knows who has had a severe sunburn. But they are almost sure death to many kinds of bacteria. You can buy special lamps that give out a great deal of ultraviolet light, as well as visible blue and violet light. Called *germicidal* lamps because they kill germs, these lamps are widely used to sterilize glassware in drugstores and restaurants, to sterilize public toilets, and to sterilize food. *Irradiated* milk is milk that has been treated with such ultraviolet light.

Still another use for these invisible rays is to make certain chemicals shine brightly even in the

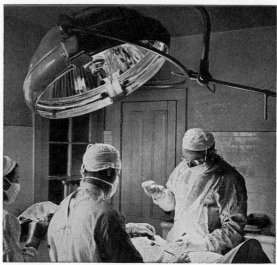

28-12. Strong mercury lights are used in operating rooms. Ultraviolet radiation from these lights kills bacteria and makes the operation safer.

dark. When struck by ultraviolet light, the atoms of some chemicals absorb the energy of the ultraviolet light and then give the energy out again in the form of visible light of various colors. For example, this is what happens to the chemicals coating the walls of fluorescent lamp tubes.

From your study of how such lamps work, back on page 312, you will remember that this effect is called fluorescence.

Wonderful stage effects can be produced by painting actors' clothes with fluorescent chemicals. With the stage entirely dark, invisible ultraviolet light is shone on the stage causing the costume to shine with a variety of bright colors.

Detectives use ultraviolet light too. Many inks and paints shine with a bright fluorescence, when they are put under "black light." Often the color of the fluorescence is quite different from the color of the ink or paint seen in daylight. This makes it easy to spot a forgery. Thus two postage stamps that look exactly alike by daylight may appear quite different under ultraviolet light. Forgeries of oil paintings and old books and letters are also identified by their very different appearance under ultraviolet light.

X rays

Can you see the inside of your stomach? Or can you tell what object is rattling inside that locked strongbox? To do so, you may say, you would need a magic lamp.

In Figure 28-14 you see a picture of such a magic lamp that really works! With this lamp you can see the fillings in your teeth without opening your mouth; you can see the cracks and holes several inches down inside steel plates; or you can see all the bones of your body without even bothering to take your coat off. This wonderful lamp is called an *X-ray tube*.

Do you remember reading about the X-ray tube in Chapter 23, page 263 (Fig. 23-6)? As you will recall, its main parts are the cathode, target, and anode. X rays are given off when electrons strike the target.

Your doctor and dentist use about 10,000 volts to pull electrons to the target. The X rays, less than a hundredth of a millionth of an inch long, will go right through your body and make a picture of your insides on camera film. Since X rays do not go through bones or through metal (like

28-14. A cosmic ray smashes into a lead plate in a cloud chamber, producing a shower of atomic particles. Cosmic ray energies are often greater than those of particles in atom-smashing devices.

fillings in your teeth) as easily as they do through soft flesh, such a picture shows bones and metal objects as shadows on the film. If your doctor wants to X-ray your stomach or intestines, he can make your stomach cast a shadow too by giving you a drink containing some of the dense but harmless metal, barium.

In industry electrons are smashed against their targets by pulls as great as 100 million volts. The X rays given off are so penetrating they will go through metal objects easily. Camera film can be exposed even through 12 inches of steel plates. X-ray pictures are often taken in this way to find air holes and dangerous cracks deep inside metal castings.

Such powerful rays as these can be very harmful to people standing nearby. Technicians using X rays stand some distance away behind lead-lined shields and turn on the X rays as briefly as possible.

While too heavy a dose of powerful X rays can severely burn you, a carefully measured exposure to just the right amount of X rays can also destroy cancer or stop its growth.

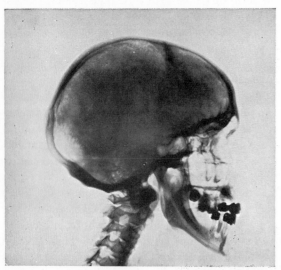

Westinghouse Electric Co.

28-13. X-ray picture of a human head. Thick bone and metallic dental fillings show as dark shadows. The thin nose and hollow cheeks barely leave a shadow.

Rays from Inside the Atom

Still more penetrating than X rays, and even more dangerous, are the rays thrown out by the nuclei of atoms. These are the *gamma rays,* hurled out by radium and other radioactive atoms as they break apart. These rays are poured into the atmosphere in death-dealing quantities during the explosion of an atomic bomb. Still shorter than X rays — only about a thousandth of a millionth of an inch long — these rays too travel at 186,000 miles a second, just as all their longer wave-length cousins do. A kind of super X ray that can go through several inches of lead, gamma rays can also be used to treat some kinds of cancer.

Gamma rays are made in great quantities in modern atom-smashing machines as atoms are torn apart. The study of these powerful rays is giving scientists a great deal of information about how atoms are put together.

The Shortest Rays of All

The highly penetrating *cosmic rays* are listed as the shortest waves of all. But the evidence is that these rays, streaming in from outer space continually, are actually protons, the hearts of hydrogen atoms. To classify them as waves is, however, possible if you recall that all atomic particles have wave properties (see page 310).

Cosmic rays are made somewhere in outer space among the stars. No one knows just where; no one knows just how. When they reach our earth, they have such enormous energy that they are able to smash any atom they strike into many pieces and scatter the fragments far and wide.

These bits of wreckage are eagerly studied by scientists because cosmic rays are a lot more successful at smashing atoms than any atom-smashing machine scientists have made so far. Scientists send apparatus high in the air in balloons and rockets. They set up laboratories on high mountain tops in order to catch and examine the pieces of atoms smashed by the furious power of cosmic rays (Fig. 28-14).

Fortunately for you, cosmic rays do not riddle your body in large enough numbers to cause you any serious damage. But scientists are interested in studying the part they may play in affecting inheritance or even perhaps in making people grow old sooner than they would normally. And they are very interested in what cosmic rays have to tell them about the secrets of atomic energy.

The Entire Spectrum of Waves

Think back over all the different kinds of waves you have just read about. How many of them are there striking your body this very moment?

Certainly radio waves are flooding over you from every nearby radio station. Certainly infrared waves are everywhere around you, made by lamps, radiators, or the bodies of nearby people. Of course your eyes can see the small group of

SPECTRUM

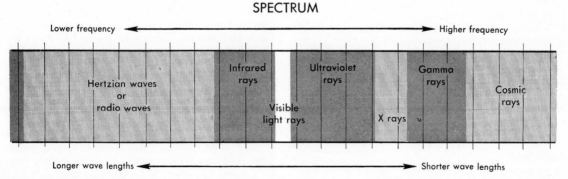

28-15. Our eyes are sensitive to only a small section of all the wave lengths. Many of the longer waves are used for communication (radar, radio). Shorter waves are used to show breaks in bones, to kill bacteria, and to treat certain diseases.

wave lengths of visible light. There is not apt to be much ultraviolet light or X rays or gamma rays in your room. But you are being steadily showered with cosmic rays from outer space.

How very little of the world you can see with your own eyes!

Looking Back . . . .

VOCABULARY

Define each of the following key words in this chapter.

1. spectrum
2. wave length
3. filter (camera)
4. spectroscope
5. infrared
6. diathermy machine
7. ultraviolet
8. germicidal lamp
9. irradiated
10. filament (X-ray tube)
11. target (X-ray tube)
12. gamma rays
13. cosmic rays
14. fluorescence

REVIEW QUESTIONS

1. How did Newton show that light is really a mixture of six colors?
2. What is color?
3. Which colors are bent most sharply by a prism?
4. Compare the speeds through glass of red and of violet light.
5. Explain the green color of green glass. What happened to all the other colors?
6. Explain the green color of green paint. What happened to all the other colors?
7. How do your eyes see color?
8. What is color blindness? Can it be cured?
9. How does a spectroscope work?
10. How are atoms made to give out their tell-tale colors?
11. Name in order all the various kinds of rays beginning with those of long wave length.
12. Which kinds of waves are in your room at this very moment?

EXPLAIN WHY:

• A photographer sometimes puts colored filters over the lens of his camera.
• A housewife puts bluing in the water when she washes white clothes.

• Yellow paint mixed with blue paint makes green paint.
• You are cooler in summer if you wear white clothes instead of black clothes.
• Many clothing stores and restaurants use "daylight" fluorescent lamps instead of filament lamps.
• Violets are blue.
• A spectrum is formed when white light passes through a prism.
• A green object looks green in green light but black when seen by red light.
• Clothes that look dark blue in daylight look black by tungsten filament bulbs.

Going Further . . . .

APPLYING PRINCIPLES

1. If a room received very little sunlight, how could you paint it in order to make it appear brighter?
2. Name some questions the spectroscope might answer that were not mentioned in this chapter.
3. How is a colored magazine picture printed?
4. Describe two practical uses of fluorescence.
5. If a doctor finds that his X rays are not powerful enough to take a picture of a broken bone, how can he make them more penetrating?
6. How might a food chemist use the spectroscope? an astronomer? a detective?
7. Name several uses for ultraviolet light.
8. Name several uses for infrared light.
9. Name several uses for X rays.

THINGS TO DO

1. If you can obtain some fluorescent paint and an ultraviolet lamp bulb, you can see many interesting effects. Try painting various objects with fluorescent paint and making them light up in the dark. You should also shine your ultraviolet lamp on such objects as your teeth, eyes, and fingernails. You will be surprised to see them glow in the dark! Some soaps and detergents and candles fluoresce brightly too, and many colored objects change their color completely under ultraviolet light.

2. To see how many-colored objects look in light of one color make yourself some yellow sodium light. You can do this easily by putting some borax in a metal jar cover and wetting it with denatured alcohol. When you set the alcohol on fire, it will presently heat up the borax and burn quietly with a bright yellow flame. In a darkened room examine

brightly colored objects by the light of this flame. Only yellow colors look yellow. All the other colors become shades of gray — including the colors in your face and clothes.

3. Without blinking, stare hard at the blue-green circle inside the back cover of this book. After you minute fix your gaze on a sheet of white paper. You will see a *red* circle! This is because the blue and the green cells of your retina have become tired. Hence the light reflected from the white paper is unable to stimulate them. It is only able to stimulate the red cells.

You can repeat this experiment by staring hard at circles of other colors! How does this experiment show you how your eyes see color?

4. You can experiment with mixing colors if you make the color top pictured on this page. If you spin overlapping halves of yellow and blue the top will look green! Try mixing all six colors of the rainbow and see if you can't make white.

5. Look up the article on color in *Life* magazine of July 3, 1944, and report on it to your class.

6. Try taking pictures with infrared film. Why will the sky look black in your pictures?

TRY THESE

1. What will be the color of a red necktie seen in (a) red light, (b) white light, (c) blue light?

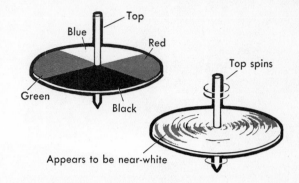

Top

Blue

Red

Green

Black

Top spins

Appears to be near-white

2. If you paint each of the spokes of a six-spoke wheel with one of the six colors of the spectrum, what does the wheel look like when it's moving fast?

3. How can three people looking at the same object each see a different color?

4. If you put red cellophane on top of blue cellophane, what color would you see when you looked through them? What if you put yellow on top of blue? red on top of purple? Try out these and other combinations to see if you are right.

5. Does a filament lamp give off any green light? Explain.

6. A scientist thought his landlady was using left-over meat from his plate to make hash. How did he use his spectroscope to make sure?

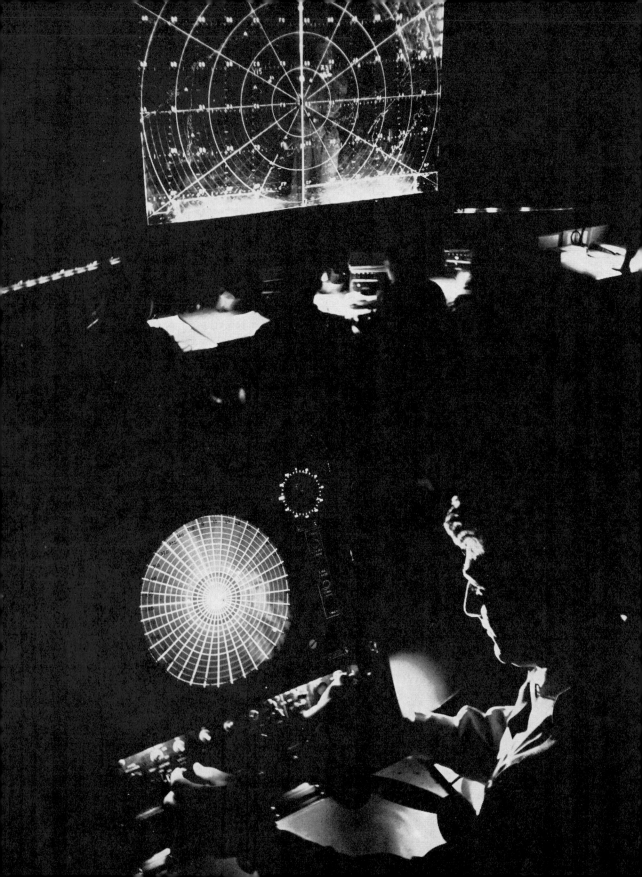

Communication – Wire and Wireless

Sound waves, vacuum tubes, light — and distant objects are revealed on a radar screen.

You MAY not mind living ten miles from your nearest neighbor. But suppose you lived ten miles from your nearest neighbor and had no radio or TV, no mail service, no telephone? Unless you enjoyed being a hermit, this would be a great hardship. To lead happy and useful lives nearly all of us must communicate with our neighbors.

Our town, state, and national governments are all controlled by voters who freely elect their candidates for political offices. If you are to vote intelligently, you must be informed by radio, TV, newspapers, word-of-mouth. Our country's government depends on communication between neighbors.

Your health and safety depend on quick communication with your doctor, your police force, and your fire department.

Your professional or business career will surely depend heavily on communication with your customers and your employer.

Think how many of your pleasures depend on communication with your friends by mail, by spoken word, by telephone. How many hours a week do you spend with TV, with your radio, with a newspaper, with books, magazines, phonograph records?

Your life is tied up in a web of communications with your neighbors. Certainly we should learn how the most common means of communications work. We should learn how sound waves carry our spoken words, how our spoken words are sent along wires by the telephone and ride through space on radio waves. We should understand in a general way how TV works, and radar, too. After all, these are part of your modern day-to-day life; they are part of your physical world.

CHAPTER

29

Our Sound-filled World

All day long your life is filled with sound. Even late at night the world around you is never completely quiet.

Most sounds tell you something. The squeal of tires tells you how fast a car is going around a corner. The way a hen cackles tells you whether she has laid an egg or is frightened. The striking of a clock, the sound of airplanes overhead, the music of an orchestra, the beat of a sick man's heart, the rush of wind in the trees, the roar of city traffic — all tell you something about the world around you. Scientists have even invented apparatus to allow you to hear corn growing, fish under water, and radio signals from outer space.

Much of the sound you hear during the day is talk. Some talk is very hard to understand. You may not understand the language used by a bank teller, an auto mechanic, or a medical doctor. But someone can understand their talk. You can understand it too if you study it hard enough.

All these sounds have a meaning. They give you information. They can mean danger, happiness, illness, or many other things.

In this chapter, we shall learn how sound is produced, why sounds differ from each other, and how we hear them.

VIBRATIONS

Firmly hold one end of a ruler down on a table and pluck the other end (Fig. 29-1). What do you hear? Pluck it again and this time look carefully at the ruler. What does it do when it is plucked? Try the same thing with a kitchen knife, a magazine, a laboratory tuning fork, a string bean, a banana.

Vibrations and Sound

What did you find? The ruler, the kitchen knife, the tuning fork produced a sound you could hear. The magazine, the string bean, and banana made no sound at all. You can test many other objects besides these to find which ones produce sound.

If you look closely at the objects which made a sound after plucking, you saw that they moved back and forth in the direction of plucking. They moved rapidly, some faster than others. Those objects that could not be made to move back and forth (vibrate) did not make a sound. If you tested enough objects in this way, you should be able to say that *objects that give off sounds can be made to vibrate*. Those that will not vibrate will not produce sounds.

Observe as many musical instruments as you can. Locate the vibrating parts that produce the sound. Strings, reeds, drum heads, radio loudspeakers, human vocal cords (in your throat) are a few of the vibrating parts which produce the sound.

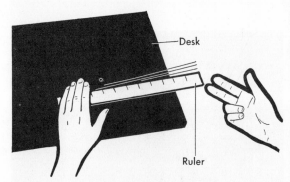

29-1. Like most vibrating objects, the vibrating ruler produces sound waves in the air.

336 COMMUNICATION—WIRE AND WIRELESS

Look at the banana again for a few moments. It did not vibrate when plucked and so did not give out any sound. What happens when a banana is dropped on the floor? Yes, it's mashed a little. Also it *does* give off a sound when it hits the floor. Try it. If you do this with each object you tested before, you will hear a sound when each hits the floor. Some may make less sound than others, but you will be able to hear most of them. True, the sound is not like the ruler or tuning fork vibrating, but it is a sound. Could it mean that two objects, banana and floor, produce sound when they hit each other?

If you examine by listening to and observing many objects hitting each other, you will be able to say " yes " to the question. When two cars, two hands, a ball and a bat, a can and your toe hit each other, a sound is produced. There is no end to the number of examples you can think up to show this principle.

A sound is produced by two objects colliding with each other.

Here then are two ways of producing sound. You saw the ruler move back and forth. You saw the banana mashed slightly. How did each of these make sound? To answer this question we shall try some more experiments.

Wave Motions

Fill a large pan with water. Wait for all waves on it to smooth out. Pluck a tuning fork and barely touch one of the arms of the vibrating fork to the surface of the water (Fig. 29-2).

What happened to the surface? It was ruffled, wasn't it? Did you see how it was disturbed? Do it again and look closely at the surface of the water. Did you see little waves go out from where the fork touched the water? You have to look closely to see them. Each time the fork hit the water a new wave was sent out. You may have seen they were shaped like circles, too. In what direction did they move? The circle of water waves should have moved away from the fork.

It is more difficult to show that waves in the air are set up by the vibrating fork, but you have seen similar waves on water. In air, the waves

Campbell-Hays from Monkmeyer

29-2. When you lower a vibrating fork into water, the vibrations set waves in motion in the water.

move away from the vibrating fork in much the same way as in water.

Over and over again the vibrating fork pushes against the air. Air pushed by the fork pushes against the air beyond it, and it in turn pushes against the air beyond *it*. Each push travels outward from the tuning fork, much like those water waves in the pan. Right behind it races the next push and the next and the next . . . (Fig. 29-3). The air that is pushed is *compressed*. The air directly behind it is thinned out, or *rarefied*. These are *sound waves*. When you listen to that tuning fork, the hum you hear is the beating of wave after wave of air pressure upon your ear.

The ruler, the kitchen knife, musical instruments, and other vibrating objects all send out a steady sound in exactly this way.

Now we should see how sound is produced by two objects bumping into each other. You will get the idea very quickly if you drop a stone in a quiet pond. You will see a big wave being sent out, usually followed by some little ones. The big wave is the important one. It is very much like the big push against the air as two objects bump into each other. When such a big push against the air travels to your ear, you hear it as a thump, a

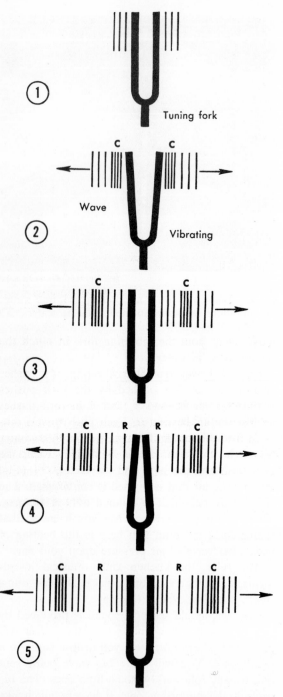

snap, or a bang. Like the single big wave in the pond, there are only one or two big sound waves given out when a hammer hits a nail or when two other objects bump together. You cannot make a steady sound unless you repeat the collision over and over again.

When a sound travels across the room, the air molecules themselves do not move far. They merely vibrate back and forth, following the back and forth motion of the tuning fork (or other sound producer). Only the wave of pressure travels, handed on from air molecule to air molecule (Fig. 29-4).

The Speed of Sound

If you have ever stood a few hundred feet from a high wall or a cliff and shouted, you may have heard your shout coming back to you as an echo. An *echo* is a sound that has been reflected, much like a ball that bounces back to you from a wall.

The farther you are from the wall, the longer it takes for the sound of your voice to travel to the wall and bounce back. It seems as if sound took time to travel from place to place. How fast do you suppose it goes?

You can find out approximately if you have a stop-watch and go to a high wall or a cliff. Make a loud noise as you start the watch. When you hear the echo, stop the watch. You have measured the time for the sound to travel to the wall and back again. Suppose the wall is 825 feet away and the sound took 1.5 seconds to make the round trip. You can then find the speed of sound from the formula

$$\text{Speed} = \frac{\text{Distance}}{\text{Time}}$$
$$= \frac{825 + 825}{1.5}$$
$$= \frac{1650}{1.5}$$
$$= \textbf{1100 feet per second}$$

Sound travels a mile in about 5 seconds.

More careful measurements show that sound waves travel slightly faster in warm air than in cold air. Also sound travels much faster through water and solid materials like the earth.

29-3. As the tuning fork prongs move in and out they repeatedly compress the air (C) and rarefy it (R). The rapid compressions and rarefactions racing away from the fork are sound waves.

You have undoubtedly noticed other effects that depend on the speed of sound. For example, you may have seen the steam from a whistle several seconds before its sound reached you. Or at a track meet you have noticed the puff of smoke from a starter's gun before you heard its sound.

Thunder and lightning always occur at the same instant, since lightning is the cause of the thunder. Thus if you hear thunder five seconds after you see the lightning, you can be sure that the lightning is about one mile away.

You needn't worry about light having a slow speed too and thus throwing off your estimate of distance. You remember from Chapter 27 that light whizzes along at 186,000 miles a second. Hence it travels all the way around the earth in the time it takes you to blink. For practical purposes you see that lightning at the same instant it occurs.

Underwater Sound

Put your head under water when your friend claps two rocks together under water several yards away. You will be surprised at how loud they sound. Water is a good conductor of sound waves.

The Navy used this fact during the last war to detect enemy submarines. Any sound made by turning propellers or by a hammer dropped inside the submarine could be heard several hundred yards away by the use of sensitive listening devices.

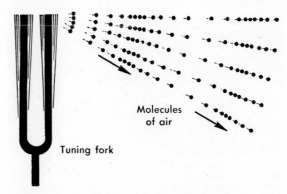

29-4. Air molecules do not travel with the sound wave. They merely vibrate back and forth as they pass along the compressions and rarefactions to their neighboring molecules.

Another important use of sound waves under water is to measure the depth of water beneath a ship (Fig. 29-5). From the bottom of the ship a sound wave is sent downward. It is well known that sound travels 4700 feet (almost a mile) a second through water. At this speed the sound wave travels downward, hits the sea floor, and is reflected back up. The time it takes the echo to return to the ship is carefully measured. The longer this time is, the deeper the water. The depth of water under a ship can be read directly on a gauge in the pilot house.

Many fish also make sounds in water, and these sounds can be heard with suitable listening de-

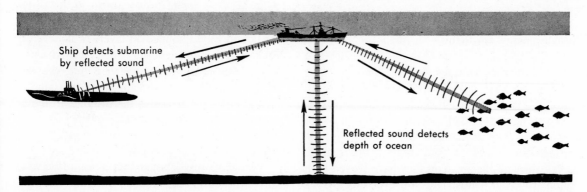

29-5. Sound waves that are sent out underwater bounce off underwater objects. The longer it takes for the reflected sound wave to return, the farther away is the object that is reflecting them.

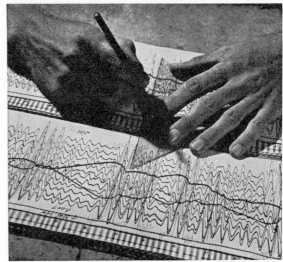

29-6. The sound waves made by the dynamite explosion travel through the ground and bounce off layers of rock deep in the ground. Instruments in the truck record the pattern of the sound wave as shown above. By examining the pattern, oil prospectors are able to locate possible oil-bearing structures deep underground.

and stretched tight makes a fairly good conductor of sound. Your voice spoken into one can causes its bottom to vibrate. The string carries this vibration to the other can. If your friend holds the can near his ear, he can hear the words you speak.

Oil prospectors often send sound waves through the ground to help them find hidden oil deposits. The sound waves are made by a dynamite explosion (Fig. 29-6). Traveling downward the sound waves bounce off layers of underground rock covering oil deposits. The reflected wave is timed. Oil prospectors can then find the depth of the deep layers of rock in much the same way as a ship's pilot measures the distance to the bottom of the sea beneath him.

No Sound in a Vacuum

You have just learned that a sound wave can travel through gases, liquids, or solids. Now, you can find out if it travels through *empty* space, too, by doing the experiment shown in Fig. 29-7.

vices. Fishing fleets often locate schools of fish by " listening " for them.

Sound Travels Through Solids, Too

So far we have talked about sound traveling in water and in air. Solids also carry sound waves.

If you have ever had a dentist drill your teeth, you know that the sound of the drill travels through the bones of your head better than it travels through the air. You may have played with sound waves in solids. Did you ever talk over a tin can and string telephone? A string fastened at each end to the center of the bottom of a tin can

As the air is pumped out of the bell jar, the sound of the bell grows fainter and fainter until you can no longer hear it. However, when you let air back in again, you can hear the sound as well as before. Evidently, sound will *not* travel through a *vacuum*.

Thus no matter how loudly you shouted on the moon you could not be heard, for our moon is an airless world. Indeed if the biggest cannon were fired right beside you on the moon, you would not hear it go off.

If you remember why sound travels through gases (like air), liquids, and solids, you will see at once why sound cannot travel through a vacuum. Sound consists of repeated pushes of molecules against their neighbors. In a vacuum there are no molecules to push, and hence there can be no sound.

PITCH

Sounds differ greatly from each other. For example, you can almost always tell girls' voices from boys' voices. Girls' voices are high-pitched; boys' voices are lower-pitched.

How does a high-pitched sound differ from a low-pitched sound? A simple experiment will show you.

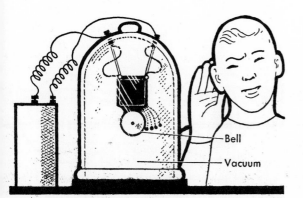

29-7. Sound waves cannot travel through empty space. Hence, when the air is pumped out of the bell jar you cannot hear the bell inside.

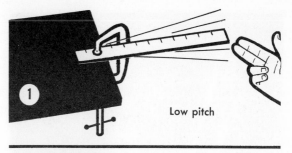

Low pitch

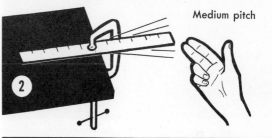

Medium pitch

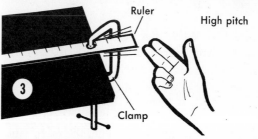

Ruler

High pitch

Clamp

29-8. The faster an object vibrates, the higher the pitch of the sound.

Pitch and Speed of Sound

Get out your 12-inch ruler and allow ten inches of it to stick out over the edge of your desk. Clamp down the two inches on the desk and pluck the end as you did before (Fig. 29-8). Now shorten the part that sticks out from the desk to eight inches and repeat the plucking. You will observe a different sound, a higher one. Note that the vibrating ruler seems to vibrate faster than before. The shorter the ruler, the faster it vibrates and the higher is its pitch.

Pitch, your music teacher will tell you, depends on speed of vibration that produces the sound you hear. On the violin, all the player has to do to make a note of higher pitch is to shorten the string by placing a finger on it. Open up a piano,

Philip D. Gendreau

29-9. The bow drawn across the strings of a violin causes them to vibrate, producing sound.

and see how slowly the big long strings vibrate. Compare their vibration rate with that of the shorter strings. If your school orchestra has a cello or a bass viol, compare the vibrations of their strings with those of the violin. You will readily see the relationship between pitch and vibration rate. The higher the pitch, the more rapid its vibration; the lower the pitch, the slower its vibration.

The pitch of your voice depends on how rapidly your *vocal cords* vibrate. Your vocal cords are a pair of stretched membranes located in your Adam's apple. They vibrate as you blow air past them (Fig. 29-10). Put your finger against your Adam's apple and feel their vibrations as you speak.

You can make a variety of sounds by changing the tension of your vocal cords and by changing the position of your tongue and lips over which the sound passes.

The voices of girls and children are high pitched because their vocal cords are rather short (like the strings at the " high " end of the piano). The longer vocal cords of men (like the strings at the " low " end of the piano) usually vibrate more slowly and hence make a lower pitch.

Air can be made to vibrate, too!

Try blowing across the mouth of a pop bottle almost filled with water (Fig. 29-11). That sound you hear is caused by the air in the bottle vibrating or shaking up and down. If you empty some of the water in the bottle, you will find you change the pitch of the sound (Fig. 29-11). Short air columns vibrate faster and produce higher notes than long ones do. An air column behaves much like the vibrating ruler you saw back in Fig. 29-8.

How many wind instruments can you recognize in Fig. 29-12? Think carefully of each one and see if it is always true that shorter air columns produce the higher pitch.

Loud and Soft

Pluck gently a stringed instrument or a rubber band as in Fig. 29-13. You can hardly hear the sound it makes.

Pluck it again much more strongly and watch it carefully. Its bigger vibrations cause greater pressure changes in the air than before. Thus, the result is a louder sound (Fig. 29-13).

Think of all the ways in which you can make a louder sound. You force air more violently over your vocal cords, you stamp your foot harder, you press the bow harder against the violin strings. In all of these cases you make larger changes in air pressure.

Distinguish carefully between the reason for

VOCAL CORDS

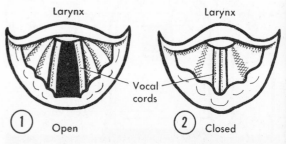

29-10. Your vocal cords are membranes in your Adam's apple (larynx). Blowing air through the opening between them causes them to vibrate, and hence to make musical sounds or speech.

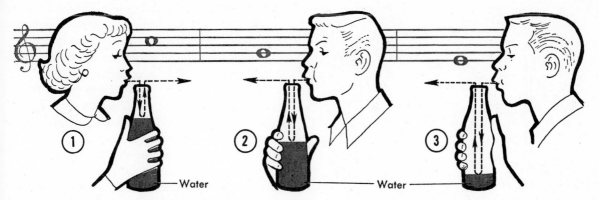

29-11. Like the vibrating ruler in Fig. 29-8, short air columns vibrate more rapidly than long ones and produce sound of a higher pitch.

pitch and the reason for the loudness of sound waves. Remember that:

- The *more rapid* the pressure changes, the *higher the pitch.*
- The *larger* the pressure changes, the *louder* the sound.

Noise vs. Music

When you press one key of a piano, you hear a very pleasant sound. Most of the sound waves hitting your ear have the same pitch. When you press two or three keys at once, the sound may still be pleasant. But if you use the length of your forearm to press ten or fifteen different notes all at once, you hear a sound that is not musical at all. Most people would call it noise.

Noise is a combination of sounds of many different pitches whose combination makes very *irregular* changes in pressure on our ears. Even the finest orchestra would make nothing but noise if each instrument were playing a variety of notes at random. The sound made by dragging your

Concert Artists, Inc.

29-12. Pitch in wind instruments is produced by changing the length and size of the air column and by using open and closed tubes.

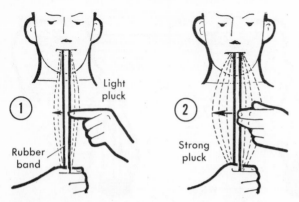

29-13. The larger the vibrations the louder sound an object can make.

feet along the floor is almost pure noise. The continuous very uneven banging of the sole of your shoe against the floor or against particles of dirt on the floor makes a great variety of sound waves with many unequal time intervals between them.

A *musical* sound is one whose vibrations are pleasing to the ear. Sounds are pleasing and musical if they consist of either one pitch or several different pitches whose combination produces fairly *regular* changes in pressure on our ears. A tuning fork makes a pure tone of just one pitch as it vibrates. The note from a piano string or a violin string is more complicated as you see in Fig. 29-14B. But the changes in pressure are still regular. There is even a regularity in the sound waves from a full orchestra if they play the proper combination of notes. It would be very hard for you to find any regularity at all though in the sound waves of a noise (Fig. 29-14C).

However, the most pleasing musical sound is not the pure note from a tuning fork. The most pleasing musical sounds are *combinations* of such pure tones. Most musical instruments, even when they play a single note, give out a combination of several sounds. Your ear hears the pitch of the loudest one. The fainter sounds that come along with it have a variety of pitches that gives the sound richness and interest. Yet you will see from Fig. 29-14B that there is still a regular pattern to the sound wave.

Perhaps you know how to play a chord on the piano. Here you are putting together several musical notes in a combination pleasing to the ear.

It is interesting that people do not always agree on what is a pleasing combination of sounds. Chords of " modern " music sound very different from the chords of " classical " music. Musical instruments played today in Asia may sound very peculiar, even unpleasant, to our ears.

It has always been true though that a musical sound is a combination of pure sounds, often very complicated, that has regularities pleasing to the listener. It is also true that noise, as we have described it, is so complicated a combination of sounds that it contains no regularities at all.

HOW WE HEAR

How often do you stop to wonder at the good fortune of having ears or to wonder how they allow you to hear the sounds around you?

The part of the ear that sticks out from your head, called the *outer ear,* is only a small part of your ear. Surprising as it may seem, you could hear perfectly well without this part. Some animals such as the rabbit and bat, however, need this outer ear to concentrate sound.

The really important part of your ear is *inside* your head. See how it is formed in Fig. 29-15.

Sound waves reaching your ear beat against the

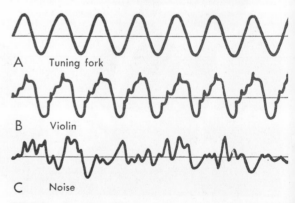

29-14. Regular changes in pressure make pleasing musical sounds; irregular pressure changes make noise.

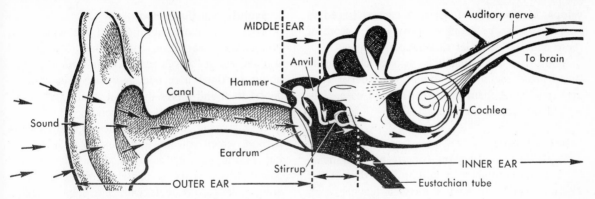

29-15. The important parts of your ear are inside your head. Here sound waves beating against the eardrum are turned into nerve signals traveling to your brain.

flexible membrane called your *eardrum,* causing it to vibrate back and forth. The in-and-out motion of the eardrum works a series of three tiny levers that pass the vibrations along to the *cochlea* (кок-lee-uh). (These three levers are the smallest bones in your body.) The cochlea, full of liquid, is an inch-long tube, coiled up like a snail. Inside it along its length is a thin flexible *membrane.* Its job is to sort out the complicated vibrations of sound and turn them into nerve signals to your brain. Resting against the membrane, all along the length of the cochlea, are the endings of the *auditory nerves* that lead to the brain.

When sound vibrations reach the cochlea, the liquid inside it is forced to vibrate. The membrane inside the cochlea vibrates too, but different parts of the membrane are able to vibrate at different rates. Thus vibrations at the rate of 128 vibrations every second cause only one short region of the membrane to vibrate. Another short length of the membrane vibrates only at 200 vibrations a second, and so on. Thus different parts of the membrane vibrate to the various pitches that exist in the original sound. Each tiny part of the membrane has its own nerve ending for signaling to your brain. In this way, your brain receives a signal for each vibration of the original sound.

Your brain can sort out the various nerve signals so that you can distinguish the various sounds from one another. Thus when you are listening to an orchestra, you can pick out the sound of the clarinet; in a room full of people busily talking, you can pick out and listen to the voice of one particular person.

Care of the Ears

Do you know anyone who is deaf or partly deaf? There are many things which cause deafness, but most of them can be avoided.

In Fig. 29-15 did you notice the *Eustachian tube* leading into the middle ear? Look for it. This tube connects with your throat and is normally closed. Swallow, and you will hear the cracking sound as this tube opens. The Eustachian tube equalizes the air pressure on the inside of the middle ear with the pressure on the outside. The eardrum won't let air through.

It is possible to infect this Eustachian tube and clog it. Earaches can result. Hard blowing of the nose when congestion of a cold appears can fill the tube with cold virus and cause congestion there, too.

There is an old saying that you should never stick anything smaller than your elbow in your ear and then you should have your coat over your elbow. The eardrum is easily damaged by any hard instrument and does not easily heal if punctured. Only your doctor should remove any foreign material that might get into your outer ear.

Measles, scarlet fever, and the common cold, if left unchecked, can affect the ear and cause deafness, too. This is particularly true if earache develops. Many cases of deafness can be traced to neglect of earache brought on by one or more of these causes. Don't let this happen to you.

Your ears are amazingly strong, considering the delicate membranes, bones, and nerve endings that make them up. With normal care, they should last you a lifetime.

Hearing Aids

More than 1½ million Americans wear hearing aids and another 4½ million need them (Fig. 29-16). You may have noticed a teacher or a fellow pupil with a hearing aid phone in his ear. It receives sound waves and makes them so much louder that the sound wave it sends into the outer ear tube is strong enough for partially deaf ears to hear. If the person's hearing is so bad that this assistance doesn't help him to hear, another device may be used. This device causes the vibrations to make direct contact with the bones of the skull near the ear which then carry the sound waves to the inner ear.

Before you or your parents invest in a hearing aid, you should visit your doctor and get a thorough hearing test. If you are hard of hearing, you need to be sure you get just the right hearing aid.

National Carbon Co. — Union Carbide & Carbon Co.

29-16. Batteries for hearing aids are being made smaller and lighter, not much bigger than the aspirin tablet on the right.

Sounds You Can't Hear

There are many vibrations in the world that you cannot hear. You cannot hear low-pitched sounds whose waves strike your ear less than about 16 times a second. Nor can your ears respond to sound waves that beat upon them faster than about 16,000 times a second.

Bats give off sounds of up to 80,000 waves a second, which you are quite unable to hear. The bat listens for the echo of these high-pitched sound waves. Like a captain guiding his ship among dangerous reefs with the help of sound echoes off the ocean bottom, the bat can guide himself about in pitch-dark places without ever bumping into anything.

Dogs can hear sounds well above the range of your ears, too. Perhaps you have seen dog whistles which seem to make no sound.

Scientists have done many experiments with such high-pitched sounds. The study of such sounds is called *ultrasonics*. Ways have been found of producing sounds with as many as a million vibrations a second and of studying their extraordinary effects.

Ultrasonic sound waves sent through liquids kill bacteria, homogenize milk, kill fish, make water appear to boil, and burn fingers dipped in by mistake.

Although you cannot hear these sounds, they can make you ill. One of the reasons people working near jet engines become ill is that the intense ultrasonic sound waves given off by these engines affect the nerves and organs of their bodies. Ultrasonic sound waves may find important uses in healing the body, too. Already they can be used to locate tumors deep inside the body and to drill cavities in teeth.

The study of ultrasonics is a new and important branch of science that is already benefiting industry and medicine. You can expect to hear more about it in coming years.

Looking Back . . . .

VOCABULARY

The following terms represent key ideas in this chapter. Define each term.

1. echo
2. pitch
3. vocal cords
4. noise
5. musical sound
6. eardrum
7. cochlea
8. Eustachian tube
9. vibration
10. auditory nerve
11. ultrasonics

REVIEW QUESTIONS

1. Explain how sound waves are used by ships for measuring the depth of the water beneath them.
2. How can you estimate the distance from you to lightning?
3. Show how sound waves are used to help locate underground oil deposits.
4. With the help of a simple diagram explain how your cochlea helps you to hear.
5. How is it possible for a common cold to spread to your ears and infect them?
6. How are tones of different pitch obtained from a piano? a trombone? an organ? a violin?
7. How are sounds of different pitch and different quality produced by the same human voice?

EXPLAIN WHY:

- Sound does not travel through a vacuum.
- The motion of the prongs of a tuning fork causes a sound.
- Objects colliding with each other give off a sound.
- Sound can travel across the room even though the air molecules do not travel across the room.
- You see lightning before you hear thunder, even though both occur at the same instant.
- Children's voices are higher pitched than men's voices.
- Some sounds are pleasant to our ears, while other sounds are unpleasant.
- Swallowing hard relieves uncomfortable pressure on your eardrums.
- You should consult an ear doctor before buying a hearing aid.
- A person who is totally deaf cannot be helped by a hearing aid.

Going Further . . . .

THINGS TO DO

1. Measure the distance of lightning. Time the interval between the lightning flash and the sound of thunder. Multiply the time by the speed of sound to find how far away the flash was.
2. Use an echo to measure your distance from a wall or a building. Time your echo and divide the time by two. Why? Multiply the result by the speed of sound to find your distance from the wall or building.
3. Make a musical instrument from drinking glasses. Find eight thin glasses that make a musical sound when they are struck. Line them up and fill each one with a different amount of water. By adjusting the amount of water in each one, you will be able to play a scale of musical notes.

EXPERIMENTS

Describe an experiment to:
1. Show that sound is caused by vibrating objects.
2. Show that sound waves can travel through a solid.
3. Show that sound can travel through the air but not through a vacuum.
4. Measure the speed of sound.
5. Show that the more rapid the vibration of an object the higher the pitch of the sound it emits.
6. Show that an irregular vibration produces a noise.

TRY THESE PROBLEMS

1. Approximately how far away is a boat if you see the steam from its whistle 4.5 seconds before you hear it?
2. If you hear thunder 8 seconds after you see the lightning flash, about how far away is the thunderstorm?
3. A ship's microphone hears echoes off the ocean bottom 0.6 seconds after the sound is sent down from the ship. About how deep is the water beneath the ship?
4. About how far away from you is a cliff that returns an echo to you in 5.3 seconds?

CHAPTER 30

Sending Words Along Wires

Do you suppose you could make yourself understood by someone the length of two football fields away? Certainly it would be hard work to carry on a conversation at such a distance unless you had the help of some voice-booster such as a public-address system.

Public-address systems can raise your normal speaking voice to a roar that can be understood a mile or two away. This is quite a noise! To be heard 150 miles away you would have to make a sound as loud as an atomic bomb. Clearly sound waves are not the most useful means of talking to your friends at a distance.

How then could you send a message to a friend 500 miles away? You can probably think of several ways. You could talk to him by telephone or by radio or even by telegraph. In all of these, you turn your message into electrical signals.

In this chapter we shall explore some of the ways in which electricity can carry your words silently and swiftly. You will find the work you have already done in electricity very useful in this study. It may be helpful to review that material before you go on.

THE TELEGRAPH

One of the early devices for sending words by electricity looks very simple. You can even make one yourself out of nails, some wire, pieces of a tin can, and several dry cells hooked up as in Fig. 30-1. This simple device, called the *telegraph,* was invented by the American artist, Samuel Morse, in 1837.

Morse's Telegraph

Morse's telegraph consisted of a battery, and a key (or switch), connected by wires to an electromagnet (Fig. 30-2). The electromagnet is arranged in such a way that when the key in the sending set is pressed, electricity flows and the electromagnet pulls down a metal arm in the receiving set with a loud click. Releasing the key "opens the circuit" again. The electromagnet no longer pulls down on the metal arm, because electricity has ceased to flow. Hence a spring can pull the arm upward with another loud click.

Basically this is how the railway telegraph works even today. If you ever visit a railroad station in a small town, be sure to examine the telegraph in operation there.

First Message

On May 24, 1844, Morse sent the message, "What hath God wrought?" from Washington, D.C., to Baltimore, Maryland, 40 miles away.

TELEGRAPH SENDER

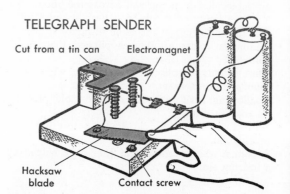

Cut from a tin can   Electromagnet

Hacksaw blade   Contact screw

30-1. Try making this simple telegraph. To send a message the electromagnet sounder can be located some distance away. Why does the electromagnet work only when the key is held down?

FIRST FORM OF KEY

IMPROVED FORM OF KEY

EARLY RELAY

FIRST WASHINGTON-BALTIMORE INSTRUMENT

American Telephone and Telegraph Co.

30-2. Many experiments contributed to the invention of the first telegraph, which depended on the development of the electromagnet.

This was the first telegraph message sent any distance. Knowing how the telegraph works, you can see that these words were not spoken as in a telephone. They were sent by a code — a code which Morse had invented.

The short time between pressing down and releasing the key Morse called a " dot." A longer time between closing and opening he called a " dash." A combination of dots and dashes is used to represent the letters of the alphabet. For instance, one dot and one dash represent the letter " a," and three dots and one dash, the letter " v."

A very similar code — the International code — is used today in many cross-country and trans-oceanic wire systems. Radio amateurs use this code, too. You will find the entire telegrapher's code in a radio amateur's handbook listed at the end of this chapter.

Modern Telegraphs

In this book you have read of many jobs that grew too big for men to do without help from machines. Here is another one. Millions of telegrams are sent in a year. There are simply not enough telegraph operators in all the country to send so many messages by hand. The job has to be done with the help of machines.

In a modern telegraph office, messages are turned into code by machines, sent by automatic machinery, and received by machines that decode them and type out the letters on a paper tape. A message that used to take several minutes of key-tapping by a trained operator can be sent today in a matter of seconds.

So great is the flood of messages over modern telegraph wires that ways have had to be found of sending many messages at once over the same wire. The next time you visit a large telegraph office perhaps you will be able to see some of this remarkable machinery.

Teletype Machines

Many railroads use the hand-operated telegraph. Big telegraph companies which send personal messages for you handle their large volume of business with the help of high-speed automatic machines. Still a third kind of telegraph equipment is used by modern airports, government agencies, newspapers, big railroad stations, and even weather stations. This is the *teletype machine*.

A teletype machine is a special kind of a typewriter connected electrically to other such typewriters far away. When you press the letter " a " of a sending machine in Washington, all the other machines connected to it will type the letter " a " too, even though they may be in San Francisco or New York or New Orleans. Thus the messages typed in a newsroom in Washington appear simultaneously on unmanned typewriters in other newsrooms all over the country.

Each key of the sending typewriter acts as a telegraph key. Each letter of the receiving type-

Western Union Telegraph Co.

30-3. The teletype machine has largely replaced the earlier telegraph key and sounder for the sending and receiving of telegraph messages.

writer is operated by a separate electromagnet. Hence when the sender presses the " j " key, he telegraphs to all the " j " keys of the receiving typewriters. They all print " j." Other keys on the teletype machine cause the motion of the paper and turn a sending typewriter into a receiving typewriter.

Samuel Morse's simple telegraph has grown to a very important means of communication in our daily lives and in industry.

THE TELEPHONE

On March 10, 1876, Alexander Graham Bell said to his assistant, " Mr. Watson, come here. I want you." Mr. Watson was out of earshot several rooms away, but he heard the message. The first *telephone* message had been sent. Since that time there has been a steady improvement of the telephone, until it is today a very efficient tool for communicating by means of electricity.

The Transmitter

In order to see how the telephone turns sound energy into electrical energy look at Figs. 30-4 and 30-5 which show the *transmitter* (or mouthpiece) parts.

The transmitter contains a flexible diaphragm, whose action is similar to the action of your eardrum. As a sound strikes the diaphragm, the diaphragm vibrates in and out, pushed and pulled by the sound waves.

Connected to the diaphragm is a small box filled with loose *grains* (or granules) *of carbon*. Current from a battery passes through these carbon grains and then along the telephone line all the way to the receiver. When a sound wave pushes in the diaphragm, the carbon grains are pressed more tightly together. When pressed together, carbon grains make better contact with each other and let more current flow through them (Fig. 30-4). In this way current increases through the telephone line when a sound wave hits the diaphragm.

Following the wave of sound, the pressure on

the diaphragm is released. The diaphragm springs back, releasing pressure on the carbon grains. Thus their resistance to the flow of current is increased and less current flows through the telephone line. In this way, any sound — simple or complex — can be changed into electric current and sent out over telephone wires.

If 256 sound waves hit the diaphragm each second, then there will be 256 increases and 256 decreases in current through the telephone line each second.

Remember Ohm's Law? The change in current as the resistance of the carbon grains changes is an excellent example of this law.

You probably realize that it is not your voice that travels over the telephone wires. A changing electric current controlled by the sound vibrations of your voice does the traveling.

The Receiver

The electric current from the transmitter is changed back into sound waves by the *receiver* (or earpiece). The receiver is relatively simple, as you can see in Fig. 30-5.

Coils of wire are wound around the poles of a permanent horseshoe magnet. A flexible steel diaphragm is then supported just above the poles of the magnet. If you open up the receiver end of a telephone, you can easily find these parts.

As waves of increasing and decreasing current

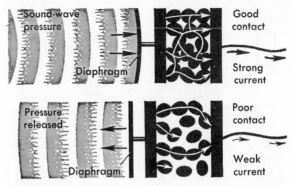

30-4. The sound-wave pressure which acts upon the telephone transmitter causes corresponding changes in the electric current flowing through it. Changing air pressure squeezes the box of carbon grains and changes their resistance to the flow of current.

pass through the coils, the strength of the permanent magnet is increased and decreased. The steel diaphragm vibrates first toward the magnet, then away from it. The vibration of the steel diaphragm, following the varying electric current, creates sound waves that are sent to your ear. These sound waves are fair copies of the original sound waves that entered the transmitter.

Telephone Lines

Between your phone and that of your friend at the other end of the line are many complicated

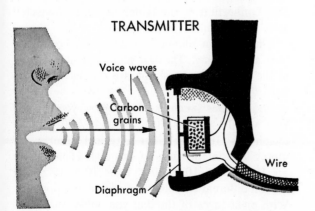

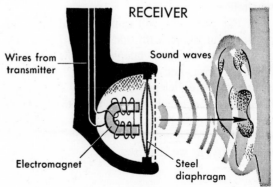

30-5. The sound waves are changed to currents of electricity in the transmitter. The telephone receiver turns these electric currents sent by the transmitter back into sound waves. The rapidly changing current through the electromagnet makes the steel diaphragm vibrate. The vibrating diaphragm creates sound waves.

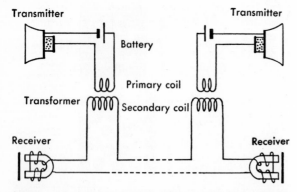

Transmitter   **Transmitter**

Battery

Primary coil

Transformer   **Secondary coil**

Receiver   **Receiver**

30-6. As you see here in this two-way telephone circuit, a practical telephone needs a step-up transformer to produce a strong signal at the other end of the line.

electrical circuits. Fig. 30-6 shows a simplified two-way telephone circuit.

As you talk, the varying current from the transmitter passes through the *primary coil* of a small step-up transformer right inside your telephone. By transformer action a varying current at a higher voltage is set up in the *secondary coil*. The higher voltage is needed to ensure a strong signal in your friend's receiver at the other end of the line.

Notice how the current from the transformer passes through the receiver at your own ear on its way out onto the telephone line. This is why you can hear your voice in your own receiver as you talk.

In Fig. 30-6 you will notice dotted lines connecting your phone with that of your friend. This dotted area contains telephone poles, a great length of wire, and many electrical switches for connecting your telephone with any one of millions of other telephones. It may even contain vacuum-tube amplifiers for giving your voice signals a boost now and then on a long trip across the country, as we shall see.

Dial System

We have seen how the telegraph companies are forced to use automatic machines to help them handle enormous numbers of messages.

How many people do you know who do *not* have telephones? Clearly the telephone company handles an enormous volume of messages, too. And the company, too, can do it only with the help of automatic machines.

The *dial system* is part of the machinery that helps. The dial system automatically connects your telephone with the telephone you are calling.

The dial on your telephone is a switch that opens and closes an electrical circuit from one to ten times, each time you spin the dial. Your clicking dial operates switches in the telephone exchange that search out the connection with the telephone you are calling.

Watch what happens when you dial a number such as 6557 (Fig. 30-7). As you dial the first number, 6, current is turned on and off six times. This is caused by the tap of a key inside your dial. Six taps sends six short pulses of current to an electromagnet in the telephone exchange. And inside the telephone exchange the electromagnet lifts an iron switching device one notch for each pulse of current. When you dial the number 6, the electromagnet lifts the switch six notches and stays there. Through the sixth connection of the switch you are connected to a second similar electromagnet.

The second number you dial is 5. The second electromagnet moves a switching device five notches and stops at the fifth notch. Through this fifth connection of the switch you are connected to a third similar electromagnet.

The last two numbers you dial are connected in a similar way. The last number connects you to the actual telephone you are calling and starts its bell ringing.

Four figures (such as 6557) allow you to connect with $10 \times 10 \times 10 \times 10$ or 10,000 possible telephones. In large cities a typical number requires 7 different turns of the dial. Hence there are $10 \times 10 \times 10 \times 10 \times 10 \times 10 \times 10$ or ten million different combinations of switches possible. With eight turns of the dial you could select one telephone out of 100,000,000. There are not yet that many telephones in the United States. In some parts of the country, long distance calls may

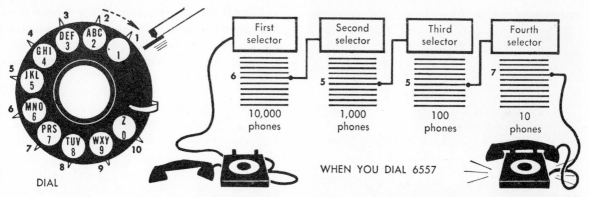

DIAL

WHEN YOU DIAL 6557

| First selector | Second selector | Third selector | Fourth selector |
| 10,000 phones | 1,000 phones | 100 phones | 10 phones |

30-7. Dialing 6557. As your telephone dial turns back to its starting position from the number 6, you can hear it click six times. With each click a short pulse of electric current moves a switch in the " First Selector." After the sixth pulse you are connected to the " Second Selector," ready to connect your second number. Since there are 10 routes through each selector, this dial exchange can connect you to any one of $10 \times 10 \times 10 \times 10$ or 10,000 different telephones.

be dialed directly. This service has already become widespread.

The dial-telephone system is tremendously complicated. At any moment during business hours there are tens of thousands of people dialing numbers, and hundreds of thousands of electromagnets quickly and accurately selecting the proper wires for their calls. Electromagnets have made

30-8. This maintenance man is inspecting the switches of a dial-telephone system in a large city exchange.

all this possible. Indeed this one application of the principles of electricity spares thousands of telephone operators the drudgery of making all those connections by hand. In this and in many other ways electromagnets help to make this a " push-button " world.

Wire Photographs

A Chinese proverb says " one picture is worth 10,000 words."

" Wirephoto " is a credit you have seen under many newspaper pictures. Over telephone lines specially built for this purpose these pictures were sent out to all newspapers subscribing to the wire-photo service. Several hundred such pictures a day are frequently sent this way.

The principle involved is relatively easy to understand if you understand the telephone. Light reflected off the photograph must be turned into electrical current to send over a telephone line. At the other end of the line the electrical current has to be turned back into light. You probably have done both of these things yourself. You turn light energy into electrical energy when you use a photoelectric exposure meter. You turn electrical energy into light energy every time you turn on an electric light.

A picture is placed on a rotating drum (Fig. 30-9). A sharp needle of light is shone on the

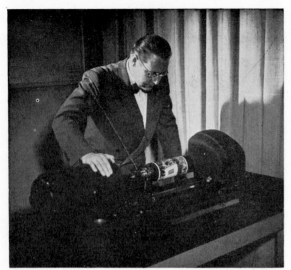

American Telephone and Telegraph Co.

30-9. "Still" pictures such as photographs and drawings, as well as messages, may be sent over wires.

picture, and the light's reflection from the picture is directed into a photoelectric cell. Where the picture is white, more light is reflected and more electric current is produced by the photoelectric cell. Where the picture is dark, little light is reflected and little electric current is produced. As the picture revolves, the needle of light slowly moves from one end of the drum to the other. Varying electric currents from the photoelectric cell are amplified and sent over telephone lines to receiving sets. The varying electric currents correspond closely to dark and light parts of the picture.

In the receiver, light from a special lamp is focused in a needle-like beam onto a sheet of unexposed photographic film. The varying current from the telephone line passes through this special lamp, which glows dimmer or brighter as the current follows the dark and light parts of the picture being sent. The photographic film is on a drum rotating at the same speed as the sending set, while the special bulb moves from one end of this drum to the other.

At the end of picture-sending, the paper is removed from the drum and developed in a dark room to produce the picture. Notice that the pic-

ture is not sent over the wire; only a varying electric current is sent. Light has been converted to electrical current by a photoelectric cell, sent over a telephone line, amplified, and converted back into light again.

Need for Amplifiers

One of the things you learned in Chapter 22 was that wire has a resistance to electric current.

American Telephone and Telegraph Co.

30-10. An air view of a radio-relay station in Nevada. At an elevation of 10,000 feet, this is the highest station on the transcontinental radio-relay system.

The longer the wire, the higher the resistance. Of course it is possible to reduce resistance of wire by making it thicker. However, that becomes expensive for long telephone lines in use today. A message sent out over a telephone wire 1000 miles long would be too faint to hear at the other end.

Engineers have found ways of giving the message a boost from time to time along its way. When the faint signal is strengthened, it is said to be *amplified*. On its way across the United States your telephone conversation has to be amplified many times (Fig. 30-10). This is done with the help of vacuum tubes rather similar to those in your radio.

VACUUM TUBES

Your world is full of weak signals of all kinds. Many of them can be turned into electricity and amplified by vacuum tubes until they are strong enough for us to see them or hear them. For instance:

Telephone messages in long-distance lines must be amplified before they are strong enough for you to hear them.

Radio signals fill the room around you right now. One of the things a radio set does is to amplify them so that the original sound may be extracted from them.

Hearing aids amplify the energy of sound waves enough for most deaf people to hear them.

The faint echoes of very short radio waves are amplified and changed in other ways in a radar set until they are strong enough to make visible marks on a viewing screen.

The faint impulses picked up by a phonograph needle are usually amplified so that you can hear them more clearly.

The faint electrical signals given off by your heart can be amplified enough to make a graph such as you see in Fig. 30-11. Such graphs (called *cardiograms*) help doctors detect heart disease.

Invisible tiny changes in the light of a distant star can be amplified enough to help us find out how far away the star is, how hot it is, and even how heavy it is.

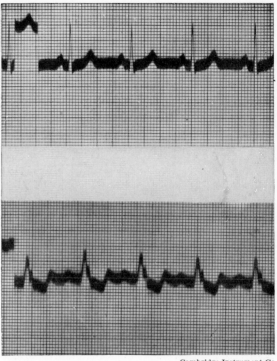

Cambridge Instrument Co.

30-11. These two cardiograms show the electrical charges produced by the beating of the heart. The downward surges in the lower photograph indicate faulty heart functioning.

Still other amplifiers using vacuum tubes are used to count pills, prospect for uranium, aim the guns of battleships, measure the purity of drinking water, or set off burglar alarms.

See how many more uses you can think of. Yes, your world has hundreds of uses for amplifiers. And at the heart of most amplifiers are vacuum tubes like those in your radio.

How does a vacuum tube make little electrical signals into big ones?

Boiling Electrons

Do you remember how an ordinary lamp bulb works? (See page 311.) Those swarms of electrons streaming through the wolfram filament make it so hot that it glows brightly. It's hot enough to boil some electrons right off the filament inside the light bulb, too. Around the fila-

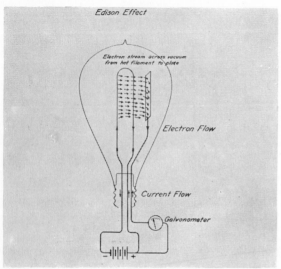

Electron stream across vacuum from hot filament to plate

Electron Flow

Current Flow

Galvanometer

Edison Foundation

30-12. The Edison effect was the beginning of many discoveries that led to modern electronic tubes.

ment of all glowing light bulbs a kind of "electron vapor" is formed. When the light bulb is turned off, these electrons "condense" back onto the filament.

Current Through a Vacuum

Thomas Edison was the first to notice these "boiling" electrons back in 1883. He sealed a metal plate inside one of his filament bulbs as you can see in Fig. 30-12. Then he connected the metal plate to the positive (+) end of the battery. When the plate was connected to this end of the battery, he found that the battery forced a current to flow through the tube. Electrons were flowing from the filament to the plate across the vacuum inside the tube. From the plate the battery forced them around the circuit through the galvanometer and back to the heated filament once more.

Edison found that if the filament were allowed to cool off, current could no longer be forced through the tube. Moreover he found that if he connected the plate to the negative (−) terminal of the battery, no current flowed through the tube. It seemed clear that the current through the tube was made of the electrons boiling off the heated

filament and being attracted across the tube to the positive plate.

A vacuum tube (like Edison's) that contains just a filament and a plate is called a *diode*.

A USE FOR EDISON'S DISCOVERY

Back in Chapter 22 you learned what an alternating current is and why it is useful. With the help of the diode it becomes easy to turn alternating current into *direct current*. All we need to do is to put a source of alternating current in place of the battery that drives current through one of these diodes.

When the plate is made positive, current will flow through the circuit as before. But when the plate is made negative, no current will flow through the tube. Hence current flows through the tube for only half the time but always in the same direction.

Nearly every radio set contains diodes for turning alternating current into direct current. We shall learn more about this, as well as other devices, in the next chapter.

An Important Addition

Up to 1906 the only vacuum tubes that were known were diodes. As you have just read, diodes are good for changing alternating current into direct current. But diodes cannot amplify the small currents set up by telephone transmitters, radios, hearing aids, and all the other devices that need amplifiers. To see how a vacuum tube can amplify small currents we need to know about the wire screen that Lee De Forest added to a diode in 1906.

The wire screen, called a *grid*, is put between the filament and the plate as you see in Fig. 30-14. The vacuum tube now contains three parts — *filament, grid,* and *plate*. A vacuum tube containing these three parts is called a *triode*.

Such a tube is able to amplify tiny electric currents of many sorts. For instance, the rapidly changing but weak electric current created by your voice when you talk into a telephone can be amplified thousands of times by such tubes until it is able to operate a loudspeaker. Indeed, if your telephone message is to travel across the country, it must be amplified by such tubes in booster stations every few hundred miles or the voice signals will weaken beyond recognition. Let us see how a triode amplifies a weak telephone message in such a long-distance booster station.

Control by Grid

The filament and the plate are connected precisely as before. Now the small rapidly changing current from a telephone transmitter is led through a resistance that is connected between the grid and and the filament (Fig. 30-13).

The changing current in the telephone line flows through the resistance, R, and causes a changing voltage across it. Thus there is a changing voltage between the grid and the filament. This changing voltage copies exactly the changing pressures of the sound waves from your voice at the transmitter.

When no current happens to be flowing through R, there is no voltage on the grid, and current flows through the tube exactly as in a diode. But when the small changing current through R happens to give the grid a negative voltage, an important thing happens (Fig. 30-14). The negative voltage on the grid *repels* the negatively charged electrons that are boiling off the filament, and decreases the number that can flow through the tube. Moreover, a *very small* negative voltage on the grid can cause a *very large* decrease in current through the tube.

See what happens when the small telephone current flows through R in the opposite direction (Fig. 30-13). Now the grid is given a small positive voltage. The positive grid *attracts* the electrons from the filament (Fig. 30-14). Of course some electrons will now hit the grid. However, because the grid is made of fine wires with considerable space between them, most of the electrons whiz past the grid to the plate. Even a *very small* positive voltage on the grid can cause a *very large* increase in current through the tube.

Thus, a small varying current flowing through the resistance, R, between the filament and the grid can cause very large changes in current through the tube. The changing current now flowing through the tube is an enlarged copy of the tiny electric currents flowing through R, caused by the changing sound-wave pressures. In other words, the tube has amplified the tiny current in the telephone line.

Ohm's Law Applies

If you remember Ohm's Law, it should be easy for you to see the last step of all. The changing current through the tube must now be turned into a changing voltage to apply to a telephone receiver or perhaps to the grid of another triode for even more amplification.

To do this we need merely make the amplified current flow through a resistance, L, as it leaves the plate of the tube. Ohm's Law says that the voltage across this resistance will be the resistance in ohms times the current in amperes flowing through it.

If the grid is negative enough to stop all current through the tube, then of course there is no current through L. The voltage across L must now be zero. As the grid lets more and more current through the tube and hence through L, the voltage across

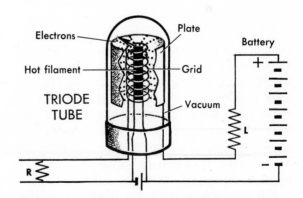

30-13. In this amplifier *weak* varying currents flowing through the resistance, R, are magnified by the vacuum tube to make *large* varying currents through L. If L is a loudspeaker, the resulting sound may fill your living room!

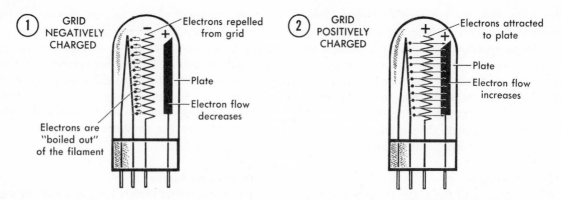

30-14. A small charge on the grid controls a much larger flow of electrons from the filament.

L grows larger and larger. In fact, the voltage across L varies in exactly the same way as the current through it from the tube, just as Ohm's Law requires.

A Typical Case

A weak current in a telephone wire may vary by one ten-thousandth of an ampere which may cause a weak telephone signal with a voltage change of only 0.4 volts as it reaches our amplifier. But it comes out the other side of the amplifier strong enough to cause voltage changes of 25 volts.

In the section " Going Further " at the end of the chapter, you will see this mathematically worked out according to Ohm's Law.

If necessary we can put our current through a second amplifier tube and boost its voltage still farther. Or if the current we have just amplified is a cross-country telephone message, we can now send it along its way for another few hundred miles. In an amplifying station thousands of vacuum tubes are amplifying small voltages into higher voltages and sending them out along the lines to the next amplifying station or to the telephone exchange in your city.

Not all vacuum tubes are diodes or triodes. Many vacuum tubes have four or five or more electrodes inside them. Several of the tubes in your radio have many electrodes, as you can tell by counting the prongs on their bases. If you go fur-

ther in science you will learn that they work on the same principles we have just been studying, and can be used for many purposes besides amplifying.

TRANSISTORS

For many electronic devices the vacuum tube is inefficient because the currents to be passed through the tube are smaller than those needed just to heat the filament. Electronic computors, for example, require only very small currents to represent the numerical information being processed. But when vacuum tubes are employed for this purpose much energy is wasted in the heat generated by the filament current.

The transistor, a device familiar from its use in pocket radios, is capable of amplifying voltages and small currents without the use of a filament. Transistors employ the flow of charges within certain types of crystal, rather than the passage of electrons from filament to plate through a vacuum. Since the charges flow within a crystal, it is possible to eliminate the glass envelope and substantially reduce the size of transistors as compared to vacuum tubes (Fig. 30-15).

In addition to its lower power requirements, the small size and simpler construction of the transistor are distinct advantages. This is evident if one considers, for example, that since 1940 the number of electronic parts used in a military aircraft has increased from one thousand to one hundred thousand.

SOUND AMPLIFIERS

Of course you know that sound can be amplified. You may have a sound amplifier in your school auditorium, or perhaps you have heard one used for announcements at a ball game or a country fair. They are called public address systems — or P.A. systems for short.

You already know the basic principles of a P.A. system, but it will be useful review for us to examine one briefly.

Sound into Electricity

When the announcer speaks into a microphone, the sound waves of his voice strike a movable diaphragm. You have seen how the motion of a diaphragm can squeeze a box of carbon grains, changing their resistance. Although most telephone microphones are built in this way, there are other common ways of turning sound waves into a changing electric current.

One of the best ways is to attach a tiny coil of wire to the moving diaphragm. The coil is arranged so that it lies between the poles of a fixed permanent magnet (Fig. 30-16). As the vibrating diaphragm moves the coil in and out, its motion through the field of the magnet induces tiny varying currents in the coil. These tiny varying currents are a copy of the original sound waves. They can be amplified just like the varying currents in a telephone line.

The varying current from the microphone flows through a *resistor* (R in Fig. 30-13) between the filament and grid of a tube. The tube amplifies the current in just the same way as described earlier (page 357). In public address systems the amplified signal is passed along to a second tube to be amplified still more. In fact, some amplifiers use as many as four to six tubes of various kinds to boost the tiny microphone current up until it can operate a big loudspeaker.

Loudspeakers — Electricity into Sound

Loudspeakers are rather like large-sized telephone receivers. However, they can produce much more sound.

Fig. 30-16 shows you how one works.

The large cone-shaped diaphragm is supported around its edge by a metal frame. The point of the cone is replaced by a cardboard cylinder. This cardboard cylinder fits around the pole of a permanent magnet but does not quite touch it.

Several loops of wire are coiled around the cardboard cylinder. Through this coil flows the amplified current from the last vacuum tube, making an electromagnet of it.

As the amplified current goes through the coil in one direction, the coil's magnetism repels the pole of the permanent magnet. Hence the cone of the loudspeaker is pushed away from the permanent magnet.

As the amplified current drops to zero, the coil springs back to its original position.

As the amplified current goes through the coil in the opposite direction, the coil's magnetism at-

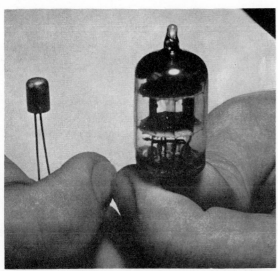

Bell Telephone

30-15. The diode transistor (left) employs silicon crystals whose electrons respond to an incoming voltage. It can do rectifying and switching as can the larger conventional diode.

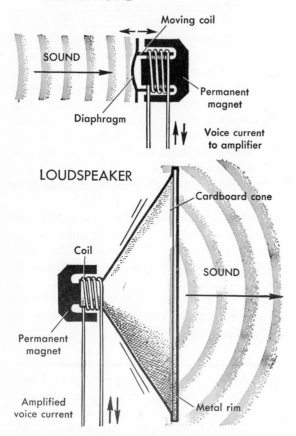

MICROPHONE

Moving coil

SOUND

Diaphragm

Permanent magnet

Voice current to amplifier

LOUDSPEAKER

Cardboard cone

Coil

SOUND

Permanent magnet

Amplified voice current

Metal rim

30-16. When sound waves vibrate a coil of wire in a magnet's field, tiny fluctuating currents are created in the wire. Current from such a microphone can be amplified by vacuum tubes and then, in a loudspeaker, converted into sound once more. The amplified current makes a magnet of the tiny coil in the loudspeaker. As in a telephone receiver, its vibrations shake a diaphragm to produce sound.

tracts the pole of the permanent magnet. Hence the cone of the loudspeaker is pulled closer to the permanent magnet.

Of course you know that those pushes and pulls are caused by amplified electric currents that copy the pushes and pulls of sound waves from the announcer's voice. Hence the vibrations of the loudspeaker cone copy the sound waves from the announcer's voice with much greater loudness.

See if you can observe the back of a loudspeaker when it is in action.

The Phonograph

Have you ever looked at a phonograph record through a microscope? Do so if you can. You will find it looks like Fig. 30-17.

Those wiggly lines are grooves in the record. It will be easy for you to see how they can be turned into sound.

As the record turns, the needle or pointed jewel in the pick-up arm follows all the wiggles of the groove. The wiggles of the needle are vibrations. The needle's vibrations can be turned into electricity in several different ways, but one of the best is the way that is used in the announcer's microphone as described on page 359. A tiny coil of wire attached to the needle vibrates between the poles of a permanent magnet. The currents induced in the coil are then amplified by vacuum tubes and finally turned back into sound again by a loudspeaker.

High-Fidelity

When you hear your friend's voice over the telephone, it does not sound *exactly* as it would if he were in the same room with you.

When you hear someone speaking over a public address system, it is usually very hard to tell who is talking.

And when you hear music or voices on a pho-

30-17. Photomicrograph of phonograph record. Grooves were cut using electrical impulses.

nograph, it is usually easy to tell that the sound is recorded.

Although it is easy to turn sound into electricity, amplify it, and turn it back into sound once more, you can see that it is not usually done perfectly. The sound comes out sounding differently from when it went in.

The small changes that are in the pattern are due mostly to imperfections in the microphone, the amplifier, and the loudspeaker. However, it is possible to reproduce the sound almost perfectly by using better quality equipment. Near-perfect reproduction of sound is called *high-fidelity* (or " hi-fi " for short).

High-fidelity equipment is usually expensive. However, more and more people are becoming interested in it because of the extraordinary perfection of the sound it can produce.

Looking Back . . . .

VOCABULARY

Each of the following expressions represents a key word in the chapter you have just studied. Show that you understand its meaning by defining each term.

1. telegraph	10. grid
2. teletype	11. filament
3. diaphragm	12. plate
4. transmitter	13. triode
5. receiver	14. loudspeaker
6. dial system	15. public-address
7. amplifier	system
8. vacuum tube	16. high-fidelity
9. diode	17. microphone

REVIEW QUESTIONS

1. Why can't the diaphragm of a telephone receiver be made of brass?

2. Why do transformers improve the operation of a telephone?

3. With the help of simple diagrams explain the operation of each of the following:

(a) the telegraph
(b) the telephone transmitter
(c) the telephone receiver
(d) the dial on your telephone
(e) picture-sending by wire
(f) a diode for turning alternating current into direct current
(g) a triode used to amplify small currents
(h) a loudspeaker

Going Further . . . .

CALCULATING AMPLIFICATION

If in a typical amplifier a current of 0.0001 amperes is passed through a resistance, R, of 4000 ohms, the voltage across R will vary by

$$0.0001 \times 4000 = 0.4 \text{ volts}$$

That is,

$$\text{Volts} = \text{Amperes} \times \text{Resistance}$$

You can see that this applies to Ohm's Law.

Using a typical triode, this much change in voltage on its grid can cause a change of 0.00025 amperes in the flow of current through the tube. Thus we have amplified the weak current changes

$$\frac{0.00025}{0.0001} \text{ or 2.5 times}$$

If the current through the tube now flows through a resistance, L, of 100,000 ohms, the voltage across L will vary by

$$0.00025 \times 100,000 = 25 \text{ volts}$$

THINGS TO DO

Make a telegraph set. Hammer a nail into a wooden base (Fig. 30-1). Then wind several hundred turns of thin, insulated wire around the nail. Mount a springy piece of metal from a steel hacksaw blade above the head of the nail so that it makes a sound when it strikes the nail. It will make another sound when it returns to its original position. Connect the batteries in series with an electromagnet and a push button or key, as shown in the picture.

READING FURTHER

Radio Amateur's Handbook, American Radio Relay League, 38 La Salle Rd., West Hartford, Conn.

Sending Messages Without Wires

When your grandfather was your age, no one could hear him farther away than he could shout. No one could see him either, once he went into the barn or rode over the next hilltop. Nowadays science has given us better ears and eyes. Today it is possible for millions of people scattered around the earth to hear your voice — all at the same time. It is possible for millions of Americans to see you at once and watch you as if you were only a few feet away from each one of them. Moreover you can now see for miles through dense clouds, and watch ships and planes through fog and in the dead of night.

In this chapter we will want to see how these everyday wonders are performed. Radio, television, and radar affect the lives of all of us nearly every day. You will be interested to see how each of them makes use of the principles you have learned in the last few units.

RADIO

Open up a radio and look at the wiring on its under side. You will agree that a radio is a *very* complicated instrument. In this chapter you will learn only the simplest outline of how it works. Yet this should be enough for you to build the simple set shown in Fig. 31-1 and to understand its general principles.

A Simple Radio

You will be pleased to find that you already know one of the most important principles of radio. You know how radio waves are produced. They are produced by a kind of a transformer.

Back on page 254 you learned how the transformer works. You saw how a changing current in one coil sets up a changing current in a second coil nearby, especially if both coils are wound on an iron core. In scientific language we say, " Alternating current in the primary coil induces an alternating current in the secondary coil."

Remove the iron core from a transformer and you will have a very simple kind of radio set (Fig. 31-2). Alternating current flowing through the primary coil sends out moving lines of force just as a radio station does. As the moving lines of force cut across the secondary coil a few inches away, they induce enough current in it to light a small lamp. In a similar way radio waves induce current in your radio receiver.

You can even send messages by inserting a switch in the primary coil. With the switch you can send dots and dashes that are faithfully copied by the lamp in the " receiving set." You are send-

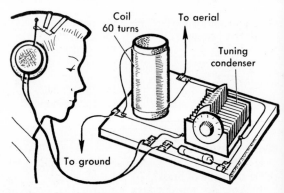

31-1. This simple radio receiver, which you can make, needs only four parts and a few lengths of wire.

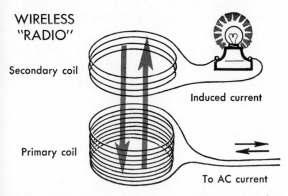

WIRELESS "RADIO"

Secondary coil

Induced current

Primary coil

To AC current

31-2. This simple experiment demonstrates that signals *can* be sent from place to place without any intervening wires — a simple "wireless" or radio. Why is it better that these coils be wound on a heavy iron core?

ing messages across a few inches of empty space without any connecting wires. You have made a very simple radio!

If you experiment with this arrangement, you will find that it has one very serious drawback. You cannot send messages more than a few inches. Obviously we must do better than this. In the rest of this section we shall see how to improve our simple set until it can send messages thousands of miles.

Radio Waves

The alternating current you used in your simple radio set probably alternated, or reversed, its direction of flow 60 times every second. It is called 60-cycle alternating current or 60-cycle A.C. Hence the lines of force around the primary coil expanded and contracted 60 times a second.

Lines of force that change as slowly as this (yes, 60 times a second *is* slow!) carry too little energy to be effective over great distances. Experiments show that lines of force that change faster have much more energy. A million cycles a second is much better. In fact, current changing direction at this rate can send out moving lines of force that induce currents in radio receivers on the other side of the world! Here is one of the principles of long-distance radio.

The rate at which the lines of force change is called their *frequency*. Your home-lighting cur-

rent probably has a frequency of 60 cycles a second. A radio station may broadcast signals that have a frequency of 800,000 cycles a second. More commonly this frequency is called " 800 kilocycles." *Kilo* means " thousand." You would tune in this station at 800 on your dial, since the dial of your radio is adjusted to read in kilocycles. Another station that you might hear at 1210 on your dial is broadcasting at a frequency of 1210 kilocycles (1,210,000 cycles per second or 1.21 *megacycles* per second). Each station broadcasts at a particular frequency that is assigned to it by the United States Government.

The rapidly alternating current travels up and down the aerial or broadcasting tower at the radio station. In so doing, it sets up rapidly changing lines of force around the aerial. Lines of force that change direction so very rapidly bubble off into space and float loose from the aerial, traveling away from it in the form of waves. These waves of alternating lines of force are called *radio waves*.

Radio waves speed through space at the rate of 186,000 miles a second, just like their cousins, the infrared waves, visible light, X rays, and others you read about back in Chapter 28.

When radio waves sweep over a metal object, the alternating lines of force of which they are made induce alternating currents in the metal. Thus your radio aerial wire this very moment has induced in it tiny alternating currents from all nearby radio stations. For that matter every pipe, wire, and other metal object in the room around you has tiny currents induced in it by the flood of radio waves pouring over it from all directions. The job of your radio receiving set is to pick out the waves from the station you want to listen to and to amplify them so that they can be made to produce sound.

You can think of the radio station aerial as the *primary* and your receiver aerial as the *secondary* of a huge and very inefficient transformer.

Messages Ride the Waves

You have seen that high-frequency radio waves travel much farther than the 60-cycle waves used in the experiment in Fig. 31-2. A radio wave can travel thousands of miles. How does it carry a message? by dots and dashes?

No, but a way has been found of making the message — voice or music — ride piggy-back on the radio wave. It works in the following way.

The announcer in the broadcasting studio speaks into a microphone. The microphone turns the sound waves of his voice into a changing electric current called the *voice current*.

The frequency of the voice current ranges from about 15 cycles a second to about 15,000 cycles a second. A typical voice current changes as you saw back in Fig. 30-5. You will see a simplified graph of its changes in Fig. 31-3A. From our experiment with 60-cycle current back in Fig. 31-2,

we know that the waves given out by frequencies as low as this will not travel very far.

Meanwhile a special vacuum-tube circuit is producing the very high-frequency alternating current called the *carrier current*. Its frequency is the frequency assigned to the radio station. It is marked on your radio dial at the position where you tune in the station.

In Fig. 31-3B you see a graph of the carrier current. Waves given out by the high-frequency carrier current will travel long distances. They are *radio waves*.

Now if the two currents are mixed by a special vacuum-tube circuit, the result will look like Fig. 31-3C. The voice current is "riding on the back" of the carrier current.

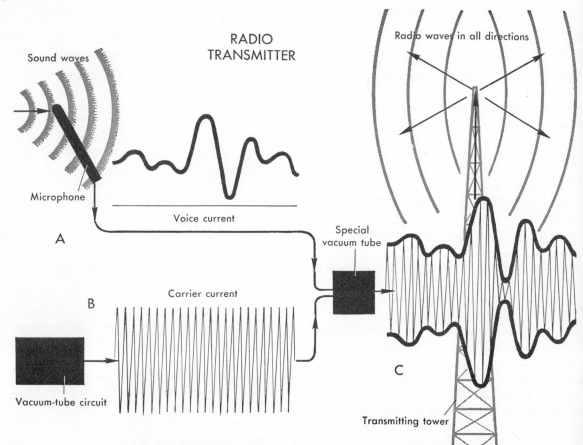

RADIO TRANSMITTER

Sound waves

Microphone

A

Voice current

B

Carrier current

Vacuum-tube circuit

Special vacuum tube

C

Radio waves in all directions

Transmitting tower

31-3. In a radio transmitter the alternating current representing sound waves (voice current) is added to the high-frequency alternating current (carrier current). The combination is able to travel long distances.

The carrier current with the voice current "riding" on it is now amplified by vacuum tubes and sent to the aerial. There the lines of force from the rapidly changing current flow out as waves — radio waves — in all directions. At 186,000 miles a second the announcer's words are "on the air."

Unscrambling the Message

The room in which you are sitting is being flooded this very moment with high-frequency carrier waves from nearby radio stations carrying their piggy-back messages. Though your ears cannot hear the waves, they are inducing tiny currents in every metal object in the room around you.

Your radio set picks out the one station you want to hear and turns its radio message into sound waves. Your radio set does this in several steps (Fig. 31-4).

First, like any other metal object around you, the aerial wire has currents induced in it by the radio waves from all nearby stations at once.

Second, your radio set selects the current induced by the one station you want to hear. This selection is done with the help of the tuning control knob which you turn to the carrier-wave frequency of the station you want to hear. This control knob adjusts a kind of electrical filter or sieve which lets through from the aerial only the one station you have selected and blocks out the currents from all the others.

Third, your radio set must now separate the voice current from the carrier current. Up until now these two currents have been together in the form of one rapidly changing current as in Fig. 31-4, a perfect copy of the changing lines of force of the radio wave. Now your radio set, with the help of special vacuum tubes. blocks off the carrier current. Only the voice current is left.

Fourth, the voice current, which is very small, must be amplified until it is strong enough to work a loudspeaker. In the last chapter you saw how this was done with telephone messages. Radio amplifiers work in a very similar way.

Fifth, and last, the amplified voice current is fed into a loudspeaker. Just as in a telephone receiver or a public-address loudspeaker, changing electric current is turned into changing air pressures or sound waves. The sound waves are nearly perfect copies of the sound waves from the announcer's voice in the broadcasting studio.

The Radio Spectrum

If two stations were to use the same carrier-wave frequency, you would hear them both at once on your radio set. Your set could not separate their messages. We have seen that each radio station is assigned a different carrier-wave frequency, so that your radio set can sort it out from all the other stations. The frequencies that work well for ordinary broadcasting stations and for special purposes such as aircraft and shipping are

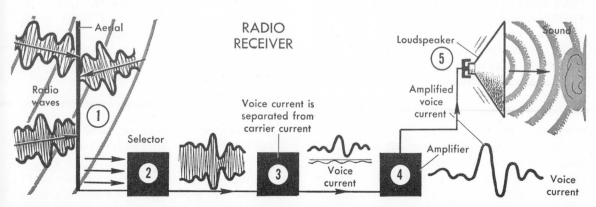

31-4. The radio receiver selects the desired signal, separates the high-frequency carrier current from the low-frequency voice current, and then amplifies the voice current enough to operate a loudspeaker.

THE RADIO SPECTRUM

Kilocycles

10   1000   10,000   100,000   1,000,000

Aircraft · Shipping · Standard broadcasting · Police calls · Ships at sea · Armed Forces · Television · Radar · Radio and television relays · Experimental

| Long waves | Short waves | Ultrashort waves | Microwaves |

31-5. Radio waves have many uses. The longest waves, often several miles long, used for long distance communication have different properties and uses from the shortest waves, only an inch or two long.

marked in Fig. 31-5. You will notice that they range from about 10 kilocycles up to 1000 kilocycles. Radio waves whose frequency is 300 kilocycles measure a little longer than 1000 yards from crest to crest. Whizzing past you at 186,000 miles a second, 300,000 such waves go by you every second.

Radio waves of higher frequency than these are used for other special purposes; the armed forces, ships at sea, police forces, and amateur radio operators all use frequencies in the 1000 to 10,000 kilocycle region.

This high-frequency region is also known as the *short-wave region* because the wave length of these waves is shorter than the waves in the standard broadcast region. A typical " short " wave, whose frequency is 3000 kilocycles, measures only about 100 yards from crest to crest.

Still higher frequencies are used for television. Radio waves used for TV range from about 10,000 kilocycles up to about 100,000 kilocycles. These waves are very short. For instance, 30,000 kilocycle waves are only about 10 yards from crest to crest. We shall learn more about these waves in the next section.

There are still shorter waves than these, whose frequency is still very high. Waves of 100,000 kilocycles up to about one million kilocycles are only a few inches long. Some of them are used for radar.

If you find it hard to see why the shorter wave

lengths should have the highest frequencies, perhaps the following analogy will help you. Imagine that you are standing on a road watching cars go by. Suppose they were all traveling at a speed of 30 miles per hour. Now if the cars were 30 miles apart, *one* would pass every hour, or at a frequency of *one car per hour*. If the cars were one mile apart, they would pass you more frequently; that is, 30 cars would pass in one hour, or at a frequency of *30 cars per hour*.

If you consider the crests of waves to be the point at which a car passes you, you can see that the frequency of the waves becomes higher as the distance between crests becomes smaller. Or, in other words, the *shortest wave lengths have the highest frequencies.*

Of course there are waves far shorter than microwaves, as you learned in Chapter 28. Review your knowledge of the other kinds of waves in the complete spectrum.

TELEVISION

Television is broadcast on radio waves, too. Waves used for TV are shorter than those used for standard radio broadcasts, but their behavior is similar. Let us see how pictures can be sent by means of such waves. We shall follow the picture from the camera in the TV studio to the screen in your living room.

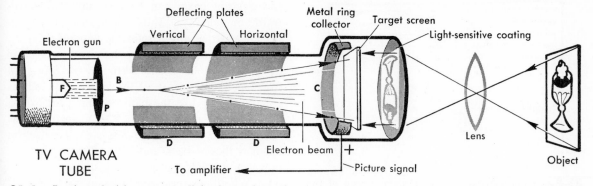

Electron gun — F, B, P

Deflecting plates — Vertical, Horizontal

Metal ring collector — C

Target screen

Light-sensitive coating

Lens

Object

D D

Electron beam

To amplifier

Picture signal +

TV CAMERA TUBE

31-6. In the television camera light focused on the target screen causes the beam of electrons to bounce off. The electrons that bounce off the light areas of the screen are collected by the ring collector, and their current, when amplified, is added to a carrier wave and sent out as the "picture signal" from the broadcasting station aerial.

The Television Camera

Inside the television camera is a large, very complicated vacuum tube, used for turning pictures into electricity (Fig. 31-6). You will notice that it looks rather like the picture tube in your television set.

When the camera tube is in use, the scene to be televised is focused on the outside of a large window by a lens (Fig. 31-6). The window and lens are arranged in the same way as the film and lens of a camera or the retina and lens of your eye.

The window of the tube is actually a very large photoelectric cell. You will remember from Chapter 27 that the surface of a photoelectric cell gives off electrons whenever light strikes it. Thus if a whole picture is focused on a big photoelectric cell, the most electrons will be given off where the picture is brightest, and in the dark parts of the picture fewer electrons will be given off. Do you see any resemblance between the window of the TV camera tube and the retina of your eye? Does it have any resemblance to a camera film?

Light focused on the window of the camera tube paints a picture in electrons. How does light do this? Where the light is brightest, many electrons will have been driven off the surface. Hence at that brightly lit spot the window will have lost negative charge — or, in other words, be positively charged. Elsewhere on the window where the picture is dark very few electrons have been

driven off. There the surface of the window will continue to have a slight negative charge (Fig. 31-7).

This "picture" painted in electric charges must now be turned into electric currents that can be put "on the air" like the voice currents of ordinary radio. The "picture" is turned into electric currents with the help of a beam of electrons created inside the tube at the end farthest from the window (Fig. 31-6).

A heated *wire filament* (F) boils off electrons just as in any radio tube. A *plate* (P) with a posi-

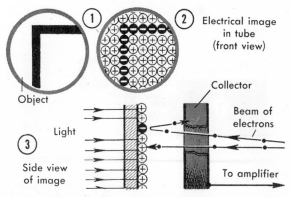

① Object

② Electrical image in tube (front view)

③ Side view of image

Light

Collector

Beam of electrons

To amplifier

31-7. Where light strikes the positively charged target screen, it gives the screen a negative charge. The negatively charged spots, of course, repel the beam of electrons, which is therefore collected by the surrounding collector ring to form the electrical "picture signal."

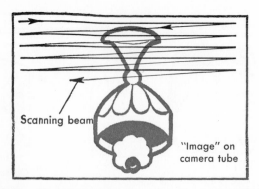

31-8. The electron beam strikes the screen of the television camera, touching all the light and dark spots as it " draws " the picture. At the end of each line it snaps back almost instantly to start another line, covering the entire screen in this way 30 times a second.

tive charge attracts the electrons just like the plate in any radio tube. The plate has a tiny hole in it, however, and as the electrons are attracted to the plate some of them hit the hole instead and go streaming through it. This stream of electrons is an *electron beam* (B). The electron beam shoots the length of the tube and strikes the window (Fig. 31-6).

Arranged along the sides of the electron beam are two pairs of *metal plates* (D). Electric charges on these plates will attract or repel the electron beam passing through them. When the charges on these plates are properly controlled,

the electron beam can be bent upward, downward, or sideways. Thus the beam can be deflected to strike any part of the window.

When the tube is in use, the electron beam is made to play back and forth in a zigzag path over the entire surface of the window. It follows a path exactly like the path of your eyes over a page you are reading (Fig. 31-8). Just as your eyes read every word on a full page, the electron beam is flicked back and forth, working its way down until it has " read " every spot on the window. What does the electron beam " see "?

You have already learned that the electron beam will " see " a surface covered with positively and negatively charged spots in the form of a picture. Whenever the electron beam strikes a positively charged spot (where bright light has driven off a lot of electrons), the spray of electrons in the beam will be attracted to the spot to replace the electrons driven off by the light. The electrons will fill up the positively charged spot in much the same way that a stream of sand particles would fill up a hole dug on a beach.

Whenever the electron beam strikes a negatively charged spot (where little or no light has fallen), the spray of electrons in the beam will be repelled. It will bounce off the window. As the electrons bounce back, they are quickly collected by a positively charged *ring of metal* (C) framing the edge of the window. These bouncing elec-

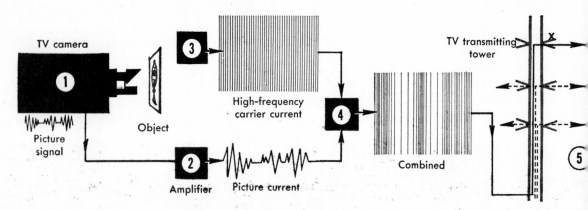

31-9. In a television transmitter the amplified "picture current" (2) is combined with a very high frequency "carrier current" (3). The resulting current (4) creates waves that travel out from the transmitting tower in all directions (5), much as in a radio transmitter. In a television receiver the waves are captured by

trons act rather like a stream of sand particles shot at a smooth hard wall. Instead of remaining against the wall, the sand particles bounce off and can be collected in a funnel.

From the collecting ring the bounced-back electrons flow to an amplifier. You will remember that the electron beam travels back and forth very quickly over the entire surface of the window; the electrons replace those already driven off by bright light in some spots (these spots are positively charged). They bounce off other spots. The bounced-back electrons flowing to the collecting plate and thence to the amplifier form a very rapidly changing electric current.

Over and over the electron beam " reads " the electron picture on the tube window. Thirty times a second the beam covers the entire picture, turning what it " sees " into a tiny fluttering current.

When this current has been amplified, it can then be combined with a high-frequency carrier current in much the same way the voice current is combined with carrier current in an ordinary radio station. The TV carrier current, with the complicated pattern given to it by the bounced-off electrons in the camera tube, is now ready to be sent out to the TV aerial.

Picking Pictures Out of the Air

Do you remember what steps are taken by your radio to turn a radio signal into sound? A TV set does the same things to the incoming television waves — except for the last of all the steps (Fig. 31-9).

First, the waves of all the TV stations in your neighborhood induce tiny, rapidly changing currents in your aerial.

Second, with the help of complicated electrical circuits your set filters out the signals from all but the one station you have chosen to see.

Third, other complicated circuits separate the high-frequency carrier current from the changing picture current put on it by the camera tube.

Fourth, the tiny picture current is amplified until it is strong enough to operate your TV picture tube.

The diagram of your TV picture tube (Fig. 31-9) looks rather like the diagram of the camera tube in the broadcasting studio, doesn't it? You will notice the filament (F) to boil off electrons, the positively charged plate (P) with the hole in it that forms the electron beam (B), the deflecting plates (D) that aim the beam up, down, and sideways, and even a screen (S) for the beam to strike.

There is another very close resemblance. The beam in your TV picture tube is made to travel back and forth across the screen of your tube precisely in step with the beam in the studio's camera tube. Thirty times each second your electron beam and the studio camera's electron beam start

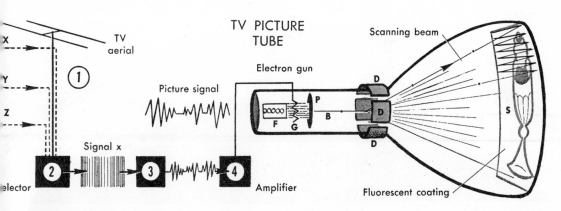

the antenna (1) and create an alternating current in it. If the selector (2) chooses the signal from station X, for example, it is sorted out (3) into the carrier current (which is discarded) and the picture current which is amplified (4) and sent to the picture tube.

together at one corner to "read" the windows of their tubes, line by line, in perfect step. This amazing linking of the two electron beams is brought about by still other complex vacuum-tube circuits in your TV set, even though your set may be hundreds of miles from the camera tube.

You will notice differences between the tube in your TV set and the camera tube in the broadcasting studio. One difference is in the window at the end of the tube. In your TV picture tube the window is not a photoelectric cell; instead it is coated with a fluorescent material. Whenever the electron beam strikes the fluorescent screen, it makes a tiny glowing spot. When the electron beam is a strong one, the spot glows very brightly. When the beam is weak, the spot hardly glows at all. As the beam weaves back and forth, it covers the entire screen with a pattern of light, 30 times every second.

Now we are about to see how the electron beam can draw a picture instead of just a square of light. Have you noticed that screen marked G between the filament and the plate of the tube? "G" stands for grid. This *grid* works in exactly the same way as the grid in the triode vacuum tube you studied in the last chapter. It controls the flow of electrons through the tube.

The grid in the TV tube is connected to the amplified picture current. (See step four.) Thus the changing charges on the grid cause similar changes in the strength of the electron beam as it weaves back and forth across the screen.

Now the electron beams in your picture tube and in the studio camera tube are moving back and forth together. Also the beam in your tube changes brightness in step with the pattern of charges on the camera-tube window. Therefore, the beam in your tube draws the very picture that is being focused on the camera tube in the TV studio.

There! The trick is done! Whatever the studio camera "sees" you will see too.

The electron beams race back and forth over the windows of TV tubes so quickly — as much as four miles every second — that every detail of a moving image is faithfully registered. In fact it is this great speed, brought about by the use of vacuum tubes, that makes television possible.

Sending Television Waves

You will remember that the carrier waves used to carry television pictures have a much shorter wave length than those used for ordinary radio broadcasting. The long waves used for ordinary broadcasting can travel through buildings and over mountains. They can even travel around the curve of the earth's surface by bouncing off the electrically charged layer of air high in the atmosphere (Fig. 31-10).

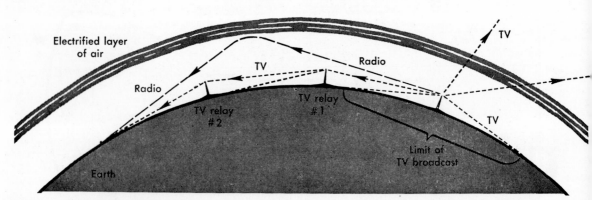

31-10. The longer radio waves can travel around the curve of the earth by bouncing off the electrically charged layer, the ionosphere, high in the atmosphere. Shorter wave lengths used for television will not do this and must be relayed from tower to tower along the earth's surface.

The shorter waves used for television cannot do this, however. They are stopped by buildings and by mountains. Moreover if you try to bounce them off the electrically charged layer high in the atmosphere they usually do not bounce. They go right through it and disappear!

Thus your television aerial has to be almost in sight of the broadcasting station's aerial — a distance rarely greater than about 50 miles. If a television program is to be sent farther than this, it has to be relayed from tower to tower around the curve of the earth's surface (Fig. 31-11).

Other short waves, such as those used to send some telephone messages or radio programs across the country, are relayed around the curving earth in the same way (Fig. 31-12). Perhaps you have seen such relay towers somewhere as you have traveled about the country.

Radio Corporation of America

Radio Corporation of America

31-11. The antenna on the top of the Empire State Building serves five TV stations. It can broadcast a number of different programs at different frequencies at the same time.

31-12. Relay towers, spaced at regular intervals, can carry television signals great distances across the country. These signals are relayed from one tower to another.

Con. Edison of N. Y.

31-13. This man in the boiler room can view on a television screen the top of the stack from 450 feet below.

The latest technique for relaying TV signals uses artificial earth satellites. The first was the privately owned U.S. Telestar, orbited in July 1962. From their great heights, satellites can receive and retransmit TV pictures across the ocean. When in a 24-hour orbit, rotating at the same rate as the earth, they hover over the same point as permanent TV relay stations.

New Uses for TV

Entertainment is not TV's only use. Television is widely used in modern hospitals. With its help each medical student can see the operating table as clearly as if he stood at the surgeon's elbow.

TV is used increasingly in schools, with special channels assigned just for education. Some classes of the future may be run entirely by TV. Television can be used to explore the depths of the sea — to hunt for sunken ships in water dangerously deep for divers.

RADAR

Like television, radar is a way of seeing distant objects by means of very short radio waves.

Unlike television, though, you would use radar to look for unseen objects such as icebergs, airplanes, or a shoreline, and to measure their distance away from you. In fact the name *radar* is an abbreviation for *Radio Detection And Ranging*.

Bouncing Radio Waves

The radio waves used for radar are very short — only a few inches long. Waves as short as these do not pass through or around solid objects. They bounce off solid objects just as light rays do.

This resemblance to light rays is the secret of radar.

In Chapter 24 you learned how light rays could be focused into a narrow beam by a light source and a parabolic reflector. In exactly the same way (Fig. 31-15), radar waves are formed into a narrow beam by an aerial and a parabolic reflector. When the radar waves hit a solid object such as an airplane, they are reflected back the way they came. By the time they return, the sending aerial has been switched over to act as a receiving aerial. The reflected radar waves induce currents in the aerial which are amplified by vacuum-tube circuits and recorded on a screen like that on your television set.

Of course you know the direction of the airplane because you know the direction your radar beam was pointed. You can find the distance to the airplane by noticing how long it took your radar waves to bounce back. It is rather like finding the distance to a cliff by timing the echoes of sound waves.

On ships, radar is used to search for other ships, islands, icebergs, or shorelines. It can do this as well in dense fog or pitch darkness as it can in clear daylight. That is why radar is so wonderfully useful for avoiding collisions and saving lives. In 1912 the great ocean liner *Titanic* hit an iceberg in a dense fog and sank with the loss of 1,513 lives. Today, with radar in widespread use on ships, we can be fairly confident that such accidents as that will rarely happen.

The radar antenna on a ship turns round and round, sweeping the sea like the rotating beam of a great lighthouse. As it collects radar echoes from nearby ships and other objects, the echoes are recorded as points of light on a screen like the screen in your TV set. To the operator the screen resembles a map on which he is at the center. Around the center in various directions and at various distances are mapped all nearby objects. So accurate is this seaborne radar that in World War II our navy was able to maneuver its ships, aim its guns, and win naval battles in the dead of night with its assistance.

In an airplane, radar is even more remarkable. Aimed downward it can not only tell the pilot the distance down to the ground, but it can also give him a map of the land and water and cities that lie below him. Land areas reflect radar waves better than water does. With the help of radar, pilots are now able to " see " and avoid turbulent clouds.

Radar is being used to protect our country in peacetime. Across Canada stretch three rows of radar stations. In each row the stations are so close together that no airplane can fly between them undetected. All three lines of radar stations are connected to our country's and to Canada's

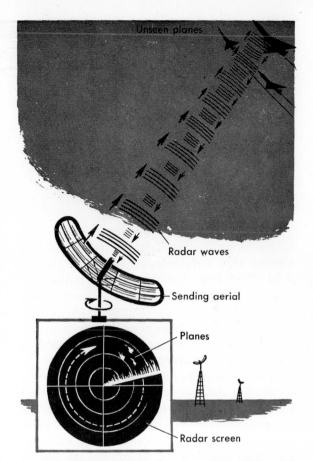

31-15. The radar set not only can detect the presence of an airplane at night, but also can measure its direction and distance.

defense headquarters. Thus radar is providing our continent with a kind of protective electric fence.

In an earlier section we saw that TV waves and radar waves travel in straight lines and hence can be used only for distances about as far as you can see. Moreover they are not bounced off the radio " roof " of charged atoms in the upper atmosphere. Put both of these facts together, and you will see why we might hope to send a radar beam or a TV program to the moon! You may be surprised to learn that radar waves actually have been bounced off the moon, the sun, and Venus to be received on earth — a feat which, you will soon see, is harder than it sounds.

Experiments with radar echoes from celestial

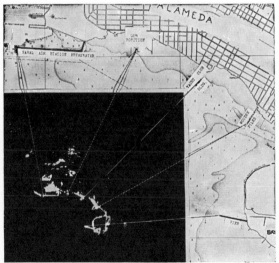

31-14. Compare this radar picture taken in the dark with the map of the region. Can you pick out various details?

bodies are not just fancy tricks. We can obtain very exact measurements of astronomical distances using this technique. For example, the distance to the moon can be determined with an uncertainty of only about one thousand feet. This is quite an accomplishment when you consider that the total distance to the moon, in feet, is about 1 billion, 260 million. Put another way, this figure represents an error of only one foot for every 1 million, 260 thousand feet. How are such radar measurements carried out?

Measuring Distance with Radar

You have already been introduced to a method for measuring distances using the time it takes for a sound wave to be reflected back to its starting point. This is how ships with sounding instruments found the distance to the ocean floor beneath them (see p. 339).

Let us take a moment to see how such sound-echo measurements are carried out, for the method used in radar measurements is quite similar.

Firstly, it has been determined that in still water of uniform density, sound will travel at about 4700 feet per second. How could we calculate the distance to the ocean bottom beneath a ship which receives an echo in, say, 6 seconds? In examples involving constant speed, we can use the general formula —

$$\text{Speed} = \frac{\text{Distance}}{\text{Time}}$$

In this formula we should substitute the known value of the speed, the measured value of time, and then solve the distance. For the speed we should then put the value 4700 feet per second. But for the time, should we put 6 seconds? If you said " no," you were right; 6 seconds is the time it takes for the sound wave to travel *twice* the distance, that is, to the ocean bottom and back again. We should, therefore, use only *half* this measured time, or 3 seconds — the time for a one-way trip of the sound wave. Our formula will now read like this —

$$4700 = \frac{\text{Distance}}{3}$$

Solving for distance, we get —

Distance = 4700 × 3 = 14,100 feet

Let us now compare sound-echo and radar measurements. The basic principle is the same, and so the same formula would be used. Knowing the speed of the radar wave — 186,285 miles per second — and using half of the time, we would solve for the distance.

But there are also some important differences between sound-echo and radar-echo measurements. For one thing, radar measurements are much more accurate over great distances. Why is this? Distance calculations involving the simple formula we have been using require that the speed be constant. Now the speed of sound is not quite constant. It varies with the temperature and density of the water or air through which the sound is traveling. When traveling many thousands of miles, there would be considerable variation in its speed. As a result, calculations made for great distances using sound-echo techniques are not very precise.

But there is every indication that the speed of radar, and of all other electromagnetic waves, is *absolutely constant in empty space*. Thus, for only the tiny fraction of a second while the radar wave is passing out and back through our atmosphere might its speed vary.

In 1957 the distance to the moon was computed at 238,865 miles using radar-echo signals involving over 50,000 separate measurements averaged together. (The averaging of many separate measurements to eliminate possible errors is an important scientific technique.)

Radar signals reflected from the moon are quite strong and show up as definite " blips " on receiving apparatus. Although radiant energy spreads as it travels through space, the moon is close enough to receive a substantial fraction of the originally transmitted energy and to bounce back a significant amount. But radar reflections from, say, Venus, 30 million miles away are considerably weaker and much harder to detect. In addition to their low intensity, signals reflected from Venus are difficult to distinguish from other signals emitted by the sun, hydrogen gas in space, and other radiant sources. We are, thus, faced with the basic problem of " background noise." In order to help distinguish them from background noise, the signals that are used in radar-echo measurements are " coded " — that is, they are sent out in a definite pattern or sequence — similar to the pattern of electrical impulses in a wire carrying a Morse-code message.

Then, with the aid of mathematical computors, the thousands of incoming signals — many of them part of the background noise — can be sorted out in a search for the code pattern originally sent.

You have seen how radio waves provide us with keen eyes and keen ears. We can be quite sure that when men travel in space they will be accompanied by many vacuum-tube and transistor devices for handling radio waves. They will be used to navigate space ships, to communicate with earth, to control flight. Radio waves have already opened up new worlds of experience for us in our daily life. Yet their usefulness has hardly begun.

Looking Back . . . .

VOCABULARY
The following expressions are key words in this chapter. What is the meaning of each?

1. radio waves
2. frequency
3. voice current
4. carrier current
5. kilocycle
6. short-wave region
7. radio spectrum
8. grid
9. radar

REVIEW QUESTIONS
1. Explain the steps by which your radio set singles out the one radio station you want to hear and turns its message into sound waves.
2. How does a TV camera tube work?
3. Explain the general steps by which your TV set singles out the one station you want to look at and turns its message into a picture on your screen.

4. What does a radar set do? What are the general principles of its operation?
5. Explain the steps by which a radio announcer's voice is put " on the air."

Going Further . . . .

APPLYING PRINCIPLES
1. In what ways does radio transmission resemble the transmission of pictures by television?
2. In what way does the formation of images on your TV screen resemble the pictures cast by a movie projector?
3. Why must the motion of the electron beam in the TV camera be exactly the same as the motion of the electron beam in your picture tube?
4. Why do you see horizontal lines through your TV pictures when you look at them closely?
5. Why must radar signals be sent out in brief pulses?

TRY THIS PROBLEM
On a given date the distance to a certain asteroid is to be determined using radar-echo methods. (Asteroids, also known as minor planets, are large chunks of rock whirling about the sun between the orbits of Mars and Jupiter.) The information below records several separate measurements of the time elapsed between sending and receiving a radar signal to the asteroid. Find the average time and use it in a calculation of the distance of the asteroid, taking the speed of radar to be 186,000 miles per second.

first measurement — 174 seconds
second measurement — 172 seconds
third measurement — 170 seconds
fourth measurement — 174 seconds
fifth measurement — 170 seconds

READING FURTHER
Television Works Like This by Jeanne Bendick, McGraw-Hill, 1954

TV and Electronics as a Career by Ira Kamen and Richard Dorf, J. F. Rider, New York, 1951

Radar and Other Electronic Inventions by Frank Ross, Jr., Lothrop, Lee and Shepard, 1954

All About Radio and Television by Jack Gould, Random House, 1953

UNIT 10

The Universe

◀ *A great collection of stars and gas, the spiral galaxy in the constellation Ursa Major.*

LEARNING ABOUT the stars and our closer neighbors in space, the planets, is one of America's most popular scientific hobbies. More than 50,000 amateurs, many of them as young as yourself, have built their own telescopes in order to get a better look at the wonders of the sky.

As you look into the night sky you may wonder how far it is to the farthest bit of light you can see. About 30,000,000,000,000,000,000,000 miles! Can you even imagine such a distance? Remember when you thought the distance across our country, about 3,000 miles, was large?

Enormous distances are common in astronomy. The student of astronomy soon gets used to thinking in terms of such distances. He, and often she (for many astronomers are women), also soon gets used to the idea that the earth is but a tiny outpost in a vast universe of stars.

But on this outpost, from which man has already taken his first space journey, we have learned much about basic physical processes — about the atom and its nucleus, about how chemical energy can be changed to heat energy, about light and electricity, to name a few. And all that we have learned here on earth is used by the astronomer to build a picture of the universe at large.

CHAPTER

32

A Star and Its Satellites

Many people, if asked how a star would look if it were much nearer the earth, might reply " It's hard to say — all you ever see is a twinkle of light." They forget that our own sun is a star. What do we know about this closest of stars?

OUR SUN

It is not easy to imagine a temperature of 6000° C. (Steel melts at 1500° C.) Nor is it easy to imagine a ball 866,000 miles across (the earth is only 8000 miles across). Yet you have to imagine both at once if you are to have an idea of the fiery globe which is our sun. It is big enough to contain over a million earths (Fig. 32-1), hot enough to boil steel easily. The surface of this enormous furnace is a twisting, churning mass of hot gases.

Spots and Eruptions

Sometimes we see dark spots on the sun's surface. These are *sunspots*. Sunspots are gigantic extra-violent tornadoes on the sun that look dark because they are somewhat cooler than the rest

of the sun (Fig. 32-2). You can see sunspots quite safely and easily (if there are any to be seen) by following the instructions on page 395.

If you watch sunspots carefully, you will find that some come and go in a few days. Others — usually the big ones — may last weeks or even months. Astronomers count the number of spots that they see throughout an entire year and record their counts year after year. When they make a graph of their yearly counts (Fig. 32-3), they notice a remarkable fact about sunspots. Their number rises and falls regularly about every 11 years. This odd behavior of sunspots has never been fully explained. It is suspected, however, that it may be caused by great up-and-down currents deep within the sun.

What appears through a telescope as a relatively quiet surface on the sun is actually in violent turmoil.[1] Special movies show spikes of hot gas continually shooting up several thousand miles within only a few minutes (Fig. 32-4). Sometimes they form great clouds of glowing hot hydrogen, called *prominences,* that may hang above the sun for hours before breaking up with explosive violence. Although some of this glowing hot hydrogen seems to be blown completely away from the sun, most of it goes up only a few thou-

[1] *Caution:* Do not look at the sun through a telescope. The intensity of the light is harmful to your eyes.

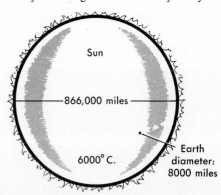

32-1. The sun, a great ball of hot gases, has a diameter more than 100 times that of the earth. It would require more than a million earths to fill the great volume of the sun.

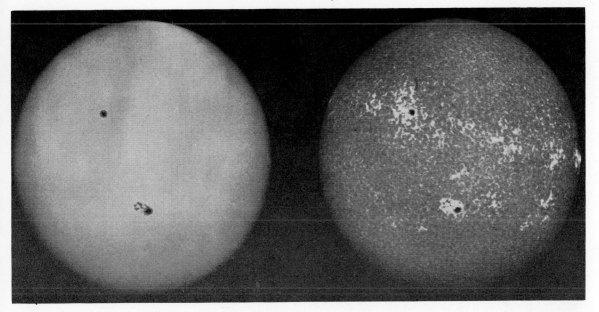

32-2. The left photograph shows the sun with two dark sunspots. A sunspot may get as large as 50,000 miles in diameter. The right photograph shows the sun on the same day photographed by special cameras that allow only certain wave lengths of light to enter.

sand miles and then rains back onto the sun again.

The prominences are under constant study. We want to know if their curved paths as they arch downward are due to the sun's magnetic field. Also we are curious about the sources of the huge amounts of energy responsible for their motions.

When the bright body of the sun is briefly blocked off by the moon during a total eclipse, a large faint whitish glow around the sun can be seen (Fig. 32-5). This is called the *corona*, or

crown. What it is made of remained a mystery for many years. Since it was high above the sun, it seemed to be made of some very light gas like hydrogen or helium. But the odd light it gave off could not be matched with light from any known material on the earth.

Finally, in 1940, a young Swedish astronomer named Edlen announced that he had found what the corona was made of — a hot gas of iron atoms! But for these iron atoms above the sun to give out

SUNSPOT CYCLES (since 1750)

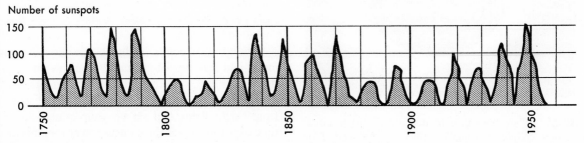

32-3. Sunspots are more numerous some years than others. As you can see, they come and go in a cycle of about 11 years.

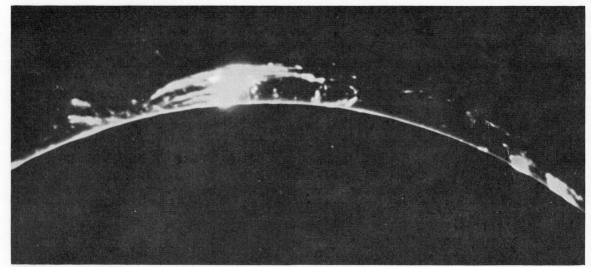

32-4. Solar prominences, great clouds of glowing hydrogen, rise above the sun's surface. Motion pictures show these clouds to move up, down, and sideways at high speeds.

such light, they must be far hotter than the sun's surface below. The evidence for such a very hot "iron crown" has been carefully examined by many skeptics, but Edlen's answer to the mystery is now generally accepted. To find iron at such a temperature high above the sun has made astronomers realize that the sun is probably surging and changing violently in ways we cannot see. (We already know from Chapter 10 that nuclear fusion keeps the sun hot and bright. In Chapter 33 we shall look at this process in detail.)

The Path of the Sun

Day and night the great arch of the sky seems to turn over our heads, carrying with it our sun and moon and the stars. A friend of yours living on the other side of this round earth would tell you that he sees the same motion of the sky that you do. To people all around the earth the sun and moon and stars appear to move as if they were points on great rotating hollow spheres that enclose our earth.

Around what points in the sky do the sun and moon and stars appear to turn? You can find out the answer for yourself if you have a camera. On a clear, moonless night, find a place well away from bright lights and set up your camera for a time exposure. Point the camera toward the northern sky and open the shutter for several hours. If your camera has not moved during the entire long

32-5. When the sun is blotted out by the moon at a solar eclipse, the sun's corona can be seen. Fine brush-like streamers show above the sun's poles like iron filings above a magnet.

exposure, your developed film will probably look something like Fig. 32-6. The star that has hardly moved at all is the North Star — sometimes called Polaris (po-LAHR-iss). Near it is one end of what appears to be the great axis of rotation of the sky.

You can see that all the stars, as well as the sun and the moon, seem to travel in circles around the north and south poles as the great sphere of the sky turns around once every day. The *farther* a star is from the pole the bigger a circle it travels in, as you will see by looking at Fig. 32-6. For example, our sun and moon always stay far from the pole star — Polaris — so they appear to move in a very long curve across the sky. You can see only part of the big circle the sun moves in. The rest of it curves around the far side of the earth beneath your feet.

THE NIGHT SKY

As you watch the great dome of sky turning over your head night after night, you may begin to get the impression that the bodies in the night sky are all fastened motionless upon it like figures on a revolving stage. But if you study the sky carefully you will see that each night its appearance is slightly different. On the revolving stage of the sky some of the actors are actually quite lively. Let's watch some of them and make a list of some of their actions that you can easily see for yourself from night to night.

Changes in the Sphere of the Sky

1. If the moon is up, you will see that its position among the stars changes from night to night. Each day the moon appears to move eastward among the stars, so that each night the turning sky brings the moon above the horizon about 50 minutes later than the night before.

Notice the path the moon follows among the stars. The moon never wanders off it. It takes an average of 27⅓ days to go all the way around its path.

2. The moon keeps its same face toward us all the time, but it changes its appearance each night.

It takes 29½ days to go from full moon through all its changes and back to full moon again.

3. If you study the stars near the path that the moon seems to follow night after night, you may notice that one or two of the brighter starlike objects actually change position each night. If you look at them closely, you may also notice that they do not twinkle as much as neighboring stars. These bright moving objects are not stars. They

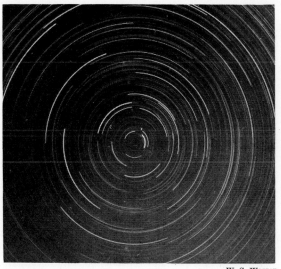

W. S. Warren

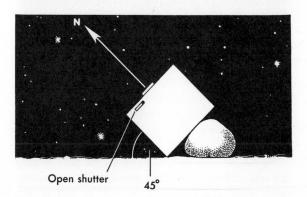

Open shutter   45°

32-6. On a clear, moonless night, set up your camera pointed toward the North Star. If you can adjust the camera's iris, make it as small as possible to keep out the stray skylight. Then make a time exposure of several hours. You will have a photograph, like the one shown above, of the star trails around the North Pole of the sky.

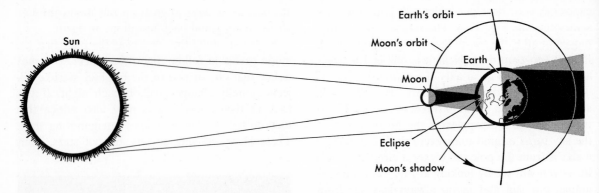

32-7. An eclipse of the sun occurs when the moon moves between the earth and the sun. Since we see the sun and moon as nearly the same size in the sky, the moon can completely cover the sun as seen from a small section of the earth. Here we see a total eclipse. A partial eclipse is seen in the shaded area.

are among our closest neighbors in space. They are the *planets*. The names of the ones you can see most easily without a telescope are Venus, Mars, Jupiter, and Saturn. Later you will meet several more that are very distant and faint.

4. If you notice what stars are overhead on two nights several months apart, you will discover that you do not always see the same part of the sphere of the sky all through the year. Each month the stars rise two hours earlier.

Each month the sun with its blinding daylight blots out for us a different part of the sphere of the sky. It seems as if the sun moves across the sphere of the sky, too, just as the moon does. But the sun takes an entire year to go all the way around its path across the sphere of the sky.

The sun, the moon, and the planets, too, *all* travel in the same narrow band among the stars. This band is called the *zodiac*. You will never see them anywhere in the sky except in the band of the zodiac.

5. As the sun travels along on its path among the stars once a year, the moon travels around the same track about thirteen times. The zodiac is a band wide enough for the moon to pass beside the sun most of the time. But occasionally the moon overtakes the sun on what appears to be a collision course. It may pass directly across the face of the sun, blotting out its light for a few minutes. This is one of the most spectacular events in all the

changing sky. It is called an eclipse of the sun (Fig. 32-7) and it occurs rather infrequently.

Thus you can see that even without a telescope the revolving stage of the sky presents you with an ever-changing spectacle.

EARLIER ACCOUNTS OF HEAVENLY MOTIONS

We have just described how the sky *looks*. From what we see with our unaided eyes, it *looks* as if the sun, the moon, the stars, and the planets were

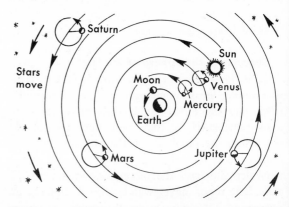

32-8. Ptolemy's universe: a motionless earth at the center, around which move the planets and stars. Note that the planets have two orbital motions — the epicycles, as well as the larger orbits, or deferents.

lighted points on great invisible spheres surrounding the earth. And from what our unaided eyes tell us it *looks* as if these spheres carrying the sun, the moon, and the stars move around a motionless earth once every day.

An Earth-centered Universe?

The conception of a geocentric (earth-centered) universe was fully described in the year A.D. 150 by a Greek named Ptolemy (TOL-eh-mee) (Fig. 32-8). And until about 300 years ago, most people who watched the sky and saw the motions you have just read about *did* think that our earth was held motionless in the center of the revolving heavens, just as Ptolemy said.

Ptolemy's explanation of the motions of the heavenly bodies was a great accomplishment; he was able to describe not merely the nightly rotations, but also more complicated motions. For example, it was long known that the eastward drift of the planets along the zodiac was not at all steady. They changed speed and even went westward occasionally (Fig. 32-9). (The word *planet* comes from the Greek word for "wanderer.") Could the motions of these wanderers be traced upon the surface of the sphere of the heavens?

Here is where the Ptolemaic theory really became ingenious. Suppose that a planet, instead of moving steadily around the earth, was traveling in a smaller circle whose center moved steadily around the earth (Fig. 32-10). Such a circling motion with a steadily traveling center was called an *epicycle*. Now if you follow the planet in its motion, you will find that, every so often, it does indeed move sideways and loop backwards in its path — that is, it undergoes *retrograde motion*.

You may find it strange to think of a body moving in an epicycle, that is, in a circle whose center is simply a moving point in empty space. But in ancient times, circular motion was considered as the "natural" form of movement for heavenly bodies. The ancient scientists were influenced by a generally held view of the heavens as the realm of "perfection," in contrast to the lower and "imperfect" earth. And of all figures, the circle was thought most perfect.

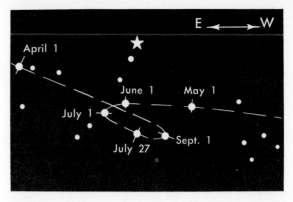

32-9. If the path of Mars is traced nightly, relative to the stars, one obtains occasional looping patterns on dates which vary from year to year.

Ptolemy was able to solve the problem of finding a systematic description for the heavenly motions by combining three ideas of movement: rotating spheres that produced the nightly turning of the stars and planets; smaller spheres for the planets than for the stars to explain the wandering of the planets against the background of the stars; and finally, the epicycles that produced the occasional retrograde motion of the planets.

All this may understandably result in a feeling

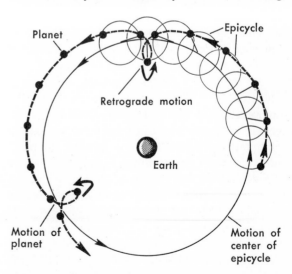

32-10. According to Ptolemy, retrograde paths resulted from a planet's double motion. Follow the planet in its epicycle while the center of the epicycle itself moves in a larger orbit.

of dizziness. But what is worse, epicycles on the epicycles were added each time some further motion was noticed. Each time the theory could be made to work again, but only at the expense of adding more and more different motions to the planets.

Yet the basis for a simpler theory had been available for many years. In fact, such a theory had been hinted at three hundred years before Ptolemy. The only trouble was that it involved one basic idea which seemed to fly in the face of common sense — the idea that the earth moved.

A Moving Earth?

Today most of us accept without question that the earth is kept swinging through a huge curve in space by the gravitational pull of the sun. But suppose you were to demand evidence?

In particular you might wonder, as did the ancients, why the stars did not then appear to shift their positions during a year. For when an object is viewed, first from one, then from a different position, it will appear to shift, as you can easily check for yourself (Fig. 32-11). Such a shift, called *parallax,* was sought many times but never observed even by the most careful of the ancient astronomers. Indeed it wasn't until 1838 that such a stellar parallax was recorded. So, the idea of the ancients that the earth was stationary seemed to agree with what they were able to observe.

Yet the idea of a motionless earth was running into trouble. By the sixteenth century, the terrible complexities of the Ptolemaic calculations — together with their increasing failure to agree with observations (constantly requiring more complexities to explain each failure) — had led to great dissatisfaction. And notions of the size of the universe had changed. Estimates of the distance of the star sphere had increased to 2000 times the previous figures. Thus a reasonable explanation for the lack of observed parallax became available. Perhaps it has already occurred to you — the stars were so distant that the shift would be too small to detect. (Try a sighting as in Fig. 32-11, but on a pencil held by a friend some 20 or more feet away.) Furthermore, how could such faraway objects travel at the terrific speeds needed to carry them all the way around our earth in just one day?

A NEW ACCOUNT OF THE HEAVENS

To defy centuries of tradition and promote a theory based on a moving earth required great courage. And to develop a description of the heavenly motions which could successfully compete with the Ptolemaic description required great skill. Both qualities were exhibited by the Polish mathematician and astronomer Nicholaus Copernicus, who published his revolutionary theory of the heavens in 1543.

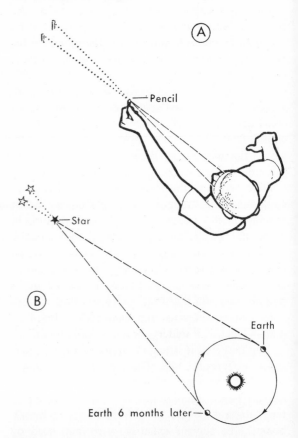

32-11. A pencil held at arm's length seems to shift position when viewed from one eye, then the other. Similarly, if the earth were moving, a close star would seem to shift when viewed from different positions in our orbit.

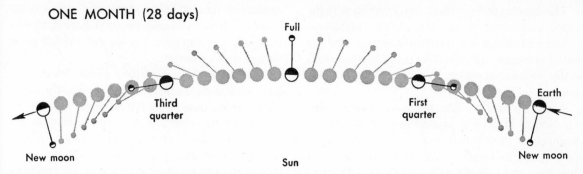

ONE MONTH (28 days)

Full

Third quarter

First quarter

Earth

New moon

Sun

New moon

32-12. The moon goes around the earth each month, but the earth is moving around the sun. The line connecting the earth to the moon symbolizes gravity. In this case, it behaves like a rigid bar that keeps the same side of the moon always facing the earth.

The Earth's Motion

According to Copernicus the earth rotates like a marshmallow on a spit — the sky does *not* turn. Of course to you, standing on the turning earth, the sky *seems* to turn around you, just as the carnival crowds seem to whirl by you in a circle as you ride on a merry-go-round. According to Copernicus our great earthly merry-go-round turns around on its axis once each day. Thus, once each day the entire carnival of the sky seems to flash past us — now the sparkling lights of the distant stars, and now the brilliant glaring of our sun, so close to us that it blots out all the fainter, more distant, stars.

Of course (in addition to its daily rotation around its axis), Copernicus also had the earth moving around the sun, along with the other planets. This was the really daring feature of his theory. It put the earth on the same footing as the other planets, thus helping to destroy the notion that the laws of the "perfect" heavenly bodies were different from those applying to the "lowly" earth.

The moving earth theory can easily explain the seasonal changes of the sun at noon — low in December and high in June — if we assume that the earth's axis is not straight up from the plane in which we move around the sun. In June the earth's north pole would be tipped toward the sun, and in December tipped away.

You can make a model showing this by using one fist as the "sun" and a finger of the other hand to indicate the earth's axis. Tip the axis a bit away from your face. Then move the "earth" around the "sun," always keeping the axis pointed in the same direction. What will be the month when the "earth" passes between your eye and your fist ("sun")? When the earth is on the far side of the "sun" from your eye? One full trip of the earth around its orbit is a year.

The Moon, Our Nearest Neighbor in Space

"But what about the moon?" you say. "The moon seems to go all the way around the sky *thirteen* times a year. Did Copernicus also think we circle around the moon times a year?" Before such a thought makes you dizzy, let us say quickly that the answer is "No." While the earth revolves around the sun, the moon revolves around the earth, only 240,000 miles away. See Copernicus' idea of the moon's motion in Fig. 32-12.

Notice that our drawing explains two things that you have already noted about the moon. It shows how the moon always keeps the same side facing toward the earth as it circles around us. Therefore no man has ever seen the other side of the moon from the earth. (That is why rockets have been fired around the moon. With cameras and TV transmitters, they have shown that the far side of the moon is much like the side we can see, except that it seems to have fewer craters. See Fig. 34-5.)

The drawing in Fig. 32-12 also explains why the appearance of the moon's face changes nightly.

When the moon is directly between you and the sun, you cannot see any of its sunlit surface. This is the position in which it is commonly called a *new moon* (Fig. 32-13).

About seven days later the moon has traveled one quarter of the way around its path and its appearance is then called *first quarter*. How does the moon in first quarter look to you as you see it from the earth? That's right — half lit, half dark. You might say when the moon is " in first quarter " that it is " half full."

In another seven days it will get around to the position marked *full moon*. Now you face it with the sun directly behind you, so all of the moon's earthward face is lit up. Since the sun and the moon are now on exactly opposite sides of the sky from you, you can probably see why the full moon always rises at sunset.

Every day the moon rises about 50 minutes later, due to its steady progress around the earth. About seven days after full moon it rises in the middle of the night. It has now gotten so far around the earth that it is in the position marked *last quarter* in our picture. How will the moon look in the last quarter? Half full again. Only this time it's the other half.

Finally, in the last quarter of its swing around the earth, the brightly lit area of the moon that we see gets thinner and thinner. At last we see only a thin crescent, then the moon passes between us and the sun again — new moon — and the whole 29-day cycle starts over.

During this time the earth has moved about one-thirteenth of its way along its yearly orbit.

Notice that the plane of the moon's orbit around the earth lies in nearly the same plane as the earth's orbit around the sun. This explains why the sun and the moon, as you look at them from our earth, seem to follow nearly the same path around the sky — within the narrow band of the zodiac.

Our Sun's Family of Satellites

If the earth and the other planets are all part of a sun-centered system of planets, how can the occasional westward wanderings of the planets among the stars be explained? What did Copernicus offer to replace Ptolemy's epicycles?

Let us follow the moving earth. According to Copernicus, it, and the other five planets then known, revolve about the sun at different distances from the sun. Since the earth is traveling around its orbit faster than more distant planets, like Mars, what will happen? Won't the earth occasionally scoot past between them and the sun? If, at the right time of year, you watch from the earth as we hurry past Mars, you will see Mars appear to slow down in its eastward drift across the sky and start going westward (just as a moving car appears to be going backward at the moment you

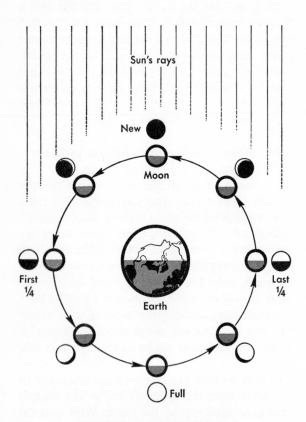

PHASES OF THE MOON

32-13. The outer circles show the shape of the moon as it appears to us on the earth. Explain why there is a new moon about once a month.

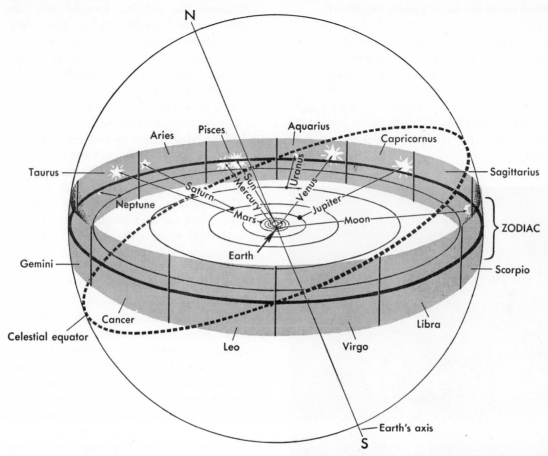

32-14. Why we see the planets along the zodiac. All the planets move in nearly the same plane, like marbles rolling in circles on the floor. From the earth we see them along the zodiac. As shown in the drawing, we would see Jupiter among the stars in the constellation of Capricornus, and Saturn in Aries.

pass it on the highway). Saturn and Jupiter will also appear to move backward as the earth overtakes and then hurries past them. According to Copernicus, it is thus the motion of the earth relative to the other planets, and not the epicycles, that causes the backward or retrograde motions of the planets.

Copernicus had his six planets moving around the sun in perfect circles. Not even he was able to overcome the ancient prejudice in favor of circular motions. In fact, he even had to retain some of the epicycles. But he laid the foundations for the work of Johannes Kepler, who, after years of detailed calculations, was the first to declare that the planets did not move in circles. Thanks to Kep-

ler, we now know that the orbits of the planets are slightly oval curves called ellipses. It was Kepler, too, who eliminated the last epicycles from astronomy and thus made the sun the focal point of *all* planetary motions.

Today we know of eight planets besides the earth — and a large number of minor planets and comets, as we shall note later. The sun and its family of planets and comets is called the *solar system*. All the planets revolve around the sun in the same direction, and their paths all lie in very nearly the same plane. It is due to this rather remarkable fact that, as we watch them from the earth, they all *seem* to follow nearly the same path around the sky in the zodiac (Fig. 32-14).

What Holds the Solar System Together?

Year after year the planets follow the same paths around the sun. What keeps them from drifting off into outer space to be lost forever?

You have already read about the answer (page 5). Gravity applies to the planets as well as it does to drops of water falling from a leaky faucet. The kind of force that pulls you down toward the center of the earth also pulls the planets toward the sun.

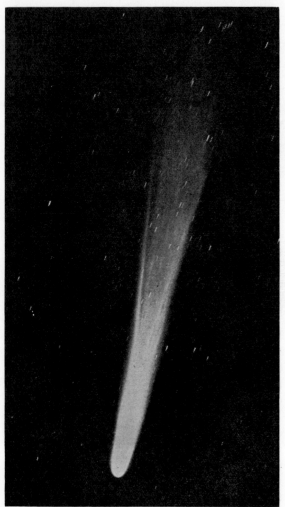

32-15. This is a photograph of Halley's Comet taken May 6, 1910. The comet's tail was many millions of miles long. Stars show as streaks.

Whereas the ancients thought that circular motion of the heavenly bodies was "natural," Newton correctly conceived that any motion not in a straight line at a steady speed required an outside force. Thus the planets, which tend to travel in straight lines, are pulled into curved paths by the sun's enormous force of gravity.

Later we shall see how Newton's Law of Gravity still operates even in the farthest known regions of space. It describes the motions of the stars in their courses; in fact, one of the interesting things about Newton's Law of Gravity is that it seems to work *everywhere.* This is indeed a change from the time when the laws governing heavenly bodies were thought to be quite distinct from the laws applying here on earth.

Comets and Meteors

Since the time of Copernicus we have learned that comets and meteors belong to our sun's family, too. Most comets travel around the sun in long, closed loops that carry them out among the most distant planets or even far beyond. Some of them take hundreds of years to make one trip around the sun. As a comet comes inward toward the sun it brightens rapidly as it receives more and more sunlight, and it begins to "grow" a tail. Quickly the tail grows longer until it may become several million miles long. A comet's tail is very thin (Fig. 32-15). It is made of gas and is so light in weight that even the gentle pressure of light rays from the sun keeps the streaming tail pushed away from the sun.

No one knows for sure what the head of the comet is made of. However, the latest idea is that it is a mass of spongy frozen gases with small solid particles mixed in.

Big comets are rare, but you can hope to see a small comet every few years with your unaided eye. Halley's comet, the most famous, appears every 75 years. The last appearance was in 1910 and it is expected back in view about 1985.

"Shooting stars," called *meteors,* are much easier to see. Every day our earth encounters millions of tiny rocks floating in space. Pulled around the sun by the force of gravity, they meet

32-16. Very rarely does a meteorite of great size strike the earth's surface. The world's largest meteorite crater near Flagstaff, Arizona, shown above, is three-quarters of a mile wide and 600 feet deep.

the earth at 20 to 40 miles a second. Fortunately for us nearly all of these cosmic bullets are burned up and vaporized by their friction with the upper atmosphere. Occasionally one is big enough so that at least a certain fraction of it survives its fiery trip down, and it falls to the surface of the earth. It is then called a *meteorite* (Fig. 32-17).

You will see meteors almost any evening you spend looking at the stars. In fact, with a little patience you can see with your naked eye nearly everything described in this chapter.

MEET OUR NEIGHBORS

Ever since the time of Copernicus scientists have been busy learning more about the objects we see in the sky. Much of what they have discovered since then has been with the use of telescopes. For example, around 1609 Galileo (gal-ih-LAY-oh) made a simple telescope and used it to inspect the sky more closely. He saw sunspots, he saw mountains on the moon, and he saw several tiny moons revolving around the planet Jupiter. With a small telescope you can see these same objects.

In the rest of this chapter we shall find out what modern telescopes have revealed about our closest neighbors in space, and take a guided tour of the solar system. (Our tour will be on paper. But in your lifetime, men may make it in person.)

32-17. Meteorites typically are of two kinds — stony, similar in composition to the earth's crust, and iron, about 90% iron, 8% nickel. The centimeter ruler to the left indicates size.

32-18. The moon at third quarter. On the surface are huge, flat dry areas. These are large craters, some of which are hundreds of miles in diameter.

Resort Life on the Moon

Do you have an overpowering desire sometimes to get away — far away — for a BIG change? If so, you may have thought about traveling to the moon and setting up housekeeping there — 240,-000 miles away from home. A rocket voyage there would only take two or three days. What sort of resort life could you expect when you landed?

You will find the moon is hot in the sunlight but cold in the dark. On the sunlit side of the moon the temperature goes above the boiling point of water, but when night falls it goes down to about 150° C. below freezing.

If you are not discouraged by such a climate, you might enjoy the scenery. There are great flat plains — the dark patches you see from the earth. People once thought they were seas, but now we know there is no water at all on the moon. Then there are some 33,000 mountains, on the earthward side of the moon, some nearly as high as Mt. Everest. Many of them are *craters* (Fig. 32-18). There is still some doubt whether the craters are due to extinct volcanoes or whether they were made by meteors crashing into the moon from outer space. Certainly on a visit to the moon you would want to explore the craters.

In one way, mountain climbing on the moon would be easy. The pull of gravity is only one sixth as great as it is on the earth. Thus if you weigh in at 120 pounds on earth you would weigh only 20 pounds on the moon! Because the moon's gravitational pull is not great, there is no air to breathe. Any atmosphere the moon may once have had, has gradually escaped into space.

Thus the moon is an airless, lifeless world. It is a world in which no sounds can be heard, because sound cannot reach your ears through a vacuum. And without an atmosphere to protect it, it is a world pelted with meteorites and scorched by deadly ultraviolet light from the sun.

Other Worlds in the Solar System

Besides the earth, our sun has revolving around it a family of 8 large planets, 30 moons, and over 1500 minor planets or *asteroids* for us to consider for a visit. Naming them outward from the sun, the planets are Mercury, Venus, Earth, Mars, the asteroids, Jupiter, Saturn, Uranus, Neptune, and Pluto.

To get a better idea of the sizes and spacings of the planets, let us imagine a scale model of the solar system. Starting from the front door of your school, which you would take as the sun's position, the planets might be thought of as mounted on posts. Table 32-1 gives an idea of this model.

TABLE **32-1** A MODEL OF
THE SOLAR SYSTEM

OBJECT	DISTANCE FROM SUN		DIAMETER	MODEL OBJECT
	Actual (millions of miles)	Model (feet)	Actual (miles)	
Sun	—	—	866,000	large toy balloon
Mercury	36	82	3,100	small grain of sand
Venus	67	154	7,700	pea
Earth	93	215	8,000	pea
Mars	140	327	4,200	large pinhead
Jupiter	490	¼ mile	89,000	orange
Saturn	890	⅖ mile	71,500	orange
Uranus	1,800	¾ mile	32,000	plum
Neptune	2,800	1¼ miles	31,000	plum
Pluto	3,700	1½ miles	3,600(?)	grain of sand

Our moon is about 2,000 miles in diameter and averages 240,000 miles from our earth. In the model it has a diameter of a small pinhead seven inches from the earth.

The nearest star is about the same size as the sun. Its distance from the sun is 270,000 times the earth's distance. How many miles from the sun would the nearest star be in the model?

What Other Worlds Are Like

Let's begin with the planet Mercury. It is so close to the fiery sun that its surface is hot enough to melt lead, and like our moon it has lost its atmosphere. The next planet, Venus, does have an atmosphere, but with almost no oxygen and with hundreds of times as much carbon dioxide as our earth. Its surface is hidden by a dense blanket of clouds. What the surface of Venus is like under the cloud layer no man as yet knows.

The next planet out from the sun is our earth, which we have already looked at in the first unit.

Then comes Mars. On Mars conditions are such that some forms of life as we know it would not be impossible. Some scientists think that life does exist on Mars — plant life like our earthly lichens perhaps. At least this is the most popular explanation for the periodic changes in the surface areas which turn from chocolate brown to blue-green and back again once each Martian year. Such plant life, together with any explorers who may someday visit it from the earth, must be able to endure temperatures below freezing most (but not all) of the time, must be able to live on less than 1% as much oxygen as we have here on the earth, and must get along with almost no water. On the earth the closest we come to such conditions as these is on the summit of Mt. Everest.

The lines or " canals " on Mars have never been satisfactorily explained. Are they optical illusions caused by the momentary combined appearance of many small dark spots? No scientist still believes they are the remains of actual canals once used by some dead civilization to transport water melted from Mars' thin ice caps (Fig. 32-19).

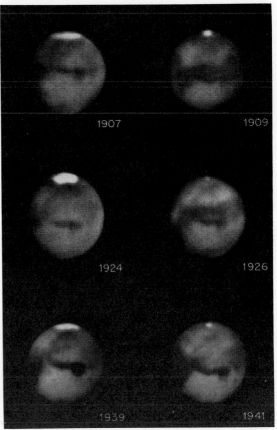

E. C. Slipher, Lowell Observatory

32-19. The Martian polar caps show seasonal variations in size. The views on the left were taken during the Martian spring season in the years shown; those on the right, during summer. The caps are probably frost or light snow and not thick ice such as is found at the earth's poles.

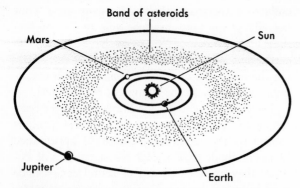

32-20. Many little planets, called asteroids, move around the sun. Most of them stay between the paths of Mars and Jupiter. Some, however, cross the earth's path and threaten us with collision.

And what of those occasional moving orange patches — are they desert dust storms? To answer questions like these we usually wait until the earth is close to Mars and then use our telescopes. But at best the " seeing " is always subject to haziness — the effect of our atmosphere upon the incoming light. Perhaps better answers await space travel to Mars or the use of automatic television transmitters mounted in man-made satellites.

Mars has two small natural satellites, one of which is rather close to the planet.

Beyond Mars is the realm of the midgets, the 1500 or more *asteroids* or minor planets (Fig. 32-20). Ceres (SEER-eez), the largest of these, is only about 500 miles in diameter. Ceres' gravitational pull is too feeble to hold an atmosphere, and if you were to land on it you would find yourself almost weightless. A single leap would carry you upward several miles from Ceres before you fell gently back. Without an atmosphere, of course, Ceres and all of its many smaller companions must have surface conditions similar to our moon. Some of these tiny planets are hardly more than flying mountains — cold, jagged rocks — midget, lifeless worlds orbiting around the sun.

Mt. Wilson and Palomar Observatories

32-21. Jupiter, spanned by great cloud bands, exhibits marked flattening as it spins on its axis in less than 10 hours. Note the Great Red Spot, upper left, which may be an erupted cloud of metallic vapors.

Beyond the asteroids, some 500 million miles out from the fiery furnace of the sun, lies the cold, giant planet Jupiter, attended by its twelve satellites. Jupiter, bigger than 1000 of our earths all rolled together, is covered by ice and ammonia and the marsh gas, methane, all at about 200° C. below zero. You can see this great planet through a small telescope, but its surface is hidden from you by clouds of methane and ammonia (Fig. 32-21). Should man ever penetrate that cloud bank, it would be difficult to return. For, in contrast to the asteroids, the enormous bulk of Jupiter would pull down a rocket ship with 2½ times as much gravity as our earth. A 150-pound man would weigh 400 pounds on Jupiter and could not lift himself erect or move about. After all, Jupiter's mass alone is more than twice that of all the other planets combined (see Table 32-2, page 394).

You may be wondering whether Jupiter's great mass might influence the motion of other bodies in the solar system. The answer is yes. This is especially true of the short-period comets — comets which return in a century or less. Over 60% of these have periods of between 5 and 7½ years. That this is no mere coincidence seems evident when you see that many of these comets pass within 15 million miles of Jupiter's orbit — actually quite close in astronomical terms (about twice as close as Venus is to the earth).

It is now generally agreed that the short-period comets have been "captured" by Jupiter — their present orbits are the result of being swerved from their original paths by Jupiter's gravitational pull.

Traveling farther out to Saturn you would find the living conditions there just as bad, if not worse. For Saturn, too, has an atmosphere of ammonia and methane. In addition, being further from the sun it is still colder. But perhaps someday a space traveler will land briefly on one of its nine icy airless moons and from there observe the great cloud-covered bulk of the planet and its famous rings (Fig. 32-22).

Mt. Wilson and Palomar Observatories

32-22. The rings of Saturn were probably formed when one of its moons broke apart due to action of tidal forces. The critical distance at which such forces are strong enough to do this is known as Roche's limit.

TABLE **32-2** INFORMATION ABOUT
THE SOLAR SYSTEM

Body	Diameter (miles)	Mass, compared to Earth's	Distance from sun. Earth=1	Yrs. to go around sun	No. of moons
Sun	866,000	330,000			
Moon	2,160	0.012			
Mercury	3,100	0.05	0.387	0.240	0
Venus	7,700	0.85	0.723	0.615	0
Earth	8,000	1.0	1.00	1.00	1
Mars	4,200	0.11	1.524	1.88	2
Jupiter	89,000	319.	5.203	11.86	12
Saturn	71,500	95.	9.54	29.46	9 (plus rings)
Uranus	32,000	15.	19.19	84.02	5
Neptune	31,000	17.	30.07	164.8	2
Pluto	3,600(?)	0.1(?)	39.60	249.7	0

Even from our earth you can see the rings around Saturn through a small telescope. Close up you would see that they are not solid at all, but are made of a dense swarm of sand and gravel-sized particles. The ring is a band almost 42,000 miles wide, while its thickness is only about 10 miles (about in the same ratio as the width of a five-foot ring cut from newspaper is to its thickness).

Out beyond Saturn the solar system gets even more cold and dark. Uranus is so cold that much of its ammonia-methane " atmosphere " lies frozen solid on its lifeless rocks. Neptune and Pluto are colder still, several billions of miles away from us and from the sun.

The discovery of Neptune is interesting, for its existence was predicted in 1846 before anyone had actually seen it through a telescope. Astronomers, having difficulty in accounting for the motion of Uranus, reasoned that there must be some unseen planet beyond Uranus which was disturbing its motion. Upon calculating where such a disturbing body should be, a telescope was trained on the predicted position — and there it was!

With Pluto we have reached the outer boundary of our star's family of planets — at least so far as is presently known. In the next chapter we go be-

yond the solar system to other stars — fiery hot objects like our sun, and incredibly far away. If you imagine that the width of your little finger represents the 93,000,000 miles from the sun to our earth, then on this same scale of distances the nearest star (other than our sun) is two miles away.

Looking Back . . . .

VOCABULARY
Each of the following is a key word in the chapter you have just studied. Define each one to show you understand its meaning.

1. asteroids
2. rotate
3. Polaris
4. planet
5. zodiac
6. meteor
7. solar system
8. comet
9. meteorite
10. corona
11. prominences
12. epicycle
13. parallax

REVIEW QUESTIONS
1. Around what point in the northern sky do the stars seem to turn?
2. About how much later each day does the moon rise?
3. How many days pass between full moons?
4. How many full moons can be seen each year?
5. Why did most ancient astronomers refuse to believe the earth moved?
6. How did Copernicus overcome objections to a moving earth?
7. What would be the effects on the earth if the moon were to turn around it in 10 hours instead of once a month?
8. What evidence do we have that comet tails are very thin gas?
9. Why do temperatures on the moon rise higher and fall lower than on the earth?
10. Could you live on the moon?

Going Further . . . .

THOUGHT QUESTIONS
1. What leads us to believe that the temperature of the sun's corona is above a million degrees?

2. How could you demonstrate that the sun generates over a thousand million times the energy that falls on the earth?

3. How might we conclude that the sun has generated about the same amount of light for at least the past 500 million years?

4. What might be responsible for a change in the orbit of a planet?

THINGS TO DO

1. In the bottom of a candy box lay a piece of blueprint paper. Put the top on the box. Then in the top make a small, but clean, pinhole. Set the box in sunshine and leave it for several hours or all day. Then take the box back out of sunlight and remove the blueprint. Develop it in water with a small amount of potassium dichromate added. You will have a long arc showing how the sun moved across the sky during the exposure.

2. Use a star map to locate the position of a bright planet that can be seen in the evening. If it rises in the east as the sun sets, watch the planet carefully night after night. Which way is it moving among the stars? Which way do the planets generally move?

3. With binoculars or a small telescope (perhaps made by an amateur astronomer) observe the moon. Notice the long shadows near the line where the sun-lit part ends. Also notice the short shadows where the sunlight falls more directly on the mountains. Can you figure out a way by which the heights of the mountains on the moon might be found?

4. Notice that when the moon is near " last quarter " you can see it during the day, west of the sun.

5. Read more about Mars and report to the class on how we know of conditions on it.

6. Through binoculars or a small telescope observe the four bright moons of Jupiter as Galileo did in 1610. Sketch their positions at various times for several nights. Do they seem to go around Jupiter as the planets go around the sun?

7. Observe any spots that may be on the sun. Use a long pinhole camera to form an image of the sun. If you use a small telescope DO NOT LOOK AT THE SUN THROUGH IT. Instead, project the sun's image on a sheet of paper held some feet behind the eyepiece. Sketch the position and size of the spots. Repeat these observations for several days and see

TABLE OF STRONG ANNUAL METEOR SHOWERS

Date of maximum	Name of shower	Radiant position	Best hours for observing
Jan. 3	Quadrantid	northern Boötes, near end of handle of Big Dipper	early A.M.
April 21	Lyrid	Lyra, near Vega	A.M.
May 4	Eta Aquarid	east of Alpha Aquarius	A.M.
July 29	Delta Aquarid	near Delta Aquarius	A.M.
Aug. 12	Perseid	between Perseus and Cassiopeia	after midnight
Oct. 22	Orionid	northern Orion	A.M.
Nov. 17	Leonid	in sickle of Leo	after midnight
Dec. 12	Geminid	near Castor	all night

how the spots move as the sun rotates. Note also that no sunspots appear near the poles of the sun.

8. Observe a meteor shower. Note the number of bright, medium, and faint meteors you see. Notice also that the shower members fan out from the same point in the sky — called the radiant point. The information in the table above may help you plan your observations.

9. If you are seriously interested in astronomical observing, and have a good deal of patience, you may want to construct your own reflecting telescope. The first reference below will give detailed instructions.

READING FURTHER

Amateur Telescope Making by Albert G. Ingalls, Scientific American Publishing Co., 1935. Practical information to help you build your own telescope.

Between the Planets by Fletcher G. Watson, Doubleday-Anchor, 1962

Earth, Moon and Planets by Fred L. Whipple, Grosset & Dunlap, 1958

Our Sun by Donald H. Menzel, Harvard University Press, 1959 (2nd ed.)

Sunspots in Action by Harlan T. Stetson, Ronald Press, 1947

The Starry Universe

Throughout the ages man has wondered about the stars he saw in the heavens. At first he lacked facts, and his picture of the universe was often fantastic.

The science of astronomy has greatly changed our picture of the universe. Yet some of the facts astronomers are discovering are as fantastic as anything our ancestors imagined.

THE STARS

Year after year the stars seem to keep the same patterns in the sky. Some of these patterns, like the Big Dipper and Orion (oh-RY-un) were named long ago (Fig. 33-1).

Of course, these patterns will not really remain the same forever. Like everything else in the universe the stars are in motion. But they are so far away that they appear stationary (much as an airplane flying at great height or distance appears to be motionless for a moment). In the few thousand years that these patterns have been observed, and for thousands of years to come, they will appear to change very little.

Today, all the sky is divided into 88 major areas, called *constellations*. Most of these constellations include some bright stars that we see in patterns easy to recognize.

Mapping the Stars

The earliest astronomers, thousands of years ago, divided the narrow band of the zodiac (Fig. 32-14) into twelve sections, each with its own constellation. They probably did this because during a year the full moon occurs twelve times (in some years, thirteen times), and each time it is in a different constellation. The names or symbols of many of these constellations of the zodiac appear in old Egyptian and Babylonian writing as well as in the Bible. Along the zodiac we find, to name a few, the Ram (Aries), the Bull (Taurus), the Fishes (Pisces), the Lion (Leo), the Virgin (Virgo), and the Goat (Capricornus).

A few dozen of the brighter stars have names. Many have old Arabic names in which the prefix *al* means " the," as in Altair (the flyer) and Algol (the demon). As more stars became of interest, another system of naming was used, too. Within each constellation the stars were labeled, in the order of their brightness, by Greek letters — alpha, beta, gamma, delta, etc. Thus some stars have several labels; for example, Betelgeuse (BEET-'l-jooz) is also called Alpha Orionis (AL-fuh o-RY-o-nis) because it is the brightest star in the constellation Orion. Many fainter stars are known only by their numbered places in star catalogues. More thousands of even fainter stars are too numerous to name or to number.

How Far Away Are the Stars?

The answer to one question — " how far are the stars? " — goes hand in hand with the asking of still another question — " how do you measure the distances to stars? " Not only is there no direct way of measuring their distances, but also, some stars may appear closer than others just because they are brighter. Look for instance, at Fig. 33-6 (on p. 401). Which star appears closest? Actually, many of the fainter stars are closer. The apparent brightness of a star is not, then, a sure indication of its distance. What could we use instead?

You may already have thought of a method. Remember from the last chapter that a star will seem to shift slightly when viewed from opposite ends of the earth's orbit. The closer the star, the

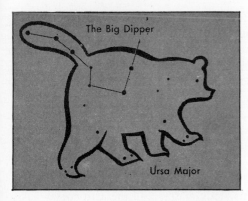

Magnitude of stars

0 ✷
1 ★
2 •
3 ·
4 ·

33-1. Two of the best-known star patterns, or constellations, are the Big Bear (Ursa Major) and the hunter Orion. The Big Dipper forms the hind parts and tail of the Big Bear. Orion contains several very bright stars and the line of three that form Orion's belt.

greater this shift — or parallax — will be. By using the 186 million miles across the earth's orbit as a base line, together with the angle of the shift, a triangle can be constructed (Fig. 32-11); from this triangle the star's distance is easy to calculate. (Surveyors often use a similar method for indirectly measuring distances here on earth.)

Although the distance to almost 2000 of the closer stars has been found by using their parallax, the vast majority of stars are much too far away to exhibit any shift even when the best instruments are used. However, still other ways have been discovered, as you will see later.

The Light Year

The very nearest to us of all the stars in the sky is 270,000 times farther away from us than the sun is. Its name is Alpha Centauri (sen-TOH-ry), a bright star far down in the southern sky. Its distance from us is so vast that the light from it, traveling as it does 186,000 miles every second, takes over four years to reach us. This distance is close to twenty-four millions of millions of miles. And this is the *nearest* known star. All of the bright stars you can see in the sky any evening are much farther away than this.

Astronomers need a bigger measuring stick than the mile to measure distances like this. So they use as their measuring stick the distance light travels in one year, about six million million miles. This distance they call a *light year*. Alpha

Centauri is a little more than four light years away.

Imagine receiving a radio message from an earth rocket with a powerful transmitter near Alpha Centauri. The message would be a little over four years old by the time we heard it, since radio waves also travel at the speed of light. In the same way, we never see Alpha Centauri as it is but only as it was when its light started on its journey to the earth. And, the farther away a star is in space, the older is the light that we receive from it. Yes, when you look out into the immense distances of space you are also looking back into the immense past of the universe.

Not All Stars Are Alike

The stars differ greatly both in the amount and color of light each puts out. Some actually put out more than a hundred million times more light than others. This difference is like comparing a match to a searchlight.

To rate the light output, or *luminosity,* of the stars, we compare them to the sun. Many stars give off about as much light as our sun does, or perhaps a hundred times more, or a hundredth as much. A few stars, however, are 10,000 times more luminous. Others are only 1/10,000 as luminous as the sun. There may be stars even less luminous, but they are very difficult to observe.

The rare, highly luminous stars are of two types. Some are blue-white and very hot, like Deneb in the constellation called the Swan. Oth-

Dominion Astrophysical Observatory, Canada

33-2. The triangular prisms of the spectroscope break up the light "fed" into it from a telescope to which the spectroscope is attached.

ers are red and have low temperatures like Betelgeuse in Orion and Antares (an-TEHR-eez) in the Scorpion. If we bring together some information you already know, we can draw some very interesting conclusions about these stars.

You know that as a poker in the fire or the filament of a lamp bulb gets hotter, the color changes from dull red to yellowish to blue-white (or "white hot"). You can probably see that the color of a glowing hot object is a good measure of how hot it is. Thus we know that blue-white stars have higher surface temperatures than our yellowish sun. Likewise red stars such as Betelgeuse and Antares are cooler than our sun.

Measurements of the color of the red star Antares show us that its surface has a temperature of 3000° C., only half as hot as the sun. Thus *each square inch* of Antares' glowing surface is giving out much less light and heat than our sun is. Now this is rather odd because other measurements show us that altogether the whole surface of Antares is pouring forth a total of 2000 times as much energy as our sun is. The only sensible conclusion we can draw from these two facts is that Antares, while cooler, is also very much bigger than our

sun. How much bigger? About 160 times as big in diameter! This star is as large across as Mars' path around the sun. Betelgeuse and a few other red stars are even larger. They are truly *red giants*.

Most of the stars are, however, much more like the sun. The white-hot stars, like Sirius, Vega, and Deneb, have diameters only a few times that of the sun. All of the sun-sized stars are known as "dwarfs" in comparison to the red "giants."

Star Sleuthing

In his study of stars, all the astronomer has to work with are faint specks of light that he examines. Yet what a wealth of information he gets from this light! He can, for example, tell how hot a star is, its chemical composition, and how fast a star is moving toward or away from the earth.

Much of this information is obtained through an instrument used for the analysis of light — the spectrograph — a combination of a spectroscope and camera (Fig. 33-2). Apart from the telescope itself, the spectrograph is the astronomer's most valuable tool.

A large telescope, which is used as a light trap, collects as much light as possible and feeds it into a spectroscope (Fig. 32-2). A spectroscope is an instrument that breaks up light into its colors. As you may remember from Chapter 28, the resultant breakup of light into its separate colors is known as a spectrum (see front end papers).

Thus when the telescope captures the light from a distant star, the spectroscope spreads out all its separate colors. When this spectrum is photographed astronomers can then carefully examine it.

The spectrum of a star seems to be a continuous band of color like that of a rainbow. You can see this by pointing a spectroscope (Fig. 28-8) at the sun. But a more careful look reveals dark lines cutting across the spectrum. First seen in 1814 by the German scientist Fraunhofer, these lines were not explained until nearly 50 years later. A continuous band of color comes from a hot solid (like the filament of a light bulb), a hot liquid, or a hot gas under great pressure like the inner parts of the sun. Cooler gases through which the continuous light may pass, like the outer layers of the sun, absorb their particular colors. The absorption of these colors by the cooler gas shows up as the dark lines which appear cutting across the continuous spectrum.

In the laboratory you can discover that each different chemical element has its own pattern of lines of absorption of light from the spectrum. These have been called the " fingerprints of the elements " (see page 325). When they appear, we know that a certain element is present. By careful comparison of the spectra of distant stars with those of laboratory materials, many of the chemicals in a distant star can be identified!

In the laboratory we also find that the pattern of lines in, say, the spectrum of vaporized sodium will change in a definite way as the sodium's temperature increases. And this is true of all the other elements. Knowing this, an astronomer can, by examining a star's spectrum, find its surface temperature.

The Doppler Shift

Even more information can be found from a star's spectrum. Usually all the patterns of lines in a star's spectrum are shifted a little toward the red or the blue as compared to the lines of a spectrum produced in the laboratory on earth. What does this mean? As Fig. 33-3 shows, the light from a

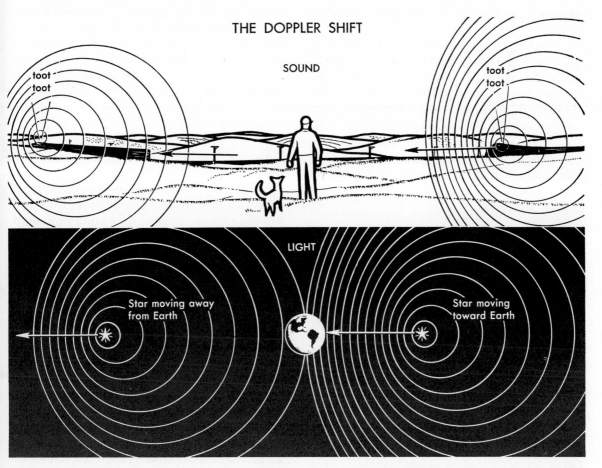

THE DOPPLER SHIFT

SOUND

toot toot

toot toot

LIGHT

Star moving away from Earth

Star moving toward Earth

33-3. Sound from an approaching source is shorter in wave length and hence higher in pitch than if the source were standing still. From a receding source the pitch is lower. This is called the Doppler shift in pitch. Light from a moving source is changed in the same way.

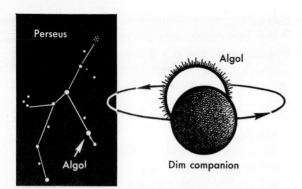

33-4. The dimming or winking of the star Algol in the constellation of Perseus is caused by a companion star that circles around it.

star moving toward the earth will have a slightly higher " pitch " and seem a bit bluer than if it were not moving toward us. If the star is moving away, the light is shifted a bit toward the red. The greater the speed, the greater the shift. From the amount of these shifts, astronomers can measure speeds as slight as two or three miles per second.

Some stars are rushing toward us at speeds up to 60 miles a second. The North Star, Polaris, on the other hand, is running away from us at 15 miles every second. It is several hundred miles farther away from you now than when you started to read this section.

Multiple Stars

Aside from a star's twinkling — an effect due to changes in the earth's atmosphere — you might think that stars have constant brightness. But even your unaided eye will show you a few surprises. With the help of a star map and Fig. 33-4 you may want to locate the star named Algol. Watching Algol nightly long ago, the Arabs noticed this star growing dim for several hours every 2.9 days. No wonder the name they gave it means " the demon."

Does this remarkable wink mean that Algol is running low on its hydrogen fuel supply? Not at all. Algol has a dim companion star that circles it. When the dark companion comes between Algol and us, it cuts off some of Algol's light. Thus Algol is partly eclipsed every few days.

Many other stars have companions, too. In fact, about one third of all the stars you see are really double, or even triple, stars, endlessly wheeling round and round one another. Several of them, like the Algol pair, are lined up in such a way, relative to the earth, that you can see them cut off one another's light from time to time. With a telescope, over a thousand such eclipsing stars have been found through their rhythmic change in brightness.

Many other double stars, not properly lined up to appear as eclipsing, can nevertheless be detected through the Doppler shift. In their orbital motion about each other, the two stars will regularly swing toward, then away from, the earth. As a result, their spectra will just as regularly be shifted — to the blue as they swing toward us, to the red as they move away. Whenever an astronomer observes this recurring shift in the spectrum of a star, he can conclude that the star is actually double — another use of the spectrograph as an instrument for probing the universe of stars.

Stars That Pulsate

As astronomers looked more and more closely at the sky, they began to find a great many stars whose brightness varies. Such stars are called *variable stars*. At first astronomers thought all these variable stars were eclipsing stars like Algol. But when the observations for many were studied, the calculations showed the nonsensical result that

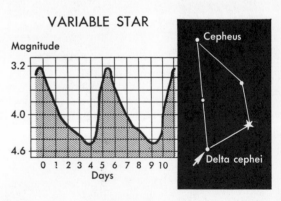

33-5. Some stars change in brightness without being eclipsed. These stars, like Delta in the northern constellation of Cepheus, regularly swell up and shrink with a change in brightness.

one of the stars would have to be inside the other star. They then realized that many of these variable stars must actually be single stars — stars that expand, then shrink, rhythmically.

A well-known example of such a star, which you can observe, is Delta in the faint constellation of Cepheus (SEE-fyoos) near Cassiopeia (kas-ee-oh-PEE-ah) (Fig. 33-5). This star takes 5.366 days to go through one complete cycle of variation in brightness. Year after year it repeats the same variations of brightness. The North Star also varies in brightness by about 10 per cent every four days. Many of these stars which vary regularly, like Delta in Cepheus, are called *Cepheid variables*. All these Cepheid variables are at least a hundred times more luminous than our sun.

In 1912, a woman astronomer, Henrietta Leavitt of the Harvard Observatory, discovered that the Cepheid variables with the slowest wink were the most luminous. This discovery was the key that astronomers needed to help them measure the size of the universe!

For now when astronomers find a Cepheid variable star, they measure the time between its winks. From the time between winks they know how luminous it really is — "long time between winks" means "very luminous." When they know how luminous a star *is* and they observe how bright it *looks,* it is easy for them to figure out how far away it must be. Here at last is a method for measuring the distances of stars too far away to show a parallax shift. Of course, not all stars are Cepheid variable stars. But most of the big important groups of stars we'll look at shortly have at least a few Cepheid variables within them.

There is still a third kind of star whose brightness changes. Occasionally some sharp-eyed observer notices in the sky or on an astronomical photograph a star not seen before. This is a *nova* or "new star." Actually, it is a star which within a few days becomes thousands of times brighter (Fig. 33-6). We may notice such stars when they are bright, but they are not actually "new." For reasons not well understood, these stars seem to "burp" out a cloud of hot, bright gas. After a few days or weeks they begin to fade and return

Mt. Wilson Observatory

33-6. Nova Persei, 1901. This star flared up a millionfold in brightness in a few days (top). The bottom picture was taken seven months later when the brightness had declined.

to about their original brightness.

Much more rarely a star suddenly becomes millions of times brighter; this is a *supernova*. When brightest, such a star may be a hundred million times more luminous than our sun (Fig. 33-7). We are seeing a star in the process of blowing up! Here is an explosion that makes even the fury

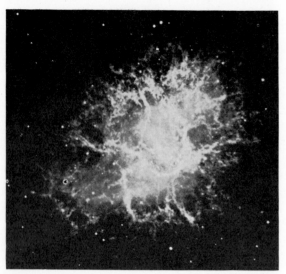

Mt. Wilson Observatory

33-7. The Crab Nebula in Cancer, as seen photographed through a large telescope. This star was seen as a supernova in 1054 A.D. Now it is surrounded by hot, expanding gases.

of our own sun's furnace look like a candle — the most stupendous explosion in the universe. Supernovas are quite rare. Fortunately, there is not much chance of our sun becoming one, at least as we now understand the nature of a supernova.

THE HISTORY OF STARS

You have read about multiple stars, pulsating stars, stars that explode, and stars like our sun which seem "well behaved." You have also read that stars come in a variety of sizes, masses, and colors or surface temperatures. All this knowledge from what at first appear only as pinpoints of light in the evening sky!

Can the modern astronomer make any sense out of this variety of stars? Is it possible that he is seeing stars in different stages of growth and development — that, for example, a blue star will later become cooler and redder? Is a supernova the last stage or death of certain stars? And what about the sun's family of planets? Is this, too, part of general star history, or is the solar system a unique feature of only one star — our sun?

We are going to take a brief look at these big questions — questions whose final solution will require detailed and patient examination of evidence as well as great imagination. Let us start with the last question first — the problem of the formation of a planetary system.

How Did Our World Begin?

Man has long speculated on the origin of the earth and the heavenly bodies. But not until Isaac Newton developed his laws of motion and gravitation did mankind have the basis for a scientific theory about the origin of the solar system.

Suppose we start with a gigantic cloud of gas drifting about in space, with all its atoms slowly rotating about some center. What will happen to these atoms? According to Newton's law of gravitation, gravitational force would pull these atoms closer together. While condensing, the spinning of the whole cloud would increase according to the same law by which a figure skater goes into a faster spin — he merely " condenses " his outstretched arms. Gradually, the cloud would flatten, just as the spin of our earth causes flattening at the poles and bulging at the equator. But the atoms of a gas are held together more loosely than the atoms of a solid planet. The swelling equatorial bulge of the gas cloud might finally tear away and surround the cloud like a great smoke ring (Fig. 33-8A). Suppose that as time went by, numerous gas rings tore away from the condensing cloud of gas. As each ring cooled, it might condense into a solid ball of matter, while the central gas cloud became the sun.

This gas cloud theory was proposed in 1796 by a French mathematician named Laplace. Do we still believe it to be a good theory today? No, for later mathematicians were able to show that each ring whirled off the sun would, instead of forming into a single body, condense into a whole string of droplets.

The Star-Encounter Theory

The rejected Laplace theory would have accounted not only for the formation of the planets but for the sun as well. The Star-Encounter Theory, on the other hand, says nothing about how stars are formed. It proposed that when two stars happened to pass close together, a huge amount of gas was pulled out and formed the planets (Fig. 33-8B).

According to this theory, planetary systems must be quite exceptional since the chance of two stars passing close like " ships in the night " is very, very slim indeed. But even if an encounter took place, it has recently been shown that the gas pulled out of the sun would, because of its high temperature, scatter before it could condense into planets.

The "Incompleted Double-Star" Theory

A recent theory to hold favor was proposed by the astronomer Gerard Kuiper. His concept of the origin of planets is also related to the formation of stars from large clouds of hydrogen gas drifting in space. Imagine two condensation centers in the process of forming within a gas cloud. One, because of local irregularities, might have ten times more gas than the other. The big mass continues to condense into a single star, but the smaller one cannot. The gravitational effect of the larger mass creates tidal disturbances in the smaller mass so that the gas of the smaller cloud breaks up into many small clouds. These are the *protoplanets* — the stuff out of which the planets will eventually form (Fig. 33-8C). This theory explains both the formation of planets and the existence of single stars. If the two clouds are about equal in size, a double star would result. (Almost half of the stars within some 150 light years of the sun are double stars, including our nearest stellar neighbor, Alpha Centauri.)

A theory of the origin of the solar system must account for everything we can presently observe about the solar system; for example, the sizes of the planets, their distances from the sun, the degrees of tipping of their orbits from the plane of the sun's equator, and the kinds of atoms of which the planets are made. You can see that astronomers who develop theories for the origin of the

solar system must meet strict standards!

But whether or not Kuiper's theory will prove satisfactory in all these details, most astronomers now seem to agree that planets may develop as one stage in the life cycle of a normal star.

The Life Cycle of a Star

No one has lived long enough to see a star form from the clouds of hydrogen gas that are widely distributed throughout certain regions of space. Hundreds of thousands or millions of years pass while the gas clouds slowly pull themselves together to form stars. But we do see dark clouds of gas that may in time form stars. Also astronomers find blue stars that are very hot and bright, and still surrounded by clouds of gas. These are probably very young stars — perhaps only a few million years old.

The original gas must have been drawn together by gravitational attraction until the temperature at the center got so high that the atoms were broken up into separate electrons and atomic nuclei. With further increases in temperature to over 20 million degrees, these nuclei would move with tremendous speeds and collide so vigorously that nuclear fusion would occur transforming a small part of their mass into radiant energy. (We shall look at this process in a moment, remembering that the hydrogen bomb, page 124, involves just such a nuclear reaction.)

The contracting gas has now begun its life as a fiery star. But consider the effect of the production of radiant energy upon the mass of contracting gas. There will be an outward radiation pressure which opposes, and may prevent, further contraction, or may even cause an expansion. Perhaps alternate stages of expansion and contraction take place before the battle between outward radiation pressure and inward gravitational attraction reaches at least a temporary balance.

The particular kinds of nuclear reactions that produce stellar energy may vary from one type of star to another. Different nuclear reactions may also occur in a star as it grows older.

For a star such as our sun, estimated to be

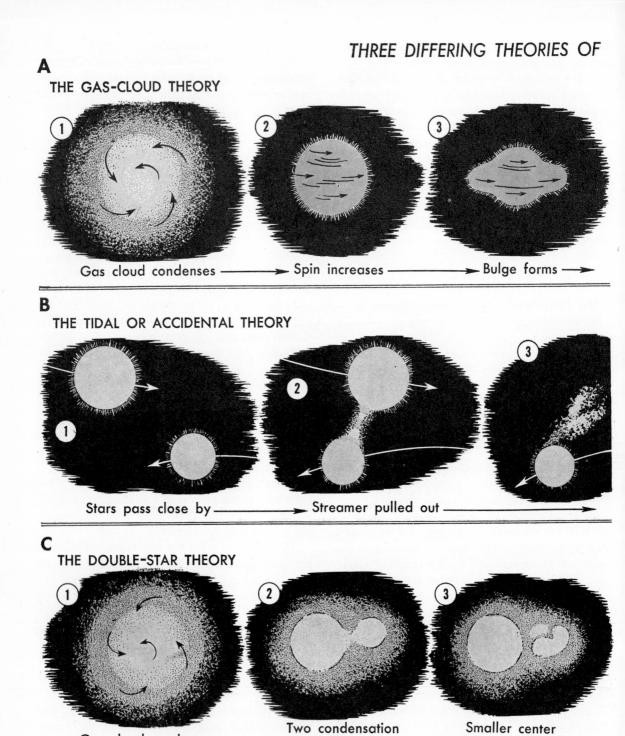

A THE GAS-CLOUD THEORY

Gas cloud condenses ──────⟶ Spin increases ──────⟶ Bulge forms ⟶

B THE TIDAL OR ACCIDENTAL THEORY

Stars pass close by ──────⟶ Streamer pulled out ──────────────⟶

C THE DOUBLE-STAR THEORY

Gas cloud condenses ──────⟶ Two condensation centers form ──⟶ Smaller center becomes unstable ⟶

33-8. One of man's greatest scientific adventures is his attempt to

THE ORIGIN OF THE SOLAR SYSTEM

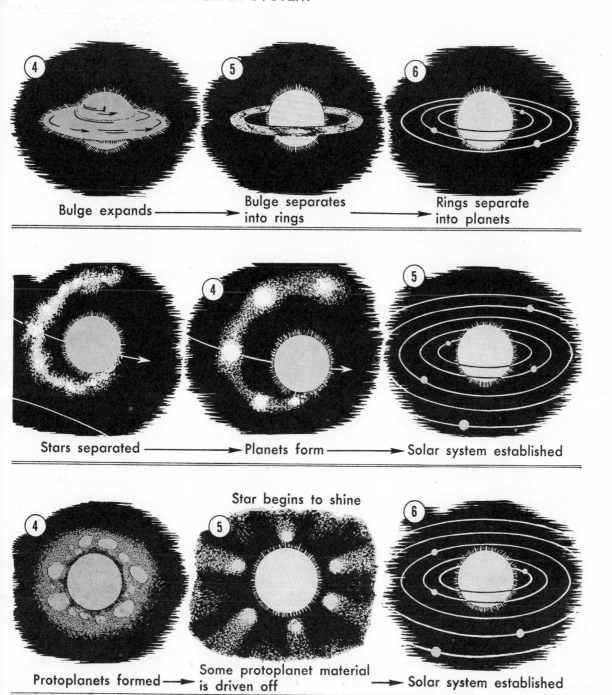

Bulge expands ⟶ Bulge separates into rings ⟶ Rings separate into planets

Stars separated ⟶ Planets form ⟶ Solar system established

Protoplanets formed ⟶ Some protoplanet material is driven off ⟶ Solar system established

Star begins to shine

develop satisfactory theories of the evolution of the solar system.

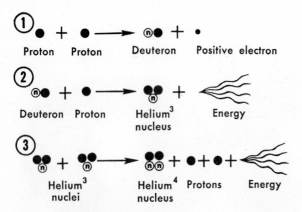

33-9. The nuclear process producing most of the sun's energy is the proton-proton cycle. (1) Two protons collide. One of the protons changes into a neutron by emission of a positive electron, and a deuteron, or heavy hydrogen nucleus, results. (2) The deuteron collides with a proton to form a helium[3] nucleus. The difference in mass between a helium[3] nucleus and the deuteron and proton separately is converted into energy. Finally, (3) two helium[3] nuclei collide to form an ordinary helium[4] nucleus plus two protons; again, a difference in mass is converted to energy.

about 5 billion years old, the main nuclear reaction has been shown to be the " proton-proton cycle " (Fig. 33-9). The net result of this reaction is the conversion of four protons (hydrogen nuclei) into a helium nucleus. In the course of each such cycle, a minute amount of mass is converted into energy according to Einstein's famous $E = mc^2$ formula.

What do we think will happen when a star such as our sun converts much of its hydrogen into helium? As the sun's core, where the proton-proton cycle operates, becomes surrounded by helium the radiant energy will have more and more difficulty escaping to the surface. At the core, the trapped radiation will build up the temperature enormously and produce an outward pressure. As a result, there will undoubtedly be a change in the size of the sun. In perhaps three billion years it may swell up, engulfing the inner planets, or even become a nova.

Finally, as the remaining nuclear fuel of the sun is consumed or blown away, the sun will shrink rapidly to end its life as it began — a contracting body of gas — but with its nuclear " fires " now largely quenched.

THE PATTERN OF THE UNIVERSE

You may wonder how the stars and cosmic gas are distributed in space. Is there a generally uniform scattering throughout all space or is there some other, more highly organized structure to the starry universe? Perhaps you are also wondering whether the thousands of stars visible to us came from a common parent body of gas.

Again, you can get at least the beginning of an answer for yourself by looking into the night sky.

The Milky Way

On a clear moonless night, go out well away from the city lights and look at the way the stars are scattered about the sky. You will notice at once that in some directions you can see more stars than in others. The faint band of light where you see the most stars is called the *Milky Way*.

When Galileo in 1609 looked at the Milky Way with his little telescope, hardly stronger than a pair of modern binoculars, he found that much of the light of the Milky Way came from many, many faint stars. Through modern telescopes, even more faint stars are photographed. Away from the Milky Way the stars are fewer.

What can this mean? It looks as if the stars are arranged in the shape of a great flat disc, rather like a fried egg (Fig. 33-10). Since the Milky Way is much brighter in one direction than in the opposite direction, it also appears that our sun and its planets are out near one edge of the system — far out in the white of the egg.

When the distances of the stars in the Milky Way from the earth were measured, astronomers found they do indeed form just such a disc. The disc is close to 100,000 light years across and 20,000 light years thick. From the outside it must look something like Fig. 33-10.

Now a great collection of stars arranged in this way could not stay flattened unless it were rotat-

Harvard College Observatory

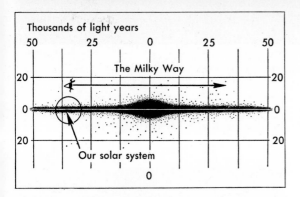

33-10. Our Milky Way system is a great rotating galaxy made up of gas and billions of stars. In the photograph the bright star near the left edge is Alpha Centauri, the nearest known star to the sun. The dark areas are caused by clouds of gas and dust between the sun and the distant stars.

ing. When astronomers make very careful measurements of the motions and distribution of the stars in various parts of the sky, they find them arranged in spiral arms whirling about a central accumulation of stars — like an enormous Fourth of July pinwheel. One trip of our sun all the way around takes 200 million years. Since our sun's family of planets was formed, it has probably made over 20 trips around. This vast pinwheel of stars contains all the stars you can see and at least 1000 million more stars besides, visible only through telescopes. It is called a *galaxy* — the Milky Way galaxy.

In recent years it has been discovered that the stars within the Milky Way Galaxy seem to be divided into two major groups, called Population I and Population II.

Our sun belongs to Population I. These stars are generally found in the spiral arms of the galaxy in regions where there is much cosmic hydrogen and dust. Population I stars are relatively young or middle-aged, and some still gather in the cosmic hydrogen from which they originally were formed.

Population II stars lie toward the center of the galaxy and, perhaps, in the space between the spiral arms in regions relatively free of cosmic hydrogen. Population II stars are older; long ago they swept up their original nuclear fuel of cosmic hydrogen.

If you look more closely at the Milky Way, you will find many interesting objects in addition to the individual stars. For example, you will find great *clusters* of stars moving together through space. The Pleiades (PLEE-yuh-deez) is a small

33-11. The Seven Sisters, or Pleiades: stars surrounded by a haze of hydrogen which they illuminate.

cluster of this sort that you can see easily with your unaided eye (Fig. 33-11). There are much bigger clusters, too, some of them containing millions of stars (Fig. 33-12). You can see one of these with your unaided eye. It appears as a faint, fuzzy blob, 34,000 light years away in the constellation of Hercules. Try locating it some clear summer evening with the aid of Fig. 33-13.

There are great clouds of dust and gas in the Milky Way, too. Much of this gas is not itself giving off visible radiation. But it can be detected through radio telescopes, which are increasingly useful in astronomical research. These new additions to the astronomer's arsenal of instruments are basically huge radio aeriels (Fig. 33-15, p. 411) and are capable of being accurately tuned in on radio waves emitted by cold hydrogen gas floating in space far beyond our solar system. By directing the antenna to different regions of the sky, and through co-operation between radio astronomers throughout the world, a map of the cosmic hydrogen distribution is built up for the entire sky.

When a cloud of gas is near a hot bright star, it may be made to glow brightly like the gas in the familiar neon sign. When this happens you see a *nebula* (NEB-yoo-luh), or luminous gas cloud, like

33-12. The Hercules star cluster: thousands of stars drawn together by gravitational attraction.

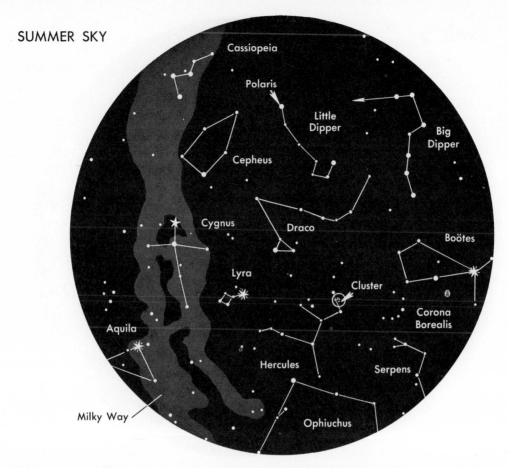

33-13. This map shows the position of the constellations during the month of May. Compare their location with the map in Fig. 33-14. Such star charts are published for all months of the year and are very useful in doing serious star-gazing.

the famous nebula in the constellation of Orion, which can be located by using Fig. 33-14. Although you can just barely see the Orion nebula with your naked eye, it is really so big that light takes 15 years just to go *across* it. It is in such nebulae that the hot blue stars are thought to be born. We find hundreds of nebulae scattered about in the great circular arch of the Milky Way.

Sometimes the clouds of gas and dust have no hot star near enough to make them glow. Then they merely cut off the light of stars very much farther away, much as rain clouds darken the light of our own sun. This is the reason for the dark patches you see among the stars in Fig. 33-10.

Other Life in the Milky Way?

Serious efforts are underway to explore the possibilities that intelligent beings exist on planets moving about other stars. Amazing as this may seem, many scientists have concluded that such life may exist and may even be sending radio signals to us!

The theory runs like this. We now believe that the formation of planetary systems around certain stars is a common occurrence. Possibly 1 in 20 stars would have planets at distances favorable for temperatures like the temperature range on earth. To be life-bearing, the planets would also need to be of the proper mass to retain, by gravitational

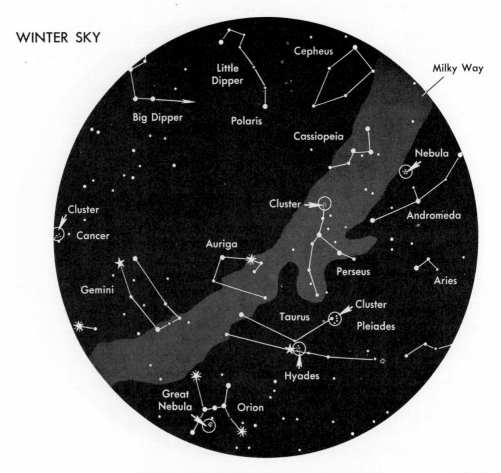

WINNING SKY

33-14. The winter sky as seen from the United States about 9 P.M. in January to 7 P.M. in February. To use this star map, face south and hold the map up over your head. The bright yellow star nearly overhead is Capella in Auriga.

attraction, an atmosphere which is neither too dense nor too thin. If the mass of a planet were too great the atmosphere retained might be so dense that life-supporting radiation from its sun would be blocked. If, on the other hand, the mass of a planet were too small, the atmosphere retained would be too thin, and incoming radiation would be of deadly intensity. Out of the suspected hundreds of thousands of planetary systems, however, some planets could be both of the proper mass and the right distance from their sun.

Today scientists know something of how the essential ingredients of living matter could have been built-up from the mixture of chemical sub-

stances believed to have existed on the earth long ago.[1] Similar chemical mixtures may exist on planets formed by other stars, for the spectroscope tells us that many stars have a chemical composition like that of our sun.

[1] The major chemical structures in all living cells are the giant molecules of various proteins. And all proteins are composed of combinations of some 21 amino acids. In 1953, an experiment by Dr. Stanley Miller and Prof. Harold Urey showed that at least three of the amino acids could be formed by passing electric sparks through a mixture of gases including ammonia, methane and water vapor. It is this very mixture which is believed to have composed the early atmosphere of the earth.

To imagine that living things might exist on the planets of other solar systems is quite a change from the viewpoint of a few hundred years ago, when men thought that the earth was the center of everything. Now we know that the earth revolves around the sun and that the sun is only an average star like millions of others in our galaxy. That life may, therefore, exist elsewhere on other planets of other stars is not a wild conclusion.

But to have living matter on another planet does not mean that it can produce radio signals. Only within the last century have we on the earth learned how to send and receive radio signals. In other solar systems, life may have developed long ago to the same point. Can you imagine intelligent beings on another planet wondering, as we do, if life exists elsewhere? How would they find out? Would they send strong pulses of radio signals in some sort of code toward each of the nearer stars? Possibly this would be in the form of 1, 2, 3, and then 4 dots. Such patterns do not occur by chance.

With the great radio transmitters and radio telescopes now built or being built, detectable signals can be sent as far as 100 light years. Within that distance from the sun are perhaps 10,000 stars. Already, giant radio telescopes (Fig. 33-15) have been pointed to selected stars that might have planetary systems, and a careful search begun for patterned signals. If any are detected, strong blasts of radio signals will then be sent out. Possibly years later an answering signal will be picked up. Surely, this is a long-term project. To send a radio signal to the nearest star and get back a reply would take nearly 9 years. For the farthest stars we can reach with our transmitters, 100 light years away, the reply would come 200 years after our signal was sent.

There is even a best wave length on which to send such signals. This is a wave length like that emitted by cosmic hydrogen. Any beings at, or beyond, our level of scientific development would probably have discovered this radiation. They would probably conclude that others elsewhere would be exploring the location of hydrogen in space and be likely to pick up their signal on a

British Information Service

33-15. The radio telescope at Jodrell Bank, England, has a steerable 250-foot "dish" which can aim accurately at various points in the sky.

wave length close to that of cosmic hydrogen.

It is possible that coded patterns of signals have been aimed at the sun and earth for centuries. Admittedly, the chances of success are perhaps one in a million. Yet, as in all of science, we shall never know unless we try. But imagine the thrill if *you* were the one to pick up such a signal!

Island Universes

In the constellation of Andromeda (an-DROM-eh-duh) you can see a faint, fuzzy blob with your unaided eye. Astronomers have found that this blob cannot be part of the Milky Way. The farthest objects in the Milky Way are about 100,000 light years away. Yet that tiny blob of light must be 1,500,000 light years away! Observations of Cepheid variable stars found in the blob assure us that this must be its distance away from us. A good look through a big telescope shows us that we are looking at another galaxy similar to our own.

This galaxy is the most distant thing you can see with your unaided eye. It is so far away that its light, racing toward you at 186,000 miles every second, had already been on its way to the earth

33-16. A spiral galaxy seen edge-on presents this appearance. The almost solid appearing edge is composed of millions of stars and cosmic hydrogen.

for more than a million years when the earliest cave men were living on earth.

This galaxy, with a spiral shape similar to our own, has in it the same sorts of objects we have just seen in the Milky Way. It has its dust clouds and nebulae, its clusters and its variable stars, just as our galaxy does. It is easy to wonder if there may not be suns like ours, too, with planets some of which, like our earth, carry living things.

There are other galaxies, too, visible only through telescopes (Fig. 33-16). Some are detectable only by radio telescopes. In fact, there are over 100 million galaxies — many of them vast islands of stars like our own Milky Way.

Many galaxies are spirals with different degrees of development of the spiral arms. Some have no spiral arms at all; others look torn and shredded, perhaps by a collision with another galaxy. Astronomers today are busy trying to find out how these great star systems develop and whether their various forms indicate that we are seeing galaxies in varying stages of evolution.

All of these galaxies together, including our own Milky Way, make up what we call the *universe*.

The History of the Universe

The fainter, more distant, galaxies are moving away from us. We know this because a spectroscope shows that the color of their light is shifted toward the red. What is more, when the shift in color is measured (Fig. 33-17), we find that the farthest galaxies seem to be racing away from us the fastest, some as fast as 50,000 miles a second. This surprising discovery has given rise to the term " expanding universe," for if all the galaxies

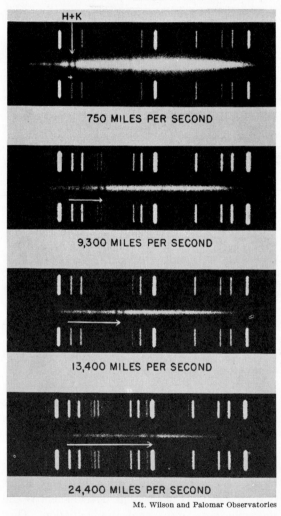

H+K

750 MILES PER SECOND

9,300 MILES PER SECOND

13,400 MILES PER SECOND

24,400 MILES PER SECOND

33-17. The farther away a galaxy, the more its spectral lines — in this case, hydrogen (H) and potassium (K) — shift to the red. This in turn, shows the more distant a galaxy, the faster it recedes.

are getting farther from us, they are getting farther from one another, too.

According to one viewpoint, if the universe has always been expanding at its present rate, then some six to eight thousand million years ago all the galaxies must have been jammed together. All the material and all the energy of the universe would have been squeezed together in a very hot and very small volume — a sort of " cosmic egg." We can only guess what this was like as we reconstruct what might have happened.

" In the beginning," this cosmic egg may have been filled with neutrons at a temperature of several billion degrees. This egg exploded. Within the first few minutes the neutrons would have combined rapidly and built up the present supply of atoms of the lighter chemical elements. Within a short time, the expansion would have cooled the material so much that atom-building would stop. After that the parts, often whirling like eddies in a stream, would move away from each other, gradually forming into separate galaxies. Within each galaxy, stars (and perhaps even a few planets around some of the stars) would form from the swirling gas.

Another theory of the origin of the universe suggests something different from the " exploding egg " idea. Perhaps matter is somehow created in the space of the universe. This theory holds that there was no " cosmic egg " beginning of the universe and neither will there be any end. The universe could be in a " steady state " of existence — thus for every galaxy that tends to fly away from us into remotest space, enough new gas appears to form a new galaxy.

If the fuel of the stars consists of hydrogen atoms that are " burned " to form helium, then the steady-state theory must somehow account for the production of new " fuel " in the universe as fast as the old fuel is consumed. On this basis, we can estimate the necessary rate of production of new hydrogen atoms. Imagine a section of space the size of an ordinary room. If one hydrogen atom were created inside that space every 1000 years, this would be enough to replenish the hydrogen of the universe. And so, the matter of the universe would just go on being at about the same concentration forever.

Which of the two theories is correct — the " exploding-egg " theory, or the steady-state? Is either correct? We do not yet have enough information to know. The expansion of the universe seems easiest to understand from the idea of an " exploding egg " origin, but calculations of the amount of matter and its concentration in space seem to favor the steady-state concept. Perhaps neither of these theories is correct, and new knowledge and understanding will give rise to better theories of the history of the universe.

Looking Back . . . .

VOCABULARY

The following expressions are some of the key words in this chapter. Show that you understand them by defining each term.

1. light year
2. luminosity
3. multiple stars
4. Cepheid variables
5. nova
6. supernova
7. Milky Way
8. galaxy
9. nebula
10. universe
11. star cluster
12. constellation
13. Doppler shift
14. proton-proton cycle
15. steady-state universe
16. cosmic hydrogen
17. protoplanet

REVIEW QUESTIONS

1. In what ways is our sun a typical star?
2. What part of the sun is observed well only during a total eclipse of the sun?
3. Compared to the sun, how much more or less luminous are some of the stars?
4. How can you tell that some stars are hotter and others cooler than the sun?
5. How is the spectrograph used for determining star temperature?
6. How can Cepheid variables be used to show their distances from the earth?
7. What is a possible life cycle for a star like the sun?
8. What is the shape of our galaxy which we see as the Milky Way?

9. Where in our galaxy is the sun located?
10. How many galaxies are known?

EXPLAIN WHY
- Early astronomers divided the zodiac into 12 constellations.
- Even the nearest stars through big telescopes never appear bigger than pinpoints of light.
- The most luminous stars are not always the brightest ones in the sky.
- Cepheid variable stars can be used to measure distances in the universe.
- The stars do not appear to move across the sky, even though some are traveling many miles a second.

Going Further . . . .

THOUGHT QUESTIONS
1. Explain how the speed of a star's motion toward, or away from, the earth can be measured.
2. What is meant by the "expanding universe"?
3. What evidence do we have that many other galaxies are similar to our Milky Way?

THINGS TO DO
1. Locate and identify several of the largest constellations. Record also the names of the brightest stars in each of these constellations, and their colors. Find out as much as you can about the distances, luminosities, and possible companions of these bright stars.
2. Look for pictures showing spectra of the stars. Note especially spectra of double stars which show two sets of spectral lines.
3. With binoculars observe some of the brighter star clusters and nebulae.
4. Make a model of the Milky Way indicating the position of the sun.
5. With binoculars observe the Great Galaxy in Andromeda, marked on some star maps as M-31. Find pictures of it made with large telescopes showing its individual stars, star clusters, and nebulae.

READING FURTHER
Introducing the Universe by James C. Hickey, Dodd, 1951
The Real Book About Stars by Harold L. Goodwin, Garden City Books, 1951
Book of the Stars by Louis Sutherland, Bernard Ackerman, 1944
The Stars: Stepping Stones into Space by Irving Adler, New American Library (paperback), 1958

34

Exploration in Space

Thirty-three chapters ago, you began this book by reading about " our home in space " — the earth. Actually, our home *is* space, for the earth itself is a space traveler, following (as well as revolving around) our sun.

Today man has become dissatisfied with the " flight schedule " of his earth. Any morning's newspaper is likely to headline his next advance toward developing his own space plans.

WHY SPACE RESEARCH?

Men are curious. They want to go where they haven't been before, see what they haven't seen before, know what they haven't known before. No sooner had they learned how to build ships that would sail the oceans than they began to wander far from their homelands. As they also learned better ways to tell their position on earth while at sea, they began to chart the whole globe.

Eventually men learned to make " lighter-than-air " balloons, then airplanes, and they began to explore the atmosphere. Today they make rockets powerful enough to escape the earth altogether, and it is only a matter of time until they climb aboard their space-bound rockets for a trip to the moon or elsewhere. Already they have succeeded in manned space flight around the earth, and they have sent valuable payloads of scientific instruments to and around the moon, toward Venus, and into orbit around the sun.

Today, almost all that we know of what lies beyond our atmosphere — the rest of the solar system, the stars, and the vast reaches of space between the stars — we have learned from a study of incoming light, both visible and invisible. But our surrounding atmosphere cuts off much ultraviolet and infrared light from which we could get more information. In our studies of local space as well as the more distant heavenly bodies, our atmosphere has been a nuisance. Here is one important reason for using rockets to send up space satellites. The proper instruments, once they are orbiting hundreds of miles up, can gather and relay back to us information without much interference from our atmosphere. Think what it will mean for astronomy when we can get telescopes and spectrographs up beyond our obscuring atmosphere to provide photographs of the planets and stars.

Biology, too, will benefit from space research. For example, we know next to nothing of what prolonged living in the absence of the earth's gravity and rotation may mean in terms of changes in animal behavior. Animals born in space satellites (where they will be weightless) may grow up with interesting changes in their activity that might cast light on just how gravity influences life here on earth. And there is, of course, the possibility of investigating alien life on Mars and, less likely, on Venus. That is why scientists insist that rockets intended to land upon or pass very close to these planets be carefully sterilized upon leaving the earth. Otherwise they might infect Mars and Venus with earth bacteria which, if they spread rapidly, might make it impossible ever to tell what the alien life was like in its original state.

There seems no limit to the possibilities for space projects. You yourself may come up with a new idea for employing space satellites and rocket-borne laboratories in the search for answers to puzzles of the universe.

We are soon going to take a look at some results of our initial ventures into space. But before you learn *what* we are finding out about space it will be interesting to see *how* space explorations are carried out.

ROCKETS AND SATELLITES

You have already read why a rocket is best suited for its job — it carries its own fuel and oxygen and can therefore travel far up into or even beyond the atmosphere. Also, its rate of acceleration (that is, change in velocity) is small as it rises through the denser air near the ground. This is an important advantage. If a rocket were started abruptly at a speed of 5 miles a second (18,000 miles an hour), it would be melted by friction between its surfaces and the air. Delicate scientific instruments would probably collapse or be badly damaged and any passengers would be crushed.

If, in theory, rockets are admirably suited for their job, in actual development they nonetheless present many problems to their designers. Among these problems fuel, guidance systems, and tracking systems are most critical.

The Problem of Fuel

Raising rockets to great heights requires high-energy fuels that produce a large force, or thrust, for each pound burned. Think of an explorer who must carry all his food on his back. How far he can go depends upon how much he can carry. Naturally he takes food with the most energy concentrated in the least weight. He knows, too, that the last meal of his trip must be carried all the way.

You would think our explorer very silly if he carried his food in a heavy refrigerator. You would expect him instead to carry light packages and to throw them away when they are empty. This is just what is done with rocket fuels.

At present no *single* rocket carrying a substantial payload is powerful enough to break away from the earth or reach altitudes of hundreds of miles. However, several rockets together can, as you may remember (Fig. 16-11, p. 195). When

the first rocket has burned up its fuel, it is cast off. Then the fuel in the second rocket burns. This rocket has less of a load to push, so it can accelerate to a greater speed. When it is burned out, it too falls off, and the fuel in the third-stage rocket burns and provides still greater acceleration. When the third rocket is out of fuel, our three-stage rocket has finally reached its greatest speed. It is at this point that placing a satellite into orbit around the earth is possible. On the trip upward, the satellite has been protected within the strong nose cone of the three-stage rocket. The nose cone now opens, and the satellite, containing a radio transmitter and other equipment, is propelled from the rocket by a spring. The rocket and the satellite have nearly the same speed, so both often move around the earth together.

Until Sputnik I was launched in 1957, the record rocket flight had been about 650 miles up from the earth. This had been made earlier the same year by the United States Army Jupiter rocket.

Sputnik II soon followed. It was not a little ball, like Sputnik I, but the whole rockethead, which weighed about half a ton — including a dog. It is estimated that the take-off thrust of the Russian rocket that put Sputnik II into orbit was 600,000 pounds. The Russians said that they had used a new fuel, like boron hydride, to power this rocket. Several such fuels are known, but all are so explosive that they are difficult to handle. However, a powerful *solid fuel* like boron hydride is preferable to a *liquid fuel* of the same energy yield per pound because the latter requires elaborate fuel pumps which take up space and weight that a solid-fuel rocket could use for either more fuel or more payload.

At present, much research is being done on both solid and liquid fuels.

The Problem of Orbit

Why does a satellite move in its orbit without returning to earth? After all, satellites are not driven by engines, as rockets are. Evidently artificial satellites move much like the moon, the earth's natural satellite. But then why is it that

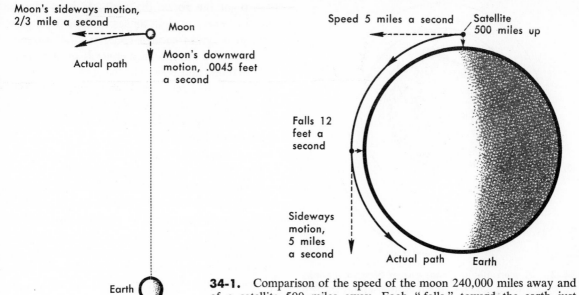

34-1. Comparison of the speed of the moon 240,000 miles away and of a satellite 500 miles away. Each "falls" toward the earth just enough each second to stay in a path around the earth.

the moon does not fall to earth? As you probably know, this is a question that puzzled Isaac Newton almost three hundred years ago.

Newton devised an explanation that was to destroy the notion of heavenly bodies acting upon each other with forces different from those acting upon the earth. He speculated that the same force of gravity that pulled an apple to earth was also pulling on the moon. In fact he proposed that gravitational attraction was universal — that all bodies in the universe attracted each other. But if gravitational attraction alone influenced the moon, it would certainly fall as an apple does. The reason it does not fall is that it is moving at great speed sideways, or at right angles to the earth's pull.

Suppose, for a moment, that there were no gravitational attraction. Then the moon would simply continue its own motion in a straight line off into space away from the earth. Galileo first led us to recognize that *when a body is moving, it keeps moving with steady speed in a straight line unless acted on by an external force.* Now Newton reasoned that there is such a force acting — namely, the earth's gravitational attraction. The earth's pull on the moon opposes the moon's tend-

ency to fly away in a straight line. Every second, the moon moves about two thirds of a mile along its path. But every second, due to the earth's pull, *it also falls toward the earth* by 0.0045 feet ($\frac{1}{20}$ of an inch). The combination of these two motions — constantly sideways *and* accelerating downward — results in the moon's traveling in its nearly circular path (Fig. 34-1).

Now how about a satellite? If released from a rocket fired straight out from the earth at, say, five miles a second, it would certainly reach a great height. But after a while it will fall back to earth. The trick is to have the rocket gradually turn on its way up until, just before the satellite is released, the rocket is moving at right angles to the earth's gravitational pull. When released, the satellite will then, like the moon, have both a sideways and a downward motion. And, provided its sideways motion is in proper ratio to its downward motion, the resulting curved path will just match the curvature of the earth — it will continue to fall around the earth without getting any closer (Fig. 34-2).

Let us again compare a satellite's motion with that of the moon. If a satellite were 500 miles up,

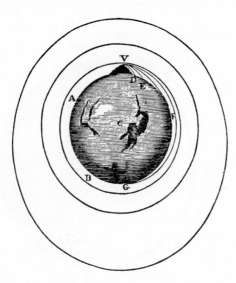

34-2. A reproduction from one of Newton's books showing his original conception of how a body thrown from earth could go into orbit.

the earth's pull on it would be about three fourths the force of gravity at the earth's surface. Since a body near the earth's surface will fall 16 feet in a second, a satellite 500 miles up falls three fourths of 16 feet, or 12 feet, in a second. We can then calculate that to keep curving around the earth, the satellite must have a sideways speed (at right angles to the earth's pull) of almost 5 miles a second (Fig. 34-1).

Notice that since the satellite is closer to the earth than the moon is, the gravitational pull on it is greater. As a result the satellite falls toward the earth more rapidly — 12 feet per second as compared to .0045 feet per second for the moon. Thus the satellite must also have a greater velocity sideways if it is to stay in orbit — 5 miles each second instead of the moon's ⅔ of a mile per second.

And what is true of a satellite orbiting 500 miles up holds as well for any other distance. For each distance at which it orbits, a satellite must have just the right combination of sideways and downward motion if it is to keep curving around the earth.

Now you can see why launching a satellite is such a complicated job. The satellite must be sent

to a point far above the earth. It must also be aimed to move at right angles to the earth's gravity, and be given enough speed to "fall around" the earth. All the guidance controls must be carefully planned and built into the rocket before it is fired. And they must work as they are supposed to; otherwise, the rocket will fall back to earth, or the satellite will be released with the wrong speed or direction.

The Problem of Tracking a Satellite

Keeping track of a satellite's location is very important. Observations of position can be made in three ways — by radio, by photography, and by visual means.

If the satellite sends out radio signals, radio observers can record when it is in the sky over them. Of course, how long it will send out signals depends upon the type of battery used. A chemical battery will run down, but it may be recharged, as when a " solar battery " like a large photoelectric cell is used to create current that can be stored in the chemical battery. If the battery " goes dead," there are no radio signals and tracking is more difficult.

The radio signals will be on short waves that can go through the ionosphere to us below (see page 14). These short waves, which bend very little, will follow straight lines as light does. So an observer can receive the signals only when the satellite is in the sky above his horizon. On one trip around the earth, this will be for fifteen to thirty minutes, depending upon the distance of the satellite from the earth (Fig. 34-3).

From the diagram, you can see that the " beeps," or signals, from a satellite can be received over a large area. When it is five hundred miles from the earth, signals can be received over an area larger than the United States. When it is nearer the earth, the area is not so large.

However, just receiving radio signals from a satellite does not tell us much about its location. Directional antennas and radar are needed to locate it more exactly. The highly sensitive radio telescopes already mentioned in connection with astronomical research are also widely used in satel-

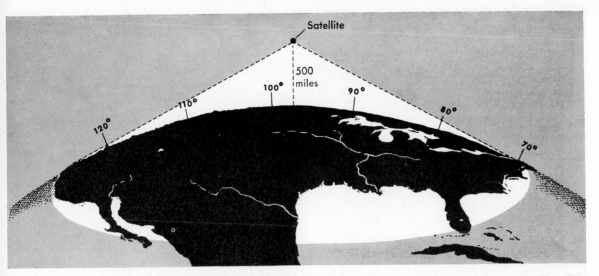

34-3. All of the United States and much of Canada would be able to receive signals from a satellite 500 miles above Minnesota. The numbers in degrees represent longitude.

lite as well as interplanetary rocket tracking.

You may yourself want to observe satellites in orbit. An observer needs to know the *time* when, and the *direction* in which, the satellite will appear. The direction should tell two things: where the satellite is *around the horizon* and where it is *above the horizon*. These should be given in angular measurements (Fig. 34-4). You know that there are 360° in a full circle and 90° in a right

angle. The direction around the horizon starts with 0° at North, goes eastward with 90° at East, 180° at South, and 270° at West. Also, there are 90° between the horizon and the point directly overhead.

A small body only a few feet across, even if highly polished, will not be very bright. Remember that it will be several hundred miles away. The final-stage rocket appears bigger and brighter.

34-4. Given the information pictured on this diagram, in what direction from where you are now would you look for a satellite? All location of objects, whether on the earth or in space, requires some method for indicating two directions. Such a system, once decided upon, becomes an international agreement making possible joint efforts by scientists throughout the world.

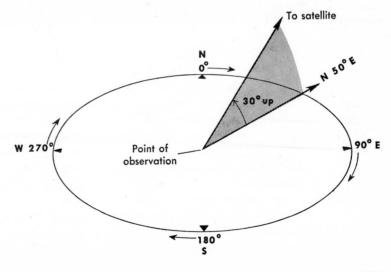

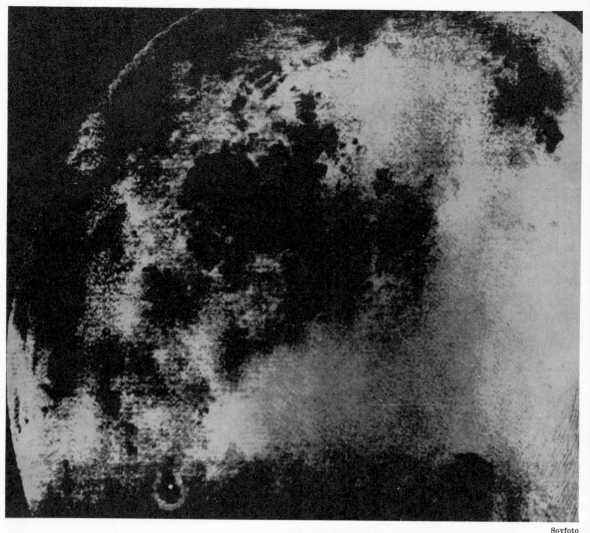

34-5. The first view of the moon's other face — a televised photograph from a Russian rocket.

Millions of people saw the rocket that carried Sputnik I, but few saw the fainter satellite.

Unless a satellite carries a light (and some may), you cannot see it at night, for both you and it are in the earth's shadow and no light falls on the satellite to be reflected to you. During the day the sky is too bright for us to see the stars — or a planet-like satellite. So the only time when we can see it is during twilight. Then the distant satellite high above us is still in sunlight, but we are in the earth's shadow and our sky is dark. You can see this effect by noticing that clouds a few miles high are often pink or red in bright sunlight after the sun has set for us on the earth.

The observations made in the United States and in other countries are put together to chart an orbit, or path, and to work out a time table for the satellite. This work is done, for example, at the Smithsonian Astrophysical Observatory in Cambridge, Massachusetts. The observations are fed into a giant computing machine (a so-called " electronic brain ") which quickly puts them together, making allowance for the earth's rotation, for the extra pull of the earth's bulge at the equator, and for the pull of the moon. The computing machine's analysis of the figures gives us a description of the satellite's path and a time table telling where it will be for the next few hours or days.

ROCKETS BEYOND THE EARTH

Up until now we have discussed the rocket primarily as an instrument for placing a satellite into orbit around the earth. But a rocket, or rather its final stage, can also be used to explore space far beyond the earth. In 1959, both the Americans and the Russians tried to hit or circle the moon but at first failed. Then, in September 1959, the Russians hit the moon. The rocket required 35 hours for the trip. A few months later, a Russian rocket went around behind the new moon, that is, while its far side was illuminated. A camera photographed this never-before-seen side of the moon. These pictures were developed automatically, then scanned and sent to earth by television (Fig. 34-5).

Both Russia and the United States have sent rocket-borne instruments into orbit around the sun. And with further careful planning we can even place such miniature laboratories into orbit around another planet. Of course, to accomplish this, the last stage of the rocket must first achieve escape velocity — about seven miles per second — before it can break away from the earth altogether and pursue a path into outer space. But this is only one of many problems involved in successful interplanetary explorations.

Gravity " Pits "

As you know, the earth's gravitational pull becomes less at increasing distances from the earth. We can think of this in terms of a great " gravity pit " about the earth. A smaller pit exists around the moon. To shoot a rocket to the moon is rather like a problem a golfer might have. Suppose that he is in a deep trap or valley. The cup (in this case, the moon) is on an in-sloping green on a high, flat surface some distance away. The golfer must blast his shot up out of the valley. Then the ball will roll (without friction in this case) toward the green. There it will " fall " toward the cup and speed up a bit. If he can aim the shot just right and hit the ball just hard enough, he can get the ball in the cup. But, unlike the golf cup, the moon is a moving target, even harder to hit. This is why the Russian moonshot in 1959 was so notable an accomplishment.

Earlier attempts by both Russia and the United States to hit the moon had failed. The rockets were swerved by the moon's gravitational field — that is, they " rimmed the cup " and moved into orbits around the sun to become the first two artificial planets. Radio contact with both was lost at about the moon's distance, so that we do not know for certain where they are.

Interplanetary Navigation

The first rockets that were sent to gather information about the sun or planets could not be navigated while in space. Once they escaped from the earth they pursued paths under the influence of their initial escape velocity as modified by the gravitational pull of the sun. To develop rockets whose control equipment enables us to guide them continuously to the desired region of the solar system poses many problems. One problem is to pack all the additional weight of fuel and equipment into the last stage and still provide enough lift energy to achieve escape velocity. Another problem is to develop radio instruments powerful enough to maintain constant contact over tens of millions of miles — so that we can know just where the rocket is and radio back signals for altering its course when necessary.

Until such time as navigable rockets were developed, the engineers who planned rocket flights had only the first few minutes of powered flight to accomplish all their aiming.

Early in 1961, a rocket scheduled to pass close to Venus was fired by Russia. It was designed to transmit back important data on the cloud-blanketed planet, but the mission failed.

But in August of 1962, the United States

launched its Venus probe — the 447-pound Mariner 2 spacecraft. Its ingenious navigation equipment enabled fine corrections to be made in its path during a 180-million-mile journey to the vicinity of Venus where it rendezvoused in mid-December. The data transmitted by Mariner 2 will, after analysis, add much to our knowledge of a planet which has long intrigued astronomers.

WHAT SPACE VEHICLES HAVE REVEALED

Since October 4, 1957, when the Soviet Sputnik ("traveler") opened the space age, both the United States and Russia have fired many satellites and space probes. What we have learned from these space projects has added much to our store of knowledge about both the earth and the space that surrounds it.

Satellites Study the Earth

Signals from satellites have provided much new knowledge about the earth and its atmosphere. For example, we now know that our atmosphere extends higher than we previously thought. This

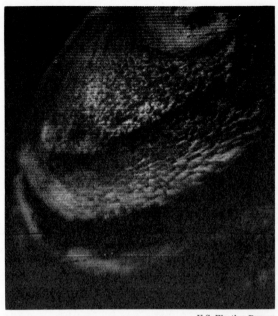

34-7. One of the many photographs taken by the Tiros satellite shows cloud formations associated with a storm 800 miles west of southern California.

means that the outer reaches of the atmosphere are hotter than previously calculated. Exposed to the direct radiation of the sun, the atmosphere above about 80 miles has a temperature averaging about 2000 degrees Fahrenheit, although this changes by some 600 degrees from the early morning to the late afternoon. Much has also been learned about the composition of the atmosphere. Perhaps most important is the discovery of great layers of oxygen, helium, and hydrogen which you saw diagrammed in Fig. 3-19, page 44.

Extensive weather observations are being transmitted from satellites. Since the weather in one part of the world is influenced by that elsewhere, truly world-wide weather information is essential. But observers in some parts of the world, like the polar regions and the middle of the oceans, are few and far between. Tiros (Fig. 34-6), the TV weather observation satellite, was fired into a 468-mile-high orbit around the earth in April 1960. Its sides were studded with 9200 solar cells to keep its batteries alive. Two TV cameras, one

34-6. One of the most useful satellites in the U.S. space program, Tiros transmits thousands of pictures of cloud formations from all over the world.

wide- and one narrow-angled, took pictures every 30 seconds, photographing 3500 miles of the earth's surface every 16 minutes. The pictures of cloud formations taken by Tiros over much of the earth has enabled skilled meteorologists to determine where storms are active, how they are moving, and what was likely to occur elsewhere (Fig. 34-7). From such observations of cloud patterns on the sunlit side of the earth new and better procedures for forecasting the weather on a worldwide basis will develop.

Even the size and shape of the earth can be studied from the motions of a satellite. As the satellite passes over areas on the earth with differing densities, the gravitational attraction of the earth upon the satellite varies. And small though these variations may be, they often are enough to cause detectable changes in the satellite's orbit. We can calculate what the orbit would be if the earth were perfectly round and had uniform mass throughout. Variations in the orbit allow us, therefore, to reconstruct the earth's true shape and the actual distribution of mass.

One series of observations has indicated that the earth has, in addition to its equatorial bulge, an extra bulge of some fifty feet in the Northern hemisphere. This raises many questions about the structure of the earth's interior.

The Space Environment

Explorer I, the first U.S. satellite sent up early in 1958, went up to 1552 miles at the highest point, or apogee (A-puh-jee), of its orbit around the earth. This satellite carried several Geiger counters to record the rate and kinds of cosmic rays that shower onto the earth. While these instruments worked well and radioed back information part of the time, at other times they failed and just sent a buzz. Apparently the equipment was not working properly. Then someone noticed that the buzz always came when the satellite was far from the earth in certain definite directions. Could the seeming failure really be a new discovery? It was. The equipment was overloaded with signals and could not work properly. Far above the earth there was a zone of intense radiation —

"clouds" of charged particles that triggered the equipment beyond its capacity to transmit.

Two major zones, or bands, of radiation were then thought to be detected and named the *Van Allen belts* after one of the leading scientists in this space research program. Later data gathered by satellites indicated, however, that the earth is ringed by only a *single* radiation band extending out from 30,000 to 40,000 miles (Fig. 34-9).

This great band of radiation, now known as the *magnetosphere*, is not to be thought of as part of the atmosphere. The magnetosphere is, rather, a region in which charged particles — electrons and protons — are trapped by the earth's magnetic field. (Recall from J. J. Thomson's experiments on the relation between the electron's mass and charge, that electrical particles are deflected by magnetic fields — see page 260.)

In 1960, a satellite called Pioneer V was sent to probe the space between the earth and sun near the orbit of Venus. With great paddlewheels containing solar batteries, Pioneer V recharged its batteries and sent strong radio signals for almost four months (Fig. 34-8). Numerous small instruments reported to us on the strength of the sun's radiations in various colors of the light spectrum,

NASA

34-8. Launched in 1960, the Pioneer V satellite was highly successful in transmitting data using a radio powered by solar cells on its "paddlewheels."

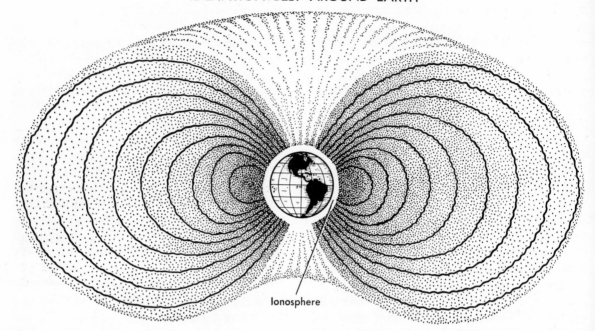

Ionosphere

34-9. The radiation belt, or magnetosphere, surrounding the earth consists of charged particles. Many of these emitted by the sun are swept toward earth, and become trapped by its magnetic field.

on the strength of cosmic rays nearer the sun, on the existence of clouds of charged particles in space and on the magnetic field of the sun. From this satellite we have the first information of conditions in the solar system far beyond our moon.

The Earth-Sun System

The discovery of the magnetosphere surrounding the earth, and of the streams of particles coming from the sun which interact with these radiation belts, is leading toward new ideas about the earth's relationship to the sun. We have, of course, for many years known the earth and sun to be related in a gravitational system. But now we are coming to realize that the earth and sun are also related through a complicated system of magnetic fields and electrical particles. In a real sense we can think of the sun's gases as extending all the way out to the earth, and of changes in the earth's magnetic field as linked to changes in the sun's electrical activity.

During the violent eruptions of hydrogen gas

on the sun's surface (known as solar prominences, see pp. 378–79) electrons and protons — the building blocks of hydrogen atoms — may escape completely from the sun's gravity. Streaming outwards as a kind of *solar wind,* these charged particles are swept along by the pressure of sunlight. Like all moving charges, they are accompanied by magnetic fields. What happens when particles of the solar wind are trapped by the earth's magnetic field? The magnetic field of the solar wind will interact with the earth's field, causing changes or fluctuations in it which are detected as magnetic storms. In generators, a changing magnetic field gives rise to electrical currents. So too, the fluctuating field during magnetic storms generates currents in transmission lines on earth.

MAN IN SPACE

The Soviet experiment with a dog in a Sputnik first showed that the larger vertebrates could survive the rapid acceleration of a rocket take-off. Laboratory experiments, and now rocket flights, have shown than man, too, can survive violent accelerations for short intervals.

Getting launched into space in a sealed cabin has its hazards. But the greatest danger comes in a return trip to the earth. On the outward trip through the air, the rocket speeds up slowly. It gains most of its speed after it is in very thin air. As a result, the temperature of the rocket nose stays fairly low, and the sealed cabin can be kept comfortable. But on the return trip, the last rocket stage (or satellite) plunges into increasingly denser air with a speed of 4 or 5 miles a second. The nose cone may reach a temperature as high as 12,-000° F, a bit too warm for the comfort of passengers in the sealed cabin!

Several things can be done to hold down the temperature within the cabin. For example, the forward part of the nose cone can be covered with special materials, ceramic like chinaware, that melt and blow off, thus carrying away part of the heat. In addition, parachutes can be used to slow the descent.

The return to earth of space capsules or satel-

34-11. The United States' first astronaut, Col. John H. Glenn, Jr., shown in his space capsule, readies himself for launching — Feb. 20, 1962.

lites was first demonstrated in August 1960, when the United States recovered a capsule from 200 miles up. Somewhat later the Russians first succeeded in guiding back to earth a life-bearing satellite. The two dogs, the plants, and the mice seemed not to have suffered from the effects of either weightlessness or radiation.

Then on April 12, 1961, Soviet Flight Major Yuri Gagarin became the first human space traveler (Fig. 34-10). He circled the earth in 108 minutes and returned safely. Soon afterwards, the United States successfully initiated its Project Mercury test flights with Navy Commander Alan Shepard and Air Force Captain Virgil L. Grissom. Other men, both Soviet and American, were scheduled to follow with longer trips.

Major Gagarin reported that he had no difficulties in his physical reactions while weightless in space. He could write and use his hands freely. Also, he reported eating and drinking a little during his flight.

In August 1961, the second Soviet space-traveler, Major Gherman Titov (Fig. 34-12), completed 17 orbits around the earth in a journey

34-10. The first man to orbit the earth — Maj. Yuri Gagarin — waves good-by to technicians as he prepares to enter his space capsule.

which lasted almost 24 hours. Major Titov has been reported as declaring that weightlessness did gradually begin to affect him, causing some discomfort.

In February of 1962, the United States Project Mercury, after painstaking preparations, launched its first astronaut into orbit — Colonel John H. Glenn, Jr. The entire nation watched his flight on television, from the initial count-down on the launching pad at Cape Canaveral, Florida, to the safe landing of his capsule in the Atlantic after three orbits of the earth. In following months, flights with greater numbers of earth-circling orbits were made as both U.S. and Soviet programs for an eventual moon-shot swung into gear.

United States astronauts have described their journeys as exciting and exhilarating experiences. Their engineless capsules sped silently across the blue-black sky, held in the grip of the earth's gravitational field. As they passed from the daylight to the night side of the earth they witnessed sunrises and sunsets flashing by.

Of course there are many potential hazards to entering and returning from orbit. Still greater hazards are involved in the forthcoming journeys across space to the moon — the ultimate purpose of the Project Mercury program. We shall look at some of these problems in a moment. But it is worth remembering that all the data gathered by satellites, both manned and unmanned, is carefully analyzed to provide plans for the most foolproof engineering of space journeys that is humanly possible.

PROBLEMS OF SPACE TRAVEL

What would you need to live in a satellite or interplanetary rocket? If you have studied biology, you know that many conditions must be met for us to stay alive. Any living animal must:

1. take in food and water
2. take in oxygen
3. eliminate solid and excrete liquid wastes
4. exhale waste gases, mainly carbon dioxide

In addition, a man in space must be protected

Wide World

34-12. U.S. astronaut Glenn and Soviet cosmonaut Titov examine Freedom 7 space capsule during Major Titov's tour of the United States in 1962.

against any other alien environmental factors that might endanger his life or health.

Of course, a proper atmosphere and pressure for breathing is needed. Unless the cabin is completely sealed and pressurized, the gases within the body and blood would expand rapidly, and the spaceman — or astronaut (from *astro,* meaning star and *naut,* meaning navigation) — would explode. Not only is the cabin pressurized, but a pressurized g-suit (Fig. 34-11) is provided in order, among other things, to aid the circulation of the blood.

The air exhaled must be enriched with oxygen and freed from excess carbon dioxide and water vapor before it can be reused. How to accomplish this is one of the problems. Taking water vapor from exhaled air would, fortunately, help solve another problem, that of supply and storage of food and water. The food and water for a space trip must be of very limited weight and volume and still enable the crew to survive the duration of the trip.

To solve the three-fold problem of food, water,

and air, scientists are trying to devise ways of using the initial supply of each of these necessities over and over again, with chemical treatment following each use. If we can convert waste materials to usable form again, the original amounts of food, water, and air needed can be greatly reduced (and the problem of storage of waste products can be eliminated or almost so, at the same time). This procedure of recovery and conversion of waste materials is called *recycling*.

Aside from food, water, and air, there are still other problems of space travel. For example, after the rockets burn out, the astronaut and his space cabin will be falling together around the earth at exactly the same rate. He will not, therefore, push against the cabin floor — another way of saying he will be weightless. By prior experience, under laboratory conditions, an astronaut may be trained to be accustomed to weightlessness.

Perhaps more serious problems are posed by the magnetosphere of charged particles. When such high-speed particles hit a metallic object, like a satellite, they release X rays. By a similar process, the dentist produces X rays to study your teeth. But the X rays in a satellite are *continuously* produced in uncontrolled quantities. On a single trip through the magnetosphere an astronaut can get a dose estimated at about 20 to 40 roentgens. This is far less than the deadly dose of 500 roentgens, but enough to be dangerous. If a man were in a satellite moving in and out of these belts on each trip around the earth, he would gather a deadly dose within a few days. However, if the satellite orbits not more than two or three hundred miles high, the dosage is low. Furthermore, it is possible to work out a system of shielding which, while not absorbing all radiation, can guard against dangerous exposures.

The magnetosphere is not the only source of radiation danger to space travel. There are also the tremendously energetic cosmic rays, which outside the earth's atmosphere are about 85 per cent protons (hydrogen nuclei), 14 per cent alpha particles (helium nuclei), and one per cent heavier particles. There is some evidence that the cosmic rays themselves may not cause much cell damage, but when they collide with the space ship they produce secondary particles that may indeed be a hazard. Since some changes in the frequency of cosmic ray bombardment parallel changes in the activities of the sun, it may be possible to time space voyages to coincide with low cosmic ray activity. As yet not enough is known to be at all sure this would be a solution.

The longer the space trip, the greater each of the problems already discussed becomes — and new problems are introduced. For example, how will a man react to isolation from a normal environment for a considerable length of time? Under experimental conditions, men placed in isolation and given complex duties to perform over a period of a week or more became increasingly weary, tense, and erratic in their sleeping habits. What does all this mean in terms of the space project we would like to get under way?

Of one thing you can be sure. Despite all the problems and dangers, scientists and engineers will continue to work toward the goal of getting man across space to the moon and to the planets.

The U.S. Lunar-Landing Project

The physical science you have studied in this book (and a great deal more) will, in the hands of engineers, be put to use in the greatest technical undertaking of this century — the lunar-landing project. Even to a greater extent than with the atomic bomb project, the U.S. government has assembled men and equipment in a massive effort that will cost some 10 billion dollars.

Final plans for accomplishing the landing of men on the moon have not yet been decided. But one plan that has strong support is shown in Fig. 34-13 on the next page.

Prior to this, however, carefully executed intermediate stages will be accomplished — increasing the number of orbits a man may make and developing two-man orbital flights (as in the Gemini capsule). Finally, three-man orbital flights will take place as practice for the three-man team that will take the great plunge into space toward the moon.

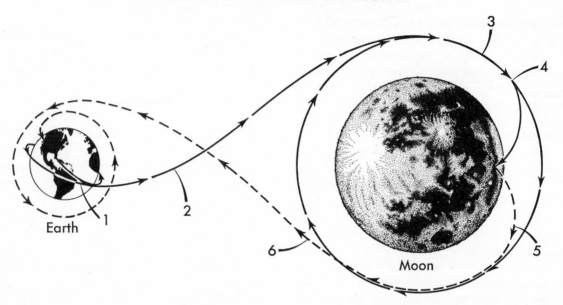

34-13. One proposed U.S. strategy for landing on the moon: A rocket will place a spaceship, with attached lunar-landing vehicle, or "bug," into orbit around the earth (1). Spaceship with bug then heads for the moon (2). After "parking" in an orbit around the moon (3), bug detaches from spaceship and descends to the moon (4). Later bug rejoins spaceship (5), and is returned to earth (6).

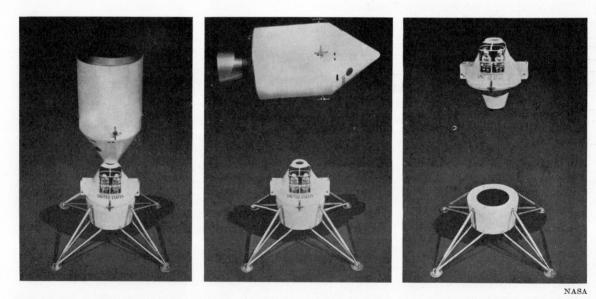

NASA

34-14. Tentative models of spaceship and lunar-landing vehicle. *Left:* spaceship with attached "bug" as it will orbit moon. *Center:* bug carrying two "astronauts" descends to moon. A third astronaut remains in "parked" spaceship. *Right:* the upper, mobile part of bug leaves its landing assemblage on moon and heads for rendezvous with parked spaceship which will carry it back to earth.

Going Further . . . .

THOUGHT QUESTIONS

1. List the various areas of science (for instance, astronomy) which you believe have been important in the development of an earth satellite.
2. If you were to be the first human passenger in a space rocket, what information would you want to have gained from experiments and trials with previous rockets and satellites?

THINGS TO DO

1. Write an imaginative report on how you lived for a day in a rocket. Use popular books, magazine articles, and newspaper reports for information and ideas.

2. If you were headed toward the moon in a rocket with a view-port or window, how would the sky look to you? (See *Life* magazine, November 4, 1957, and more recent articles.)

3. Make a model of a real earth satellite.

4. Find what is meant by the " thrust " of a rocket in relation to horsepower.

5. Design and use a test-firing stand for rockets, using carbon dioxide cartridges or other compressed gases for your test " fuel."

A DIFFICULT PROBLEM

The earth has a natural satellite, the moon, which goes around the earth once in about 660 hours at a distance of 240,000 miles. We also know that the period, P (the time for one complete circle), of a satellite changes with its average distance, d, from the center of the earth according to

$$P^2 \text{ changes as } d^3$$

By comparing a satellite like Sputnik to the moon, we have

$$\frac{P^2_{\text{sat}}}{P^2_{\text{moon}}} = \frac{d^3_{\text{sat}}}{d^3_{\text{moon}}} \quad \text{or} \quad P^2_{\text{sat}} = d^3_{\text{sat}}\left(\frac{P^2_{\text{moon}}}{d^3_{\text{moon}}}\right)$$

We have substituted the numbers in hours and miles for the period and distance of the moon and have solved the equation for the period of the satellite

$$P_{\text{sat}} = 5.6 \times 10^{-6} \times d_{\text{sat}} \sqrt{d_{\text{sat}}}$$

The figure 10^{-6} is the same as 1 divided by 10 multiplied by itself six times.

Example: Find the period of a satellite 10,000 miles from the center of the earth (or 6,000 miles about the surface of the earth).

$$P_{\text{sat}} = 5.6 \times 10^{-6} \times 10^4 \times 10^2 = 5.6 \text{ hours}$$

Notice that we can write 10,000 as 10 multiplied by itself four times, or 10^4, just as we write 100 as 10 multiplied by itself twice, or 10^2.

Now try these problems:

1. Find the period of a satellite 40,000 miles from the earth's center.
2. What would be the period of a satellite only 4,000 miles from the earth's center?
3. From the results above, make a graph of the relation between period in hours and distance from the earth's center. At what distance would the period of a satellite be just 24 hours?

READING FURTHER

Satellites and Space Probes by Erik Bergaunt, Putnam, 1959

Rocketry Through the Ages by Donald Cox and Michael Stoiko, Holt, Rinehart & Winston, 1959

Rockets Through Space by Lester del Roy, Holt, Rinehart & Winston, 1960

Guide to Scientific Measurements

If someone told you that an artificial satellite was traveling 120, wouldn't you ask " 120 what "? Suppose he said " 120 minutes." Would that tell you enough? Not at all. He would need to tell you how far it goes in that time, for example, that it circles the earth once every 120 minutes. Then you would know two quantities — *time* and, in this case, the approximate *distance*. If he also told you its *weight* you would know still more. These three units, *time, distance* (or *length*), and *weight* (sometimes, *mass,* as we shall explain shortly) are three basic, or *fundamental,* quantities used in physical measurement.

While you are undoubtedly familiar with the measurement of length and time using measuring sticks and clocks, the measurement of *mass* is more difficult to explain. Let us think of mass as *the quantity of matter in a given object, which resists changes in the motion of that object.* We say that a locomotive has more mass than, say, a baseball, because it takes more force to change a locomotive's motion (from 2 feet per second to 3 feet per second, for example) than it does to change a baseball's motion. However, for our general purposes, we can talk interchangeably about mass and weight (as they are measured on any part of the earth's *surface*). But keep in mind that the scientist thinks of mass as different from weight, as you will learn later.

UNITS FOR MEASUREMENT OF LENGTH

Wouldn't it be confusing, if you ordered a foot of expensive platinum wire from France and found that the French unit for measurement of a foot was different from yours? Clearly, we need agreed-upon, or *standard,* units for measuring length.

Length in the English System

From past experience you have learned how to use a system for indicating length in inches, feet, yards, and miles. The system you use is:

$$1 \text{ foot} = 12 \text{ inches}$$
$$1 \text{ yard} = 3 \text{ feet}$$
$$1 \text{ mile} = 5{,}280 \text{ feet}$$

This system, the English system, is widely used in the United States. But the French don't use it — nor do the Italians — nor do scientists when they can help it. Instead, they have agreed upon a different system — the metric system. Why? Let us see if there are advantages in using the metric system.

Length in the Metric System

The unit of length in the metric system is the meter (ME-ter). Originally, it was set at one ten-millionth of the supposed distance from the equator to the North Pole. As you shall see, a meter is just a bit longer than a yard. Until recently, a durable alloy of platinum and iridium marked in this length, and kept under laboratory-controlled conditions near Paris, was the world's scientific standard for the metric unit of length. From it, other extremely accurate copies were made for use throughout the world.

Recently, a much more accurate physical standard of length has been adopted by the world's scientists. It is based on a certain wave length of light given out by an atom of krypton when its electrons vibrate. But this standard, while important for the extremely precise measurements needed in advanced research, will not replace the use of the meter stick in junior and senior high school laboratory measurements.

The table shows how the metric system may be used to indicate measurements merely by moving the decimal point to the right or left.

The Metric System — Length

1 meter (m) = length of the standard bar
1 decimeter (dm) = $\frac{1}{10}$ of a meter (0.1 meter)
1 centimeter (cm) = $\frac{1}{100}$ of a meter (0.01 meter)
1 millimeter (mm) = $\frac{1}{1,000}$ of a meter (0.001 meter)
1 kilometer (km) = 1,000 meters

Multiplying and Dividing Lengths in the Metric System

Suppose you want to change 43,791 feet into miles. You divide 43,791 by 5,280. But what if you want to change 43,791 *centimeters* into meters? Simply divide by 100 or move the decimal point two places to the left and you have your answer, 437.91 meters. Refer to the table and you will see that a centimeter is 1/100 of a meter.

Now try these problems, making use of the table when necessary.

1. How many centimeters in 3½ meters? How many millimeters?

2. What fraction of a meter is 75 centimeters? What fraction is 750 millimeters?

3. How many meters are in 58 kilometers? How many in ⅞ of a kilometer?

4. What fraction of a kilometer is 400 meters?

Changing from One System to the Other

Earlier we spoke of the iridium-platinum meter bar that is kept in Paris. How long is it when measured in inches? You will find that:

$$1 \text{ meter} = 39.37 \text{ inches}$$

How many centimeters are equal to 1 inch? Since 1 meter, which is also 100 centimeters, equals 39.37 inches we see that:

$$39.37 \text{ inches} = 100 \text{ centimeters}$$
$$\text{or}$$
$$1 \text{ inch} = \frac{100}{39.37} \text{ centimeters}$$

Therefore, 1 inch = 2.54 centimeters and 1 yard (36 inches) = 0.914 meters.

UNITS FOR MEASUREMENT OF WEIGHT

You probably know the English system of measurement of weight as well as you know the English system of measurement of length. (Note we used the word *weight* not *mass*. For many purposes, weight at sea level is generally interchangeable with mass. But it is important to remember that weight and mass are *not identical*. Mass is related to a body's resistance to changes in its motion. But weight is the measure of the pull of gravity on a body. Thus the farther a body is from the center of the earth, the less the pull of gravity, and hence the less its weight. But its mass will not change. Yet, we repeat, at sea level, we can measure mass in terms of weight units.) The units in the English system are given below:

$$16 \text{ ounces (oz.)} = 1 \text{ pound (lb.)}$$
$$2,000 \text{ lb.} = 1 \text{ ton}$$

Weight in the Metric System

Just as there is a standard of length, there is a standard for mass that scientists have devised. In the metric system, it is the *kilogram*. Here again, scientists find the metric system more convenient. Do you remember what the prefix " kilo " means?

For the standard kilogram, a water-filled cubic box 10 centimeters at each inside edge is used. The water must be pure and at a temperature of 4 degrees centigrade. The weight of the water at 4° C. in this cubic box is defined as 1,000 grams — or 1 kilogram. (Put another way, 1 cubic centimeter of water at 4° C. weighs 1 gram.) Standard blocks of metal can be made whose weight is exactly the same — 1,000 grams or 1 kilogram — as this mass of water. Then, in any laboratory, other weights can be accurately compared with these standard blocks. The following table gives the units of weight in the metric system.

The Metric System — Weight

$$1 \text{ kilogram (kg)} = 1{,}000 \text{ grams}$$
$$1 \text{ gram (gm)} = \tfrac{1}{1{,}000} \text{ or } (0.001) \text{ kg}$$
$$1 \text{ milligram (mg)} = \tfrac{1}{1{,}000} \text{ or } (0.001) \text{ gm}$$

$$1 \text{ kg} = 2.2 \text{ lb. (approximately)}$$
Therefore, 2.2 pounds = 1,000 grams.
Therefore, 1 lb. = $\tfrac{1{,}000}{2.2}$ gm = 454 gm.

How We Measure Time

You should have no difficulty with these units — hours, minutes, seconds; you're accustomed to them — and they are world-wide; that is, these units of time are used in both the English and metric systems. You may know that originally the basis for the unit of time was the rotation of the earth; one rotation actually takes a few minutes less than 24 hours, about 23 hours and 56 minutes.

Today, scientists are able to measure time in billionths of a second. For ordinary measurement of time, the regular swing of a pendulum can be counted — such as 60 swings in a minute. It has been found the particles inside atoms (electrons, protons, neutrons) vibrate regularly, too. So it should not surprise you that, just as in the case of length, atomic standards have been adopted; highly accurate clocks are being developed based on the regular vibrations of atomic particles and will be developed for wide use during your lifetime.

UNITS FOR MEASUREMENT OF VOLUME

Units for expressing the volume of an object can be *derived* from units of length. You've already measured length, as well as area (which is length × width), with a ruler. *Volume* is the amount of space an object occupies.

Suppose you want to measure the volume of a car battery. You find it is 10 inches long by 8 inches high by 6 inches wide. How do you find the volume? You say:

$$\text{Volume} = \text{length} \times \text{width} \times \text{height}$$
$$= 10 \times 6 \times 8 = 480 \text{ cubic inches}$$
$$(\text{or in.}^3)$$

Or to find the volume of a room, you would measure the length, width, and height of the room in feet to get the result in cubic feet (cubic feet or ft.^{3}).

In measuring volume we really measured *three lengths,* even though we called them length, width, and height. We might say the formula for measuring a cube is L^3 or in this case, cm^3.

When indicating measurements in the metric system, we use cubic centimeter, abbreviated cc or cm^3, or we use ml. (milliliter — one thousandth of a liter) for liquid measurement.

Volume Units in the English and Metric Systems Compared

1,000 cm^3 is called 1 liter
and
1,000 cm^3 = 1.1 quarts (qt.)
32 oz. = 1 qt.
The liter is then equivalent to 1.1 quarts.
1 oz. = 28.4 cm^3

UNITS FOR MEASUREMENT OF SPEED

It would be simple if everything we measured required only units for length, time, or mass (weight). Actually, many combinations of these units must be used.

Scientists *derive* many units from the *fundamental* ones we've discussed. We've already derived units for *volume* from the units for *length*.

Another derived unit you will often use is based upon the units for *time* and *length*. This derived unit is used to express measurement of *speed*.

You have often seen signs that say: " Speed limit — 50 miles per hour." Notice that units for *length* (miles) and *time* (hours) have been combined into a new, or derived, unit (*speed*).

How, for example, could you measure the speed of a car (assuming the speed remained constant)? You might measure the length of a strip of road and use a stop watch to time the cars as they moved over this measured distance. Then you would use a formula such as this one:

Speed = distance per unit of time;

per means " divided by." Therefore,

$$\text{Speed} = \frac{\text{distance}}{\text{time}}, \text{ or } s = \frac{d}{t}$$

Thus, if a car traveled 1,000 feet in 20 seconds, its speed would be

$$\text{Speed} = \frac{1,000 \text{ ft.}}{20 \text{ sec.}} = 50 \text{ ft./sec.}$$

In the English system speed may be expressed in feet/second or miles/hour. Of course, when using the metric system, speed is expressed in cm/sec., m/sec., km/sec., or km/hr., etc. Again, notice that the units used to express time are identical in the English and metric systems.

ACCURACY — SIGNIFICANT FIGURES

Scientists use measuring instruments because with their aid more exact observations are possible than with unaided senses. But understanding how measurements are standardized and the meaning of the units used for time, velocity, volume, weight, mass — is not enough. Measurements must also be expressed in *significant figures*. Let's find out the meaning of " significance " with regard to the following statement of measurement:

The sun's mass is found to be about 2,200,-000,000,000,000,000,000,000 tons.

Now how *significant* would the .1 be in a statement that the mass of the sun is about 2,200,000,-000,000,000,000,000,000.1 tons?

Does the 0.1 of a ton add anything to our knowledge if the word " about " precedes the figure? No, the 0.1 isn't significant since, if we don't have a measurement accurate enough to place digits in decimal places for trillions, millions, hundreds of thousands, etc., it hardly makes sense to insert a digit in a decimal place for tenths of a ton.

In determining the accuracy of your measurement, *you do not count any zeros included merely for purposes of locating the decimal point*. Thus, when you write " length = 15 centimeters," it means that you have measured the object to the *nearest centimeter* and used *two* significant figures. Recording a measurement to the *nearest hundred,* say 1,500 cm, *would also involve only two significant figures,* even though there are four figures to the left of the decimal point. The zeros here are used to indicate decimal position and do not count as significant figures.

But if you recorded a measurement such as 15.0, it would mean the .0 *is* a significant figure. You would be indicating *three* significant figures since you recorded digits for the tens, units, and tenths places. Your measurement could likewise have been correctly indicated to *three* significant figures, to the nearest tenth of a centimeter, as 15.3 cm, or to the nearest tens place, as 1,530 centimeters, if you had a measuring instrument which could indicate three significant figures.

Do you see that 15. cm or 15.3 cm is a more accurate measurement than is 15 cm? And that 1,530 is more accurate than 1,500 cm?

You should never record 51 cm if your measurement was made to the nearest tenth; it should be written 51.0. Similarly, 51.03 would mean that you had measured the length to the nearest hundredth of a centimeter and that *four* figures are significant.

Thus you express your measurements in the number of figures which indicate the precision, *regardless of where the decimal point is*.

For most junior and senior high school work, measurements of length in meters or weight in grams is sufficiently accurate when indicated to three significant figures — for example, 249, 24.9, 2.49, or 0.249 meters, or 7280, 728, 72.8, or 0.782 grams. All of these measurements are accurate to three significant figures. In the school laboratory, your teacher will indicate the number of significant figures he desires.

FURTHER EXPERIMENTS IN PHYSICAL SCIENCE

If you wish to go further and deeper into the principles and the applications of the principles of physical science, these 84 experiments offer a sound basis for laboratory work. They are suitable for individual or group research, classroom demonstration, or laboratory use at home or school.

1. Physical Properties

We can often recognize materials around us largely by their *physical properties*.

(a) Examine crystals of salt, sugar, iodine, mica, and potassium permanganate under a magnifying glass. Examine larger crystals of quartz, dogtooth spar, calcite, and galena. A magnifying glass is not necessary for these. How do sugar and salt compare in appearance? How do iodine and mica resemble each other? Break a small piece from the galena. How does the small segment compare with the original sample? Does the shape or appearance of the crystals help to identify some materials?

(b) Try putting a small quantity of each substance in water. Do they react alike? Compare their hardness by crushing small samples or scratching them with a knife. Are there noticeable differences in *color* and *luster*? These differences are only a few of the physical differences that you can use to identify your materials. What other physical differences can you name?

2. Chemical Properties

Chemical properties are not so easy to observe. They tell how a substance reacts with other substances. Differences in chemical properties (especially when added to physical properties) help you to recognize and identify substances.

(a) To a pinch of cornstarch in a dish add a few drops of dilute hydrochloric acid. Now add a little of the acid to a pinch of baking soda. Is there a noticeable difference in the two reactions?

(b) Place small pieces of lead in one test tube and magnesium in another. Add a few drops of dilute hydrochloric acid to each. Again, is a difference apparent?

(c) Place a few crystals of iodine and a few crystals of sulfur on opposite edges of a wire gauze. Heat each edge separately with a Bunsen flame. Is the reaction quite different? These different reactions are only a few examples of how the chemical properties of substances differ.

3. Physical Change

Dissolve a small piece of sulfur (pea size) in 10 ml. of carbon disulfide. When it has completely dissolved, pour it into a shallow dish, such as a watch glass or saucer. Has the sulfur changed? Allow it to stand undisturbed until the carbon disulfide has evaporated. (*Caution: Keep away from open flame as carbon disulfide is inflammable!*) Examine under a magnifying glass the sulfur crystals formed in the dish. Has the sulfur been recovered?

Those changes which affect the size, shape, and general appearance without changing what the substance is made of are called *physical changes*. Melting, freezing, dissolving, boiling, mixing, and shrinking are all examples of physical changes. Can you name and describe some more?

4. Chemical Change

A *chemical change* is one in which new substances with new properties are formed. Examine a clean strip of copper foil or thin copper sheet. Is it flexible? Does it have the characteristic reddish color of copper? Does it have a luster? Examine some powdered sulfur. Feel its texture by rubbing it between your fingers. Is it soft? Note its yellow color.

Now place about 1 inch of powdered sulfur in a Pyrex test tube and heat it until it boils.[1] Insert the strip of copper into the melted sulfur and continue heating for a few minutes. Remove the copper from the test tube. When it is cool, compare the luster, flexibility, and color with the original copper. Has the surface of the copper been changed? Repeated bending should cause some of the surface scale to flake off. Does it have the properties of either the copper or the sulfur? Has a chemical change taken place? The reaction is:

copper + sulfur → copper sulfide

Chemists, of course, are primarily interested in chemical change, action that will bring about the formation of new and sometimes useful products. Simple chemical changes are of four types: (1) Decomposition, (2) Composition, (3) Displacement, (4) Double Displacement. The following experiments will illustrate these types.

---

[1] Always use Pyrex test tubes unless the instructions read otherwise.

5. Decomposition

(a) Strongly heat ½ g. of lead peroxide (PbO_2) in a Pyrex test tube. Lead peroxide is composed of lead and oxygen. Light a splint of wood and blow it out so that it just glows. Thrust the glowing splint into the test tube while the tube is still being heated. What happens to the splint? Repeat the test two or three times to be sure. If the splint bursts into flame, this shows the presence of *oxygen* gas. Remove the tube from the flame, cool, and examine the substance that remains in the tube. How does its color differ from the lead peroxide with which you started? Has the lead peroxide been changed? We can describe this reaction as:

lead peroxide → lead oxide + oxygen

brown   yellow

(b) Place a few marble chips which are composed of calcium, carbon, and oxygen ($CaCO_3$) in a Pyrex test tube fitted with a delivery tube (Fig. 1). Heat the marble as hot as possible with a Bunsen burner.

Allow any gas that escapes to bubble into a test tube filled with limewater. If the limewater turns milky, the presence of carbon dioxide (CO_2) gas is indicated. Where did it come from? What has happened to the marble chips?

calcium carbonate →

    calcium oxide + carbon dioxide

(c) Mix 3 g. of potassium chlorate ($KClO_3$) with 1 g. of manganese dioxide (MnO_2). (The manganese dioxide acts as a catalytic agent only, and does not take part in the decomposition.)

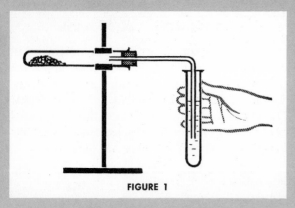

FIGURE 1

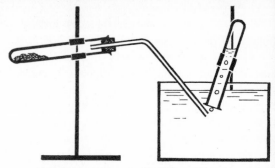

Collecting gas by displacement of water

FIGURE 2

Place in a test tube fitted with a stopper and glass delivery tube. Heat the tube gently and collect some of the gas formed by displacing water from a test tube (Fig. 2). Test for the presence of oxygen by inserting a glowing splint into the gas collected. Is it oxygen?

In this case of decomposition:

potassium chlorate →

    potassium chloride + oxygen

6. Composition

Many chemical compounds are made by direct chemical combination of two or more elements. The following examples are but a few.

(a) Hold a small piece of charcoal (carbon) in a tongs or deflagrating spoon and ignite it in a Bunsen flame. Hold the burning charcoal in an empty wide-mouth bottle, placed mouth *upward,* until it burns itself out. Thrust a burning splint into the bottle. Does the gas formed in the bottle support burning? Add 10 ml. of limewater to the bottle and shake. The formation of a white precipitate indicates the presence of carbon dioxide gas. What two elements have *combined?*

carbon + oxygen → carbon dioxide

(b) Ignite a piece of sulfur and hold it in an empty wide-mouth bottle placed mouth upward.

sulfur + oxygen → sulfur dioxide

Cautiously note the odor of the gas formed. Check with a burning splint to determine whether the gas burns or supports combustion. Moisten the petals of a red or blue flower and place it in the sulfur dioxide gas for several minutes. What happens to the color?

(c) Mix together thoroughly 1 g. finely powdered zinc and ½ g. powdered sulfur. Heap in a small mound on a piece of asbestos, and heat one corner of the mound with a Bunsen burner held at arm's length. Step back when the material begins to glow where heated. What happens? The name of the white powder formed is zinc sulfide. Does this reaction generate its own heat once started? Here the combination is:

zinc + sulfur → zinc sulfide

7. Simple Displacement

Simple displacement occurs when an active element displaces a less-active one from its compound.

(a) Place about 5 g. of granular zinc in a wide-mouth bottle or flask fitted with a delivery tube and a funnel tube. Add dilute sulfuric acid (H_2SO_4) (5 water to 1 acid) through the funnel tube until the zinc and the bottom of the tube are covered by the acid (Fig. 3). (*Precaution:* Do not allow sulfuric acid to come in contact with your clothing or body. When mixing, always add the acid to the water very slowly while stirring to prevent spattering due to excess heat. If the acid does come in contact with your skin or clothing, wash with water — good amounts of water — and notify your teacher at once.) In this reaction zinc has displaced hydrogen.

zinc + sulfuric acid → zinc sulfate + hydrogen

8. Double Displacement

In many chemical reactions two compounds exchange parts. Such reactions are called *double displacements*. In each of the following examples one of the products is an insoluble precipitate.

(a) To 5 ml. of silver nitrate ($AgNO_3$) solution in a test tube, add a few drops of dilute hydrochloric acid (HCl) (1 acid to 5 water). Shake to coagulate the precipitate formed. Add more acid a drop at a time until no more precipitate forms. The precipitate is silver chloride. Note its color.

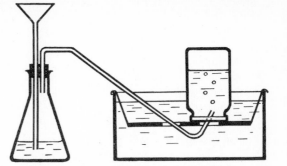

Generator with funnel tube and delivery tube

FIGURE 3

How does it change upon standing? What must be the other product formed in the reaction?

silver nitrate + hydrochloric acid →
silver chloride + nitric acid

(b) Add sodium hydroxide (NaOH) solution a drop at a time to 5 ml. of ferric chloride ($FeCl_3$) solution. Handle the same as the silver solution. What is the color and consistency of the ferric hydroxide ($Fe(OH)_3$) formed?

sodium hydroxide + ferric chloride →
ferric hydroxide + sodium chloride

(c) Repeat the procedure using 5 ml. of lead acetate ($Pb(C_2H_3O_2)_2$) and adding potassium iodide (KI) solution a drop at a time. Lead iodide (PbI_2) is the precipitate. What is the color? What other product is formed?

lead acetate + potassium iodide →
lead iodide + potassium acetate

(d) The main function of baking powder is to free CO_2 gas during the baking process. The carbon dioxide that is set free causes the dough to rise, and the cake or biscuits to be porous and light. Mix ½ teaspoonful of baking powder with 5 ml. of vinegar (acetic acid) in a test tube fitted with a delivery tube. Is any gas freed? Pass the gas into limewater. Do you get a test for CO_2? What is meant by a " leavening agent "? Try some cream of tartar in water instead of vinegar. What happens?

sodium bicarbonate + acetic acid →
carbon dioxide + water + sodium acetate

What chemicals would you expect to find in " ready mix " for cakes?

9. Solutions

By dissolving a substance in water we easily get a uniform distribution of the material when it is used. This is also an easy way to keep the substance from being too concentrated or too strong. For example, if you want to use an insecticide, such as nicotine sulfate, to kill aphids (sucking insects) on roses, the nicotine must be diluted with a very large amount of water or it will burn the plant. The water is also needed as a spreading agent so that a small quantity of the nicotine sulfate will reach all parts of the plant.

Does it not seem unusual that quite a bit of sugar may be added to a full cup of tea or coffee and the cup does not overflow? Did you ever stop to think what happens to the sugar? Can any particles be seen? Where does the sugar go?

(a) Take a clean test tube and fill it ¾ full of water. On a piece of paper, weigh out 5 g. of table salt. Add a pinch of salt to the water, and placing your thumb over the mouth of the tube shake vigorously until the salt has dissolved. Keep adding small amounts of salt to the test tube, shaking until no more salt will dissolve. A small quantity of salt in the bottom of the test tube indicates that the solution is saturated. Weigh whatever unused salt is left on your paper. How much salt was dissolved in the water? Take a second test tube and repeat the experiment using sugar instead of salt. Is water capable of holding more sugar or more salt under these conditions?

(b) Hold the test tube containing the salt solution in a test-tube clamp and warm it gently with a Bunsen burner. Did the excess salt in the bottom of the test tube dissolve? Add more salt to the solution to see if it will dissolve. Try the effect of heat on the sugar solution, adding sugar until no more will dissolve. Is the solubility of the material increased by heating? Add a small amount of starch to some cold water in a test tube. Will it dissolve? Heat the water to boiling. What happens to the starch?

10. Supersaturated Solutions

For ease of handling and measuring, and for the sake of appearance, it is often desirable to have chemicals and food products like salt and sugar in the form of crystals. Uniform small size crystals are produced by quick precipitation from supersaturated solutions.

Half fill a test tube with sodium thiosulfate (hypo) crystals and add just enough water to cover the crystals. Heat the test tube gently over a Bunsen flame until all the hypo has dissolved. Carefully cool the test tube under running water, but do not shake or disturb the solution in it. When the tube feels thoroughly cool to the touch, set it in a rack and drop one small crystal of hypo into the solution. Watch what happens. Are the crystals large or small? Note the temperature of the tube when the reaction has been completed by holding it in your hand. Does the temperature of the tube seem to have changed? What kind of a solution is shown by such rapid crystal formation?

11. Suspensions

Suspensions are mixtures of solid particles distributed throughout a liquid or gas, like dust in the air. Unlike those in a solution, the particles in a suspension are large enough to be seen, and, if not stirred, they will eventually settle out. Many medicinal preparations are suspensions. The direction to " Shake well before using " is a way of getting the materials thoroughly mixed again after settling.

Some suspensions take a long time to settle out. The size and weight of the suspended particles have a lot to do with the time. Fill a gas-collecting bottle with water and add a pinch of sand and a pinch of china clay or chalk to the water. Stir thoroughly and allow the particles to settle. Which substance settles out first? Why?

Paints are generally suspensions of finely ground pigment (solid) in oil. The fineness of particles and the thickness of the oil slow the settling process so that the paint generally stays mixed for several hours or even for days. To 10 cc. of linseed oil in a test tube add enough zinc sulfate

($ZnSO_4$) to give a thick suspension. Only a gram or two of the zinc sulfate is needed. Allow the mixture to stand overnight. What does it look like? When mixed it could be used as a paint, but is not recommended because the oil dries slowly. A drying agent could be added.

12. Colloids

Jell-o is a type of suspension in which water (the solvent) clings to the small particles of gelatin, and instead of settling out, the whole mixture gels or becomes rather solid. This is a special kind of a suspension generally called a *colloid*. It is in between a true solution and a suspension. The water is said to be occluded (absorbed) by the gelatin.

(a) Use 2 g. of commercial gelatin dessert (like Jell-o) and mix it with 10 ml. of boiling water. Set aside and allow to cool. On the next day, examine the consistency of the mixture. Is it still liquid? Have any solid particles settled out? Heat will cause it to liquefy again. Will it regel upon cooling?

(b) A small amount of egg white shaken with water in a test tube will form a colloid. Heat the solution in the tube. What happens? Can the colloid be restored?

13. Electrolysis

Matter is essentially electrical. The electrical nature of matter is evident in electroplating, electrolysis, and ionization. Experiments with these can be carried out with simple equipment. *Electrolysis* is the decomposition of a substance by passing an electric current through it. The substance to be decomposed must be either in solution or in a molten state.

Strip the insulation from the ends of two lengths of copper wire; bell wire or #18 wire will do. Fasten each wire to a short piece of carbon rod. The center electrode from an old dry cell can be used as a source of carbon rod (see Fig. 4-8).

Make a saturated solution of copper chloride solution ($CuCl_2$) by dissolving as much copper chloride as possible in 300 ml. of cold water. Fill two test tubes with the solution and invert them in a beaker containing the remaining solution. Insert one carbon electrode into the mouth of each tube. Connect the wires from the electrodes to four dry cells connected in series. Allow the current to flow through the solution for several minutes. Does gas begin to collect in one test tube? If great care is used, the odor of this gas may be noted by cautious sniffing. Examine the second electrode. Is there any deposit on it? Could it be copper?

copper chloride → copper + chlorine

14. Ionization

Acids, bases, and salts (called *electrolytes*) produce many electrically charged particles, or *ions,* when dissolved in water. Other materials such as sugar, starch, and alcohol do not ionize. They are called *nonelectrolytes*. Commercial electroplating, refining of metals, and the preparation of many chemicals depend upon the fact that ions are present. (The ability of a solution to conduct an electric current will indicate how well it is ionized.)

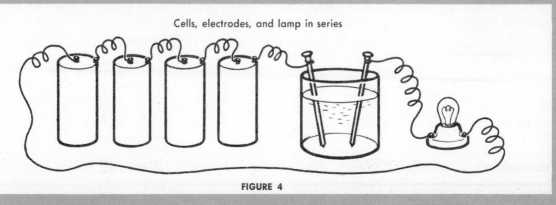

Cells, electrodes, and lamp in series

FIGURE 4

(a) Connect four dry cells in series. To one terminal, connect in series a 6-volt pilot bulb and a large iron nail. To the other terminal of the cells, connect a second nail. Touch the two nails together briefly. A current should flow through the lamp. In a glass of distilled (pure) water, now place the nails so they are *not* touching each other (Fig. 4). Does the lamp light up? Drop a pinch of salt in the water. What effect does it have on the lamp? Does adding more salt have any effect?

Starting with pure water in every case, try the effect of adding sugar, baking soda, cornstarch, vinegar, ammonia, rubbing alcohol, soap powder, etc. Does the lamp light up in every experiment? Which substances are ionized?

(b) Insert the nails directly into an apple or tomato. Does the bulb light up? Those materials that conduct the current are called *electrolytes;* all others, *nonelectrolytes.*

15. Electricity from Chemicals

The electrical nature of matter is shown by the fact that electricity can be obtained directly as the result of chemical action.

Fill a beaker with dilute sulfuric acid made by adding 10 ml. of acid to each 100 ml. of water used. Firmly attach a foot of copper wire to a strip of zinc metal. Do the same with a copper strip. Hang the two metal strips in the acid so that they are not in contact with each other. Connect the free ends of the wires to a low-reading voltmeter or a 1½ volt flashlight bulb. Is there a chemical reaction taking place? Is electricity being generated? Do gas bubbles collect on the copper strip? Does it help to agitate the metal strips occasionally? What does this accomplish?

16. Electroplating

Electroplating is the process of coating an object with a metal by passing an electric current through a solution. The solution is an electrolyte containing ions of the plating metal. The object to be plated, called the *cathode,* is connected to the negative side of a direct current source. The plating metal is connected to the positive side and is called the *anode* (Fig. 22-4).

Make a plating solution by dissolving 50 g. copper sulfate ($CuSO_4$) and 15 g. sulfuric acid in 200 ml. of water. Use a strip of clean copper metal for the anode and a clean carbon rod for the cathode. (The center rod of an old dry cell makes a good cathode.) Clean the carbon rod in a strong detergent and rinse thoroughly with water. Connect the two electrodes (anode and cathode) to a source of direct current, such as a storage battery or four dry cells in series. Be sure the carbon cathode is connected to the negative terminal of the battery. If an ammeter is available, connect it in series with one of the electrodes. The amount of current flowing should not exceed 0.2 ampere for each square inch of surface to be plated. After the current has been flowing for a few minutes, raise the cathode to inspect the deposit. Has copper been deposited on the carbon electrode? Is it bright? Can a hard deposit be obtained?

17. A Typical Acid

Many acids can be made with the help of sulfuric acid. For example, to make hydrochloric acid (HCl) place about 10 g. of sodium chloride (NaCl) in a flask fitted with a delivery tube and a funnel tube. Add about 25 ml. of dilute sulfuric acid (2 parts acid to 1 part water). Warm the flask gently and collect the gas by allowing it to accumulate in a dry bottle standing mouth upward. Cautiously note the odor of the gas. Add 10 ml. of water to the bottle, quickly cover tightly with the palm of your hand, and shake the bottle to mix the water and gas.

Is your hand pressed down when you try to remove it from the bottle? What does this indicate? Taste the solution by bringing a drop or two to the tip of your tongue. A sour taste is typical of acids. Test the solution with strips of red and blue litmus paper. Acids cause blue litmus paper to turn red. Drop a small piece of magnesium ribbon (a metal) into the solution. Is the magnesium dissolved? Acids dissolve many metals.

18. A Typical Base

Household ammonia is a typical base. It may be prepared by mixing 5 g. of dry ammonium chloride (NH_4Cl) with an equal amount of dry calcium hydroxide ($Ca(OH)_2$). Place in a test tube fitted with a delivery tube, heat gently, and collect the gas formed by displacement of air from a dry bottle held mouth downward. Cautiously note the odor of the gas. Add 10 ml. of water to the bottle and tightly stopper with the palm of the hand. Is there suction on the hand when you try to remove it? Test the solution with litmus paper. A base will turn litmus blue. Has a base been formed?

19. Identification of Acids and Bases

Many materials used about the house or in the kitchen are acids or bases. It is often useful to be able to identify these materials. The strength of an acid depends upon the number of hydrogen ions present in the solution. The strength of a base depends upon the number of hydroxide ions present. The degree of acidity or basicity is designated in terms of " pH " numbers. " pH 1 " indicates the strongest acid; " pH 7 " indicates a neutral condition like that of water. Numbers above 7 indicate a base, " pH 14 " indicating the strongest base.

Test the following materials with commercial " pH " paper which has a wide range of " pH " values. Rank the tested material in order, strongest acid first to strongest base last: household ammonia, baking soda, washing soda, face soap, laundry soap, detergent, bleaching solution, lye, drain-cleaning compounds, lemon juice, vinegar, tomatoes, tooth paste, cream of tartar, sour milk.

20. Neutralization

An acid and base react together to neutralize or counteract each other. A salt and water are formed in the process. The chemical activity of these substances can be controlled in this way, or new products made by their interaction.

Put 10 ml. of dilute sodium hydroxide (NaOH) in a beaker. Add dilute hydrochloric acid (HCl) one drop at a time until a piece of blue litmus paper floating in the solution just barely changes to pink. If too much acid has been added, add a few drops of sodium hydroxide. A point will be reached where one drop of either chemical will change the color of the litmus. Take a small portion of the neutralized solution and evaporate it in an evaporating dish over gentle heat or a water bath. Taste a grain or two of the residue. Is it salt?

sodium hydroxide + hydrochloric acid →
sodium chloride + water

21. Hydrolysis

Hydrolysis is the opposite of neutralization. In some cases when a salt is dissolved in water, it will react with the water to form an acid and a base. If one of the products formed is more highly ionized (stronger) than the other, the salt solution will actually give an acid or basic reaction.

Dissolve a pinch of baking soda in water and test the solution with litmus paper. Is it acidic or basic? Do the same for aluminum sulfate, sodium chloride, washing soda, and silver nitrate. Why does the sodium chloride give a neutral reaction?

Baking powder has as its main ingredients salts such as baking soda combined with aluminum sulfate or calcium hydrogen phosphate. Why would carbon dioxide gas be freed if this powder were moistened with water?

22. Dehydration

Sulfuric acid is frequently used in the preparation of other chemicals; in many cases it is present as a dehydrating agent. A dehydrating agent has the property of absorbing water, even extracting hydrogen and oxygen from some compounds in the proportion of 2 hydrogen to 1 oxygen.

Place a heaping spoonful of table sugar in a beaker and add concentrated sulfuric acid until all of the sugar is moist. Observe what happens after the acid has had a few minutes to react. This sugar has the formula $C_{12}H_{22}O_{11}$. What is the appearance of the residue? Could it be carbon? Has the sulfuric acid acted as a dehydrating agent?

23. Electrochemical Series

Chemical elements vary in their chemical activity, some being very active while others are quite inert. This fact is particularly easy to observe in the case of metals. It is possible to arrange the metals in a list in order of their activity, the metal at the top being most active, and that at the bottom the least active. A more active metal can replace a less active one in a compound. We use this ability of one metal to replace another for many useful reactions.

(a) An interesting reaction to watch is the replacement of lead from solution by zinc. Fill a 150 cc. beaker with a saturated solution of lead acetate $(Pb(C_2H_3O_2)_2)$. Suspend a strip of clean zinc in the center of the beaker. The top end of the zinc strip may be bent and supported on a wood stick across the top of the beaker. Set the beaker aside where it will not be disturbed until the next day. What is the appearance of the zinc? What chemical change has taken place?

. (b) Try strips of zinc, aluminum, or iron in solutions of silver nitrate, copper sulfate, mercuric nitrate, iron sulfate, and sodium chloride. Is there a reaction in every case? List all the metals used, either in strip form or in solution, in the order of their apparent activity.

24. To Clean Silverware by Displacement

Household silverware is subject to oxidation or tarnishing. This is especially noticeable when foods contain sulfur compounds.

Take a silver plated spoon and allow it to stand in a jar of mustard. Notice how the spoon begins to blacken after 10 minutes or so. This is direct combination of silver and sulfur to form black silver sulfide. The action can be reversed and the silver cleaned without use of silver polish or wearing away of the silver plate. Place the silver in an aluminum pan with about 1 qt. of water and a teaspoonful each of baking soda and salt. Warm the solution and keep hot until the tarnish has disappeared from the silver. Aluminum ions from the pan unite with the sulfur. This leaves a clean surface of pure silver again. Would this action have taken place if a glass container had been used? Has the silver been damaged by this cleaning process? This is an *electrolytic process*.

25. Chemical Pictures

Beautiful artistic effects can be obtained by following the simple steps needed to develop a photographic print. In a dark room illuminated with only a dim red light place a few sprays of fern, leaves, or flowers on a piece of " glossy " photographic paper, emulsion side up. Expose the paper with its arrangement to a bright white light for about one to three seconds. Develop the paper as an ordinary print by immersing for several minutes in a solution of developer until the picture is in good detail. (Under the red light the picture will look darker than it really is.) Rinse the picture in water and then soak in hypo solution for 20 minutes to remove unused chemicals. Finally wash thoroughly for 30 minutes in water and roll out face down on a waxed metal plate to dry. By changing the exposure time or the time spent in the developer, you will get a variety of effects. Tubes of developer and fixer are quite inexpensive, and directions for use are on the tube. A saturated solution of hypo (sodium thiosulfate) will make an adequate fixer.

26. Make a Blueprint

In a dark room, coat one side of a sheet of smooth white paper with a solution of ferric ammonium citrate. Place in a darkened drawer to dry. When the paper is dry, place an opaque object on the treated side and expose to bright sunlight for five minutes. Develop the print by placing it face downward in a pan containing a potassium ferricyanide solution. Allow to remain several seconds. Then remove unused chemicals by washing the paper thoroughly in water. Upon drying, a permanent picture should result. A photographic negative may be held tightly to the blueprint paper by using a printing frame, and can be exposed and developed in the same manner.

27. Oil Paints

Paint is largely a combination of a finely ground solid pigment (coloring matter) mixed with a suitable liquid vehicle. The vehicle serves to spread the colored pigment over the surface being painted. Oil, water, or a host of synthetic combinations are commonly used for vehicles.

(a) Take about 3 g. of zinc oxide (ZnO) and make a thick paste by adding linseed oil a drop at a time while mixing with a spatula. Thin the thick paste by adding turpentine a drop at a time until the paint can be spread with a small brush. On a test board paint a band of this paint.

(b) To 10 ml. of raw linseed oil in an evaporating dish add ½ g. of manganese dioxide (MnO_2) and heat the oil until it boils. Keep hot for a few minutes and then filter out any solid particles that remain. Using this oil as a vehicle, add 3 g. of zinc oxide to make a thick paste. Thin with turpentine and paint a strip on the test board next to the sample from part (a). Set the board aside to dry until the next day. The manganese dioxide added to the oil will help promote drying of the paint through more rapid oxidation of the linseed oil.

Examine the two test samples. Does paint (b) have better drying properties than paint (a)?

28. Plastics

Plastics are becoming more and more common in our daily lives. There are a great many ways of making plastic material. One method of preparation is called *polymerization*. Polymerization is described in your text on page 103 when sulfur is changed into a plastic. Natural rubber is also the product of polymerization.

(a) To about 20 ml. of latex (rubber tree sap) add strong acetic acid a few drops at a time while stirring. When the latex is completely thickened, knead under water to remove excess acid. Is it elastic? Will it bounce?

(b) While many plastics must be heated in order to make them polymerize and set, a thermoplastic material, when mixed with an activator, generates its own heat while undergoing polymerization and setting. This type may be purchased at most hobby centers along with the activator. Buy the colorless type. Make a small mold out of a round can cover about one inch deep with a flat top. Wax the inside so that the plastic may later be removed. Mix up enough plastic to form a layer ½ inch deep. Pour into the mold. When the plastic has set, place an object such as a coin or dried insect on its surface. Mix up a second batch of plastic and carefully pour into the mold

until the object is well covered. Allow to set overnight before removing.

(c) Molded plastic objects may be made by using a thermosetting powder. Fill a small mold with a general-purpose thermosetting powder obtained at hobby stores. Place the mold under pressure in a vise or hydraulic press. Heat for two minutes. Release the pressure to allow gases to escape, compress and heat again for two or three minutes. Allow to cool and remove from mold.

The Periodic Table — A Study of Relationships

When we first study the elements it may seem as though they are unrelated; for example, it may seem that their chemical properties of combining with each other do not follow any particular pattern. But scientists constantly seek for such patterns wherever they can.

29. Relating the Elements

As early as 1815 (only a few years after Dalton's atomic theory was announced), William Prout tried to show that all atomic weights are multiples of the atomic weight of hydrogen. At that time, of course, Prout didn't know that each element has several chemically identical isotopes. Thus he couldn't know that an element's atomic weight should be calculated as the average of the differing weights of its various isotopes.

30. An Early Attempt

In 1829, Dobereiner, a German chemist, listed chemically similar elements in groups of three, basing his grouping upon their relationships in atomic weight; for instance —

Atomic Weight		Atomic Weight	
1. chlorine	35.5	1. calcium	41.
2. bromine	80.	2. strontium	88.
3. iodine	127.	3. barium	137.
	81.*		89.*

* Numerical average of the atomic weights of first and third elements in each group.

Do you notice the relationship between the average atomic weights of the first and third elements in each group and the atomic weight of the second element? Calculate these averages for yourself. Dobereiner believed that this was an approach toward predicting the atomic weight of the middle element in his system of grouping.

31. Another Effort

Attempts to seek further relationships followed. In 1864, Newlands, an Englishman, suggested an arrangement of the elements in octaves, that is, in groups of eight. The *eighth* one seemed to have properties similar to the first one. For instance, in the grouping that follows, sodium is chemically similar to lithium:

1. lithium
2. beryllium
3. boron
4. carbon
5. nitrogen
6. oxygen
7. fluorine
8. sodium
9. magnesium
10. aluminum
11. silicon
12. phosphorus
13. sulfur
14. chlorine

This pattern seemed promising — but it failed to work in later series of octaves.

32. The Periodic Table

In 1869, Mendeleev (men-deh-LAY-yef), a Russian, discovered a pattern for the chemical properties of the elements, which — but for slight modifications — is in many respects satisfactory even today. This pattern, known as the *periodic table,* is illustrated in an abridged version on this page (several periods, or groups, of elements whose valence is variable, have been omitted).

What use has the periodic table? In a word — *predictability*. A study of the periodic table can provide an understanding of the relationship of the elements, so that if you know the behavior of one,

THE PERIODIC TABLE
(Abridged)

I A	II A		III A	IV A	V A	VI A	VII A	0
1 H 1.008								2 He 4.003
3 Li 6.939	4 Be 9.012		5 B 10.81	6 C 12.011	7 N 14.007	8 O 15.9994	9 F 19.00	10 Ne 20.183
11 Na 22.9898	12 Mg 24.31		13 Al 26.98	14 Si 28.09	15 P 30.974	16 S 32.064	17 Cl 35.453	18 Ar 39.948
19 K 39.102	20 Ca 40.08		31 Ga 69.72	32 Ge 72.59	33 As 74.92	34 Se 78.96	35 Br 79.909	36 Kr 83.80
37 Rb 85.47	38 Sr 87.62		49 In 114.82	50 Sn 118.69	51 Sb 121.75	52 Te 127.60	53 I 126.90	54 Xe 131.30
55 Cs 132.91	56 Ba 137.34		81 Tl 204.37	82 Pb 207.19	83 Bi 208.98	84 Po [210]	85 At [210]	86 Rn [222]
87 Fr [223]	88 Ra 226.05							

Atomic weights in this table are based on the Carbon 12 isotope as standard. Those in square brackets have been determined only approximately.

you may reasonably *predict* the behavior of another.

The basis for the periodic table lies in the laboratory, where the chemical properties of the elements are experimentally investigated. But the findings of experimental science can then be used to reason with, to imagine with — that is, facts can be reflected upon, assembled, and reassembled in one's mind. The purpose of the " problems " which follow is to give you such an opportunity — to use the facts of experimental science in your armchair, and from these facts, to reflect, to reason, to predict.

33. Predicting Valences

Consider the list of elements in the column, or chemical " family," headed IA in the periodic table. Do you recognize any from their symbols? No doubt you recognize Na — sodium. What valence does Na have? Do you recall from table 7–1 on page 82 that it has a valence of 1^+? In accordance with the pattern discovered by Mendeleev, K (potassium), which is listed in the same chemical family, would also have a valence of 1^+. What valences would Li (lithium), Rb (rubidium), and Cs (cesium) have? 1^+, of course. Now all the elements in the IA family have atoms which can *lose* one electron. On the other hand, Cl, as do all the other numbers of the VIIA " family," has a valence of -1 (that is, it can *gain* one electron).

34. Predicting Compounds

If Na formed a compound with chlorine (Cl), what would the compound be? *NaCl* (common salt). What would be the formula for the chloride of K? *KCl,* of course. And of Li? *LiCl.* An element whose *atoms can lose one electron joins with elements whose atoms can gain one electron.* Now write the formulas of the chlorides of Rb, Cs, and the radioactive Fr.

35. Predicting Compounds (continued)

Notice once again that *families of elements* (elements with similar properties) are in columns headed IA, IIA. Now the numerals I and II can

be used, in these cases, to refer to positive valences. What, then, would be the valence of B (boron)? Of Al (aluminum)?

Atoms of Be, an element from the IIA family, *can lose two electrons* and so may join with *two atoms, each of which can gain one electron.* Thus the formula of beryllium chloride would be $BeCl_2$. On the basis of your study of the periodic table, you can now write the formulas for:

magnesium	(Mg)	chloride
calcium	(Ca)	chloride
barium	(Ba)	chloride
aluminum	(Al)	chloride
boron	(B)	chloride

36. The Zero Valence Family

The family of elements marked zero is interesting. Probably you recognize the symbol He (helium). If the heading IA indicates a valence of 1^+, what would the heading zero indicate? Zero valence, of course. The elements of this family have atoms which can neither gain or lose electrons. These elements, except under very special conditions, do not combine with other elements, and so are called *inert* elements.

(a) Would you expect to find a substance such as KrO? If not, why not?

(b) He and Ne are gases. In what state are the other inert elements?

(c) Suppose X, a new element, was found which had a valence of zero. And suppose it belonged below Rn in the periodic table. Would you expect its state to be solid, liquid, or gaseous?

(d) A newspaper article reports a compound with the formula *RnCl.* You know that Rn is in the inert family and so has no combining power with other elements. You suspect a misprint. Can you hunt out the element whose symbol was incorrectly printed?

37. Periods of Elements

Now reading the periodic table horizontally, note the H-He row, or period. What do the numbers 1 and 2 mean? Does it help to know that hydrogen has 1 proton in its nucleus, and helium has 2?

(a) What do the numbers 3, 4, 5 in the Li-Be-B period of elements stand for?

(b) From your reasoning, what is the number of electrons in Li, Be, and B?

(c) Here are three pieces of information to be related:

First, you know that the numbers at the top of our abridged periodic table refer to valences, or to the number of electrons that can be lost or gained.

Second, you know that the numbers directly above the symbols for the elements stand for the number of protons or electrons in each atom.

Third, from examination of the diagrams of atomic structure on pages 66 and 79, you can see that the first, or inner, shell of electrons around the nucleus has two electrons.

What then is the number of electrons in the outer shell of

(i)   Li, Be, and B?
(ii)   Na, K, Rb?
(iii) Mg, Ca, Sr?
(iv)   Al, Ga, In?

38. More About Periods of Elements

The number below the symbol of each element refers to the atomic weight; thus H has the atomic weight 1.008, He, 4.003, and Li, 6.940.

By proceeding from left to right in the periodic table, that is, as you read the periods of elements, decide which statement in each of the following pairs of statements is true.

The atomic weights increase.
The atomic weights decrease.

The atomic numbers increase.
The atomic numbers decrease.

The number of electrons in the outermost shell increases.
The number of electrons in the outermost shell decreases.

39. The Activity Series

The periodic table may also be used to relate the greater or lesser activity of elements. As you may remember from experiment 23 in this blue section a chemical is rated as more active than another if it can replace it from a compound.

1. First, note that simple laboratory work can show the relative activity of chlorine (Cl) compared with bromine (Br) and iodine (I).

(a) If some carbon tetrachloride (about an inch in a test tube) is added to chlorine water, the chlorine will be dissolved and the carbon tetrachloride will turn yellowish. Carbon tetrachloride will also dissolve bromine and iodine, but only if these substances are uncombined.

(b) Now chlorine water (water in which chlorine has been dissolved) may be shaken up with potassium bromide (KBr). Almost immediately, the carbon tetrachloride turns *brown* — the color of bromine. (Iodine, you may recall, exhibits *violet* crystals.) The bromine has been *displaced* from KBr by the *chlorine*.

Shake up a solution of potassium iodide, chlorine water, and carbon tetrachloride. What color would you expect the carbon tetrachloride to turn? Why?

2. On the basis of these reactions, which of the elements above (Cl, Br, I) is most active? If you could get a solution of At, would it displace chlorine from KCl? Or would chlorine displace it from KAt?

3. How does this activity series appear in the periodic table?

40. Force

Force is a push or pull. To a common brick or object of similar size lying on a smooth table top, attach a spring balance. With the balance pull the brick across the table. How much is the reading on the balance? This is the force needed to move the brick. By separate cords or strings, attach two balances to the same brick. Pull with the two balances in the same direction. Does the sum of the readings on the two balances just equal the pull when one balance is used alone? Should the readings on each balance be the same? Why?

Change your experiment so that the forces exerted by the two balances 'oppose each other. Does the brick move? Compare the readings on each balance. What happens when each balance reads the same? What happens when one balance reads more than the other? Now attach the balances so that they are pulling at right angles to each other. How does this affect the direction of motion of the brick? Does it follow the path indicated by either balance — or does it take a path somewhere in between the two forces? When two or more forces act upon an object, the motion of the object is in the direction of a third force, called the *resultant*.

(c) Suspend a one-pound weight by two cords each attached to a spring balance. Start with the balances close together, then gradually move them apart horizontally and note the increase in the balance readings. Is it possible to have an extremely high force built up in the cord while it is supporting only a small weight?

41. Inertia

The tendency of a body to resist change in motion is known as *inertia*. This effect is frequently seen on a streetcar or a bus. A sudden stop of the bus causes a person to lunge forward in the direction of travel, while a sudden start frequently causes a lunge or loss of balance in the opposite direction.

(a) When an object is at rest, it tends to remain at rest. Place a piece of smooth cardboard about four inches square over a water tumbler. Place a light weight or coin on the cardboard. Flick your finger against the edge of the cardboard with a quick snap so that the cardboard flies off in a horizontal direction. What happens to the coin?

(b) Place a book on a smooth sheet of paper. Grasping the edge, quickly jerk the paper from under the book. If the book moves, try it again. Why does the book tend to remain unmoved?

(c) Suspend a heavy metal ball or weight weighing two to five pounds by a light string. Attach a piece of the same string to the bottom of the weight.

So that the heavy weight will not do damage when it falls, tie a heavy cord loosely from the support to the top of the weight to catch the weight after the light string breaks. By pulling the lower string slowly, and gradually increasing the tension, which string breaks — the one above or the one below the weight? Repeat, but this time pull the lower string with a quick jerk. Which string breaks this time? Why?

(d) Place a one-pound weight on a small car. If necessary place a piece of cardboard on top of the car to provide a smooth surface for the weight to rest upon. With a piece of string attached to the car set it in motion with a jerk. What happens to the weight? Repeat the setup but this time start the car very gradually until it has good motion; then by means of a string attached to the rear of the car, stop it suddenly. What happens?

42. Acceleration

When an object increases its velocity, it is said to be *accelerated*. Sir Isaac Newton was able to show that the rate of acceleration depends upon the force; the greater the force, the greater the acceleration. He also showed that as the object increases in mass (weight) it becomes harder to accelerate. These facts are summed up in one of the fundamental laws of motion: *the acceleration of an object is directly proportional to the force acting on it and inversely proportional to the mass.*

(a) Weigh a small-wheeled car. Tie a string to the car and place it on a smooth table. Pass the string over a roller or pulley fastened to the edge of the table. At the end of the string fasten a light weight (Fig. 5). Does the weight descend? Does the car move? Move the car back and use a heavier weight. Does the car pick up speed? Try increasingly heavier weights. What effects do they have upon the acceleration of the car?

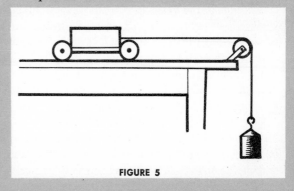

FIGURE 5

(b) Start the experiment over again, but this time place a 500 g. weight in the car. Does it move as rapidly now? Increase the load in the car. Is the acceleration reduced? Why?

43. Action (Force) and Reaction (Equal and Opposite Force)

When a rifle is fired, the bullet takes off in one direction and the rifle takes off in the opposite direction. Anyone who has fired a rifle or shotgun knows this: "The gun kicks." Because of its small size, the bullet moves off at high speed, while the rifle, because of its comparatively large size, moves slowly. As Newton said: *For every action* (*force*) *there is an equal and opposite reaction* (*force*).

(a) Weigh two wheeled cars like those used for the inclined plane experiment. Select two that weigh nearly the same, or add weight to one until they are equal. Compress a coiled spring between the ends of the two cars and tie the cars together with a piece of string so that the spring stays compressed. Place them on a smooth surface, such as a table. Use a match to burn the string. This allows it to be broken without touching or disturbing the cars. What happens? Do the cars move at the same speed? Do they travel the same distance?

(b) Try loading one car so that it is twice as heavy as the other, then repeat the test. How does this increase in weight affect the speed of each car? Load one car so that it is four times as heavy as the other. How does the speed of the two cars compare now? What effect does adding weight to one car have upon its speed?

44. Friction

Friction is the resistance to movement of one surface over another surface. It is a desirable thing between auto tires and the roadway, but in many cases (such as a piston moving in its cylinder or a wheel rotating on an axle), friction is not wanted. But to reduce or increase friction we must know those factors that influence it.

(a) Tie a string around a common brick or a heavy book and pull it across a smooth table top by means of a spring balance attached to the other end of the string. Does it make any difference in the balance reading whether the narrow surface of the brick or the broad surface is in contact with the table? Now pull the same brick over a roughened surface such as a thick carpet. Repeat the trials, but this time move the carpeted surface of a blackboard eraser over both a smooth and rough surface. What effect does the smoothness of the surfaces have upon the amount of friction developed? Does the area of the surface in contact have any effect?

(b) Place the brick on a group of rollers (nails with heads removed would do) or on a wheeled cart and repeat the experiment. What effect do roller bearings have upon the amount of friction developed?

(c) Place two or three bricks on top of each other and pull across the table top; then try again with rollers below the bricks. What effect does this increased weight have upon the friction as indicated by the reading on the spring balance? What factors determine the amount of friction?

45. Conservation of Momentum

The product of the mass of an object and its velocity is called *momentum*. When two objects collide, their total momentum before collision equals the total amount after collision. This is known as the *Law of Conservation of Momentum*. Conservation of momentum can be easily shown.

(a) A level board with a " v " groove cut in its surface can serve as a guide. Place several glass balls or marbles of the same size in contact with each other in the groove. Move one ball to one side and roll it along the groove so that it strikes the bunched-up balls. What happens? Try rolling the ball slowly. Now try rolling it rapidly. Is there any difference in the velocity of the balls displaced?

(b) Draw two balls to the side and repeat the process, rolling the two balls together. Do the same thing with any number of balls until only one ball remains as the target. How does the number of balls put into motion after collision compare with the number of balls rolled along the groove? Does there seem to be conservation of momentum?

46. Gravity

Gravitational force causes objects to fall to earth. In a vacuum all objects would fall with the same acceleration. The effect of the shape of the object, and of the air resistance acting on it, cause different objects to gain speed at different rates. Release a sheet of paper and a pencil so that they start to fall together. Which one hits the floor first? Now take the sheet of paper and crumple it into a tight wad. Again drop the paper and pencil together. How do their times of fall compare now? Why?

All machines are combinations of one or more of the following simple machines: the lever, wheel and axle, pulley, and inclined plane. An understanding of the simple machines makes it possible to understand complex machines.

47. Levers

Levers are generally bars that can rotate about a *fulcrum*. By having the fulcrum close to the load to be lifted and the force far from the fulcrum, we can move a large load with a small force. A crowbar and a claw hammer are good examples of levers.

(a) Support a meter stick at its midpoint on a narrow-edge fulcrum. Place equal weights at each end. Do they balance each other? Move the fulcrum so that it is closer to one end. Does it now require more or less weight at the other end to balance the stick? What is the effect of moving the fulcrum very close to one end?

(b) Try to crack a walnut by squeezing it in your hand. Now place it in the jaws of a pliers or a nut cracker. Is there a mechanical advantage? Is this a double lever?

(c) Drive two sixpenny nails about one half of their length into a piece of soft wood. Pull one nail out with a pliers and the other one using a claw hammer. Are all levers equally effective? Why?

48. The Wheel and Axle

The *wheel and axle* is a kind of continuous lever. The carpenter's hand brace for drilling holes and the crank on a hand-operated food grinder or egg beater are examples of the wheel and axle. In the wheel and axle the force acts at a point some distance from the axis of rotation, or fulcrum. This force exerts a turning force, or *torque,* on the wheel and axle. The amount of torque is found by multiplying the force by its perpendicular distance to the axis of rotation. The greater the force or the greater the distance, the larger the torque.

(a) Remove the knob from the shaft (or axle) of a door lock. Is it difficult to open the door when the wheel (knob) has been removed? Why?

(b) Start several one-inch wood screws in a pine board with a few taps from a hammer. Turn the screws into the wood using different size screwdrivers, from very small to large. Why are those with larger diameter handles more effective? Try a carpenter's brace with a screwdriver bit. Is it the easiest to use? Why?

49. Inclined Plane

The inclined plane is often used when we wish to move heavy loads. Sliding loads up and down a plank instead of directly lifting them is a common application of the inclined plane.

With a cord, attach a spring balance to a block of wood or metal. Note the weight of the block as recorded on the spring balance. Now rest the block on a smooth board set at an angle of about 15° and pull the block up the board by means of the attached balance (Fig. 6). How does this reading of the balance differ from the first reading? What is an apparent advantage of this inclined plane? Try the effect of setting the plane at a 45° angle instead of a 15° angle and note the balance reading. What two conclusions can be drawn from these trials?

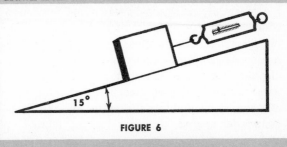

FIGURE 6

50. The Screw

A screw or bolt is actually a very flat inclined plane. As it progresses into the wood or into a nut, a complete turn gives a very short advance. A relatively small force applied to the screw can overcome a large resistance.

(a) On top of an ordinary screw-type jack (like a house jack) place a heavy weight. Tie a spring balance to the end of the handle and measure the pull needed to raise the load. Is there a high mechanical advantage? Measure the height of the load from the table top and measure again after one full turn of the handle. How far has the jack handle moved? How much has the load been lifted? How does the efficiency of this screw jack compare with other types of machines?

51. Power

It is often useful to know the power produced by a machine. This measurement is often made in a unit called the *horsepower. Power* is the amount of work done in a unit of time; for example, 100 foot-pounds of work per second. When work is done at the rate of 550 foot-pounds per second, it is being produced at the rate of one horsepower. Most household appliance motors range from $\frac{1}{10}$ horsepower to $\frac{1}{4}$ horsepower.

To measure the power output of engines and motors that have a rotating shaft, a form of brake is used. Loop a heavy cord over a pulley on the shaft of a small electric motor and attach a spring balance to each end of the cord. Fasten the spring balances to an overhead support, start the motor, and read the force indicated on each balance. The difference in readings is the force exerted by the motor.

During each revolution of the motor, this force acts through the distance of one circumference of the pulley. By using a stop watch and revolution counter, you can find the number of revolutions per second. The work done by the motor in one second equals the force times the circumference of pulley (distance) times the number of revolutions per second. The horsepower developed is determined by dividing the power by 550 foot-pounds per second.

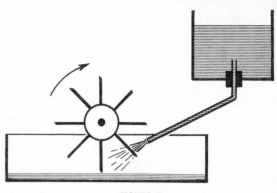

FIGURE 7

52. Turbines

A steam turbine is an engine that derives its power from steam working against bladed wheels mounted on a shaft which turns.

(a) You can easily observe the principle of the steam turbine by fitting a flask with a stopper and a right angle glass delivery tube. Put a small amount of water in the flask, heat it to boiling, and direct the steam from the delivery tube against a bladed wheel. Make the wheel from a cork with strips of metal, such as pen nibs, in it to act as blades. A knitting needle driven lengthwise through the cork can serve as an axle. Support the axle at its ends on a smooth surface having a groove or depression to keep the wheel from rolling away. The pouring spouts of two beakers make good axle supports. Try changing the angle at which the steam strikes the blades and also the angle of the blades to the cork.

(b) Your turbine wheel can be a water wheel pushed around by water trapped behind a high dam as in dams and power projects. Punch a hole in the bottom of a can large enough to hold the rubber stopper and the glass delivery tube from the flask used above (Fig. 7). Fill the can with water and direct the stream from the delivery tube against the wheel. Again the shape of the blade and the angle of impact of the water are important.

53. Jet Propulsion

The jet engine is a typical action-reaction engine. The principle of jet propulsion can be illustrated by cementing a balloon to a toy automobile so that the opening of the balloon is pointed toward the rear. Place the car on a smooth surface, inflate the balloon and release it. What is the action force? What is the reaction?

A very simple engine can be made from a paper milk carton and four short pieces of glass tubing. Put about one inch of water in the milk carton. Above this water line in each side of the carton insert a right-angle glass bend about two inches long overall. Have all the bends pointed in the same direction, either clockwise or counterclockwise. Suspend the carton by a string fastened to its top and drop a few pieces of dry ice into the water. How does this show action and reaction?

54. Heat Conduction

(a) The difference in the abilities of different substances to conduct heat is of use in both heating and insulating. Place 50 ml. of water in a glass beaker and 50 ml. in a metal can of about the same shape and size. Compare the time required to bring water to a boil, in each case using the same heat source. Are glass utensils as efficient as metal ones in conducting heat?

(b) With a coil of wire hold a piece of ice at the bottom of a test tube of water. Heat the upper part of the tube to boiling with a Bunsen burner. What happens? Is water a good insulator?

(c) Place a copper or iron screen about two inches above a Bunsen burner. Turn on the gas and ignite the gas below the screen. Is the flame stopped by the screen? Turn off the burner, allow the screen to cool, and light the burner again, but this time ignite the gas *above* the screen. Does it burn below the screen? What accounts for the effect of this screen on the flame?

(d) Obtain several rods of equal length and shape, each made of a different metal. At one end of each attach a drop of wax. Hold the other end in a candle flame. Note the difference in time for the wax to melt at the other end. Which metals are the better conductors?

55. Convection Currents

Heat is distributed in fluids mostly because of convection currents set up in the fluid. Unequal heating in different parts of the fluid causes differences in densities, and starts the circulation going. How convection currents are set up in our atmosphere can be shown as follows:

Cut two holes in the side of a wood or cardboard box so that two chimneys may be fitted as shown in Fig. 8. Chimneys may be made from empty tin cans with both ends removed. Place a candle under one chimney and light it. Completely cover the front of the box with a piece of glass and make it as airtight as possible. Ignite a small piece of tar paper over the chimney which is not immediately over the candle. Notice how the smoke travels down, around, and up again.

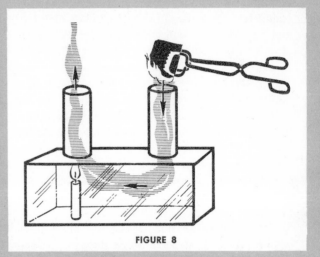

FIGURE 8

56. Radiant Heat

(a) Take two sheets of aluminum. Coat the surface of one with black paint or soot from a candle; keep the other shiny. Fasten a lump of wax on the back of each sheet. Direct the rays from an electric heater at the faces of the two sheets when they are held side by side in a vertical position. Which plate is the better absorber of radiant heat? To reduce the radiant heat absorbed by a material, what should be the condition of its surface? Try the same tests using copper or aluminum foil. Are they as effective insulators?

(b) Place a lighted candle at the focal point of a parabolic reflector (Fig. 9). Place your hand about two feet away from the flame. Can any heat be felt? Carefully place a second reflector about four feet away so that the heat from the candle is directed toward it by the first reflector. Place your hand at the focal point of the second reflector. Is there a noticeable heat? If a radiometer is available, note the reaction when put in the two positions you held your hand. Are the heat rays visible? Can they be focused like visible light?

57. Radiation Thermometer

Radiant heat energy has very little effect upon the air through which it passes. Upon striking an object, however, this energy is absorbed, and the temperature of the object rises. Ordinary mercury thermometers usually receive their heat mainly by conduction from the surrounding air or material, and because their bulbs are shiny they are poor absorbers of radiant energy. However, they can be converted to radiant thermometers.

Seal the bulb of a mercury thermometer in a hollow metal sphere, such as plumbers use for toilet floats, and paint the sphere dull black. Allow heat from an electric heater to fall on an ordinary mercury thermometer in the air and on the radiation thermometer just made. How do the readings differ? Is there a type of heat present not readily measured by the usual mercury in a glass thermometer?

Not all metals are equally effective in shielding against radiant heat. Hold a thin sheet of polished aluminum between the source of heat and the thermometers. How does this affect the readings of the two thermometers? Replace the aluminum with a thin sheet of iron. Is the iron as effective as the aluminum in cutting off the radiant heat? How can you tell?

58. Refrigeration

Evaporation is a cooling process which is widely used in refrigeration.

Put about ½ inch of alcohol in a shallow dish. Note the air temperature on a thermometer and then place the bulb of the thermometer in the alcohol. Blow vigorously across the surface of the alcohol. What effect does this have on the temperature registered on the thermometer?

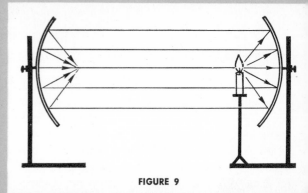

FIGURE 9

Insect repellants in pressurized cans generally use the same gas for propellant that the home refrigerator uses in its cooling coils. Release the gas from the repellant can so that it travels through a piece of copper tubing. Coat the outside of the tube with water. What happens to the water? How does this illustrate the principle of the refrigerator?

59. Boiling at Reduced Pressure

Evaporation is increased by reducing the vapor pressure above a liquid. Fill a round bottom flask half-full of water and bring the water to a boil. Remove the flask from the heat source and quickly stopper. Invert the flask, and run cold water over the surface to cool it. As the flask cools, does the water inside begin to boil vigorously again? Before boiling has come to a complete stop, remove the stopper and take the temperature of the water. Does the thermometer read less than 212° F.? How was reduced pressure obtained in the flask? Would water boil at a temperature less than 212° F. if you were up high in mountain country?

60. The Barometer

Change in air pressure is one of the causes of change in local weather conditions. Pressure changes are measured with a barometer. To make a barometer take a glass tube 34 inches long and close one end by heating it in a Bunsen flame. When cool, fill the tube completely with mercury, cover the open end tightly with a finger tip, and invert the tube into a dish of mercury. Remove

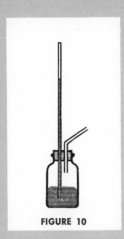

FIGURE 10

your finger which closed the tube. The mercury will fall slightly in the tube. Place a meter stick or yard stick behind the tube and read the atmospheric pressure in inches or centimeters of mercury. The measurement is made from the top of the mercury in the closed tube to the surface of the mercury in the dish.

You can make pressure changes and see the effect on the barometer. Invert the mercury tube into a wide-mouth bottle, as illustrated in Fig. 10, instead of an open dish. Attach an exhaust pump or pressure pump to the short open tube. When the pump is operated, the effect of pressure change on the mercury column can readily be seen.

61. Humidity Indicator

The relative amount of moisture in the air can be indicated by using a human hair as the measuring device. Remove the oil from a long human hair by soaking it for a time in alcohol or ether. Dry the hair and fasten one end of it to a cardboard sheet with a pin. Fasten the other end to a lightweight cardboard pointer as indicated in the diagram (Fig. 11). Pin the pointer to the sheet so that the pointer is free to rotate. Moist air coming in contact with the hair, as from a beaker of boiling water, will cause the pointer to sag. This will give the low or wet position. A lighted bulb held close to the hair will dry it, and give the top or dry position. With these two extremes marked,

the space between can be divided to give relative readings between wet and dry.

62. Dew Point

The *dew point* is the temperature to which air must be cooled in order that its moisture will begin to condense. This temperature is important in weather forecasting as it shows how near precipitation may be. When the dew point and air temperature are close to each other, a slight drop in air temperature may cause precipitation. Airlines and farmers in particular need this type of information.

Place a thermometer in a beaker of water and add a few ice cubes to the water. Stir the water gently with the thermometer and watch the outside of the beaker for any condensation. As soon as the beaker becomes clouded with condensed vapor, read the thermometer. This temperature is the dew point. Read the air temperature. Would these readings give some idea as to the relative humidity of the air? If the temperatures read were quite far apart, is the air relatively dry or wet?

63. Static Electricity

Static electricity is generated in practically every case where two different kinds of materials rub together. Running a plastic comb or brush through dry hair will give the characteristic snap and crackle of discharging static electricity. Poor conductors have a tendency to store the static charges. In this way it is possible to store up very large charges.

You have learned that there are two kinds of static charges: *positive* and *negative*. You have also learned that like charges *repel* and unlike

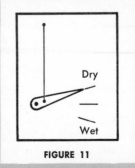

FIGURE 11

charges *attract*. This can be shown by using a pith ball suspended on a thread. (Pith comes from the inner part of hollow stemmed plants like the sunflower.)

(a) Charge a hard rubber rod by rubbing it with a piece of fur. Bring the tip of the rod close to the pith ball. Is it attracted? Does it then fly away and keep its distance as you follow it with the tip of the rod?

(b) Touch the pith ball to discharge it. Charge a glass or lucite rod by rubbing it with silk. Bring it close to the pith ball. Does the ball react the same way as when the rubber rod was used? So far, could this pith ball be used to distinguish between negative and positive charges? Touch the ball to discharge it again.

(c) Place a negative charge on the pith ball by touching it with a charged rubber rod. Now place a charge on a stick of sealing wax by rubbing it with a piece of flannel. Bring the charged sealing wax close to the charged pith ball. Is the ball attracted or repelled? Is there a negative or positive charge on the sealing wax?

(d) An electroscope (see Fig. 21-5) is a simple instrument used to detect the presence of a static charge of electricity. Bring an uncharged rubber rod to the knob of an electroscope. Does anything happen to the two leaves at the other end? Put a charge on the rod with the wool and again bring it up to the electroscope. What happens to the leaves of the electroscope now? Touch the metal knob with your fingers. What happens to the leaves of the electroscope?

(e) To show that the charges on glass and rubber are different, do the following. Tie a thread to the mid point of a hard rubber rod and suspend it so that it hangs in a horizontal position. Place a charge on one end by rubbing it with a piece of fur. Now place a charge on a second hard rubber rod. Bring the two charged ends close to each other but do not let them touch. What happens?

Replace the charge on the suspended rod if it has been lost by touching it, and bring near it a glass rod that has been charged by means of the silk cloth. What happens?

From this it should be apparent that like charges repel and unlike charges attract. Did your results indicate this?

64. Make an Electroscope

Use an ordinary screw-cap glass jar as the shell of the electroscope. Cut a hole in the lid large enough to take a rubber stopper. Insert a nail through the stopper so that the point is well into the jar. The rubber stopper serves to insulate the nail from the cover. Cut two strips of metal foil about ½ inch by 2 inches from candy or gum wrappers. Place the upper ends together and cement or tie to the lower end of the nail. When a charged object is touched to the head of the nail, the metal leaves will fly apart. A second like charge brought to the nail will cause the leaves to diverge further. An opposite charge or grounding will cause the leaves to collapse.

Try charging such materials as glass, lucite, a hard rubber comb, phonograph records, sealing wax, or a photo negative by rubbing each of them with a piece of fur, wool, nylon, silk, or cotton. Use your electroscope to determine what type of charge has been obtained.

65. The Permanent Magnet

Knowledge of magnets is over a thousand years old, but their use for anything except compass needles is a modern development. Our understanding of magnetic fields makes telephones, radio, television, and electric power stations possible.

(a) Touch a needle with the end of a bar magnet. Will it be attracted to either end? Try the magnet on iron filings, tacks, copper wire, zinc, lead, or any other object. What type of material is attracted?

(b) Place a bar magnet under a sheet of white paper. Sprinkle iron filings over the paper and note the pattern that takes form. Where is the magnetism concentrated in this magnet? Follow the lines traced by the filings with a small compass. How does the needle change direction in passing from one end (pole) to the other (Fig. 12)? (To distinguish the poles one is marked N, for north pointing and the other S, for south pointing.)

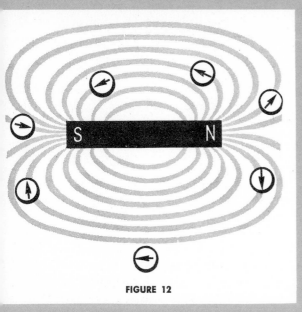

FIGURE 12

(c) Bring the like poles of two magnets up to each other. Do they attract or repel? Do the same with unlike poles. Make a pattern that shows these facts by sprinkling iron filings on a sheet of paper placed over the magnets.

(d) Does a magnetic field penetrate solid materials? Suspend a strong magnet by one end. Tie a paper clip with a thread so that it is held within ¼ inch of the lower end of the magnet. Slide various sheets of metal, glass, wood, etc. between the magnet and the paper clip. Is the material penetrated by the magnetic field? Is there any material that interferes with the field?

66. The Electromagnet

On page 250 of your text it was pointed out that when an electric current flows through a wire, a magnetic field surrounds the wire. If a long piece of insulated wire is wound around a straight rod, the spiral coil formed will be a magnet and will have a north and south pole like an iron bar magnet. If an iron rod is placed inside of this coil, a better pathway for the magnetic field is provided and a stronger magnet results. The principle of the *electromagnet* is widely used in building electrical equipment. It is used in the operation of electric generators, electric motors, switches, relays, telephone circuits, and many other devices.

Here's how an electromagnet can be constructed and how it acts.

(a) Set up a simple circuit containing a length of fine insulated copper wire, a dry cell, and a switch. Wind the wire about a pencil to form a helix or coil. Close the switch and bring a compass up to the coil. Does this coil have north and south poles? Will this coil attract light metal objects such as steel pins or iron filings?

(b) Insert an iron nail in the coil instead of the pencil. What effect does this have upon its strength? Use a much longer length of wire wrapped around the nail. Does this give a stronger magnet (Fig. 22-12)? Use two or three dry cells in series instead of just one. Is there a definite increase in the magnetic field? Can your magnet be used like a magnetic crane to pick up, move, and release steel or iron objects?

67. Primary Cell

Great numbers of dry cells are used in flashlights, portable radios, and camera flash attachments. Dry cells or batteries are a convenient source of power but their life is relatively short. Let us see why.

(a) Fill a beaker or glass with dilute sulfuric acid (10%). Firmly attach copper wire leads to a carbon rod and strip of zinc and place each in the solution so that they do not touch. Attach the wire leads to a voltmeter or to a flashlight bulb (1 to 3 volt) held in a suitable lamp base. Is a current being generated? What is taking place at the zinc electrode? Does the amount of current flowing seem to decrease? Shake the bubbles off the carbon electrode. Does this restore the current to its peak again? Is one electrode being consumed in this process? Leave the cell connected until you are sure.

(b) Cut away part of an old dry cell, such as a flashlight battery, so as to expose the center electrode. What is the composition of the center electrode, and what is the metal that is used in the outer case?

Ammonium chloride paste is used in the dry cell as the electrolyte instead of sulfuric acid. Manganese dioxide is added to the electrolyte to oxidize any hydrogen gas that accumulates when the cell is used. What is the appearance of the zinc case on a very old cell? Could this type of cell be recharged?

There are several other kinds of chemical cells that can be made to generate electrical energy. How to make a lead storage cell is described on page 257.

68. The Relay

A small current from a dry cell may be used to control a very much larger current. One device that can be made to illustrate this action is the *relay*. In order to avoid the use of high voltage, the lamp circuit used in this demonstration takes the place of appliances that might operate on 110 volts or higher.

Construct a relay as follows: Wind several layers of fine insulated copper wire around a soft iron core. Mount the coil on a block of wood so that it is stationary. Bend a piece of light iron (from a tin can) so that it is free to pivot on a nail driven in the block as indicated in Fig. 13.

When the switch is closed in the electromagnet circuit, the piece of metal will be attracted to the magnet. When the current is cut off, a light spring will pull the metal back, breaking the circuit.

Now if the relay is connected in a circuit as shown in Fig. 13, closing the switch in the electromagnet, or relay circuit, will cause a larger current to flow in the lamp circuit. Opening the switch will stop the current in the lamp circuit. We now have a way of controlling the flow of current in a high-voltage circuit by using a very weak source of current.

69. Resistance

Pass current from three dry cells wired in series through 25 ft. of #18 copper wire. With an ammeter (range 1 to 30 amp) in series with the wire, read how much current is flowing. Use the same source of energy, but this time pass the current through 50 ft. of #18 wire. What effect does it have on the ammeter reading? In place of #18 wire use a finer wire such as #28. Again what is the effect as read on the ammeter? How do length and cross sectional area affect the resistance of wire and consequently the amount of current flowing?

In place of copper wire use a piece of iron wire of comparable length and size (gauge number). Does iron offer greater resistance than copper? Do all materials conduct equally well? Make a further check by using such wire as tungsten, nichrome, and aluminum.

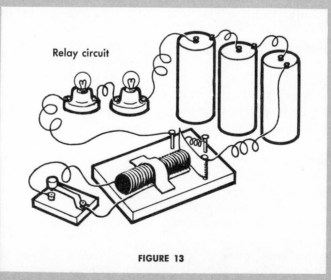

Relay circuit

FIGURE 13

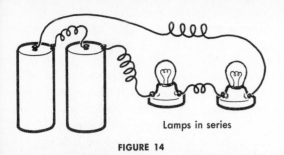

Lamps in series

FIGURE 14

70. Resistances in Series and Parallel

When resistance is added to a series circuit, what is the effect upon the amount of current flowing?

Connect two dry cells in series and pass the current through a 3-volt flashlight lamp. Add a second lamp to the circuit in *series* with the first one (Fig. 14). What effect does this have on the brightness of the lamp? Why? What will be the effect of putting a third lamp in series? Try it.

Again connect two dry cells in series with a 3-volt lamp, but this time add a second lamp in *parallel* with the first (Fig. 15). What is the effect on brightness? Are both lamps equally bright? Has the amount of current flowing been decreased? Add a third lamp in parallel. How does its brightness compare?

71. The Generator

Chemical reactions and friction can produce electrical energy as you have seen. But for large amounts of economical energy the generator is used. When a magnetic field moves across a wire which is part of an electrical circuit, an electric current flows in the wire. The magnetic field is said to have *induced* the current (caused it to flow).

To see induction take place, make a compact coil about one inch in diameter by winding about 25 turns of #18 covered copper wire one turn on top of another. Connect the ends of the coil to the terminals of a galvanometer (see Fig. 22-17).

Insert the end of a magnet into the coil. Does the galvanometer needle deflect? Withdraw the magnet. How does the needle react this time? Move the magnet in and out at various speeds. Does this affect the amount of current generated?

Insert a stronger magnet in the coil or use two magnets with like poles adjacent. Does a stronger magnetic field induce more current? Replace the wire coil with one having many more turns and again move a magnet in and out. Is there greater deflection of the galvanometer? What is the effect of rate of motion, size of coil, and strength of magnet on the amount of current produced?

72. The Induction Coil and Transformer

When a pulsing current flows in a coil of wire, it causes a magnetic field to move back and forth as the current changes strength. This magnetic field moving over a second coil in a separate circuit will induce a current in the second coil.

The intensity of current flowing in the secondary coil depends in part upon the number of turns in each coil. If the two coils are close together, and there are twice as many turns in the secondary as in the primary, they will induce twice as much voltage in the secondary. Ten times as many turns in the secondary will give ten times the voltage in the primary, half as many turns, one half of the voltage. Thus we have a means of raising or lowering voltage at will. High voltage is needed to get a spark to jump (as in the spark plugs of an auto), or to cause an electron stream as in a TV tube.

Wind a few turns of insulated bell wire around one end of an iron rod. Connect the wire to a dry cell through a simple key (switch). Wind a few turns of a second piece of wire around the other end of the rod and connect its end to a galvanometer. Is the galvanometer needle deflected when the switch in the first circuit is closed? Does

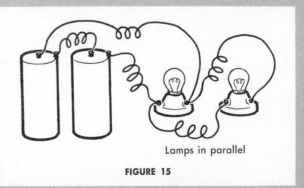

Lamps in parallel

FIGURE 15

it stay deflected? Open the key. What happens?

Open and close the key rapidly. Is a pulsing current flowing in the galvanometer circuit? Place more windings in the galvanometer circuit by wrapping more turns of wire around the rod. What effect does this have upon the intensity of current flowing as indicated on the galvanometer? How is this principle of induction used in a step-up or step-down transformer?

73. Heating Effect of Electric Current

In studying the resistance offered to an electric current it should be remembered that the flow of electricity always produces some heat. This is an advantage where heat is a desired result as in stoves, toasters, electric furnaces, etc. It can be a very great disadvantage under some circumstances because it uses up some of the electric energy being sent through wires and conductors. It can create a fire hazard and must be guarded against by selection of proper wire size.

Connect six feet of number 26 gauge iron wire in series with six feet of number 26 gauge copper wire. Stretch the wire back and forth on a board around insulated knobs or binding posts. Connect the wire in a series with a 6-volt storage battery and a *rheostat* (a variable resistance of about 18 ohms for regulating current).

The amount of current flowing in the circuit may be varied by adjusting the resistance of the rheostat. Increase the current flowing until the iron wire begins to glow. How is the temperature of the copper wire affected? How does the resistance of the iron wire compare with that of the copper wire? Would this account for the heating effect?

What kind of wire would be suitable for use in the heating element of a toaster? Why should a larger size wire be used when aluminum wire is used in place of copper wire?

74. Lenses

Eyeglasses, cameras, projectors, binoculars, microscopes are a few instruments that make use of the ability of lenses to bend light beams. Hold a double convex lens (burning glass) in direct sun-

light and move it back and forth until the smallest and most intense spot of light falls on a sheet of paper (see Fig. 25-3). The light passing through the lens has been refracted (bent) and hence brought to a point. The distance from the lens to this sharp spot of light is called the *focal length*. If convex lenses of different thicknesses are available, find their focal length in the same way. What effect does the thickness of a lens have upon its focal length?

In a darkened room allow light from a candle to pass through a small hole in a cardboard screen at least 1 foot square. On the side opposite the candle place a white sheet of paper and move it to and from the screen until an image of the candle flame is obtained. Does the image appear upside down? Do light rays bend or travel in straight lines?

Allow the light from a candle to pass through a double convex lens and catch its image on a screen. Move the screen back and forth until the image is sharp. Is it inverted? What effect does moving the candle to or from the lens have upon the size and distance of the image from the lens? What effect would lenses of different thicknesses have upon the image? Why is it necessary to move a camera lens to obtain sharp focus?

75. Spectrum

Refraction is the bending of light rays when passing from one medium to another. Since water bends different wave lengths of light by different amounts, raindrops in the air can cause a rainbow to form from sunlight. A similar effect is caused by allowing sunlight to fall upon one face of a triangular glass prism. Direct the refracted light onto a white screen or wall in a darkened room. What is the order of the colors? Which one has been refracted most? Which least?

76. Polarized Light

Polaroid film will pass only those light rays that are vibrating parallel to the axis of the polaroid. By viewing a light source through two pieces of polaroid held one in front of the other, it

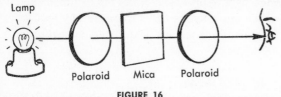

FIGURE 16

is possible to block out most of the light. This is done by rotating one piece of polaroid. (Polaroid is generally mounted in a frame like a circular lens.) After passing through a single polaroid film, light is *polarized*. Polarized light passing through some transparent materials shows a color pattern.

Place a thin layer of mica between two pieces of polaroid. In a darkened room allow light from a 25-watt bulb to pass through the polaroid and mica to the eye (Fig. 16). What is the appearance of the mica? Rotate one of the polaroid films and note the change in the color pattern. Try bending or flexing the mica. Is there a change in the color pattern? Could polarized light be used to study stresses in plastic models of gears, machine parts, etc?

77. Sound Waves

In many respects sound waves act like light waves. They can be absorbed or reflected, brought to a focus, or caused to interfere with each other.

(a) *Absorption.* Construct a box in the form of a long tube, 6 inches square and at least 4 feet long (the longer the better). Use hard wood, masonite, or any other material handy to get a hard, smooth surface for the interior of the box. Suspend a door bell that can be operated from dry cells at one end of the box. Close completely this end of the box. Leave a 1 inch hole in the end opposite the bell so that the sound can escape. Ring the bell and note the loudness of the sound coming from the box. Now line the box with an insulating material like glass wool. Again cause the bell to ring. How has the loudness of the sound been affected? Is the glass wool a better absorber of sound than the original hard surface of the box?

(b) *Focusing Sound Waves.* Hang a ticking watch at the focal point of a large metal parabolic reflector (Fig. 17). Note the loudness of the sound as you move back about four feet from the reflector. Place a second reflector at this point so that sound from the first reflector will be directed to it. Connect about two feet of rubber tubing to the end of a funnel. Place the free end of the tube in your ear and move the funnel end around and about the focal point of the second reflector. This funnel acts like a doctor's stethoscope. Can you locate a point where the ticking sounds much louder? Are sound waves being brought to a focus here?

78. Interference of Sound Waves

You will need two tuning forks of the same frequency, each mounted on a resonator box. Strike both forks so that they will vibrate at the same time. Is there a steady, loud sound that gradually dies down?

Tightly wrap a rubber band around one prong of one of the tuning forks. Set each fork vibrating again. Is there a noticeable difference in the steadiness of the sound? Is there a rise and fall in the loudness? Try moving the rubber band to different positions on the fork or add another rubber band to the second prong. The added weight changes the vibration rate of this fork. It is possible to get very marked interference when the vibration rate of one fork is changed slightly.

79. Frequency

All objects have a natural *frequency of vibration.* This may be different for each substance de-

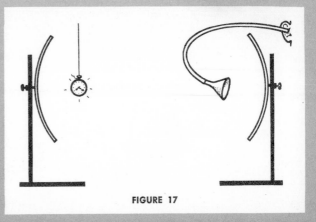

FIGURE 17

pending upon its size, shape, density, etc. Strike different types of water glasses a light blow with a pencil and note the difference in sound. Suspend pieces of metal, solid or tubular, of different lengths, and note the difference in the frequency of the sound when each is struck. Wood blocks can be used in the same way.

80. Resonance

Resonance is the build-up of sound as one sound wave reinforces another. To do this the waves must be in step with each other. If a metal ball is suspended by a string two or three feet long and set swinging, its amplitude of swing can be increased if it is struck a series of light blows at just the right position in its swing. If your timing is off, the ball may be slowed up and stopped, but if your timing is right, the swing will become greater and greater. This reinforcement of the vibration is called *resonance*.

Vibrate a tuning fork over a tall cylinder. While keeping the fork vibrating, gradually add water to the cylinder. A point will be reached where the sound will increase to maximum loudness, and then decrease as more water is added. At the point of maximum loudness the vibration of the air column is just the correct rate to cause resonance with the tuning fork. The principle of resonance is also used in electrical circuits to tune in a desired frequency and tune out all others.

Resonance can be used to determine the velocity of sound, the frequency of the sound, or the wave length producing it. The air column that has been set in vibration will be approximately ¼ the length of one wave. From the fact that velocity equals wave length times frequency ($V = L \times f$) any one factor may be determined if the other two are known.

81. The Diode

Use a 6H6 dual diode to show the effect of heat on the emission of electrons from the cathode of a vacuum tube. Connect one plate (anode) of the tube in series with a milliammeter and the positive terminal of a 6-volt battery. Use pin #3 of the tube. Connect the negative side of the battery to the cathode of the tube, pin #4. Does any current flow through the ammeter? Connect the low side of a 6-volt transformer to the heater element of the tube by attaching one wire to pin #2 and the other to pin #7. As the heater warms the cathode, does current flow through the ammeter? Electrons released from the cathode enable the plate circuit to be completed. Try a lower voltage on the heater. Is the current reduced in the plate circuit? (Fig. 18.)

Reverse the leads connecting the tube to the 6-volt battery so that the plate is now connected to the negative side. Will any current flow in the plate circuit when the plate is made negative? Could a tube like this be used to rectify an alternating current so that current will flow only when the plate is positive?

A 117Z3 diode could be used instead of the 6H6 dual diode; this would also eliminate the need to use a transformer. The heater can then be connected directly to the 110-volt source. But in general it is best to use the setup as shown.

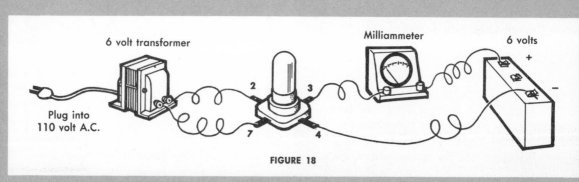

FIGURE 18

82. The Choke Coil

When a straight wire conductor is wound into a coil, it becomes something more than just a resistance. A variation in voltage in the circuit will cause a back electromotive force to be set up in the coil. This back EMF always opposes the change that has induced it to take place. The coil opposes any increase or decrease of current in the circuit. This property is known as *inductance,* and is an important factor in the design of generators, motors, and radio and television circuits.

To see the effect of a coil of wire when placed in an alternating current or direct current circuit, do the following: Wind about 400 turns of bell wire on a cardboard tube 6 inches long and 1 inch in diameter. Connect this coil in series with a 100-watt lamp and 110-volt alternating current through a double switch.

Close the switch so that alternating current is flowing in the circuit. Does the lamp light? Is it very bright? Now slowly insert a soft iron core into the coil. What effect does this have on the brightness of the lamp?

Repeat the procedure with direct current from the B battery. Try the effect first with the iron core removed and then with the iron core fully inserted. Does this coil seem to have any effect upon the brightness of the lamp when direct current is used? Does this coil act as a " choke " for alternating current or direct current?

83. The Capacitor

The *capacitor,* or condenser, is an electrical device capable of storing electrical energy when it is connected to a source of current. The *capacitance* is a measure of the amount of energy the capacitor may store. In use, the capacitor can store electrical energy until fully charged, and then has the ability to discharge a large amount of energy *quickly.* A capacitor may be used to produce resonance in a circuit by helping to control the frequency of the current. This is important in radio and television circuits. The capacitor also has the peculiar ability of blocking direct current

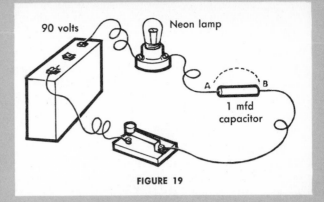

FIGURE 19

and allowing alternating current to flow relatively unhindered.

Connect a 90-volt B battery or direct current generator in series with a neon glow lamp and a 1-microfarad, 400-volt paper capacitor. Include a key or switch in the circuit to control the flow of current (Fig. 19).

When the key is closed, does the lamp glow for an instant? Why does it not continue to glow? Open the key and short out the capacitor by touching a wire (insulated where held by hand) from A to B. Is there a slight spark or sound of a discharge? Was the capacitor charged by the direct current? A capacitor of great capacitance will produce a more noticeable spark.

Replace the battery with a 110-volt alternating current source. Close the key. Does the lamp light? Does it stay lit? Open the key and replace the capacitor with a .1-microfarad capacitor. Is the lamp as bright? What is the effect of greater capacitance on the amount of current in the circuit?

84. Timing Circuit

An interesting adaptation of the capacitor is its use in a timing circuit. The circuit is completed with a resistor in series with the lamp and the capacitor in parallel with the lamp. The source of current is a 90-volt B battery or direct current generator. The bulb will flash when the capacitor is charged to about 80 volts. The capacitor builds up its charge again and the light again flashes as the capacitor discharges through the bulb. Increased resistance in the circuit increases the time it takes to fully charge the capacitor. A capacitor of greater capacitance also takes longer to charge. By varying either or both resistor and capacitor, the light can be made to flash with different time intervals between succeeding flashes. Try the effect of using a fixed resistor of from .5 to 1 megohm. Also try changing the size of the capacitor from 1 through 5 microfarads (400-volt paper capacitors are satisfactory) (Fig. 20). The neon bulb with screw-type base is suitable for use on the regular 110-volt line (General Electric NE 34).

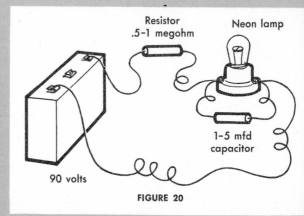

Resistor .5-1 megohm

Neon lamp

1-5 mfd capacitor

90 volts

FIGURE 20

Index to Further Experiments

References enclosed within parentheses indicate experiment numbers.

Glossary

A

absolute zero. The lowest possible temperature. According to one theory, it is thought that at this temperature, $-273°$ C, the motion of atoms and molecules altogether ceases.

absorb. When light rays (or some other kinds of rays) strike an object, the rays that are not reflected enter the object and are said to be absorbed.

absorption. When radiation strikes an object and is turned into heat, the radiation is said to be absorbed.

adhesion. The force of attraction between molecules of two different kinds of substances. It is the force that holds water to skin, paint to wood, etc.

alloy. A fusion or mixture of two or more metals in which the metals cannot be distinguished from each other or separated by ordinary means.

alpha particle. The nucleus of a helium atom, consisting of two protons and two neutrons. Alpha particles are shot out by many, but not all, radioactive elements.

alternating current generator. A machine for producing electrical energy from mechanical energy by rotating coils of wire in a magnetic field.

ammeter. The most common device for measuring the flow of electric current.

ampere. The unit for measuring electric current. It is the current which flows when an electromotive force of one volt is applied across a resistance of one ohm.

amplifier. An electronic device whose purpose is to create strong electrical signals that are exact replicas of the weak signals fed into it.

anode. The positive $(+)$ terminal of an electroplating apparatus or a vacuum tube.

argon. A gaseous element which is very inactive chemically. It is used to fill lamp bulbs under low pressure to prevent the filament from vaporizing.

asteroid. One of the many small planets revolving around the sun between the orbits of Mars and Jupiter.

astigmatism. A defect in vision in which the lens is curved differently in one direction than in another (like the side of a football), so that it is impossible to see all of an object in focus at once.

atmospheric pressure. The pressure exerted by air as a result of the weight of the earth's atmosphere. At sea level the atmosphere exerts a pressure of about 14.7 pounds on every square inch.

atom. The smallest particle of matter than can take part in a chemical reaction. There are over 100 elements, each with its own kind of atom, but all made of the same electrical parts — electrons, protons, and neutrons — in various combinations.

atomic number. The number of protons in the nucleus of an atom. It is also equal to the number of electrons revolving around the nucleus. Each of the approximately 100 elements has, of course, a different atomic number.

atomic pile. Another name for " reactor."

atomic weight. The weight of any atom compared with the weight of an oxygen atom (which is taken as 16). The atomic weight is approximately equal to the total number of protons and neutrons in an atom's nucleus.

auditory nerve. The nerve that carries impulses from the inner ear to the brain.

automatic transmission. A device on modern cars that replaces the manual gearshift.

B

balanced equation. A chemical equation showing not only what kinds of molecules and atoms take part but also how many of each. The number of atoms reacting is equal to the number of atoms in the substances produced as a result of the reaction.

barometer. The most common device used to measure the pressure exerted by the earth's atmosphere. There are several different kinds; among them, the mercury barometer and the aneroid barometer.

basalt. Dense, dark rock containing magma occurring in subsurface layers of the earth's crust. (In its molten form it is basaltic lava or volcanic lava.) There is some evidence that the ocean basins have foundations of basaltic rock.

Bernoulli's Principle. A principle which states that the more rapidly a gas or liquid flows over a surface or through a passage, the less pressure it exerts on its surroundings.

beta particle. An electron shot out by a radioactive atom.

bifocals. Spectacles whose lenses are each divided into two parts, the upper part of the lens to assist in looking at distant objects, the lower part for seeing clearly objects close at hand.

blast furnace. The huge furnace used in the steel industry to extract the iron from iron ore.

C

candlepower. The unit by which intensity of light sources is measured. An ordinary candle has about one candlepower.

carburetor. The device in an internal-combustion engine that mixes air and fuel in the right proportion for proper explosion in the cylinders.

carrier current. In a radio transmitter or receiver, the high-frequency alternating current whose fluctuations correspond to the radio waves traveling from transmitter to receiver.

catalyst. A chemical that hastens a reaction without taking part in the reaction itself.

cataract. A disease of the eye in which the lens becomes opaque, causing blindness.

cathode. The negative ($-$) terminal of an electroplating apparatus or a vacuum tube.

cathode rays. A stream of electrons given off at the cathode (negative terminal) of a vacuum tube.

cell. An arrangement of chemicals in a container for the purpose of producing electrical energy from chemical energy.

centigrade scale. On this scale of temperature water boils at 100° and freezes at 0°; hence a centigrade degree is 1/100 of the temperature difference between boiling and freezing water.

Cepheid variable. A star whose brightness varies regularly because it rhythmically swells and shrinks.

chain reaction. The reaction in which the neutrons produced by fission of U 235 or plutonium are able to cause fission of still more U 235 or plutonium atoms, resulting in the production of more neutrons.

charge. An accumulation of electricity of only one kind (as on a cloud, or rubber rod).

chemical equation. A precise description, by means of formulas, showing what takes place in a chemical reaction; for example, the burning of carbon in oxygen is $C + O_2 \rightarrow CO_2 +$ heat.

chemical reaction. An event in which atoms change their partnerships to form new molecules. Heat is usually given out or absorbed in a chemical reaction, and the properties of the final products always differ from the properties of the original material.

chromatic aberration. A defect of a lens in which various colors of light are brought to a focus at different distances from the lens.

cirque. Deep basin "eaten out" by a mountain glacier at its point of origin.

clouds. Water that has condensed in the form of tiny droplets above the surface of the earth. If the droplets condense at ground level, they are called "fog."

cluster. A group of stars moving togther through space, usually looking like a faint fuzzy patch; for example, the Pleiades.

cochlea. The fluid-filled spiral tube in the inner ear from which the endings of the auditory nerve send impulses (the result of sound waves acting on the fluid) to the brain.

cohesion. The force of attraction between molecules of the same material. It is the force that pulls water into drops, keeps a stretched wire from breaking, and makes solid objects keep their shape.

comet. A mass of frozen gases including small rocky bits and dust traveling around the sun, with a gaseous tail made visible by reflected sunlight when the comet is closest to the sun.

commutator. The part of the rotating armature of an electric motor or generator through which current flows from (or to) the motionless brushes that rub against it.

composition (chemical). A chemical reaction in which atoms or molecules combine to form larger molecules.

compound. A material made of two or more kinds of atoms held together in a chemical combination; for example, carbon dioxide, CO_2.

compression ratio. In an internal-combustion engine, the ratio between the volume of the fuel-air mixture before and after compression in the cylinder.

concave lens. A lens that is thinner at the center than at the edges.

condensation. The conversion of a gas into a liquid with the release of heat; for example, steam condenses to form water.

condenser. In electricity, a device for storing electric charge; for example, a Leyden jar is a simple condenser. In chemistry, a device for cooling a gas or vapor in order to convert it into a liquid.

conduction (heat). The flow of heat from place to

place, passed along by collisions between adjoining molecules.

conductor. Any material through which electricity or heat flows easily; its property is opposite to that of insulators.

cones. Those nerve endings in the retina of the eye which are sensitive to color.

conglomerates. Rounded pebbles cemented together to form a rock.

Conservation of Matter. A law which states that during a chemical reaction, matter (and hence mass) is neither created nor destroyed.

constellation. A pattern of stars visible to the naked eye in a small area of the sky. The entire sky is divided by astronomers into 88 such constellation areas.

contact process. The most important industrial process for making sulfuric acid out of sulfur, air, and water.

continental shelf. Shallow ocean beds bordering the continents and declining sharply to the ocean depths.

contour plowing. Plowing around the surface of a slope to prevent erosion.

convection currents. Currents in a gas or a liquid caused by uneven heating. The moving convection currents carry heat from the warmer to the cooler regions of the gas or liquid.

convertiplane. An airplane that can take off vertically like a helicopter and then, supported by wings, fly forward like a conventional airplane.

convex lens. A lens that is thicker at the center than at the edges.

Copernican system. Astronomical description which has the earth rotating daily on its axis and, along with the other planets, revolving around the sun; proposed by Nicholaus Copernicus, Polish astronomer, in 1543.

cornea. The hard, transparent protective coating on the outer surface of the eye.

corona. The beautiful faint glow seen around the sun during a total eclipse.

cosmic hydrogen. Hydrogen gas, occurring in space, which has not condensed into stars.

cosmic rays. The most penetrating rays with the shortest wave length known. They shower the earth from outer space; their source is still unknown.

cracking. The process of splitting large molecules of petroleum into smaller ones; used in making large quantities of gasoline.

current (electric). A measure of the rate of flow of electric charge; commonly measured in amperes.

cylinder. In an engine, the space in which a hot gas (such as steam or exploding gasoline) expands, doing work against a piston.

D

decomposition. A chemical reaction in which molecules come apart to form smaller molecules or even separate atoms.

dehydration. The process of removing water from a material.

delta wing. An airplane wing shaped like a triangle (seen from below); sometimes used for airplanes that fly close to the speed of sound.

depth of field. The range of distances in front of a camera within which all objects are in clear focus. Depth of field is greatest for high *f*-numbers.

detergent. A compound that removes grease and dirt from an object by reducing the force of their adhesion to the object's surface.

deuterium. Hydrogen whose atoms contain one neutron as well as the one proton in their nuclei. Hence deuterium atoms weigh twice as much as ordinary hydrogen atoms, and are sometimes called " heavy hydrogen."

dew. The water drops formed on the surface of solid objects when water vapor in the air condenses.

dew point. The temperature to which air must be cooled in order to begin the formation of dew. At the dew point the relative humidity is 100%.

dial system. The complex refinement of a modern telephone system that replaces the switchboard operator by automatic machinery operated by the dial on the transmitting telephone.

diaphragm. In optics, the adjustable opening behind the lens of a camera to control the amount of light entering during an exposure; also called " iris diaphragm." In sound, the part of a microphone which is forced to vibrate in and out by an arriving sound wave.

diathermy machine. An instrument which produces invisible, long wave-length rays capable of heating the interior of solid objects; used by doctors to produce local artificial fever.

diesel. A kind of internal-combustion engine that ignites the gas-air mixture in the cylinders by means of the heat generated upon compression, instead of by means of an ignition system and spark plugs.

dihedral angle. The slight upward tilt given to the wings of some airplanes (from body of plane to wingtip) in order to increase lateral stability.

dikes. Vertical bands of igneous rock which, in molten state, have pushed up through a crack in other rocks.

diode. A vacuum tube containing only two electrodes. *See also* triode.

direct current. An electric current that flows in only one direction around a circuit instead of reversing direction repeatedly as an alternating current does.

displacement. A chemical reaction in which part of a molecule is displaced by new atoms, and a new and different molecule results.

distillation. The process of heating a liquid in order to convert it to a gas and then condensing it elsewhere in order to separate it from undesirable impurities, which are left behind.

Doppler shift. The change in pitch of a sound wave or the change in frequency (hence color) of a light source as the source moves rapidly toward or away from an observer.

double displacement. A chemical reaction in which two different molecules exchange parts, and two new and different molecules therefore result.

drag. The resistance exerted by air to the motion of an airplane.

drive shaft. In an automobile or truck, the rod that connects the motion of the crank shaft of the engine to the rear axle.

drumlins. Oblong hills composed of glacial drift.

dry-bulb thermometer. One of the two thermometers in a common form of hygrometer, used to measure humidity of moist air.

E

earthquake. A trembling in the earth caused by cracking or slipping of rock due to strains in the earth's crust.

echo. A sound or radio (radar) signal that has bounced back from a distant obstruction.

eclipse. The shadowing of one object by another. In an eclipse of the sun, the moon comes between the earth and the sun and cuts off the sun's light; in an eclipse of the moon, the earth cuts off the light of the sun shining on the moon.

efficiency. In the case of a machine, the fraction of the work input that is converted into useful work output;

or, efficiency = $\dfrac{\text{useful work output}}{\text{work input}}$. In the case of

a lamp, the number of candlepower of light given off for each watt of electric power consumed.

effort force. The force put into a machine; for example, the force of your finger on a typewriter key.

electrochemical series. A list of elements arranged in order of their tendency to form ions when the free element is put into water.

electromagnet. A coil of wire, usually with an iron core, arranged to act as a magnet when an electric current passes through it.

electromotive force. The "push" produced by a cell

or generator of electric current; commonly measured in volts.

electron. The tiniest possible particle of negative electricity. Electrons form the outer parts of all atoms; also, an electric current is the flow of electrons along a wire. Beta rays resulting from radioactivity are a stream of electrons.

electron-gaining. A term applied to atoms of the nonmetallic elements, which gain electrons when they enter into a chemical compound.

electron-losing. A term applied to atoms of the metallic elements, which lose electrons when they enter into a chemical compound.

electron microscope. A microscope that uses a beam of electrons instead of light rays to view small objects. It can magnify as much as 100,000 to 1,500,000 times — far more than ordinary microscopes.

electron-sharing. A term applied to atoms which share electrons with other atoms when they enter into a chemical compound; for example, carbon atoms commonly react in this way.

electroscope. A simple device for detecting electric charge; its action depends on the fact that two similarly charged objects may repel one another strongly enough to be driven apart.

element. Material made of one and only one kind of atom. Over 100 different elements are known. The most common element on the earth is oxygen.

energy. The ability to do work.

energy converter. Any device that converts energy from one form into another; for example, a battery converts chemical into electrical energy, and a steam engine converts heat into mechanical energy.

enlarger. A photographer's darkroom device for making prints of various sizes from a single negative.

epicycle, planetary. A small circle in which, according to the ptolemaic system, a planet moved, in addition to its greater circular motion around the earth. When the two motions were combined it was possible to "produce" the retrograde movements of a planet.

erg. A very tiny unit of energy used by physicists especially when measuring the energy changes in single atoms; 10,000,000 ergs = 1 joule, the energy consumed by a 60-watt bulb in 1/60 of a second.

erosion. Wearing away of land by weathering agents such as wind, running water, and glaciers.

Eustachian tube. The tube that connects the middle ear to the back of the throat.

evaporation. The change of a liquid into a gas with the absorption of heat.

exposure meter. A photographer's instrument for measuring the amount of light falling on his subject and showing the values of exposure time and *f*-number at which he can set his camera.

F

f-number. The ratio between the focal length of a lens and its diameter. The higher the f-number, the "slower" the lens is at making pictures.

Fahrenheit scale. On this scale of temperature water boils at 212° and freezes at 32°; hence a Fahrenheit degree is 1/180 of the temperature difference between boiling and freezing water.

farsightedness. A defect of the eye in which the eyeball is too short, so that nearby objects cannot be brought clearly into focus on the retina, though distant objects can be seen clearly.

fast lens. A lens whose diameter is large compared to its focal length. It can therefore form a bright image on the film in a particularly brief exposure time.

faults. Definite lines of break in rock formation.

filament. In a lamp bulb or vacuum tube, the wire heated by electricity until it gives out light and, in some cases, electrons. In the X-ray tube, the negatively charged wolfram wire which is heated sufficiently (by an electric current) to give off a steady stream of electrons.

filter (camera). A piece of colored glass placed in front of a camera lens in order to prevent certain colors of light from reaching the film.

fission. The splitting of the nucleus of a plutonium or U 235 atom with the release of several neutrons and a great deal of energy.

fluid drive. A device in modern automobiles for the smooth coupling of the power of the engine to the rear wheels by means of a liquid under pressure, such as oil.

fluorescence. The process by which a phosphor gives off visible light.

focal length. The distance from a lens or curved mirror at which rays from a very distant object are brought to a focus.

focus. The point to which rays of light from an object are brought together by a lens or curved mirror.

fog. Water that has condensed in the air in the form of tiny droplets to make a cloud at ground level.

foot-pound. A unit for measuring work; it is the work done by a force of one pound moving through a distance of one foot.

force. A push or a pull.

formula. A group of symbols that describes what elements comprise a compound; for example, "CO_2" means that molecules of carbon dioxide are made of one atom of carbon and two atoms of oxygen.

fossil. Any petrified or preserved form or impression of plants and animals.

fractional distillation. The separation of the ingredients of a mixture by taking advantage of the difference in their boiling points.

Freon. A common type of refrigerant in household refrigerators.

frequency. The number of waves that pass a given point in one second.

friction. The force that resists the sliding or rolling of one object on another.

front. The boundary, often hundreds of miles long, between two air masses of different temperature and humidity.

fulcrum. The motionless point around which a lever turns.

fusion. The process in which nuclei of light atoms fuse together to form a heavier nucleus and to release energy. The energy of the sun is released by a fusion process.

G

galaxy. An enormous group of stars and nebulas — often several hundred thousand light years across — traveling through space together, usually remote from its neighbors. The Milky Way is the galaxy of which the sun is a member star.

galvanometer. A device for detecting electric current by means of the rotation of a current-carrying coil suspended in a magnetic field.

gamma rays. Waves similar to those of light but of much shorter wave length and much greater penetrating power. Gamma rays are given off by many, but not all, radioactive elements and by some artificial atom-smashing processes, including fission.

Geiger counter. A physicist's device for detecting and measuring gamma rays, neutrons, alpha rays, beta rays, and other radiation given off during nuclear processes.

generator. In electricity, a machine for creating electricity from mechanical energy.

germicidal lamp. A lamp that produces useful amounts of germ-killing ultraviolet light.

glaciers, continental. Vast, thick sheets of ice which periodically cover large areas of land, changing the climate of the world; distinct from valley glaciers.

glaciers, valley. Broad, slow-moving rivers of ice originating in mountains and forced to a lower level by the pressure of the ice above.

gravity. The force that all objects in the universe exert on one another by reason of their mass.

grid. An electrode placed between the anode and the cathode of a vacuum tube, the charge on it being intended to control the flow of current through the tube.

H

Haber process. An important industrial process for making ammonia (NH_3) out of hydrogen and the nitrogen from the air.

half-life. The length of time a radioactive element takes to decay to half its original quantity. During the next half-life, half of what remains will decay, and so on.

heat. A measure of the *total* energy of motion of all the molecules in an object. The total amount of heat energy in an object is measured in calories.

heat barrier. The increase in temperature due to air friction as a plane travels at speeds over about 1,000 miles an hour.

helicopter. An airplane supported not by wings but by a whirling overhead rotor; it can take off and land vertically and hover motionless in the air.

homosphere. That layer of the atmosphere, extending up to about 55 miles, in which oxygen, nitrogen, carbon dioxide, and other components are uniformly mixed. Above the homosphere are relatively separate layers of nitrogen, oxygen, helium, and hydrogen.

horsepower. A unit of power. It is a rate of doing work equal to 550 foot-pounds per second (or 33,000 foot-pounds per minute).

humidity. The amount of water vapor in the air.

hygrometer. A device for measuring humidity.

I

igneous extrusion. Outpouring of lava onto the surface of the earth from volcanoes or fissures.

igneous intrusion. Any pushing up of molten rock into cracks in the rock layers above.

index of refraction. A number that indicates the ability of a transparent material to bend a ray of light entering it from the air.

induce. To create an electric current in a conductor by moving it through a magnetic field, or by moving the magnetic field across the conductor.

infrared rays. Invisible rays that carry heat which can be felt, but not seen, emanating from a hot iron or a stove; their wave lengths are longer than those of visible red light.

input. *See* work input.

insulator. A very poor conductor (of heat or electricity).

internal-combustion engine. An engine whose power comes from the explosion of a fuel-and-air mixture inside the engine's cylinders; the explosion drives a piston down the cylinder and the piston can then perform mechanical work.

inverse square. The inverse square of a number, *n,* is 1 divided by the square of the number; that is,

$$\frac{1}{n \times n} \text{ or } \frac{1}{n^2}; \text{ for example, if } n \text{ is 2, } \left(\frac{1}{2 \times 2} \text{ or } \frac{1}{2^2}\right).$$

ionization. The process by which atoms (or groups of atoms, called radicals) form electrically charged particles called ions.

ionosphere. The layer of the atmosphere beginning about 50 miles up which contains electrically charged atoms (ions) able to reflect radio waves.

iris diaphragm. The adjustable opening of an eye or a camera lens whose size controls the amount of light entering.

irradiated. Showered with rays.

isostasy. The concept that mountain ranges " float " in denser rock located beneath the surface and that all other parts of the upper structure of the earth's crust are in balance with the lower portion.

isotopes. Forms of the same element which differ only in the number of neutrons in their nuclei and in their atomic weights; for example, hydrogen has three isotopes with none, one, and two neutrons in their nuclei.

K

Kelvin scale. Another term for " absolute scale " of temperature. Named for Lord Kelvin, a British physicist.

kilocycle. One thousand cycles (a second), a measure of the frequency of a traveling wave.

kilowatt-hour. A unit of work, or energy; it is the work done in one hour at the rate of one kilowatt (one thousand watts). Hence a 1,000-watt bulb burning for one hour consumes one kilowatt-hour of energy.

L

land breeze. A breeze, usually warm and usually at night, blowing from the land out over the sea.

lateral control. The ability of a pilot to control the sideways tipping of an airplane in flight.

lens (of the eye). The transparent part of the eye that focuses incoming light onto the retina.

Leyden jar. A simple device for storing an electric charge; it consists of a glass jar covered inside and out with a metal foil.

lift. The upward force caused by a combination of upward push of air on the bottom of an airplane wing and upward push resulting from low pressure on top of the wing.

light year. The distance light travels in one year — about 6 trillion miles; the unit used in astronomy for measuring distance.

lightning. An enormous electric charge flowing in a very brief time between two clouds or a cloud and the earth.

lightning rod. A pointed rod on the top of a building, connected to the earth by a heavy wire, which serves to drain electric charge from passing clouds before enough has accumulated to create a destructive lightning bolt.

limestone. A type of sedimentary rock composed chiefly of calcium carbonate.

longitudinal control. The ability of a pilot to tilt an airplane upward or downward in flight.

loudspeaker. A device used in radios, phonographs, and public-address systems whose function is to convert electrical energy into sound energy.

lubricant. A material, commonly oil, used to reduce the friction and hence wear between moving parts of a machine.

luminosity. The true brightness of a star after correcting for the effect of its great distance from us; usually measured by comparison with the sun's brightness.

M

magma. Molten rock deep within the earth; when cooled it forms igneous rock.

magnetic pole, earth's. Either of two places on earth (north magnetic pole and south magnetic pole) to which a compass needle will point. (The magnetic pole and the geographic pole are not identical; the north magnetic pole and the north geographic pole are presently some 1,000 miles apart.)

magnetism. The force by which a magnet attracts or repels pieces of iron or steel or another magnet.

magnetosphere. A belt of charged particles in nearby space trapped by the earth's magnetic field; first known as Van Allen belts.

mantle, earth's. The region starting 20 to 30 miles beneath the earth's surface, extending down some 1800 miles.

mass. The property of an object by which it resists changes in its speed or direction of motion. Inertia and the pull of gravity on an object (that is, its weight) are results of an object's mass.

mechanical advantage. The amount by which a machine multiplies a force.

metal. A chemical element that forms compounds by losing electrons.

metamorphic rocks. Rocks changed from their original form due to large changes in temperature and pressure.

meteor. A piece of rock or iron from outer space that has fallen into the earth's atmosphere and burned up as a result of friction with the air.

meteorite. A particle of rock or iron from outer space that has not been completely burned up by its passage through the earth's atmosphere and hence has reached the ground.

microphone. A device for converting sound energy into electrical energy.

Milky Way. The narrow band of faint stars circling the sky which is really our galaxy, seen from our position on the earth inside it.

minerals. Chemical compounds, or elements, usually in a crystalline state, found either in free form or, more often, intermixed to form rocks.

mirage. The displaced image seen when light coming to the eyes from a distant object is bent by passing through the boundary between layers of warm and cool air.

Mohorovicic discontinuity (Moho). The boundary between the earth's crust and mantle — named in honor of its discoverer, Mohorovicic.

molecule. The smallest part of a compound that can exist and still have the chemical properties of the compound; the parts of which a molecule is made are atoms.

musical sound. A series of identical waves or combinations of waves whose effect is pleasing to the ear.

N

natural gas. A mixture of methane (CH_4) and ethane (C_2H_6) which is found underground, commonly with petroleum.

nearsightedness. A defect of the eye in which the eyeball is too long, so that distant objects must be brought nearer to the eye in order to be seen clearly.

nebula. A great cloud of dust and gas in our galaxy, visible either as a dark obscuring cloud or as a luminous cloud.

neutron. A neutral (uncharged) particle found with the proton, and weighing about as much as the proton, in the nucleus of nearly all atoms (exception: H^1).

noise. A collection of random, nonrepetitive wave lengths of sound whose effect is displeasing to the ear.

nonmetal. A chemical element that commonly forms compounds by gaining electrons.

nova. A star that suddenly increases in brightness, apparently as a result of an explosion. Unlike the regular change in brightness of other variable stars, this change rarely happens more than once to a particular star.

nucleus. The central core of an atom, composed largely of protons and neutrons. Although very tiny compared to the size of the entire atom, the nucleus contains most of the atom's weight.

O

ohm. The unit used to measure electrical resistance; it is the resistance which will allow just one ampere to flow if an electromotive force of one volt is applied across it.

Ohm's Law. The electrical law that states that the current, I, that flows in a circuit multiplied by the resistance, R, of the circuit equals the applied voltage, E; hence $E = I \times R$.

opaque. Refers to an object through which light (or some other kind of ray) will not pass.

output. *See* work output.

P

parabolic. Refers to the shape of a surface curved in such a way that it reflects to a single point all the rays in a beam of light that strikes it.

parallax, astronomical. The apparent shift in direction of a heavenly body when seen from two differing points on the earth's surface, or from differing positions in space.

partial eclipse. The incomplete shadowing of an object (such as the earth) when its only source of light (such as the sun) is *partly* covered by some intervening object (such as the moon).

persistence of vision. The ability of the retina of the human eye to retain an image for a fraction of a second after the object has vanished.

petroleum. A thick, black liquid found in pools beneath the earth's surface; it is a mixture of useful materials including the ingredients of gasoline and lubricating oil, most of them of the general formula, C_nH_{2n+2}; an example is $C_{10}H_{22}$.

pH. "Potential of hydrogen"; it is a number that measures how strongly acidic or basic a solution is.

phosphor. A chemical compound that gives off visible light when it is struck by electrons, ultraviolet light, or some other kinds of invisible radiation.

photoelectric cell. A device that turns the energy in light into electrical energy; often used in a photographer's exposure meter, making it possible to "read" light intensity on an electric meter.

pile. *See* reactor.

pinhole camera. A very simple camera in which a pinhole takes the place of the lens.

piston. The plunger that slides smoothly up and down in the hollow cylinder of an internal-combustion engine or a steam engine.

pitch. A measure of how "high" or how "low" a sound appears to be; the pitch of a sound wave is mainly determined by its frequency.

planet. One of the many relatively cold and dark bodies revolving around the sun.

plate. The anode (positively charged terminal) in a vacuum tube.

plutonium. A fissionable man-made element, atomic number 94, which is useful as a source of atomic energy; it is made from U 238 in a reactor.

Polaris. The star in the northern sky that lies closest to the axis of the earth's rotation.

polarized. Refers to light waves whose vibrations are all in planes parallel to one another.

poles. The ends of a magnet, where the magnetism appears to be strongest.

polymer. A molecule, usually a large one, made of a large number of identical atom-groups joined end to end.

populations I and II, of stars. Population I: younger, bluer stars lying in or near the central plane and in the spiral arms of a galaxy; Population II: older, redder stars common near galactic centers as well as "above" and "below" the galactic plane.

power. The rate at which work is being done; for example, foot-pounds per minute or kilogram-meters per second; power $= \dfrac{\text{work}}{\text{time}}$.

power brakes. Brakes that operate when a gentle force on the brake pedal is multiplied by the power of the engine into a much larger force on the brake rods of the car.

power steering. The steering mechanism of a modern car that operates when a gentle force applied to the steering wheel is changed by the power from the engine into a large force turning the front wheels.

pressure waves. Vibrations caused by earthquakes, which can travel through solids, liquids, and gases. Also called *primary waves* because they are picked up by a seismograph before other vibrations.

prominences. Flame-like clouds of glowing hydrogen rising above the surface of the sun.

proton. A positively charged particle of electricity found in the nucleus of every atom; together with neutrons, protons make up most of the weight of an atom.

proton-proton cycle. The nucleur fusion process in which four hydrogen nuclei (protons) are eventually converted into a helium nucleus with the conversion of some mass into radiant energy. The sun and similar stars derive their energy from this process.

Ptolemaic system. The astronomical description which has the earth fixed at the center of the universe, about which the planets, sun, and stars revolve; proposed by Ptolemy, Greek astronomer, in A.D. 150; superseded by the Copernican system.

public-address system. A vacuum-tube device whose function is to reproduce music or a speaker's voice in very much amplified form.

pupil. The round hole through which light enters the eye on its way to the retina.

pure research. Research which is concerned only with gaining new knowledge for its own sake, not with putting knowledge to practical use.

Q

quartz. Crystalline mineral composed of almost pure silicon dioxide; always present in granite.

R

radar. An electronic device for detecting distant objects at night or through fog or clouds by recording the echoes of very short radio waves (a few inches to a few feet in wave length) returning from them.

radiation. The flow of energy in the form of rays traveling (in a vacuum) at 186,000 miles a second; for example, radio waves, infrared (heat) rays, and visible light.

radiator. In an internal-combustion engine, the labyrinth of tubes in which water cooling the engine loses its heat to the air.

radical. A group of atoms that commonly, but not always, cling together during a chemical reaction; for example, SO_4 (sulfate) and OH (hydroxide).

radioactivity. The spontaneous breaking-down of the nucleus of an atom, during which alpha particles or beta particles and gamma rays are given off and a new kind of atom is formed as a result.

radio spectrum. The range of all possible radio wave lengths — from a few inches to several miles.

radiotelescope. An electronic device, essentially a huge radio antenna and receiver, sensitive enough to pick up radio waves emitted by clouds of hydrogen and other sources in outer space.

radio waves. Electromagnetic waves whose wave lengths range from several feet to several miles.

rain. Water that has condensed in the air in drops large enough to fall to the ground.

rate of work. The speed at which work is done, or

$$\text{power} = \frac{\text{work}}{\text{time}}.$$ Rate of work is the same as power.

reactor. An assembly of fissionable atoms and material to slow down neutrons (the moderator), whose function is to release atomic energy at a controllable rate.

receiver. That part of a telephone or a radio that converts electrical impulses back into sound waves.

recycling. The chemical procedure of recovery and conversion of waste materials to usable form.

reflection. The bouncing of light (or some other kind of ray) off an object.

refraction. The bending of a beam of light when it goes from one transparent material into another having a different index of refraction.

refrigerant. A fluid such as sulfur dioxide or a Freon used in refrigerators to carry heat; it absorbs heat from the freezing compartment in order to evaporate and delivers the heat to the outside room when it condenses in the radiator.

refrigerator. Any device that removes heat energy from an object or a space and disposes of the heat elsewhere.

relative humidity. A comparison, usually written as a per cent, between the amount of water vapor actually in the air and the amount the air could hold at the same temperature.

resistance (electrical). A measure of the difficulty an electric current has in flowing; commonly measured in ohms.

resonance. When the natural period of vibration of one vibrating object is the same as the natural period of another, they are said to be in resonance. The objects may be two sound-producing instruments, two oscillating electrical circuits, or two vibrating weights.

retina. The layer of light-sensitive nerve endings lining the back of the eye.

retrograde motion (of planets). The apparent, temporary reversal of planetary motion due to the earth's bypassing the planet in its orbit. In the Ptolemaic system, retrograde movement was accounted for by the epicycles.

rheostat. A variable electrical resistance; for example, the volume control of a radio.

rods. Those nerve endings in the retina of the eye which are sensitive to light but not to color.

rotate. To turn around on an axis through itself.

S

satellite. A moon; also applied to a tiny man-made moon circling the earth.

saturated. Refers to a solvent that contains all the

solute that it can dissolve at that temperature. It can apply, for example, to water containing dissolved salt or air containing water vapor.

sea breeze. A breeze blowing in from the sea over the land, usually cool and usually in the daytime.

seamounts. Submerged mountains, many 3000 feet high, whose peaks are as much as a mile below the ocean surface.

sediment. Material such as sand, gravel, and mud deposited by settling of streams, rivers, lakes, and seas.

sedimentary rock. Rock formed by the hardening of layers of sediments deposited originally by agents of erosion.

seismograph. An instrument used for detecting and recording the vibrations caused by an earthquake.

shale. Sedimentary rock with fine layers, formed by deposits of clay, mud, etc.

shear waves. Vibrations caused by earthquakes, which travel through solids and dense, glassy liquids. Also called *secondary waves* because they travel at a slower rate than pressure waves.

shock. The sensation you may experience when an electric charge flows through your body.

shock waves. Bunched-up sound waves of very high pressure formed by an object traveling at or beyond the speed of sound.

short wave. A term commonly applied to those radio waves whose lengths are shorter than about 150 meters.

shutter. In a camera, the cover which is briefly removed from behind the lens to allow light to enter.

silicone. A newly discovered class of silicon compounds that are very stable at high temperatures and have many other interesting and useful properties.

sills. Igneous intrusions which spread out horizontally between two layers of rock.

silt. Fine particles of earth carried away by running water.

snow. Water vapor that changes directly to solid form at temperatures below freezing.

solar system. The sun, its family of planets and their moons traveling together through space.

solar wind. A stream of electrons and protons, originating from eruptions of hydrogen on the sun, swept outward by pressure of sunlight.

Solvay process. An important industrial process for making sodium carbonate and sodium bicarbonate from ammonia, salt, and carbon dioxide.

sound barrier. The sharp increase in air resistance as a speeding object approaches the speed of sound.

sound wave. One compression and one rarefaction of the air, following each other at such a rate that they can be heard by the human ear.

spark plug. A part fitting into each cylinder of a gaso-line engine (but not a diesel engine). An electric spark jumping across the end of the spark plug ignites the gasoline-air mixture in the cylinder.

spectroscope. A device for sorting out into a spectrum the various wave lengths composing a beam of light or other radiation.

spectrum. When a beam of rays is sorted out into the waves which compose it, the array of waves arranged in order by wave lengths is called a spectrum.

spherical aberration. A defect of a lens in which light passing through the center is brought to a focus at a different distance than light passing through the edges.

static electricity. An isolated charge of electricity which may either remain motionless on an object such as a cloud or a condenser or may flow in a brief time from one object to another. Unlike current electricity, it is not capable of continuous flow.

steady-state theory. The proposal that the universe as a whole had no beginning in time. Rather, it has existed forever in much the same condition or state in which it is now observed. (From observations of their Doppler shifts, the galaxies appear to be receding from each other. Since this would lead to an increasingly empty universe rather than to a steady state, it is further proposed that enough hydrogen to form new galaxies is being continually created.)

steam pressure. The pressure exerted by steam, usually on the inside of a boiler and steam engine. The higher the steam pressure, the better the engine is able to do work.

stratosphere. The cloudless layer of our atmosphere about 10 to 50 miles up.

streak. The color of a finely powdered mineral.

streamlining. Shaping a high-sped object such as a bullet, boat, or plane so that there is the least possible air or water resistance to its motion.

sunspots. Giant tornado-like storms on the surface of the sun that appear dark only because they are cooler (about 4800° C.) than the rest of the sun's surface (about 6000° C.).

supernova. The brightest kind of nova, in which a star appears to explode by a process still not understood.

supersaturated solution. A solution that contains more dissolved material than could possibly be contained if the nuclei on which precipitation occurs were available.

supersonic flight. Flight faster than the speed of sound (about 750 mph at sea level).

suspension. A solution containing particles of insoluble material too tiny to settle to the bottom yet big enough to make the liquid look muddy or milky instead of clear.

T

target (X-ray tube). The positively charged electrode whose atoms give off X rays when struck by the beam of electrons emitted by the filament.

telegraph. A device for sending messages along a wire. Unlike the telephone, a telegraph is only able to send a series of clicks whose combinations in various ways represent letters of the alphabet.

teletype. A pair (or more) of typewriters connected electronically in such a way that when a key of one is pressed, the corresponding key of the other is operated by a magnet, even though the typewriters are miles apart.

temperature. A measure of the *average* energy of motion of the molecules of an object; measured in degrees centigrade, Fahrenheit, or Kelvin.

terminal moraine. A mound of debris that is left as glacial ice melts.

thermostat. A temperature-operated switch used to control heating equipment automatically.

tide. The daily rise and fall in the level of the oceans by reason of the pull of gravity exerted on them by the sun and the moon.

time exposure. Leaving the shutter of a camera open for about 1/10 of a second or more in order to make a successful photograph in dim light.

topsoil. The top layer of soil, generally most capable of supporting plant life.

torque. A rotation-producing or a twisting force; also called a " moment."

total eclipse. The complete shadowing of an object (such as the earth) when its only source of light (such as the sun) is *completely* covered by some intervening object (such as the moon).

transformer. An electrical device for changing the voltage of an alternating current.

transmission. The part of the driving mechanism of a car which is commonly controlled by the gearshift. The transmission connects the engine to the rear wheels in various speed ratios forward and reverse.

transmitter. That part of a telephone or a radio that converts sound waves into electrical impulses.

transparent. Refers to an object that allows light (or some other kind of ray) to pass through it freely.

triode. A vacuum tube containing three electrodes.

tritium. Hydrogen whose atoms contain two neutrons in their nuclei in addition to the usual single proton and therefore weigh three times as much as ordinary hydrogen atoms.

tungsten. A metallic element (also called wolfram) whose melting point is so high that it can be heated to give off light without melting; used extensively for filaments of lamps and vacuum tubes.

turbojet. A common type of jet engine in which air is drawn into the engine as it is compressed by means of a fan or turbine rotated by power drawn from the jet exhaust gases.

U

ultrasonics. The science of sounds whose frequencies are higher than the range of human hearing.

ultraviolet rays. The group of invisible rays whose wave lengths are shorter than those of visible violet light.

underexposed. Refers to a photograph that is too dark because not enough light has been allowed to fall on the film.

universe. All of space together with all of the galaxies it contains.

V

vacuum. A space containing little or no air or molecules of any other kind.

vacuum pump. A machine for pumping air or other gases out of a closed container.

vacuum tube. An evacuated glass or metal tube containing two or more electrodes and through which an electric current is passed for any one of a wide variety of purposes.

valence. The number of electrons gained, lost, or shared by an atom when it is in a compound.

valves. Openings in the cylinder of an internal-combustion engine through which fuel and air enter and through which the burned exhaust gases leave.

Van Allen belts. *See* magnetosphere.

variable star. A star whose brightness appears to change from time to time.

virtual image. An image which the eye sees by following diverging rays back to their apparent source. Since the rays do not actually start where the image is seen, it is called a virtual image.

vocal cords. A pair of membranes stretched across your " windpipe." When air is forced through the slit between them, the motion of the vocal cords helps to form the sounds of your voice.

voice current. In a radio transmitter or receiver, the varying electric current whose fluctuations correspond to the sound waves being transmitted.

volt. The unit used to measure electromotive force; it is the force required to drive one ampere of current through a resistance of one ohm.

W

water cycle. The continual change of form of the earth's water supply from water vapor in the air to liquid water in rain, rivers, oceans, etc., and back into water vapor again.

wave (of light). A single vibration of radiant energy.

wave length. The distance from wave crest to wave crest (or trough to trough) in a series of waves.

weathering processes. Mechanical means (expansion and contraction) or chemical means (usually union with oxygen) by which rocks are decomposed.

wetting agent. A compound that reduces the force of cohesion of water drops and increases their adhesion to a surface.

wind. A convection current in the atmosphere.

work. That which is accomplished by a force moving through a distance; measured in foot-pounds, gram-centimeters, etc.

work input. The product of effort force and the distance through which it moves. The work input into a machine always equals the work output if work against friction is included with the latter.

work output. The product of the force exerted by a machine and the distance through which it moves. Taken together with work done against friction, it is always equal to the work input.

X

X rays. Very penetrating invisible rays given off by the metal target of an X-ray tube when it is struck by a stream of electrons (cathode rays).

Z

zodiac. The path in the sky along which the planets appear to move as they travel around the sun.

Index

Page numbers in boldface refer to illustrations;
page numbers in italics refer to the section entitled "Further Experiments in Physical Science."

atoms (*continued*)

gaining, 79, 80, 82; electron losing, 79, 80, 82; electrons in, 61, 64, 79, 261; electrons passing through, 260, 261; space of, 64–65; indestructibility of, 53, 54, 85; inside of, 63, 64; neutrons in, 64; nuclei of, 64–68, 108, 109, 119–24, 127, 128; as particles, 52, 53; protons in, 64; radioactive, 127–32, 333; in Rutherford's experiments, 64; splitting of, 109–111, 127; "tagged," 131, 132; weights of, 53, 54, 65–67, **109**; X-raying of, 263

atomic bomb, 54, 108, 109, 110, 111

atomic energy, 109, 111, 113–15, 117, **123**, 127, 176, 331

Atomic Energy Commission, 117, 130, 132

atomic engine, 113

atomic number: definition of, 68; of elements, 67, 68

atomic pile, *see* reactor

atomic power station, **117**

Atomic Theory, of Dalton, 54–56, 85, 115, 120, 122

atomic weight: distinguished from atomic number, 68; of elements, 67, 68

auditory nerve, 345

automatic gearshift, 183–84

automatic lateral control, of glider, 189

automobile, **143, 165,** 179; early, 179–80; of future, 181, 184–85; headlights of, 273, 288; thermostat in radiator of, 206; of today, 181–84

axis, earth's, of rotation and magnetic, 8

Azoic era, 46

B

bacteria: killed by ultrasonic sounds, 346; killed by ultraviolet waves, 329; nitrogen fixed by, 90, **92;** seen under microscope, 301, 302, 303; tuberculosis caused by, 301

Badlands of South Dakota, 19

Bakelite, 103

baking soda, 81, 83, 92, 94, 98

balancing equations, 85, 86

ball bearings, 139

barium, 330

barometer, *454*

basalt, 38

basaltic lava, 38

bases, in chemistry, *442–43*

basic research, 264, 265

bat, sound waves given off by, 346

battery: and "boiling" electrons, 356; solar, 177; storage, 247; Volta's, 245, 246

bearings, ball, 139

Becquerel, Antoine, 263

Bell, Alexander Graham, 350

Benz, 180

benzene, 164

Bernoulli's Principle, 191

beryllium, 68

beta particles (rays), 62, 63, 127, 128

Betelgeuse (Alpha Orionis), 396, 398

bifocal glasses, 288

Big Bear, **397**

Big Dipper, 396, 397

bird, flight of and low-drag wings, 196–97

black color, heat absorbed by, 218

black light, 313, 329

black mica, 39

blast furnace, 76, **77**

blood, path of radioactive iron through, 131

blue: inability to see, 325; in spectrum, 320–24

blue vitriol (hydrated copper sulfate), 75

boiling point, of water, 207

bomb: atomic, 54, 108, 109, **110,** 111; hydrogen, 124–25

boron hydride, 416; *see also* fuel

Boulton, Matthew, 157

box camera, *see* camera

brain: hearing with, 345; seeing with, 282, 285

brake, power, of automobile, 183; radar-controlled, 184

brass, used in thermostat, 205, 206

breeze, land and sea, 224, **225**

bromine: as electron-gainer, 80; in sea water, 10, 76; silver combined with, 80

Brownian motion, 200

"bug" of spaceship, **428**

bulb, light, 258, 307, 308, 321, 355, 356

Bunsen burner, safety precautions for, 56*n.*

burner, thermostat for, 206

burning, and composition, 72, 73

burning glass, 284

bus, model, 185

butane, 100

C

cadmium borate, 313

cadmium rods, in reactor, **111,** 112, 113

calcite crystals, *437*

calcium, 9; in sea water, 10; valence of, 82, 83

calcium carbonate (limestone), 9, 11, 73, 77, 81, 93, 94; decomposition of, *438*

calcium chloride, 77

calcium nitrate, 83

calcium oxide, *438*

calcium silicate, 94

calcium sulfate, 10

Calder Hall, 113, **117**

caloric, 161–62

camera: adjustments of, 293–94; chromatic aberration in, 296; and exposure time, 294, 295, 297, 298; fast, 295; filter for, 321; "good," 295, 296; image formed in, 291, 292, 293, 296, 298; parts of, 291; pinhole, 268, 269, 295; spherical aberration in, 295, 296, **297;** television, 367–70

Canada: glacial debris in, 22; radar defenses in, 373

cancer: gamma rays in treatment of, 129, 331; X-ray treatment of, 129, 330, 402

candlepower, 310, 311, 312, 313

capacitance, *463*

capacitor, 236, *463*

Cape Cod, formed by glacial changes, 23

Capella, 410

carbon, 9, 10; atom of, **66,** 67, 100; charged with elec-

focus of convex lens, 284; depth of, 298

folding, **34**, 36

folds, **34**, *see* mountains

food: nitrogen in, 90; preserved, 221

foot-pound, 138

force: electromotive, 249, 250, 253, 254; experiments with, *448–49;* and lever, 140, 141, 142; multiplying, 136, 137, 138, 140, 142, 143; of water, 25

formaldehyde, 104

formulas, writing chemical, 57, 81, 84

fossils, **38**, *see* sedimentary rocks; as calendar of earth's events, 45, 46

Foucault pendulum, 4, **5**

Fourier, Jean, 249

four-stroke cycle: of diesel engine, 167, **169;** of gas engine, 163; of gasoline engine, 164, **166**

fractional distillation, 101, 102

fractionating tower, 101, **102**

Franklin, Benjamin, 238, 239, **240**, 241, 242

Fraunhofer, 398

Freon, 220

frequency of radio waves, 363

friction, 139, 142, 143; and charging with electricity, 237; of molecules in air, 384, 386; and rockets, 416; tidal, 6

frictional drag, 196

frogs' legs, Galvani's experiments with, 244

fronts, in weather maps, 230, **231**

fuel, 102, 163–64, 175–76, 194; in rockets, 416, 421

fulcrum, of lever, 140, **141**, *451*

furnace, blast, 76, **77**

fusion, of atoms, 124; controlling fusion, 125

fusion energy, 123, 124; *see also* proton-proton cycle

G

galaxy, definition of, 407; *see also* Milky Way, *411;* evolution of, 413; Doppler shift of, **412**

Galileo, 208, 389, 406, 417

Galvani, Luigi, 244, 248

galvanometer, 248, 249, 253, 254

gamma rays, 19, 62, 63, 127, 128, 129, 331, 332

gas: bottled, 100; coal, 163; " illuminating," 163; as insulator, 211–12; natural, 100, 163, 175; neon, 259, 261, 313

gas burner, thermostat for, 206

gas engine, 163, 164, 165

gas lever, of Model T, 180

gas refrigerator, 220

gas thermometer, 207–08

gas turbine engine, 173

gasoline, 88, 89, 98, 99, 100, 102, 164; high-test, 167; as mixture, 101

gasoline engine, 163, 164, **165**

gears, turbine, 159

Geiger counter, **132**, 423

Geissler, Heinrich, 259

gems, **41**, 42

generator, 253, 254, 255

germicidal lamp, 329

glacial cycle, continental, **23**, 24

glacial till, 22; *see also* terminal moraine; drumlin

glaciers, 19, **21, 22, 23**

glass: charged with electricity, 237, 238, **456;** colored, as filter, 321; electricity insulated by, 239; and light, 271, 272, 273, **277**, 279, **280;** and magnetism, 243; manufacture of, 86, 93, **94**, 98

glass wool, 211, 222

glider, 189, 190, 196, 197

glycerine, 96, 278

gneiss, 41, *see* metamorphic rocks

Goddard, Robert H., 174

gold, plating with, 246; in sea water, 11

governor, of steam engine, 157

gram, definition of, *52n.*

Grand Canyon, **20**, 21

Grand Coulee Dam, 161

granite, **39, 40**

graphite, powdered, 139

graphite blocks, in atomic pile, 111

gravity: of earth, 4, 5, 6, 7, 316, **417**, 421; experiment with, *451;* of Jupiter, 393; measurement of, by formula of inverse squares, 316; of moon, 5, **6**, 390; Newton's law of, 170, 388; planets governed by, 388; of sun, 6, 7; pull on earth's satellite, 417, 418

Great Lakes, 22

green, inability to see, 325; in spectrum, 320–24

Greenlands, fiords of, 22

grid: in TV picture tube, 370; of vacuum tube, 357–58, **358**

Gulf of Mexico, 11, 229

Gulf Stream, **11**

guncotton, 91

H

Haber, Fritz, 91

Haber process, 91, 92, **93**, 97, 98

half-life, of carbon, 132

Halley's comet, **388**

Hawaii, 38

hearing aids, 346, 355, 357

heat: absorption of, 217, 218, *453–54;* from air friction, 386; conductors of, 210, 211; and convection currents, 212–13, 224; laws describing flow of, 249; and radiation, 42, 213, 214, 217, 218, 224; reflection of, 217, 218, *453*

heat barrier, 194–95

heat energy, 142, 160, 161–62, 202, 203–04, 218–19

heat exchanger, in atomic power plant, **113**

heat rays, 214, 217, 221, 327–28, 329, 453–54

heater, electric, thermostat for, 206

heating, of home, 214–15

helicopter, 173, 195–96

helium, 15, 31, 32, 44, 63, 79, **123;** atom of, 67, 123–24; isotopes of, 67–68; in neon sign, 313; nucleus in atom of, 121, 124; in sun, 406

hematite, 42

hemoglobin, 56, 131

Henry, Joseph, 251

heptane, 100, 101
Hercules, constellation of, 408; star cluster, **408**
Herschel, William, 327
Hertz, Heinrich, 260
hexane, 100, 101
high compression: in diesel engine, 168; in gasoline engine, 167
high-fidelity, 360
high-test gasoline, 167
Himalaya Mountains, 36
home: cooling of, 221–22; heating of, 214–15, 222
homosphere, 44
hornblende, 39
horsepower, 150–52, *452*
housefly, eye of, 289, **290**
humidity, 224, 229; comfortable, 226; healthful, 222; indicator for, *455;* measuring, 226; relative, 225–28; and seeding of cloud, 232; and thunderstorms, 230
Huygens, Christian, 307, 309
hydrated copper sulfate (blue vitriol), 74
hydrazine, 194
hydrochloric acid, *see* hydrogen chloride
hydrodynamics, 161
hydrogen, 15, 44; atom of, 65–66, 80, 100, 123–24; in displacement experiment, *439;* and dry cell, *457;* and electric cell, 247; electron-sharing atom of, **80;** heavy, 119, 124; in hemoglobin, 56; in human body, 55; in hydrogen bomb, 124–25; ions of in acid, *443;* ionized, **125;** isotopes of, 66; paired atoms of, 84; in sun, 123, 379, 406, 424; test for, 57, **58;** in thermometer, 208; in water, 55, 57–58, 73, 85, 246
hydrogen bomb, 123–25
hydrogen chloride (hydrochloric acid), 75, 76, *437, 439, 442–43*
hydrogen, cosmic, 407–08, 411–**12**
hydrogen hydroxide, *see* water
hydrogen oxide, 75
hydrogen peroxide, 73, **74,** 75, 89
hydrolysis, *443*
hydrostatics, 161
hydroxide ions, in base, *443*
hygrometer, 226, 228
"hypo," photographers', 233, *440, 444*

I

ice, 203, 204, 221; index of refraction of, 278
Ice Age, 23, 24, *see* glacial cycle
igneous: rocks, 38, 39; intrusion, 39, 40; extrusion, 39
"illuminating gas," 163
image: formed in camera, 291, 292, 293, 296, 298; seen by microscope, 303; seen through reading lens, 300, 301; thrown by enlarger, 299; thrown by movie projector, 299; thrown by slide projector, 298, **299;** virtual, 301
inclined plane, 143, 144, *451*
"Incompleted Double Star" Theory, 403
induced current, 254, *459*
inductance, *462–63*
industry, tracers in, 131–32

inert elements, *447*
inertia, *449*
infrared rays, 214, 218, 327, 328, 329, 331
ink, 96, 98; invisible, 77, 78
input, 138; and efficiency, 142
insulators: for electricity, 239, 251; of heat, 211, 212, 217
interference, of sound waves, *461*
internal-combustion engine, 163, 185
Invar (alloy), 205
inverse square law, in spread of light, 315–16
iodine, 11, 80, 81, 127; experiments with, *437;* radioactive, 128, 130
ionization, *441–42*
ionosphere, **14,** 16, **370,** 418, **424**
iris, 282, **283, 288,** 289, 293
iron, 9, 10; atom of, 68, 79, 80; as catalyst, 91; chemical activity of, in core of earth, 44, 45; in displacement reactions, 75, 76; in electromagnet, 250, 251; electron-losing atoms of, 80; electrons in atom of, 68, 79, 80, 82; as heat conductor, 211; in hemoglobin, 56, 131; melting point of, 208; oxygen combined with, 73, 80; radioactive, 130–31; sulfur combined with, 56, 58, 72, **79,** 80, 81, 82, 84; sulfur mixed with, 55, 56, 58; in sun's corona, 380; symbol for, 67, 81, 82; in thermostat, 205, 206; and zinc, 79, 80
iron nitrate, 83
iron oxide, 10, 73, 76, 80
iron sulfate, 75, *444*
iron sulfide, 56, 58, 72, **79,** 80, 81, 82, 84
irradiated milk, 329
isostasy, 36, 37
isotopes: of carbon, **66,** 124–25, 131, 132; of helium, 67–68; of hydrogen, 66; of iodine, 128, 130; made by fission, 127; radioactive, *see* radioactive isotopes; of tin, 128; of uranium, 108, 111, 115, 116, 117

J

jet engine, 168, 169, 170–73, 192, 193, 194, 196, *452*
Jodrell Bank, radiotelescope at, **411**
Jupiter (planet), 387, 389, 392; and gravity, 393–94
Jupiter (U.S. Army rocket), 416

K

Kelvin scale, 208, **209**
Kepler, Johannes, 387
kerosene, 163, 171
Killarneyan Mountains, 33
kilocycle, definition of, 363
kite experiment, by Franklin, 240–41
Kitty Hawk, N.C., 188, 190
Kuiper, Gerard, 403
krypton, 15

L

land breeze, 224, **225**
Langley, Samuel, 188

O

obsidian, **40,** *see* volcanic glass

ocean, 10; currents in, and winds, **111, 112;** floor of, 13, 14

oceanography, **12, 13,** 14

octane, 100, 101, 102

Oersted, Hans Christian, 247, 248, 250, 261

ohm, 250, 357

Ohm, Georg, 249

Ohm's Law, 249, 250, 357, 358

oil: electricity insulated by, 239; lubricating, 102, 139, 142

oil burner, thermostat for, 206

Olds, Ransom, 180

opaque object, 272, 276, **322**

optic nerve, 282, 283, 285

orbit, of earth satellite, 416–18

orbital flights, 425–26

Orion, constellation of, 394, **395;** nebula in, 409, **410**

outer ear, 344

output, 138; and efficiency, 142

oxygen: in air, 15, 44; aluminum combined with, 81; atom of, 68, 80; carbon combined with, 53, **54,** 72, 84, *438;* and chlorine, 80; in earth's crust, 9, 10; electron-gaining atom of, 80; and helium, 79; in hemoglobin, 56, 131; in human body, 55; hydrogen combined with, 55, 57, 58, **74,** 76, 80, **81;** in hydrogen peroxide, 74; iron combined with, 73, 80; lead combined with, 52, 53; liquid, 86; in magma, 38; magnesium combined with, 80; mercury combined with, 52, 53, 57, 58, 74; molecules of, 84; phosphorus combined with, 73; for rocket engine, 174, 194–95; in rocks, 26; sulfur combined with, 54; in sulfuric acid, 88; symbol for, 67, 81; test for, 57, **58;** in water, 14, 55, 57, 58, 74, 246; water combined with, 74; zinc combined with, 53

Ozarks, 33

ozone, 15

P

paints, 88, 89, 98

Paleozoic era, 46

Panhard, René, 180

paper: and magnetism, 243; manufacture of, 88, 95–96, **97,** 98

parabolic mirror, 274, **275**

paraffin, 102

parallax, 384, 397, 401

pea, nodules of, and nitrogen-fixing bacteria, **94**

pendulum, Foucault, 4, **5**

pentane, 100

periodic table of elements, *445–48*

perpetual motion machine, 139

Perseus, constellation of, 400, **410**

persistence of vision, 300

perspiration, 219, 225, 226

petroleum, 99–101, 102, 163–64

petroleum jelly, 163

*p*H numbers, *443*

phenol, 104

phonograph, 359–60

phosphor, 313

phosphoric oxide, 73, 81

phosphorus, 10; as electron-gainer, 80; oxygen combined with, 73; radioactive, 128, **129,** 130

photoelectric cell, 261, 297, 310, 354, 367

photoelectric effect, 309

photoenlarger, 299

photographic film, *see* film

photon, **309**

physical changes, 58, 59

Pikes Peak, 36

pile: atomic, *see* reactor; Volta's, 245

pinhole camera, 268, 269, 295

Pioneer V satellite, 423

piston: of diesel engine, 168; of gas engine, 163; of gasoline engine, 167; of steam engine, 155–57

pitch, of sound, 341–44

planets: in solar system, 381–82, 386–87; possible life on, 409, **410,** 411; radar signals to and from, **411**

plastics, 102–04; electricity insulated by, 239, 251; and sulfuric acid, 88

plate, of vacuum tube, 356, **357, 358,** 367–68

platinum, 89; in Crookes' tube, 259

Pleiades, 407, **408,** 410

Pluto (planet), **387,** 390–91, 394

plutonium, 117, 127, 128; and atomic bomb, 109

polar caps on Mars, **391**

Polaris (Pole Star), 25, 40, 44, 381, 400

polaroid, 308, 309, *460*

Pole (North) Star, 25, 40, 44, 381, 400

poles: of electromagnet, 251, 252; of magnet, 243, 252, 253, 260; magnetic, of earth, 7, **8**

polonium, 62, 63

polymers, 103, 104

Population I and II of Milky Way, 407

positive electric charge, 61, 62, 63, 64, 65, 79, 261; in electric cell, 247; and electron beam, **367,** 368; and electroscope, 239; fixed, **238;** and Leyden jar, 239, 240

potassium, 10

potassium bromide, 76, 81

potassium chlorate, *438*

potassium chloride, 76, 78, *438*

potassium iodide, *439*

potassium nitrate (saltpeter), 83

potassium thiocyanate, 78

power: in automobile, 184; definition of, 149; measurement of, 148–49, *452;* for rocket engine, 194–95; rotary, 157; in United States, 175; and work, 149, 151

power brake, of automobile, 183

power plant, atomic, 112–14

power shovel, **144,** 186

power steering, of automobile, 183

pressure of air, 14, 15

prism, spectrum made by, 319, 320–21, 323, 326

product, in chemical reaction, 84

Project Mercury, 425–26

Project Mohole, 45

prominences, of sun, 378–79, **380,** 424

propane, 100

protein, and nitrogen, 90
Proterozoic era, 46
proton-proton cycle, **406**
protons, 64, 65, **66**, 67, 68, 108, 119, 121–22; as cosmic rays, 331; and sun's energy, 406; in magnetosphere, 423
protoplanets, 403, 405
Ptolemy, 382–84; geocentric system of, **382**
public address system, 359
pulley, 143
pump: vacuum, 258–59; in rocket engine, 194–95; water and steam engine, 155
pupil of eye, 282, **283**, 288–89, 293
pure research, 264–65
P-waves, or pressure waves, or primary waves, 43

Q

quakecenter, 43
quartz, **38**
quartz crystals, *437*

R

radar: 328, 355, 372–73; measuring distance by reflection of, 373–75
radiant heating, **215**
radiation: of heat, 213–14, 217–18, 224; and life on planets, 410; in space travel, 427; X ray, 262; *see also* magnetosphere
radicals, 83, 84
radio instruments for space navigation, 421
radio set, 362–63, 365
radio signals, to and from planets, 411; from satellites, 422, 423
radio spectrum, 365–66
radio station, 363, 365
radio telescope, 408, **411**, 412
radio tubes, 261, 355
radio waves, 261, 328–29, 331, 362–66; bouncing, 372–73; future uses of, 374; and ionosphere, 14, 16, **370**, 418; short, 16, 366, 372; in tracking earth satellites, 418, 419; for TV, 366; in space, 408
radioactive elements, in study of earth's age, 10, 46
radioactive isotopes (radioisotopes), 127–32; in industry, 131–32; as tracers, 130–32
radioactivity, 31, 63, 109, 123, 127; discovery of, 263; within earth, 42
radium, 62, 63, 123, 127, 129, 130, 331
radon, 63, 123
rain, 228, 229, 230; man-made, 232–33
rainbow, 319
ram-jet engine, 173
rarefied air, 337
rayon, 88, 92, 94, 97, 98
rays: alpha, 62, 63, 64, 127; beta, 62, 63, 127, 128; cathode, 259, 260, 261, 262; cosmic, 111, 132, 331, 332; gamma, 62, 63, 127, 128, 129, 330, 332; heat,

214, 217, 221, 327–28, 329, 331–32; infrared, 214, 218, 327, 328, 329, 331; light, *see* light; *see also* radar; radiation; radio waves; television waves
reaction, chemical, definition of, 58
reactor, **111**, 127, 130; breeder, **116**; energy from, 112–14; research, **112**; " swimming pool," **112**
reading lens, 300–01
receiver: radio, 363, 365; telephone, 351, 352; television, **368**
recycling of waste material, 427
refinery, petroleum, 99, 100, 101
reflection: of heat, 217, 218, *453;* of light, 271–74, 322, 323
refraction: of light, 276, 277, 278–80; index of, 277, 278
refrigerator: in air-conditioning unit, 222; electric, 220; ether, 219; gas, 220, **221**; illustrating principle of, *454;* thermostat for, 206
relative humidity, 225–28
relay circuit, *458*
relay tower, television, **371**
rendezvous with spaceship, **428**
research, basic, 264, 265
residual mountains, 34, **35**
" resinous electricity," 238
resistance, to electromotive force, 249, 250, 357, *458*
resistor, 359
resonance, *461–62*
resultant, *449*
retina, 282–84, 285–89, 324
retrograde motion, of planets, **383**
revolution: of moon around earth, 385–86; of planets, 387; *see also* Copernicus; of spheres, 384; *see also* epicycles
revolution, geological, 46
rheostat, *460*
rock(s): effect of water on, 18, **19**, 25; as guide to past, 45, 46, *see* law of strata; igneous, **38**, **39**, 40; inside earth, 37; metamorphic, 40, **41**; reconstruction of age of, 46; sedimentary, 25, 26, 30, **31**, 37, **38**; uranium, **115**
rock wool, 211
rocket(s): 16; escape velocity for, 194, 421; guidance control of, 418; into outer space, 421; interplanetary navigation of, 421; landing on moon, **428**; launching from satellite of, 422; and space projects, 415–16; three-stage, 194–95, 196
rocket engine, 173–74, 194, **195**, 196; fuel for, 416, 421
Rocky Mountains, **33**
rods, of eye, 283, 285
Roemer, Ole, 306, 307
Roentgen, Wilhelm, 258, 261, 262, 264
roller bearings, 139
rotary power, of steam engine, 157
rotation: of earth, 4, 5, 385
rotor blade, of airplane, 196
rubber: charged with electricity, 237, 238, *423;* electricity insulated by, 239, 251; molecule of, under electron microscope, **264**; as polymer, 103
Rumford, Count, 162
rust, 80

Rutherford, Lord, 60, 61, 66; experiments with atoms, 64, 65

S

salt (sodium chloride), 80, 93, 96; deposits of, 93; in double-displacement reaction, 77, *407;* extracted from sea water, 10; in food, 92; physical properties of, *437;* for preserving food, 93; as product of acid-base neutralization, *443;* saturated solution of, 224, 225; and sodium bicarbonate, 93; sodium carbonate made from, 92, 93–94; and sodium hydroxide, 92–93, *439, 443;* symbol for, 81; uses of, 92–93
saltpeter (potassium nitrate), 83
sand, 26
sandstone, 25, 26
satellites: artificial, of earth, 16, 372, 416; computing path of, 420–21; launching of, 416–18; man's reactions inside of, 426–27; path of, 418, 419, 420; picture transmitting from, 420, 422; problems of travel in, 427; requirements for life in, 426–27; retrieving of, 425; rocket launching from, 422; tracking of, 418–19; transmitting data, 422–23; when visible, 419
saturated air, 224, 225, **226**
saturated " hypo " solution, 233
saturated solution of salt, 224, 225, *440*
Saturn (planet), **387,** 390–91; rings of, **393,** 394
Savery, Thomas, 154, 156
scanning beam, of TV picture tube, **369**
Schaefer, Vincent, 232, **233**
schist, 41, *see* metamorphic rocks
screw, as simple machine, 143, *452*
sea breeze, 224, **225**
seamounts, 13
sea water, composition of, 10
Sea Wolf, U.S.S., **114**
secondary waves, 43
sedimentary layer(s), **30, 31**
sedimentary rock, 25, 26, *see* shale, limestone, sandstone, conglomerates
sedimentation, 25, 26
" seeding " cloud, 232–33
seismograph, 43
selenium, 309
shale, 25, 26
shear waves, 43
ship: diesel-powered, 186, **187;** radar on, 372, 373
shock, electric, 240
shooting star, *see* meteor
short-wave radio, 366
shovel, power, **144,** 186
shutter: of camera, 291, 294; of enlarger, 299; of movie projector, 300
Sierra Nevadas, 33, 228, 229
silicon, in earth's crust, 9, 10; in magma, 38; in rocks, 26
silicon dioxide, 9, 10, 25, 26, 39
silk: and electric charge, *423;* electric wire insulated by, 251
sill, 39, 40; *see also* igneous intrusion

silt, 23, 25
silver, 80, 86, 211; for mirror, 273; plating with, 246; tarnish on, 80
silver chloride, 80, *439*
silver iodide, 233
silver nitrate, 75, 81, 83, 85, 86, *439, 443, 444*
silver sulfide, 80, *444*
Sirius, 398
Sklodowska, Marie (Madame Curie), 62, 63
slate, 40
slavery, 150
slide projector, 298–99
Smithsonian Institution, 189
soap: manufacture of, 94, 95, 96–97, **97;** testing for *p*H value of, *443*
sodium, 9, 10, 80, 81; in reactor, 112; spectrum of, 325, 399
sodium acetate, *439*
sodium bicarbonate (baking soda), 81, 83, 94, 98
sodium carbonate, 77, 86, 92, 93, 94, 95
sodium chloride, *see* salt
sodium hydroxide, 92, 95, 96, *439, 443*
sodium lamp, 313, 325
sodium nitrate, 83
sodium silicate, 94
sodium thiosulfate, 233, *440*
soil, composition of, 9, 10, *see* topsoil; conservation of, 26, **27,** 28
solar battery, 177
solar engine, 176–77
solar system, 386, 387, 390; information about, 394; model of, 391; three theories of origin of, 402–03, **404, 405**
solar wind, 424
solder, 97, **99**
solid, change to liquid, 58
solutions, chemical, *440*
Solvay process, 94, 97, 98
sound amplifier, 359, **360**
sound barrier, 192–93, 195
sound echo measurement, 374
sound waves, 192, 316, 336, 337, 338; experiments with, *461;* hearing, 344–46; and hearing aids, 346; impossible in vacuum, 340–41; interference of, *461;* and loudness, 342, 343, **344;** and music, 343, 344; and pitch, 341–42, 343, 344; in public address system, 358; in solids, 340; speed of, 338–39; in telephone system, 350, 351; ultrasonic, 346; underwater, 339–40; and voice current, 364, 365
space research: purpose of, 415; rockets and satellites in, 416–19, 421; orbital motion of satellites, 417; properties of earth disclosed by, 2, 422; earth-sun relationships discovered by, 424; weather observations from satellites, **422,** 423; U.S. lunar-landing project, 427, **428;** U.S. rocket probe of Venus, 421; environment surrounding earth, 423; man in space, 424, **425,** 426–27; interplanetary navigation, 421; tracking satellites, 418, **419;** Newton's laws in, **418**
spar, crystals of, *437*
spark lever, of Model T, 180

thrust fault mountains, **35,** 36
thunder, 231, 339
thunderstorm, 230, **231**
tides, and moon, **6**
time exposure, 295
timing circuit, *463*
tin, 75, 80, 97; isotopes of, 128
tin nitrate, 75
Tiros, **422**
Titanic, 372
titanium, 195
TNT, 91, 108
Todd, 180
topsoil, 27, 28; compounds of elements in, 9; formation of, 21
torque, *451*
torque converter, of automobile, 182–83
Torricelli, Evangelista, 155
tracers, radioisotopes as, 130–32
tractor, 185–86
transformer, 254, **255,** 362, *459;* in telephone system, 352
transistor, 358, **359**
transmitter: radio, **364;** telephone, 350, **351,** 352, 357; television, **368**
transparency, 272
trinitrotoluene (TNT), 91, 108
triode, 356, **357**
tritium, 66
truck, trailer, 185
tube: cathode-ray (Crookes'), 258, 259, 261, 262; diode, 356, 357; radio, 261, 355; triode, 357, 359; TV camera, 367–69, 370; TV picture, 258, 261, 369–70; vacuum, 355–56, 357, 358, 360, 365, 367, *462;* X-ray, 262–63, 330
tuberculosis, 301
tungsten, 312, *458*
tuning fork, 337, 338, 345, *461*
turbine: of jet engine, 171, 172, 173; steam, 159–61, *452;* water, 161
turbojet engine, 171, 172, 192, **193**
turboprop engine, 172, 192
TV picture tube, 258, 261, 369–70
TV programs, wave length for, 328
TV signals, *see* Telestar
TV weather observation satellite, **422,** *see* Tiros

U

ultrasonics, 346
ultraviolet light, 19, 313, 329, 332, 385
uniformitarianism, 20
universe: beginning of, 402, **404, 405;** definition of, 412; expanding, 412–13; of Ptolemy, **382–83;** steady-state theory of, 413
uranium: 80, 109; atom of, 46, 108–09, 110, 119, 122–23, 127–28; in atomic pile, 111; cost of, 114; enriched, 115; isotopes of, 108, 115–17; in rocks, 31; search for, 115; and vacuum tubes, 355; *see also* nucleus
uranium-lead dating, 32
Uranus (planet), **387,** 390, 391, 394

Urey, Harold, 410*n.*
Ursa Major, **397**
U 235, **109,** 110, 111
U 238, **109,** 110, 111

V

vacuum: definition of, 212; index of refraction of, 278; sound waves impossible in, 340–41
vacuum pump, 258, 259
vacuum tube, 356–59, 365, 367
vacuum-tube circuit, in radio, 364
valence, 82, 83; of families of elements, *446–47*
valley glaciers, 19, **21,** 22
valves, of steam engine, 155, **156**
Van Allen belts, 423, *see* magnetosphere
vanes, of rocket engine, 194
vapor: for gasoline engine, 164; water vapor, 15, 410
Vaseline, 164
Vega, 398
Venus (planet), 387, 390–91, 393–94, 415, 423; radar reflection from, 373–74
vibration, sound, 336
vinegar, testing for *p*H value of, *443*
virtual image, 301
virus, under electron microscope, 263, **264**
vitamin D, 329
"vitreous electricity," 238
vocal cords, 342
voice current, 364, 365, 369
volcano, 35, 36
volcanic glass, *see* obsidian
volt, 250
Volta, Alessandro, 244, 245, 246, 247
Von Guericke, Otto, 155

W

warm air mass, 229
water: boiling point of, 207, *454;* composition of, 55, 57, 58, 80; composition of sea water, 10; contraction of, 205; decomposition of, 57, **58,** 74; in double-displacement reaction, *439;* electric current for taking apart, 57, **58,** 246; evaporation of 24, **25,** 58; expansion of, 205; force of, 25; freezing point of, 207; in hydrated copper sulfate, 75; in hydrogen peroxide, 74; light refracted in, 275–77, 278; and rocks, effect on, **18, 19;** sound waves under, 339; in sulfuric acid, 88
water cycle, 24, **25**
water pump, and steam engine, 155
water, purifying of, 76
water turbine, 161
water vapor, 15, 224–25, 230, 232–33
water wheel, 153–54
Watt, James, 150–51, 156–57
wave length, 331, 332; of cosmic hydrogen, 411; of cosmic rays, 331; frequency related to, 366; of gamma rays, 331; of heat rays, 327–28; of light waves, 320–23, 326; of radio waves, 328; for TV programs, 328; in color vision, 324

" wave-particle dualism," 310; *see also* cosmic rays as protons; electron microscope

waves: pressure waves, or P-waves, or primary waves, **43;** radar, 372–73; radio, *see* radio waves; shear waves, or S-waves, or secondary waves, **43;** sound, *see* sound waves; television, 369, 370–71

wax, and static electricity, *451*

weather: 15, 18; forecast, 230, 385; man-made, 232–33; observations from satellites, 422, 423

weather maps, 230, **231**

weathering processes, **19**

wedge, 143

weed killer, tagged, 132

weight: of air, 7; as pull of earth, 5, 6

weightlessness in space travel, 424–27

wet-bulb thermometer, 226, 227

wetting agent, 202

wheel and axle, 143, *451*

white color, heat reflected by, 218

white light, 320, 321, 322, 324; *see also* spectrum

White Cliffs of Dover, 26

windmill, 152–53, 154

window, invisible, 273

winds: local, 224; over oceans, 11, 12; effect of, on erosion, **19, 27**

wing of airplane: delta, 193; lift of, 190, 191; and powered lift, **196;** and sound barrier, 192; swept-back, 193

wirephoto, 353–54

wolfram, *see* tungsten

wood: electricity insulated by, 239; heat poorly conducted by, 210; and magnetism, 243

wood pulp, 96

wool, and electric charge, *423*

word equation, 57, 84

work, 145; definition of, 137, 143; and efficiency, 142; and friction, 139; measurement of, 138; and power, 149, 151

Wright brothers, 188–90

X

X rays, 261, 332; atoms studied by, 263; " burns " from, 263, 330; in cancer treatment, 129, 330; for detecting cracks inside metal castings, **330;** discovery of, 262; of human head, **330;** and medicine, **262,** 263, 330; photographic film affected by, 262; in space travel, 427; structure of matter probed by, 263; uses of, 262, 263, 330

X-ray tube, 262–63, 330

Y

Yosemite Valley, 22

Z

zero, absolute, 208, 209

zinc, 10, 76, 79, 80, 81, 82; charged with electricity, 244, 247; in displacement experiment, 75, 76, *439;* sulfur combined with, *439*

zinc chloride, 75, 81, 82

zinc nitrate, 83

zinc oxide, 10, 53, *444*

zinc silicate, 313

zinc sulfate, *439, 440, 441*

zinc sulfide, 63, *439*

zodiac, 382, **387,** 396

Index of Activities in Text

Figure numbers in parentheses refer to illustrations that will be helpful to consult in performing activities.

THE STORY OF COLOR

(See inside back cover of this book)

A When a ray of white light passes through a prism the light is separated into separate spectrum colors.

B When red, green, and blue lights are projected onto a screen, red and green combine to produce yellow; green and blue produce blue-green (turquoise); blue and red, purple. All three combine into white light.

C Did you think we made a mistake in the printing of this illustration? According to theories held for many years, the eye required a combination of the primary colors (red, blue, and green) in order to form full-color images. And this theory still holds for the formation of color images formed from spots of light as in B. But, as recently discovered, it is *not* true for many cases involving more complete images, such as a picture of a bowl of fruit. For these, it seems that a full-color image can be formed by the eye *even though all the light received is of the same color, say yellow, so long as this light contains at least two different tints* of yellow. As shown in the illustration, two differing yellow beams have passed through black and white transparencies. In these transparencies the black and white shadings are more intense in some parts of one picture than in corresponding parts of the other. The theory of color vision is under active investigation. See page 324 of the text for a brief discussion.

D Try this experiment. Hold the book under a strong light and stare at one spot in the farm scene for about a half minute (or more) without blinking. Then stare at a bright white surface steadily. You will see the objects in this scene in different colors. This change in color occurs because you have fatigued the cells on the retina of your eye that respond to different colors, so that only the cells not used react when you stare at the white surface. Repeat by staring at other spots.

E
F Look at this pattern of dots from a distance. Go back as far as you need to until the circles disappear and blend into the background. Now look at the background color with a magnifier and you will see the same pattern of dots shown in the center. Most color printing processes produce colors in this way by the addition of separate colors from separate dots.

B
C
D
E
F
G
H
I
J

Earth tilted $23\frac{1}{2}°$

work = force x distance
energy = ability to do work
friction = resistance

How & Why Bk – Simple Machines
Wonder Book –

$\dfrac{1}{100,000,000}$ cm = 1 Ängstrom –(cosmic ray)

measurement of a ray

higher frequency – the
shorter the wave length.
Marconie –1899 – wireless telegraph
1 kilocycle = 1,000 cycles

A

B

C